W9-BYM-126

BRIGHTON CROP PROTECTION CONFERENCE
Pests and Diseases – 1992

Volume 1

BRIGHTON CROP PROTECTION CONFERENCE
Pests and Diseases – 1992

Volume 1

Proceedings of an international
conference organised by
The BRITISH CROP PROTECTION COUNCIL
held at Brighton Centre and
Brighton Metropole, Brighton, England
November 23–26, 1992

BCPC Registered Office
49 Downing Street
Farnham
Surrey GU9 7PH, UK

©1992 The British Crop Protection Council
49 Downing Street, Farnham,
Surrey GU9 7PH, UK

All rights reserved. No part of this publication may
be reproduced, stored in a retrieval system, or
transmitted in any form or by any means, electronic,
mechanical, photocopying, recording or otherwise,
without the prior permission of the copyright owner.

Up to 10% of any one paper may be reproduced
without prior permission provided The British Crop
Protection Council and the Author(s) are
acknowledged.

British Library Cataloguing in Publication Data

Brighton Crop Protection Conference: Pests
and Diseases – Proceedings – 1992
632

ISBN 0-948404-65-5
ISSN 0955-1506

Every effort has been made to ensure that the recommendations and statements made in these Proceedings are correct,
but The British Crop Protection Council cannot accept responsibility for any loss, damage, or any other accident arising from
carrying out the methods advocated.
Nothing in these Proceedings shall be taken as a warranty that
any substances or mixture of substances mentioned herein is
not the subject of patent rights and the Council does not hold
itself responsible for any infringement of said rights.

Printed in Great Britain by
THE LAVENHAM PRESS LIMITED, LAVENHAM, SUFFOLK

Contents

VOLUME 1

SESSION 1

SESSION 3A

SCLEROTINIA: ITS BIOLOGY AND IMPLICATIONS FOR DISEASE CONTROL 97

Invited Papers

SESSION 3B

TOXICOLOGY: MODERN METHODS FOR RISK ASSESSMENT 133

Invited Papers

SESSION 3C

PEST AND DISEASE RESISTANCE TO AGROCHEMICALS 163

Posters

FUNGICIDES

SESSION 4A

POST HARVEST LOSSES

269

Invited Papers

Research Reports

SESSION 4B

ADVANCES IN THE SAFER FORMULATION, PACKAGING AND APPLICATION TECHNOLOGY OF PESTICIDES

311

Invited Papers

Research Report

SESSION 4C

DEVELOPMENT OF PATHOGENS FOR BIOCONTROL

343

Posters

SESSION 5

NEW COMPOUNDS, FORMULATIONS AND USES – FUNGICIDES

Research Reports

VOLUME 2

SESSION 6A

EFFECTS AND FATE OF PESTICIDES IN WATER AND THE ATMOSPHERE

Invited Papers

SESSION 6B

ADVANCES IN IPM IN FRUIT AND VITICULTURE   497

SESSION 6C

CROP PROTECTION IN ARABLE CROPS   537

SESSION 7A

DISEASE FORECASTING AND DIAGNOSTICS IN ARABLE CROPS   687

SESSION 7B

TRANSGENIC PLANTS FOR RESISTANCE TO PESTS AND DISEASES   729

SESSION 7C

EFFECTS AND FATE OF PESTICIDES IN THE ENVIRONMENT   767

VOLUME 3

SESSION 8A

DISEASES AND PESTS OF NON-BRASSICA OILSEED CROPS

SESSION 8B

MODELS IN THE CONTROL OF INVERTEBRATE PESTS 953

SESSION 8C

ADVANCES IN THE INTEGRATED MANAGEMENT OF PESTS 989

Posters

SESSION 10

IMPLICATIONS OF MODERN REGULATORY REQUIREMENTS FOR CROP PROTECTION

THE BRITISH CROP PROTECTION COUNCIL

President	Professor J. Dekker
Vice-President	R. F. Norman
Chairman	Mr J. North
Vice Chairmen	Mr B. W. Cox, Mr A. G. Harris
Hon. Treasurer	Dr Anne Buckenham

Corporate Members:
Agricultural Engineers' Association
Agricultural and Food Research Council
Agricultural Training Board
Association of Applied Biologists
Association of Independent Crop Consultants
British Agrochemicals Association
British Institute of Agricultural Consultants
British Society for Plant Pathology
Department of Agriculture and Fisheries
    for Scotland
Department of Agriculture, Northern Ireland
Department of the Environment
Ministry of Agriculture, Fisheries and Food
    ADAS
      Pesticides Safety Division
National Association of Agricultural Contractors
National Farmers' Union
Natural Environment Research Council
Overseas Development Administration
Society of Chemical Industry, Pesticides Group
United Kingdom Agricultural Supply Trade
    Association Ltd

Individual Members:	**Hon. Vice-Presidents**
Dr D. H. S. Drennan	Mr A. W. Billitt
Dr H. C. Gough	Mr J. D. Fryer
Mr D. J. Higgons	
Dr K. Holly	
Mr J. Smith	
Mr D. Tyson	

Secretary   Mr B. J. T. Baldwin

The British Crop Protection Council

The British Crop Protection Council exists to promote the knowledge and understanding of crop protection. It was founded in 1968 when the British Weed Control Council, set up in 1953, and the British Insecticide and Fungicide Council, set up in 1962, merged to form a single body concerned with all aspects of crop protection. The BCPC is essentially a British organisation but its work is international in outlook.

The Council is composed of corporate members including Government bodies, research and advisory services, the farming and agrochemical industries, distribution and contracting services, environmental bodies and other organisations, as well as individual members with special qualifications and experience in the field of crop protection. This blend is probably unique.

Objectives

Members of The BCPC have a common objective – to promote and encourage the science and practice of pest, disease and weed control, and allied subjects both in the UK and overseas. To achieve this the Council aims:

to compile and arrange the publication of information and recommendations on crop protection for specialists;

to help the public to understand the nature of pests, diseases and weeds, and their control, and the part their control plays in food production;

to provide a forum for discussion at conferences and other meetings on matters relating to crop protection and to publish and distribute the proceedings of these meetings;

to identify short- and long-term requirements for research and development in the field of crop protection;

to act as a liaison agency and to collaborate with other organisations with similar objectives.

Further information about The BCPC, its organisation and its work can be obtained from:

The British Crop Protection Council
49 Downing Street
Farnham
Surrey GU9 7PH, UK

Brighton Crop Protection Conference
Pests and Diseases – 1992

Organising Committee:

Chairman	Mr D. J. Higgons
Members	Dr D. V. Alford
	Professor D. Atkinson
	Mr G. Beaumont
	Dr K. J. Brent
	Dr J. H. Clarke
	Dr D. L. Ebbels
	Mr R. T. R. Pierce
	Dr D. Rudd-Jones
	Mr C. J. Siddall
	Mr D. Tyson
Conference Secretary	Ms S. Simpson

Programme Committee:

Chairman	Dr D. V. Alford
Vice-Chairmen	Dr J. F. Jenkyn
	Dr J. P. Leahey
	Dr M. W. Skidmore
	Dr M. G. Solomon
Press Officer	Mr R. T. R. Pierce
Exhibition Officer	Mr G. Beaumont
Conference Secretary	Ms S. Simpson

Session Organisers	Mr D. J. Arnold	Dr D. R. Jones
	Dr S. Ball	Dr T. Locke
	Dr G. L. Bateman	Mr P. J. Mulqueen
	Dr N. Carter	Mr D. B. Pinniger
	Dr N. E. Crook	Dr K. A. Richardson
	Dr P. R. Ellis	Mr P. H. Rose
	Mr C. Furk	Dr P. E. Russell
	Dr P. Gladders	Dr M. W. Shaw
	Dr D. M. Glen	Dr J. R. Street
	Mr S. C. Gordon	Mr R. A. Umpelby
	Mrs R. Hignett	(Dr P. T. Haskell
	Dr A. D. Hill	pre-Conference
	Dr D. J. James	Symposium)

ABBREVIATIONS

acid equivalent	a.e.	nuclear magnetic resonance	nmr
active ingredient	AI	number average diameter	n.a.d.
boiling point	b.p.	number median diameter	n.m.d.
British Standards Institution	BSI	organic matter	o.m.
centimetre(s)	cm	page	p.
concentration × time product	ct	pages	pp.
concentration required to kill 50%		parts per million by volume	mg/l
of test organisms	LC50	parts per million by weight	mg/kg
correlation coefficient	r	pascal	Pa
cultivar	cv.	percentage	%
cultivars	cvs.	post-emergence	post-em.
day(s)	d	power take off	p.t.o.
days after treatment	DAT	pre-emergence	pre-em.
degrees Celsius (centigrade)	°C	probability (statistical)	P
dose required to kill 50% of test		relative humidity	r.h.
organisms	LD50	revolutions per minute	rev./min
dry matter	d.m.	second (time unit)	s
Edition	Edn	standard error	SE
Editor	Ed.	standard error of means	SEM
Editors	Eds	soluble powder	SP
emulsifiable concentrate	EC	species (singular)	sp.
freezing point	f.p.	species (plural)	spp.
gas chromatography–mass		square metre	m^2
spectrometry	gcms	subspecies	ssp.
gas–liquid chromatography	glc	surface mean diameter	s.m.d.
gram(s)	g	suspension concentrate	SC
growth stage	GS	temperature	temp.
hectare(s)	ha	thin-layer chromatography	tlc
high performance (or pressure)		tonne(s)	t
liquid chromatography	hplc	ultraviolet	u.v.
hour	h	vapour pressure	v.p.
infrared	i.r.	variety (wild plant use)	var.
International Standardisation		volume	V
Organisation	ISO	weight	W
Kelvin	K	weight by volume	W/V
kilogram(s)	kg	(mass by volume is more correct)	(m/V)
least significant difference	LSD	weight by weight	W/W
litre(s)	Litre	(mass by mass is more correct)	(m/m)
litres per hectare	l/ha	wettable powder	WP
mass	m		
mass per mass	m/m	approximately	$c.$
mass per volume	m/V	less than	<
mass spectrometry	m.s.	more than	>
maximum	max.	not less than	≮
melting point	m.p.	not more than	≯
metre(s)	m	Multiplying symbols—	Prefixes
milligram(s)	mg	mega	$(\times 10^6)$	M
millilitre(s)	ml	kilo	$(\times 10^3)$	k
millimetre(s)	mm	milli	$(\times 10^{-3})$	m
minimum	min.	micro	$(\times 10^{-6})$	μ
minute (time unit)	min	nano	$(\times 10^{-9})$	n
molar concentration	M	pico	$(\times 10^{-12})$	p

SESSION 1

THE NINETEENTH BAWDEN LECTURE

CHAIRMAN   MR J. J. NORTH

SPEAKER   PROFESSOR C. R. W. SPEDDING

SESSION
ORGANISER   DR D. V. ALFORD

MODERN AGRICULTURE: THE ROLE AND IMPACT OF TECHNOLOGY, LEGISLATION AND PUBLIC OPINION

C.R.W. SPEDDING

Centre for Agricultural Strategy, University of Reading, 1 Earley Gate, Reading, Berkshire, RG6 2AT.

ABSTRACT

Effective demand is the dominant factor shaping the European agricultural industry – its size, its products and its methods. Technology makes things possible but will be applied only when economic and acceptable.

What is acceptable is constrained by legislation (e.g. UK and EC) and by public opinion. The latter is not homogeneous and not necessarily well represented by those who attract most media attention. It is essential to recognise that the public are entitled to their concerns, even when these are based on ignorance or are poorly articulated, and they must be listened to. But they are not competent to propose solutions: this is the responsibility of the industry.

Pesticides provide an important example of concerns that should be discussed in a non-confrontational manner and should not be brushed aside: confidence and trust depend upon this. However, it must be recognised that Agriculture is vulnerable to major uncertainties, ranging from nuclear accidents to global warming.

INTRODUCTION

The title sounds formidably comprehensive, yet it leaves out economics, which is what will have the dominant impact on the shape of modern agriculture in Europe. This will be true of most parts of the world but there are often additional problems, such as drought and desertification, lack of infrastructure, lack of appropriate skills (including marketing), lack of a motivated work-force and a polluted environment. The last two are serious limiting factors in much of Eastern Europe. In dealing with modern agriculture, I shall confine my attention mainly to Western Europe, with particular reference to the EC (European Community).

Of course, technology makes things possible and legislation and public opinion may constrain the application of technology, but the scale and nature of agricultural activity is determined by the economic framework of costs and prices. This is inevitable, since farming is a business, whatever else it may also be, and farmers have to make a living and an adequate return on capital or go out of business.

The size of the agricultural industry is bound to reflect the effective demand for its products and the protection afforded by the CAP (Common Agricultural Policy) over the last few decades is unlikely to be available, to anything like the same extent, in the future.

Recent changes to the CAP have totally changed the situation that had previously obtained in which major commodities could be produced in excess of demand, in the knowledge that they would be bought into intervention at acceptable prices. The current Uruguay round of the GATT talks is likely to reinforce the price reductions and reduction of support for agriculture already agreed.

Effective demand must ultimately determine what is produced and in what quantities. Where markets are working properly, if there is no demand, there will be no production. If that demand is limited to particular qualities or, as is increasingly the case, to particular production methods, then this will have to be reflected in the nature of both product and production.

The primary role of technology, therefore, is to present production possibilities to the producer, not only, however, in terms of product and process but also of price. Technology makes it possible to create demand but may also reduce it where the consumer finds its products or processes unacceptable, even at a lower price.

Public opinion may operate directly on the producer but more commonly it will influence expressed demand.

Legislation is most commonly of a rather negative kind, legislative bodies such as the EC either laying down rules that have to be observed or banning practices.

Such legislation is often a response to public opinion but may be generated by Governments or the EC, in the public interest. Even where EC legislation is a response to public opinion, it may not be so for many of the countries to which the legislation will nonetheless apply.

The role of public opinion is to articulate public concerns, real or perceived, in order to bring about change in production patterns.

The role of legislation is to ensure that products meet specified standards of quality and safety and that methods of production are acceptable to the public (whether for reasons of environmental impact or, for example, animal welfare).

The roles of technology, legislation and public opinion therefore interact and their impact will influence demand within what is allowed by law. These inter-relationships are indicated in Figure 1.

Within the modern agricultural industry some 80% of its products are processed, to greater or lesser degree, by the food industry. The buyers of farm produce, therefore, are not so much the consuming public but, largely, processors and the multiple retailers.

Public opinion directly affects demand in the supermarkets and may be influenced by many factors, such as processing, packaging and advertising, that occur between the farm gate and purchase by the consumer. A great deal happens to the price as well as the product in this interval and the price paid to the farmer is usually less than half that charged to the consumer.

FIGURE 1. Factors affecting demand

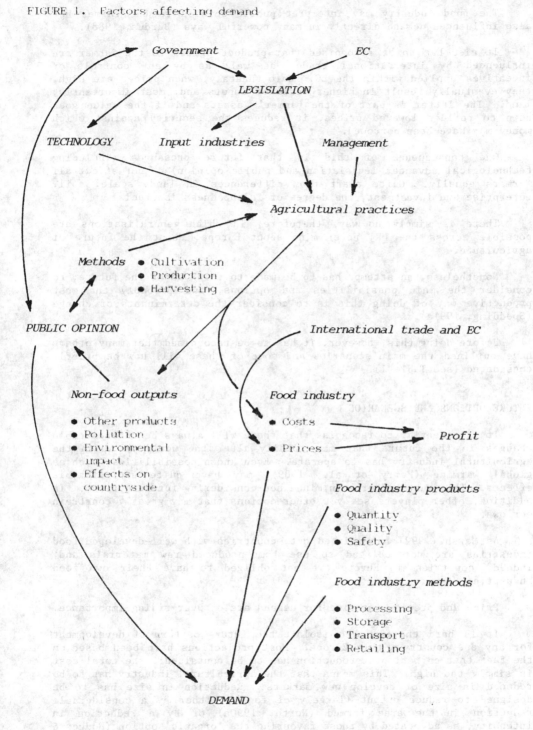

The food industry may interpret public opinion to the farmer but also influences demand directly in many powerful ways (Burdus, 1988).

It also has to be recognised that product prices to the farmer are influenced by international trade, as well as by any controls or incentives applied within the EC. Unfortunately, when prices are high, they eventually result in higher costs of inputs and, most importantly, land. The latter is part of the farmer's assets and if the value goes down to reflect lowered prices, it reduces the security against which money may have been borrowed.

One consequence of this is that future pressures (including technological advance, legislation and public opinion) do not affect all farmers equally. Quite apart from differences in land, scale, soil, enterprise and investment, the degree of indebtedness is crucial.

There is simply no way, therefore, in which generalisations are possible across the UK, never mind about Europe, about the future of agriculture.

Nonetheless, an attempt has to be made to think about the future, to consider the main possibilities and options, and probably the most productive way of doing this is to consider the determinants of change (Spedding, 1991a).

Before doing this, however, it has to be recognised that many others have outlined the main scenarios and some of these will now be briefly considered (see Table 1).

FUTURE OPTIONS AND SCENARIOS

It is essential to recognise that there will always be unforeseeable changes in the future that may totally alter the world in which the agricultural industry has to operate. Even known possibilities, such as global warming (Parry et al., 1989), may have quite unpredictable effects. This must be borne in mind when considering future options. In addition, other players see yet other options that may greatly constrain our own.

As Marsh (1992) has pointed out, countries with well-developed food industries are not obliged to use home-produced raw materials and, indeed, countries in Europe are not obliged to have their own food industries.

Price and precise catering for demand are of over-riding importance.

It is hard therefore to isolate the future pattern of development for any one country within Europe. Most projections have been based on the fact that current overproduction has to be contained: the total cost is simply too high. This means that the agricultural industry has to be reduced in size or develop new markets. Reduction in size has to be designed to reduce output (largely of food), either by a considerable reduction in the area farmed (North, 1990a) or by a reduction in intensity, as advocated by those favouring the 'organic' option (Hodges & Scofield, 1988; Holden, 1989; Lampkin, 1990).

TABLE 1. Projected scenarios.

Scenario	Reference
1. Major contraction of agricultural area	North (1990a)
2. Expansion of "Conservation" areas	HMSO (1990b)
3. Rural policy to sustain rural populations	Neville-Rolfe (1990)
4. General extensification of farming	Taylor & Dixon (1990)
5. Increase in organic farming	Hodges & Scofield (1988) Holden (1989) Lampkin (1990)
6. Major development of biofuel production	Carruthers & Jones (1983) Rexen & Munck (1984)
7. Larger-scale production of raw materials for industry	Rexen & Munck (1984) Barnoud & Rinaudo (1986)

Of course, there is no reason to suppose that the whole of agriculture has to conform to one or other of these scenarios and, indeed, Whitby (1990) argues in favour of multiple land-use. It is quite possible to imagine highly intensive production on the more fertile soils, in those areas where inputs are not constrained by environmental impact restrictions, and extensive farming on cheaper or less fertile land or in areas that are classified as environmentally sensitive.

Indeed, as is currently happening with set-aside and partial organic conversion, it is possible to have mixtures of high- and low-intensity farming within one farm. One could go further and see the incorporation of unploughed, unsprayed headlands as representing a mixture of intensity within one field.

It may be a mistake therefore to see options and scenarios as mutually exclusive: it is more a question of adjusting the nature of the farming to the prevailing pressures and constraints operating in an area. This is, in any event, a more realistic approach than to suppose that particular systems or patterns can, will or should apply across the wide range of conditions to be found within Europe.

Although economics and effective demand will be bound to have a dominant influence on what is produced, and how, technology, legislation and public opinion will be powerful determinants, whether they operate through demand or not.

Although, as shown in Figure 1, they interact, it is worth examining each in turn.

TECHNOLOGY

As already indicated, technology makes things possible but its application is governed by many factors. If it is not in the long run economic, it will cease to be applied, although it may well be tried out by pioneers - partly to discover whether it is economic in practice or not. Few farmers can currently afford such pioneering and 'set-aside' land may offer an alternative way of gaining practical experience of a new technology. The money devoted to 'set-aside' could then be seen as a sound investment in gaining information that is actually needed to enable farmers to make informed choices. However, if the technology is not acceptable to the consumer, its application will be restricted by legislation or by economic demand.

Much of this is influenced by the manner of its presentation and the rate of its introduction: clearly 'the public' needs to feel consulted and to be reassured by a trusted authority.

The present situation appears unsatisfactory in that development is hedged about in such a way that there is a risk of beneficial developments being inhibited by arrangements designed to reduce the risk of mistakes.

In the past, there have been such mistakes and this has affected public trust, but such mistakes have not been limited to particular kinds of technology: they have been spectacular, for example, in the development of biological control.

It is important to consider what potential developments may occur in the future but it is even more important to devise a satisfactory regulatory framework within which they occur.

It has to be recognised that new technology generates fears and the easiest political action to reassure the public will generally be to insist on rigorous testing. Not only may this cause delay and lead to high costs, it is never going to be entirely clear what are appropriate tests, such is the complexity of the situations in which new technology will be used. Over-testing may limit development and still fail to produce relevant information. Controlled and closely monitored practice might assist development and provide relevant data. One possible way of achieving this might be the new NERC Environmental Change Network, which is one expression of the general policy to encourge environmental impact assessments (HMSO, 1990b).

POTENTIAL DEVELOPMENT IN TECHNOLOGY

It must be recognised that some of the most important developments may be quite unforeseeable at the present time. Furthermore, developments quite outside agriculture may have an enormous impact. The development of cheap sources of virtually inexhaustible supplies of energy (whether by fusion, from renewables or some as yet unimagined source), for example, would transform the entire outlook.

All this, it may be thought, is relevant to the long-term and there are some short- to medium-term developments that can be projected – at least as possibilities. This is true but does not rule out the possibility of totally unforeseen developments in the medium-term at any rate.

It is always as well to be aware of these major uncertainties even when considering what can be considered to be developments "in the pipeline". Table 2 illustrates some of the latter.

Genetic engineering is a good example of both short-term probabilities, such as the speeding up of tree-breeding, and much longer-term but clearly foreseeable possibilities, such as the insertion of N-fixing genes in cereal crop species (Woolhouse, 1988).

The point is that, although technology will open up entirely new vistas and may thus have enormous impact, the application of such developments will depend upon their being socially acceptable, legally permissible and economically advantageous.

What is needed is open and wide discussion of technological possibililties, without sensationalism, without representing them as inevitable ("you can't stand in the way of progress"), indeed, without equating technological change with progress but recognising that society can choose amongst the possibilities created, and without dismissing new ideas by premature economic assessment. The importance of adequate information is often stressed, but there is a great deal of information: it is more a question of accessibility.

None of this is easy in a competitive industry where investment costs in R&D may be very high.

LEGISLATION

The protection of the public is an obvious function of legislation and, in agriculture, the main areas relate to food safety and quality, water quality and atmospheric pollution. It cannot be confined to the use of inputs, such as agrochemicals, since agricultural activity itself may affect these areas.

For example, the ways in which animal feedstuffs are compounded may pose a health hazard, as seems likely in the case of BSE (Bovine Spongiform Encephalopathy) (HMSO, 1990a).

Similarly, methods of cultivation (e.g. the ploughing up of permanent grassland) may release large quantities of nitrate into rivers or aquifers (and, in the latter case, reaching them many decades later). Although the risks from such leaching seem remote (Royal Society, 1983; Jollans, 1985; Jenkinson, 1988) there is nonetheless EC legislation setting limits which must not be exceeded. Since the intention of such legislation is to reassure the public, limits may be set with inadequate evidence and are difficult to change – though clearly it is most unfortunate to get trapped into such a situation. Scientific evidence is always going to change with time and it must be sensible to have mechanisms for adjusting to this.

TABLE 2. Technological possibilities for crop production.

Increased resistance to pests and diseases to frost damage	Blaxter (1986) North (1990b) Lycett & Grierson (1991)
Tolerance to salinity and other inhospitable environments	Blaxter (1986) Commins & Higgins (1988)
Response to CO_2 (including greater use of C4 plants)	Blaxter (1986) North (1990b)
Genetic engineering to produce useful organic compounds in plants	Daly (1985)
Application of molecular biology in plant breeding	Flavell et al. (1983) Day (1987) Federici (1991)
Algal culture	Pirt (1984)
Baculoviruses with B.t. genes	Sunderland (1990)
Bacillus thuringiensis	Shields (1987)
Antifeedants	Dunn (1987)
Pheromones	BMA (1992) Lampkin (1990) Hurst et al. (1991)
Transgenic plants	Vaeck et al. (1987)
Biocontrol by nematodes	Georgis & Hague (1991)
Biocontrol by fungi and viruses) Use of microbial enzymes)	Lynch & Crook (1992)
Novel machinery	O'Callaghan (1991)

Protection may also be extended to farm workers, exposed members of the public, wildlife (both fauna and flora) and its habitats, the landscape and the environment generally.

In the case of farm livestock, protection is chiefly in terms of welfare, since this includes health, nutrition and shelter as well as behavioural aspects.

Historically, agriculturalists tended to regard legislation as bureaucratic interference, to be kept to a minimum. Increasingly, however, it is seen as a necessary control on unfair competition and fraudulent claims, provided that it is universally agreed, applied and policed - at least within a trading bloc such as the EC. Where it is not, it may still be possible to claim advantages for products that result from properly controlled production processes.

The current harmonisation of welfare (and other) legislation may have far-reaching consequences (Evans, 1991).

It is too early to judge yet how competitiveness within the EC has been affected by environmental policies (Freeman, 1991) but, in any case, these are matters of great complexity.

PUBLIC OPINION

Since public opinion is never homogeneous, it is hard to be sure exactly who is represented when 'public opinion' is quoted.

Polls represent a small sample and are obliged to ask rather simplified questions. Pressure groups often appear to represent public opinion but it may be dangerous to assume that they do so, especially if they are rather extreme in their views.

Many people may support such groups, because they think it is a good thing to have active champions in the field, but it does not follow that their policies and pronouncements carry the full backing of their members.

There is a widespread assumption that intensive agriculture has greatly damaged the European environment, landscape, wildlife and their habitats (Barber, 1985; Korbey, 1985; Melchett, 1985; CAS, 1988; Baldock, 1990; Jackson, 1990) and such diverse authors as Melchett (1985) and Barber (1988) have argued that, if fields ceased to be farmed with high levels of inputs, wildlife would benefit immensely. However, Barber (1991) has subsequently judged that no irreparable damage has been done to biodiversity by intensive farming in the UK.

In response to public pressure, countries like Denmark and Sweden are taking environmental protection very seriously (Crouch & Peck, 1991; Bernson & Ekström, 1991) especially with regard to pesticide use, where there is felt to be widespread overuse (Griffiths, 1988; Taylor & Dixon, 1990).

However, in a summary of the results of opinion polls, Hodge (1990a) showed that, despite the publicity given to the impact of agriculture in rural areas, the general public continues to perceive urban-based threats as more significant.

Those who represent consumers also recognise that the role that pesticides have played in producing the abundant choice and variety of produce now available is not generally appreciated: "The benefits they have bestowed are now in danger of being swamped in a list of perceived disbenefits ..." (Graham, 1990). It is also not recognised that important consequences flow from the increased cost and timescale involved in the production of new pesticides (Finney, 1988).

Barber (1985) referred to a 1984 CLA (Country Land-owners Association) poll in which most people saw landscape and scenery as the most important benefits from the countryside, with wildlife second and food production third: an overwhelming majority disapproved of changes caused by modern farming.

However, Carter (1985) argued that high-intensity farming is quite consistent with proper regard for wildlife and landscape, and Raymond (1985) considered that lower-input systems would not necessarily lead to environmental benefit. It is often held (e.g. Hunter-Smith, 1985) that small-scale farming has less intrinsic potential for environmental damage, but there is little clear evidence in practice.

It seems likely that sweeping generalisations about systems and methods are invalid and do not help the debate at all. In other words, neither the scale of farming, nor even the nature of it, will necessarily have a harmful or a beneficial effect on the environment.

Nonetheless, there appear to be some deeply held notions that are deployed in argument as if they are self-evident truths. One example is that what is 'natural' is in some way better. As a generalised proposition it is manifest nonsense. The curious thing is that this does not stop people either using it or attacking it - both of which are wholly unrewarding activities. The fact that it is nonsense can be illustrated by the range of human behaviour, all quite natural, from bestial to saintly; or by fearful human disease and parasitism - all natural but generally judged undesirable; the behaviour of predatory animals when the prey are our pets, our livestock or ourselves; or by suffering caused by 'natural' disasters; or ... the list is endless.

It should be obvious that no-one can seriously hold the proposition to be true in this general sense, that it is not worth attacking and that poll questions about it cannot elicit sensible answers.

What we should be trying to establish is the sense, or senses, in which it is believed to be true, and this may be different from what is commonly articulated. For example, the idea that 'natural' sources of food are safer than 'artificial' (meaning synthesised, manufactured, with additives etc.) is so easily disposed of by reference to naturally occurring toxins (Fenwick & Lewis, 1989; GRO-ACT, 1991) that it can be held only by those ignorant of the facts. We should not be dismissive about this (Spedding, 1991b), however, since we are all ignorant about most subjects.

It seems more likely that the idea is simply used as a weapon with which to attack the use of substances (including agrochemicals) that arouse fears in people in no position to substantiate them. This does not make them unreal or unfounded, however.

There may be rather better grounds for suspecting that man-made synthetic chemicals damage the environment more than 'natural' ones (Hibbitt, 1990), because it is the 'natural' environment that is being considered. (If it were a hospital environment, for example, the idea would be self-evidently untrue.)

Similar considerations apply to the concept of 'risk'. It is quite understandable that human fears are not simply related to the degree of risk, even where this is understood and quantified. In fact, few of us behave rationally in relation to risk and probably few of us could quantify most of the risks to which we are exposed.

Thus the fact that people appear to rate the risks of pesticide poisoning very much higher than the facts warrant (Berry, 1990; Huckle, 1991) should not be surprising. Indeed, I was previously totally unaware that in 1988 there were nine times as many garden accidents with flowerpots as with insecticides!

The fact is that we have already adjusted (however inadequately) to old or familiar risks and we take new ones much more seriously. Similarly, we dislike involuntary risks and are offended where risk and benefit are separated (Finney, 1990).

Life abounds with risks and it really cannot be expected that people will be greatly influenced by relative risk assessments.

In any event, attitudes to risk change with age and must be influenced by a host of other factors. Attitudes thus vary greatly between countries, even within Europe. There is, for example, a general concern with conservation but most EC countries think of conservation as an "off-farm" matter (Espie, 1991) and farms in mainland Europe appear to be less aware of conservation issues than in the UK, although there are notable exceptions, such as attitudes to pollution in the Netherlands.

However it is arrived at, public opinion is now a powerful force for change in agriculture and cannot be ignored.

There are many ways of tackling the difficulties that this causes. Education and information flow (Anon., 1991) are highly desirable but they cannot solve the problem, simply because we can none of us ever be sufficiently well informed about all the issues on which we, as citizens, ought to have views.

One clear conclusion is that confrontation is not the answer.

The trouble is that there is a tendency to ignore moderates, precisely because they can be safely ignored, and to react only when this has given rise (and support) to extremists. Confrontation is then fostered by the critics and it is very hard, once this position has been reached, for those attacked to get off the defensive.

This has been most clearly demonstrated in relation to animal welfare but the principles are transferable.

The first step in reassuring concerned people is to take their concerns seriously, even when they are unfounded or exaggerated. Taking worries seriously has nothing to do with believing or confirming them and, if you brush them aside, those who hold them will not trust you at all from that time on.

Taking them seriously means listening to them and trying to understand them or, quite often, what lies behind them (Spedding, 1991b). This kind of constructive dialogue can lead to better informed debate and the possibility of education.

EDUCATION

There is no possibility of everyone being as well informed as each specialist: consider the volume of literature on pesticides alone (Schmidt, 1986; Hurst et al., 1991). Although education cannot therefore be relied upon to solve these problems, it is nonetheless one of the pillars for future progress. Probably the most important general area of biology upon which it would be worth concentrating is the ecological notion of 'balance'. The 'balance' of nature, between species, and the notion of human activity 'in harmony' with nature, lie behind some prevalent public attitudes and are deployed to support whatever action a group advocates. There needs to be a better understanding of the complexity of ecological relationships: concepts of biological control, notions about the dangers of releasing genetically modified organisms, food chains and an appreciation of what may be termed 'natural' - all depend upon this.

As Graham-Bryce (1991) pointed out, environmental aspects of pesticides are often considered in isolation without any recognition that the environment can accept some impact without impairment. He also drew attention to the difficulties in interpreting evidence, even from controlled experiments on the effects of pesticides and distinguishing these from other effects of the farming systems used. However, it is not only the public who need to think clearly about these issues.

Frequently, when the public try to get a measure of whether agrochemical usage is increasing or decreasing, they are told that a litre of one is not comparable to a litre of another. When they then move to comparisons of quantities of active ingredients, they may be told that these too are meaningless. Someone has to say how usage can be measured and compared or such arguments will be seen as designed only to confuse.

The complexity of the interactions between pesticide use and world food production is enormous (Conway, 1982) and it is hard to draw up any kind of balance sheet for and against the use of pesticides. Nevertheless, it is necessary to recognise the main arguments. The case for pesticides rests primarily on the avoidance of crop losses, during production and post-harvest.

It is generally accepted that pesticides have had enormous effects on levels of production (Rickard, 1991) and it is often assumed that the growth of world population increases the need for them (Kraus, 1988; Beyer, 1991).   However, it has to be recognised that hunger and malnutrition are primarily a result of poverty (Bunting, 1992).

Apart from the aftermath of major disasters, such as earthquakes or floods, no-one who has money goes hungry, and if the hungry had money the food they need would be produced.

The problems of hunger and malnutrition are not primarily those of lack of knowledge of how to produce food.

The main arguments against pesticides are: (1) that they endanger food safety by leaving harmful residues; (2) that they harm the environment, chiefly in terms of wildlife but also in terms of effects on operators and those innocently exposed to spray drift; (3) that they are unsustainable in terms of energy costs; and (4) that they are ineffective (and unsustainable) because of the development of resistance.

Much of the public image derives from past experience with well-known pesticides such as DDT, but the complexity of agroecosystems makes it difficult to be sure, in advance, that problems can be foreseen (Conway, 1990).

ALTERNATIVE WAYS FORWARD

Against this background of arguments for and against high-input farming (because parallel cases are made for and against fertilisers), it is clear that a wide range of options exist for the future.

The first possibility is to continue to use all available technology, but this will clearly be constrained by increasing legislation, even if public opinion is disregarded. The arguments are in any case strong for a reduced dependence on agrochemicals because of the high costs and the development of resistance where pesticide usage is both high and frequent.

A second possibility is the extension of organic farming. This, and even the terminology, are now controlled in the EC by Regulation (EC, 1992) and other countries are following suit. The word 'organic' (and its linguistic equivalents) is allowed only where products have been produced to laid-down Standards by registered producers and processors, and where producers are registered and inspected by the nationally recognised authority (in the UK, by UKROFS - the UK Register of Organic Food Standards). None of this makes any claim for the product itself, only for the production method.

Currently, organic farming represents a very small sector (Lampkin, 1990) and is no threat to any other form of agriculture, unless it reinforces in the public mind the idea that agrochemicals are 'bad' for whatever reason. Some people believe that organically produced food is better nutritionally and tastes better: others believe that, since no agrochemicals are used, there is less risk of even unknown consequences.

There is more evidence that the use of agrochemicals may damage the environment but some of the substances permitted in organic production may also do so (Graham-Bryce, 1991). Certainly one of the objects of organic farming is to minimise damage to the environment (Young, 1989) and, if it does so, the EC will look on it with favour (Johnson, 1989).

Quite apart from fully organic systems, there are many versions of lower-iinput systems, because these can include a range of intermediate levels of input.

There are possibilities for lower-input grassland systems, because legumes can provide biologically fixed nitrogen at a rate that is higher than the average application of fertiliser N in the UK (Prescott et al., 1988; Young, 1992).

It is possible that increasing dependence on clover would benefit from the use of pesticides (Lewis et al., 1991).

Such systems avoid extreme positions and are likely, therefore, to employ some form of integrated pest management.

Biological control appears to some members of the public to be the obvious way forward. Natural populations control one another all the time but, as van Emden (1987) has pointed out, co-evolution between, for example, aphids and their indigenous natural enemies is such that biological control to a level acceptable to growers of field crops would rarely occur in the absence of manipulative intervention.

Monoculture, it has been argued (Lupton, 1984), is a sort of negative biological control, oversimplifying the population mix. Most plants are not attacked by most pests and pathogens (Shields, 1987) as the majority of such enemies are host specific and natural toxins abound as defence mechanisms (Rosenthal, 1986).

The possibilities of intervention increase all the time, such as the selection of naturally occurring fungi to control nematodes (Crump et al., 1990) and the use of Baculoviruses that occur only in invertebrates (Lynch & Crook, 1992).

Meanwhile, there is an increasing awareness of the devastating errors that can be made by introducing exotic species of animals for the purpose of biological control (Johnson, 1991).

These alternative technologies have to be applied within changing patterns of agriculture, responding to other pressures.

CHANGING PATTERNS OF AGRICULTURE

Change in agriculture in one part of the world is not immune to changes elsewhere. Nuclear accidents are part of the general uncertainty but even foreseeable change cannot be predicted in either detail or timescale.

For example, there is enormous potential for increased agricultural production in Eastern Europe and the old USSR. There are also enormous difficulties in bringing it about. In World terms, production will meet economic demand and, sooner or later, there will either be intolerable social strain or the demand will rise to meet the need. It is impossible to say, however, how or when this might be brought about.

Within the EC, the immediate problems are overproduction of major commodities and the need to control the cost of the CAP.

The Uruguay round of the GATT talks may mean that even the changes already agreed in the CAP by EC Ministers may not be the final outcome. Certainly there will be reduced support for production, even if not for farmers. If production is reduced, the market for inputs will presumably decrease.

Other possibilities for reform of the CAP are under discussion (see Harvey, 1991a, 1991b; Rickard, 1991; Nix, 1992) and the economic framework finally established will have a dominant effect on the whole industry (as stated at the outset of this paper).

It is worth noting some of the policy scenarios that might be possible.

Increased production of non-food products

Agriculture has always produced non-food products (e.g. wool, cotton) and it is possible that overproduction of (mainly) foodstuffs might lead to a change in the balance, with more use of food products for non-food purposes and more production of specifically non-food products. Examples of the former are cereals as raw materials for industry (Rexen & Munck, 1984; Valentine, 1990) and, of the latter, biomass production, mainly for fuel (Carruthers & Jones, 1983; Spedding, 1990a; McLain, 1991).

Non food production has two main implications for pesticide usage. First, some of the objections to pesticide usage disappear, because the material is not going to be used for food but, secondly, pest damage may not matter greatly since quality and cosmetic appearance may not be so important and total biomass may be the main objective (all this will vary with the end use).

A change in the balance of non-food/food production would have implications for land use and landscape, and for the development of rural industry. It has an effect, therefore, on social patterns, on rural populations and on the balance of the argument as to whether the majority of the land should be agriculturally employed and thus available if the need for food production were to change in the future.

Animal welfare regulations

Considerations of improved animal welfare may greatly change livestock production systems (Evans, 1991) and thus the cropping patterns that sustain them. The importance of this may be judged from the fact that, in the UK, the two-thirds of the agricultural land in grass and some one third of the cereals are used solely for livestock production. In Europe as a whole (90 countries), the proportion of agricultural area in grass is about 43% (Lee, 1983), but an estimate for Europe more narrowly defined, suggests that 80% of the agricultural area is devoted to livestock production (van Dijk & Hoogervorst, 1983).

The impact of a significant increase in vegetarianism can be imagined (Spedding, 1990b). The size of the agricultural industry depends upon livestock production: without it, <u>all</u> the resources needed by agriculture would greatly diminish. The social implications of this to those involved in the food chain are enormous - from the input industries to processors and retailers.

Protection of the environment

Pollution caused by farm wastes (Nielsen, 1990) may be controlled in ways that change production patterns: use of wastes to generate fuel energy would be a sensible way forward. The 'polluter pays' principle is likely to operate increasingly in cases of this kind.

For positive environmental impact, government policy may take the form of protected areas such as ESAs (Environmentally Sensitive Areas) (Smith, 1989; HMSO, 1990b) or land-owners may endeavour to sell environmental land management as a service (CLA, 1989).

Certainly, the EC increasingly places environmental issues higher on the policy-making agenda (de Salis, 1990; Delbeke, 1991) and most European countries now have a 'green' party (Hodge, 1990b).

It is reported (Anon., 1990) that German farmers now receive a biological control subsidy for using predatory wasps instead of pesticides to protect maize against the European corn borer.

There is some disagreement currently as to whether there should be closer integration of agricultural and countryside policies (Rickard, 1991) or whether they should be kept separate (Barber, 1991).

Extensification

The dangers of a 2-tier structure of land use have been highlighted by Oliver-Bellasis (1991), in terms of the best land being used for low-cost production with damage to ecosystems and the poorer land not generating enough money for good stewardship.

Some would prefer to see a general extensification (Taylor & Dixon, 1990), though not necessarily to the point of organic farming.

'Extensive' and 'intensive' are terms used in a variety of ways but there is a strong public theme that inputs such as agrochemicals are not needed, since we have an embarrassment of surpluses. This may appear difficult to square with public concern about the hungry people of the world but, in fact, the answer to world hunger rarely lies in food aid.

What is required is to increase food production where it is needed, whether in Eastern Europe or in developing countries.

Achieving this is both difficult and complex but requires resources, mainly finance but also some skills: for example, book-keeping skills might make co-operatives feasible - co-operatives that included food distribution and retailing, to avoid exploitation by middle-men.

New thinking is required here. For example, a supply of cheap oil and small-scale equipment to third-world farmers could release all the land currently cultivated but producing feed for livestock used for traction and transport.

PUBLIC OPINION - THE FORCE OF THE FUTURE?

Public perceptions are a reality - even when they are ill-founded and erroneous - and can influence demand for agricultural products.

It is crucial therefore to understand how such perceptions are formed and can be changed. As Brook (1990) has pointed out, parading achievements, however genuine, is ineffective: they are regarded as irrelevant at best and as a smoke-screen at worst.

It was argued earlier that education, desirable though that is, can hardly operate on the scale required: in any event, it must not be brain-washing or persuasion but a genuine attempt to help people to make up their own minds on important issues.

Before public perceptions of agriculture can be altered, it is the industry itself that must be prepared to change (Brook, 1990) and to be seen to be genuinely doing so (Spedding, 1991b).

In the context of crop protection, industry has to be and be seen to be genuinely concerned to move with (or ahead of) justified public concerns about the use of and dependence on pesticides. But changes should not be made piecemeal without an understanding of their wider effects.

As Sir Crispin Tickell (1991) has expressed it: "We need a value system which enshrines the principle of sustainable development. Isolated measures designed to cope with one problem can make others worse."

SUSTAINABILITY

Graham-Bryce (1991) concluded that the current unifying concept bringing needs of conservation and human demands together is that of 'sustainable development'.

There is, of course, a danger that 'sustainability' will be used by different people to mean whatever 'green' package they wish to advocate, but there is some general acceptance of the Brundtland definition (Brundtland, 1987): "To meet the needs of the present generation without compromising the ability of future generations to meet their own needs." Such concepts are quite difficult to apply to individual sectors, as if they existed in isolation, but also immensely difficult to apply worldwide.

In the context of this paper, it has to be asked: What agricultural practices (and especially those of crop protection) are sustainable? Those that are unprofitable will be unsustainable economically. Some are clearly unsustainable technically, such as treatments to which organisms become resistant. High yields may be unsustainable because of the inputs required or because high-yielding crops are more susceptible to obligatory plant-parasitic pests and diseases, like aphids, mildew and rusts, mainly as a result of higher nitrogen concentrations in the attacked tissues (de Wit, 1990).

Some will be unsustainable if the public finds them unacceptable and this will reflect their perceptions and be expressed as public opinion.

What then can be concluded from this very complex mixture of themes?

CONCLUSIONS

1. There is a need for clarity of thought by both the public and the industry.

2. It is a mistake to attack the opposing extremists as if they <u>are</u> the spokesmen for the other side. This only offends the moderates and gives more power to the extremists.

3. It is wise to recognise that there are tides of opinion that tend to attract followers, who then speak out with unnatural strength, while those opposed to the tide keep quiet. Extremists try to create such tides and they are the negation of informed debate.

4. Education is needed, especially in relation to ecological balances, in the consequences of success of public pressure (e.g. the effects on commercial innovation), in the nature of risk and in the role of natural toxins.

5. Consumers should be involved in formulating the questions and identifying the problems, with access to all relevant information.

6. Industry should play a major role in funding R&D to fill gaps in our knowledge and help in the innovation of improved systems.

7. Industry should accept responsibility for devising solutions, which should then be subjected to independent testing. To avoid an overburdensome programme of testing, close monitoring of practice should be considered.

REFERENCES

Anon. (1990) Farmers Weekly, 20 July, 1990, 50.
Anon. (1991) Public access to information on pesticides. Pesticides News (14) December 1991, 18.
Baldock, D. (1990) Agriculture and Habitat Loss in Europe. WWF International CAP Discussion Paper No 3, Gland.
Barber, Sir Derek (1985) Comments on the options. In: Food production and our rural environment – the way ahead (Ed. A. Korbey) CAS Paper 17, Centre for Agricultural Strategy, University of Reading, 54-58.

Barber, Sir Derek (1988) The Countryside: decline and renaissance. Journal of the Royal Agricultural Society of England 150, 81-89.

Barber, Sir Derek (1991) The State of Agriculture in the United Kingdom. Report to the RASE, November 1991, RASE.

Barnoud, F.; Rinaudo, M. (1986) New perspectives in large-scale procurement of pulps and fibres from European agricultural products. In: Alternative uses for agricultural surpluses, CEC, 74-76 (Eds W.F. Raymond; P. Larvor) Elsevier Applied Science.

Bernson, V.; Ekström, G. (1991) Swedish policy to reduce pesticide use. Pesticide Outlook, 2, (3), 33-36.

Berry, C.L. (1990) The hazards of healthy living - the agricultural component. Proceedings Brighton Crop Protection Conference - Pests and Diseases 1990, 1, 3-13.

Beyer, E.M. (1991) Crop protection: meeting the challenge. Proceedings Brighton Crop Protection Conference - Weeds 1991, 1, 3-22.

Blaxter, K.L. (1986) People, Food and Resources. Cambridge University Press.

BMA (1992) Pesticides, Chemicals and Health. Publication on behalf of the British Medical Association by Edward Arnold.

Brook, R. (1990) The public image of animal production. Journal of the Royal Agricultural Society of England 151, 103-111.

Brundtland, G.H. (1987) Our Common Future. World Commission on Environment and Development. Oxford University Press.

Bunting, A.H. (1992) Feeding the World in the Future. In: Fream's Principles of Food and Agriculture (Ed. C.R.W. Spedding) Blackwell Scientific Publications, 256-290.

Burdus, A. (1988) Competition in the food distribution sector. Ch 4 in: Competition policy in the food industries (Eds J. Burns; A. Swinbank) Food Economics Study No 4, 68-94. Department of Agricultural Economics and Management, University of Reading.

Carruthers, S.P.; Jones, M.R. (1983) Biofuel production strategies for UK agriculture. CAS Paper 13, Centre for Agricultural Strategy, University of Reading.

Carter, E.S. (1985) Intensive systems - their effect on the environment. In: Food production and our rural environment - the way ahead (Ed. A. Korbey) CAS Paper 17, Centre for Agricultural Strategy, University of Reading.

CAS (1988) Public perception of the countryside (Eds F.A. Miller; R.B. Tranter) CAS Paper 18. Centre for Agricultural Strategy, University of Reading.

CLA (1989) Enterprise in the rural environment. Greenwell Working Party Report. CLA, London, April 1989.

Commins, P.; Higgins, J.V. (1988) New technologies and the prospects of Europe's farmers. Outlook on Agriculture 17 (1), 2-6.

Conway, G.R. (1982) Pesticide resistance and world food production (Ed. G.R. Conway). Imperial College Centre for Environmental Technology, 48 Princes Gardens, London SW7. ISBN: 0-950-7744-1-3.

Conway, G.R. (1990) Agroecosystems. Ch 9 in: Systems Theory Applied to Agriculture and the Food Chain (Eds J.G.W. Jones; P.R. Street) Elsevier Applied Science.

Crouch, J.; Peck, J. (1991) Correcting a misconception. The Agronomist, 1991, (3) 14-15.

Crump, D.; de Leij, F.; Kerry, B. (1990) Nematode pests: the need for biological control. The Agronomist, 1990, (1), 6-7.

Daly, P. (1985) The Biotechnology Business: a strategic analysis. Printer (London), Rowman and Allanheld (NJ).

Day, P.D. (1987) Crop Improvement: constraints and challenges.
    Proceedings British Crop Protection Conference - Weeds 1987,
    1, 1-12.
Delbeke, J. (1991) European policies for environmental protection.
    Ch 6 in: Green futures for economic growth (Ed. T. Barker) Cambridge
    Econometrics, 89-96.
de Salis, W. (1990) Environmental pressures on the land. In: Farming
    under Pressure. Farming Issues 5, 18-21, Lloyds Bank.
de Wit, C. T. (1990) Understanding and Managing Changes in Agriculture.
    Ch 10 in: Systems Theory Applied to Agriculture and the Food Chain
    (Eds J.G.W. Jones; P.R. Street) Elsevier Applied Science.
Dunn, N. (1987) Coming: crops that insects hate. The Furrow (2) 92, 5.
EC (1992) EC Organic Food Standards Regulation (EEC) 2092/91.
Espie, A. (1991) Attitudes of European Farmers to Wildlife
    Conservation. Journal of the Royal Agricultural Society of England
    152, 80-87.
Evans, D. (1991) European Community - implications for animal welfare
    of the 'single internal market'. In: Farm Animals: it pays to
    be humane (Ed. S.P. Carruthers) CAS Paper 22, Centre for
    Agricultural Strategy, University of Reading.
Federici, B.A. (1991) Microbial insecticides. Pesticide Outlook 2,
    (3), 22-28.
Fenwick, R.; Lewis, J. (1989) Natural is safe - true or false? The
    Agronomist (3), 14-15.
Finney, J. (1988) World crop protection prospects: demisting the
    crystal ball. Proceedings Brighton Crop Protection Conference -
    Pests and Diseases 1988, 1, 3-14.
Finney, J. (1990) Where do we stand? Where do we go? Presentation
    to the 7th International Conference of Pesticide Chemistry,
    Hamburg, August 5-10, 1990,
Flavell, R.B.; Kemble, R.J.; Gunn, R.E.; Abbott, A.; Baulcombe, D. (1983)
    Applications of molecular biology in plant breeding: the detection
    of genetic variation and viral pathogens. In: Better Crops for
    Food, CIBA Foundation Symposium 97, Pitman, London.
Freeman, R. (1991) Environmental costs and international competitiveness.
    Ch 5 in: Green futures for economic growth (Ed.T. Barker) Cambridge
    Econometrics, 69-84.
Georgis, R.; Hague, N.G.M. (1991) Nematodes as biological insecticides.
    Pesticide Outlook, 2 (3), 29-32.
Graham, J. (1990) The consumer's perceptions and responsibilities.
    In: Food safety in the human food chain (Ed. F.A. Miller) CAS Paper
    20, Centre for Agricultural Strategy, University of Reading, 39-44.
Graham-Bryce, I.J. (1991) Environmental Impacts of Crop Protection
    Products: a Perspective. Journal of the Royal Agricultural Society
    of England 152, 88-89.
Griffiths, W. (1988) Crop Production realism: the role of agro-
    chemicals. Proceedings British Crop Protection Conference,
    Brighton - Pests and Diseases - 1988, 1.
GRO-ACT (1991) Organic vs Conventional Crop Production. GRO-ACT.
    ISBN: 0-9516605-0-0.
Harvey, D.R. (1991a) Economic factors influencing the agricultural
    environment. Pt 1 Policy development and current pressures.
    Agricultural Engineer 46 (3), 71-76.
Harvey, D.R. (1991b) Economic factors influencing the agricultural
    environment. Pt 2 - policy pressures and possible solutions.
    Agricultural Engineer 46, (4) 102-104.

Hibbitt, C. (1990) Putting pesticides in perspective. Agricultural Engineer 45 (2), 61-62.

HMSO (1990a) Bovine Spongiform Encephalopathy (BSE). Report Agriculture Committee, House of Commons, London: HMSO, 10.7.1990.

HMSO (1990b) This Common Inheritance: Britain's Environmental Strategy. Command 1200, London: HMSO.

Hodge, I. (1990a) Conflict or consensus over agricultural and countryside issues? Ch 5 in: Agriculture in Britain (Ed. D. Britton) CAB, 94-104.

Hodge, I. (1990b) The Future Public Pressures on Farming. Ch 7 in: Agriculture in Britain (Ed. D. Britton) CAB, 119-134.

Hodges, R.D.; Scofield, A.M. (1988) Biological husbandry: an introduction to its scientific foundation. Modern organic farming and horticulture. 1 (1), 9-15.

Holden, P. (1989) The case for organic agriculture. Proceedings 1989 National Conference on Organic Food Production, 4-6.

Huckle, K.R. (1991) Risk Assessment - regulatory need or nightmare? Paper presented at 32nd Annual Meeting International Institute Synthetic Rubber Producers, May 1991, Washington DC.

Hunter-Smith J.D. (1985) Small-scale farming and its effect on the rural environment. In: Food production and our rural environment - the way ahead (Ed. A. Korbey) CAS Paper 17, Centre for Agricultural Strategy, University of Reading, 43-52.

Hurst, P.; Hay, A.; Dudley, N. (1991) The Pesticide Handbook, Journeyman, London, Concord, Massachusetts.

Jackson, G.H. (1990) The valleys of abundance, Journal of the Royal Agricultural Society of England 151, 10-20.

Jenkinson, D. (1988) Farming and Nitrates. Farmers Club Journal, 92, 19-26.

Johnson, J. (1991) Biologists plot revenge in war of the snails. New Scientist, August 24, 1991, 14.

Johnson, S. (1989) Organic Agriculture - its role in the EEC. In: The Case for Organic Agriculture. Proceedings 1989 National Conference on Organic Food Production, BOF and OGA, Bristol.

Jollans, J.L. (1985) Fertilisers in UK farming. CAS Rep No 9. Centre for Agricultural Strategy, University of Reading.

Korbey, A. (1985) Food production and our rural environment - the way ahead (Ed. A. Korbey) CAS Paper 17. Proceedings Symposium of Centre for Agricultural Strategy, University of Reading, 29.11.1984.

Kraus, P. (1988) Global pest management in the future. Proceedings of International Symposium on: Changing perspectives in agrochemicals. Neuherberg, 24-27 November 1987, 1-9.

Lampkin, N. (1990) Organic Farming. Farming Press, Ipswich.

Lee, J. (1983) The spatial pattern of grassland production in Europe. Proceedings 9th General Meeting of the European Grassland Federation. BGS Occasional Symposium No 14, 11-20.

Lewis, G.C.; Cook, R.; van der Ende, A. (1991) Effect of agrochemical applied at sowing on seedling emergence and herbage yield of perennial ryegrass and white clover. Grass and Forage Science 46 (2), 121-129.

Lupton, F.G.H.(1984) Biological control: the plant breeder's objective. Annals of Applied Biology 104, 1-16.

Lycett, G.W.; Grierson, D. (1991) Genetic engineering of crop plants (Eds G.W. Lycett; D. Grierson) Butterworths, Guildford. ISBN 0-408-04779-8.

Lynch, J.M.; Crook, N.E. (1992) Biological control systems. Chemistry in Britain, January 1992, 42-45.

Marsh, J.S. (1992) The food and agricultural industry: the food chain in developed and developing countries. Ch 1 in: Fream's Principles of Food and Agriculture (Ed. C.R.W. Spedding) Blackwell Scientific Publications, 1-14.

McLain, H.D. (1991) An overview of harvesting biomass crops. Agricultural Engineer 46 (4), 110-111.

Melchett Lord (1985) Farming for the public, not for ourselves. Proceedings British Crop Protection Conference, Brighton - Weeds, 1, 3-19.

Neville-Rolfe, E. (1990) British agricultural policy and the EC. Ch 10 in: Agriculture in Britain: changing pressures and policies (Ed. D. Britton) CAB. ISBN: 0-85198-655-2.

Nielsen, V.C. (1990) Farm Waste Management: The challenge of the next decade. Journal of the Royal Agricultural Society of England 151, 187-200.

Nix, J. (1992) Will there be life after GATT and MacSharry? The Agronomist (1), 2-3.

North, J. (1990a) Future agricultural land use patterns. Ch 4 in: Agriculture in Britain: changing pressures and policies (Ed. D. Britton) CAB. ISBN: 0-85198-655-2.

North, J. (1990b) Technology. Ch 3 in: Agriculture in Britain: changing pressures and policies (Ed. D. Britton) CAB. ISBN: 0-85198-655-2.

O'Callaghan, J.R. (1991) Engineering Opportunities in the Environment. The Agricultural Engineer 46 (3), 80-83

Oliver-Bellasis, H. (1991) What if? A vision of the future of our industry - a farmer's view. Farmland Market 36, 14-15.

Parry, M.L.; Carter, T.R.; Porter, J.H. (1989) The Greenhouse Effect on the Future of UK Agriculture. Journal of the Royal Agricultural Society of England 150, 120-131.

Pirt, S.J. (1984) Algal photosynthesis: the Aladdin's cave of biotechnology. Chemistry and Industry, December 3, 1984, 843-849.

Prescott, J.H.D.; Wilkins, R.J.; Stoddart, J.L. (1988) AFRC Grassland and Ruminant Research: Science for Sustainable Grassland Farming. Journal of the Royal Agricultural Society of England 150 195-210.

Raymond, W.F. (1985) Lower input systems, their effect on the environment. In: Food production and our rural environment - the way ahead (Ed. A. Korbey) CAS Paper 17, Centre for Agricultural Strategy, University of Reading, 33-42.

Rexen, F.; Munck, L. (1984) Cereal crops for industrial use in Europe. Report prepared for the Commission of the EC, EUR 9617 EN.

Rickard, S. (1991) UK Farming: The Economic Background. Proceedings British Crop Protection Conference, Brighton - Weeds 1991, 755-61.

Rosenthal, G.A. (1986) The chemical defences of higher plants. Scientific American 254 (1), 76.

Royal Society (1983) The nitrogen cycle of the UK. The Royal Society, 1983.

Schmidt, G.H. (1986) Pestizide und Umweltschutz. Vieweg, Wiesbaden, 1986. 466 pp. ISBN: 3-528-08903-2.

Shields, R. (1987) Towards insect-resistant plants. Nature 328, No 6125, 12.

Smith, E.J.G. (1989) Environmentally Sensitive Areas: a successful UK initiative. Journal of the Royal Agricultural Society of England 150, 30-43.

Spedding, C.R.W. (1990a) Opportunities for energy production. Report of RASC Conference, Peterborough, 1990.

Spedding, C.R.W. (1990b) The Impact of Organic Foods and Vegetarianism. Ch 16 in: Foods for the '90s (Eds G.G. Birch; G. Campbell-Platt; M.G. Lindley) Elsevier Applied Science, 231-241.

Spedding, C.R.W. (1991a) Shaping 21st Century British Agriculture - Pressures, Problems and Solutions. Massey Ferguson National Agricultural Award Lecture, 23.10.1991, RSA, London.

Spedding C.R.W. (1991b) Thinking about the future. Journal of the Royal Agricultural Society of England 152, 31-35.

Sunderland, K.D. (1990) The future for biological control. Professional Horticulture 4, 11-20.

Taylor, J.P.; Dixon, J.B. (1990) Agriculture and the Environment: Towards Integration. RSPB, Sandy.

Tickell, Sir Crispin (1991) What we must do to save the planet. New Scientist 7.9.1991, 16.

Vaeck, M.; Reynaerts, A.; Höfte, H.; Jansens, S.; De Beuckelear, M.; Dean, C.; Zabean, M.; Van Montague, M.; Leemans, J. (1987) Transgenic plants protected from insect attack. Nature 328, No 6125, 33-37.

Valentine, J. (1990) Oats: Historical perspective, present and prospects. Journal of the Royal Agricultural Society of England 151, 161-176.

van Dijk, G.; Hoogerworst, N. (1983) The demand for grassland in Europe towards 2000. Some implications of a possible scenario. Proceedings 9th General Meeting of the European Grassland Federation. BGS Occasional Symposium No 14, 21-32.

van Emden H.F. (1987) Paper to: Biological control of pests, pathogens and weeds: development and prospects. Royal Society Discussion meeting London, 18-19 February, 1987.

Whitby, M. (1990) Multiple land use and the market for countryside goods. Journal of the Royal Agricultural Society of England 151, 32-43.

Woolhouse, H.W. (1988) Food for Thought. Journal of the Royal Agricultural Society of England 150, 221-228.

Young, N.E. (1992) Low cost grass from home made nitrogen. Paper to the 46th Oxford Farming Conference, January 7-8, 1992.

Young, R. (1989) The Soil Association Conservation Guidelines. In: The Case for Organic Agriculture. Proceedings 1989 National Conference on Organic Food Production, BOF and OCA, Bristol.

SESSION 2

NEW COMPOUNDS, FORMULATIONS AND USES – INSECTICIDES

CHAIRMAN   PROFESSOR M. F. CLARIDGE

SESSION
ORGANISER   MR C. FURK

RESEARCH REPORTS   2-1 to 2-9

FIPRONIL: A NEW SOIL AND FOLIAR BROAD SPECTRUM INSECTICIDE

F. COLLIOT

Rhône-Poulenc Agro, Lyon, France

K. A. KUKOROWSKI

Rhône-Poulenc Ag Company, Research Triangle Park, NC, USA

D. W. HAWKINS, D. A. ROBERTS

Rhône-Poulenc Agriculture, Ltd., Ongar, Essex.

ABSTRACT

Fipronil [(±)-5-amino-1-(2,6-dichloro-α,α,α-trifluoro-p-tolyl)-4-tri-fluoromethylsulfinylpyrazole-3-carbonitrile] is a new pyrazole insecticide that provides excellent control of many soil and foliar insects on a wide variety of crops and non-crops. Fipronil at 120 g AI/ha applied to the soil effectively controls corn rootworm beetle larvae, *Diabrotica* spp., and wireworm larvae, *Limonius* spp. and *Agriotes* spp. Fipronil at 25-50 g AI/ha applied to foliage controls many chewing insect pests such as Colorado potato beetle, *Leptinotarsa decemlineata*; diamondback moth, *Plutella xylostella*; and boll weevil, *Anthonomus grandis grandis*. Rice paddy treatments of fipronil at 50 g AI/ha provide excellent control of stem borer, *Chilo* spp.; brown planthopper, *Nilaparvata lugens*; and rice water weevil, *Lissorhoptrus oryzophilus*. Additionally, insects resistant or tolerant to pyrethroid, cyclodiene, organophosphate and/or carbamate insecticides are not cross resistant to fipronil, thus making fipronil an especially effective candidate for resistance management programs.

INTRODUCTION

The insecticidal properties of fipronil were discovered by Rhône-Poulenc Agro in 1987 at Ongar, U. K. This phenyl pyrazole insecticide is a potent blocker of the GABA regulated chloride channel. Fipronil is a highly effective insecticide against both piercing-sucking and chewing insects, and can be effectively delivered via soil, foliar, bait, or seed treatment applications.

Fipronil is currently in worldwide development. This paper reports on the chemical and biological properties of fipronil.

CHEMICAL AND PHYSICAL PROPERTIES

Code Number: MB 46030
Common Name: Fipronil [BSI]
Structural Formula:

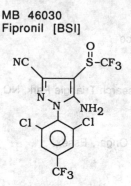

Molecular Formula: $C_{12}H_4Cl_2F_6N_4OS$
Molecular Weight: 437
Appearance: white solid
Melting Point: 200-201ºC
Vapor Pressure: 2.8×10^{-9} mm Hg at 20ºC
Solubility: water   2 mg/l
     acetone   >50%
     corn oil   >10,000 mg/l
Log P: 4.0 [by shake flask method, octanol/water partition]
Primary Formulations: 20% Suspension Concentrate
     0.2, 1.5% and 2.0% Granule
     60% Flowable Suspension

MAMMALIAN TOXICITY

Acute oral LD_{50} [rat]:   100 mg/kg
Acute dermal LD_{50} [rat]:   >2000 mg/kg
Ames test: negative
Chromosome aberration: negative
Skin irritation: not irritant
Eye irritation: slight irritant

ECOTOXICITY

Daphnia LC_{50} [48 h]:   0.19 mg/l
Mallard duck LD_{50}:   >2150 mg/kg
Pheasant LD_{50}:   31 mg/kg
Japanese carp LC_{50} [96 h]:   0.34 mg/l

BIOLOGICAL PROPERTIES

Laboratory Evaluation

The biological activity of fipronil to a wide variety of insects is presented in Table 1. For all these insects except *Musca domestica* and *Diabrotica virgifera*, the technical AI was diluted in 5% acetone + 95% water and sprayed onto host plants either pre or post infested.

Fipronil was added to 10% sucrose and provided ad libitum to adult *Musca domestica*. Fipronil diluted in 1% acetone + 99% water was added (*m/m*) to soil containing both maize seeds and *D. virgifera* larvae. Fipronil exhibits very good activity to a wide spectrum of serious insect pests, including aphids, leafhoppers, planthoppers, chewing Lepidoptera and Coleoptera, flies, and soil inhabiting Coleoptera.

TABLE 1. Biological activity of fipronil against a variety of insects measured by LC50 [or '*' LC90] in mg/l.

Species [and stadium at initiation of test]	Fipronil	Cypermethrin
Aphis gossypii [MP]	1.2	0.1
Nilaparvata lugens [L]*	0.2	0.5
Nephotettix cincticeps [L]*	5.0	5.0
Spodoptera eridania [L2]	4.0	2.0
Spodoptera frugiperda [L2]	3.6	1.6
Plutella xylostella [L2]*	0.3	0.4
Heliothis virescens [L2]	4.3	3.0
Heliothis armigera [L2]*	10.0	0.4
Helicoverpa zea [L2]	1.8	1.4
Leptinotarsa decemlineata [L]	0.03	0.23
Musca domestica [A]	0.39	5.0
Diabrotica virgifera [E]	0.03	-

'MP' = mixed population of adults + juveniles
'L' = mixture of larval/nymphal instars
'L2' = 2nd instar larvae
'A' = adult stage
'E' = egg stage

TABLE 2. Biological activity [LC50 in mg/l] of fipronil against insects resistant to cyclodiene, pyrethroid, or carbamate insecticides.

Insect and resistance	Fipronil	Cypermethrin	Dieldrin	Carbaryl
M. domestica S	0.4	-	0.3	-
M. domestica C	36.0	-	867.0	-
H. virescens S	4.3	3.0	-	320
H. virescens P	7.2	327.0	-	>500
L. decemlineata S	0.03	0.23	-	29
L. decemlineata LIR	0.34	8.90	-	>500

'S' = susceptible culture
'C' = cyclodiene resistant culture
'P' = pyrethroid resistant culture
'LIR' = Long Island, NY, USA mixed resistance culture

The mode of action of fipronil was determined to be by blockage of the GABA regulated chloride channel. Subsequent laboratory bioassays indicate that fipronil has practically no effect on acetylcholine esterase. Also, insects with known resistance to various cyclodiene, pyrethroid, or carbamate insecticides were susceptible to fipronil [Table 2].

Field Evaluation

In general, there has never been phytotoxicity by any fipronil formulation on any crops tested. Table 3 summarizes the field performance of fipronil by recommending field use rates providing the highest quality control of the various pests listed.

Soil application

Fipronil has provided consistent, excellent control of *Diabrotica* corn rootworm larvae [120 g AI/ha as modified in-furrow or narrow band incorporated at planting] and *Agriotes* wireworm larvae [50-150 g AI/ha as a band incorporated at planting] [Table 3] in numerous field trials in both the mid-western USA and Europe during 1989-1992. Fipronil's field performance against these serious soil pests [and many more currently being researched] provides control at a fraction of the use rate of current organophosphate standards. Note that like the pyrethroid tefluthrin, fipronil provides control of *Diabrotica* larvae at one tenth the rate of organophosphate standards. Fipronil must be incorporated into the soil thoroughly and properly to attain maximum benefit of its low use rate.

Granule fipronil applications to rice provide superior control of *Chilo spp.*, stem borer, and *Nilaparvata lugens*, brown planthopper. Both pests are controlled with a single low rate application of fipronil at planting [50-100 g AI/ha broadcast surface application] [Table 3]. Also, granular applications of fipronil to rice in the planter box provide outstanding field control of *Lissorhoptrus oryzophilus*, rice water weevil [50-100 g AI/ha equivalent rate] even after the treated rice is transplanted into untreated rice fields.

Foliar application

Fipronil at very low application rates [12.5-25 g AI/ha] provides rapid, outstanding control of *Leptinotarsa decemlineata* larvae and adults on potatoes [Table 3]. Additionally, fipronil provides excellent, long-lasting control of many other serious foliar pests including *Plutella xylostella*, *Trichoplusia ni*, *Pieris rapae*, *Anthonomus grandis grandis*, and *Frankliniella* spp. at 25-50 g AI/ha use rates. Fipronil is effective on these pests as both a curative and preventative treatment. This flexibility of use, coupled with its lack of cross resistance to pyrethroids, organophosphates and carbamates, makes fipronil an excellent candidate for our Pest Management conscious environment.

Seed treatment and bait applications

Fipronil is also being tested extensively for seed treatment efficacy on many crops, especially sugar beets, cotton, and maize [Table 3]. Fipronil shows promising efficacy, without any phytotoxicity, against wireworms on maize at 250-500 g AI/Q, and against thrips on cotton at 125-250 g AI/Q. Also, fipronil is being researched as a bait formulation for the control of grasshoppers/locusts. The current data suggest rates as low as 6 g AI/ha providing outstanding control of these Orthoptera pests in a bait application delivery.

TABLE 3. Summary of Fipronil field use: recommended crop use, insects controlled, use rate and method of application.

Crop	Insect	Rate [g Al/ha]	Method of application
Soil incorporated granule			
Maize	*Diabrotica* spp.	120	Modified in-furrow or narrow band, incorporate at planting
	Argiotes spp.	100-150	Band, incorporate at planting
Sugarbeet	*Agriotes* spp.	100-150	Band, incorporate at planting
Potatoes	*Agriotes* spp. and *Limonius* spp.	50-100	Band, incorporate at planting
Sunflower	*Agriotes* spp. and *Limonius* spp.	100-150	Band, incorporate at planting
Soil surface applied granule			
Banana	*Cosmopolites* sp.	.1-.2/mat	Granule application to mat
Rice	*Chilo* spp.	50-100	Granular application to paddy rice
	Lissorhoptrus oryzophilus		
	Nilaparvata lugens		
Turf	*Neocurtilla hexadactyla*	50-100	Broadcast granule application
Foliar application			
Maize	*Ostrinia nubilalis*	50-100	Whorl treatment of granule
Alfalfa	*Hypera postica*	12.5-25	Foliar spray applications
Cotton	*Anthonomus grandis grandis*	25-50	made to coincide with the appearance of the pest
	Frankliniella spp.	25-50	
Potato	*Leptinotarsa decemlineata*	12.5-25	
Peanuts	*Frankliniella* spp.	25-50	
Rangeland	*Melanoplus* spp.	6-12.5	Foliar spray or bait application
	Schistocerca spp.		
Seed treatment			
Maize	*Agriotes* spp.	250-500/Q	Applied directly to seed prior to planting
Cotton	*Frankliniella* spp.	125-250/Q	
Sugarbeet	*Agriotes* spp.	50/unit	

'Q' = quintal = 100 Kg
'Mat' = 1 plant
'Unit' = 100,000 sugarbeet seeds

CONCLUSIONS

Extensive field tests have shown Fipronil to be a highly effective insecticide on a wide range of piercing-sucking and chewing insects at low use rates. Fipronil, as a phenyl pyrazole, is a member of a new class of potent insecticides with a unique mode of action. Fipronil can be used as a foliar spray, soil applied insecticide, seed treatment, or bait. Fipronil is also very effective controlling insects with known resistance, making it an excellent candidate for use in critical pest management programs on a number of crops where pyrethroid, organo phosphate, or carbamate tolerance/resistance problems are known. Rhône-Poulenc Agro will develop fipronil for all appropriate insecticide uses world wide.

ACKNOWLEDGMENTS

The authors wish to thank Dr. Edgar W. Parnell, Dr. Leslie R. Hatton and Dr. David C. Twinn for their dedication and early work on fipronil. Also, we wish to thank all members of the Discovery Research teams in both the U. K. and the U. S. A. and Fipronil Task Force Team, especially the coordinators, Dr. M. E. Zirakparvar and R. N. C. Morgan.

REFERENCES

Hatton, L. R., Hawkins, D. W., Pearson, C. J., and Roberts, D. A. [1988] Derivatives of N-phenylpyrazoles. *E. P. Patent 295117.*

MAT 7484 — BIOLOGICAL AND CHEMICAL PROPERTIES OF A NEW SOIL INSECTICIDE

J. HARTWIG, F. MAURER, J. MAHLSTEDT

Bayer AG, Agrochemicals Division, Pflanzenschutzzentrum Monheim, D-5090 Leverkusen-Bayerwerk, Germany

A.D. COHICK, B.J. MONKE

Miles Agricultural Division, Box 4913, Kansas City, MO 64120, USA

ABSTRACT

MAT 7484, an insecticide from the organophosphorus ester group, has been developed for soil application. The compound's high activity against *Diabrotica sp.* combined with a sufficient residual activity make MAT 7484 extremely suitable for use in maize. Field studies performed with MAT 7484 since 1984 have demonstrated consistently good efficacy against all important *Diabrotica* species. Excellent efficacy was achieved with Aztec® 2.1 G, a combination of 2 % MAT 7484 plus 0.1 % cyfluthrin, even in locations infested not only with *Diabrotica* larvae but also with *Agrotis* larvae. MAT 7484 also provides good control of other soil insects such as *Agriotes sp.*, *Hylemyia platura* and *Agonoderus lecontei*. MAT 7484 plus cyfluthrin poses a low risk to birds and a minimal risk to aquatic organisms. Thus the product's chemical and physical properties address current environmental issues. Selected laboratory and field studies reflecting the effects and properties of MAT 7484 on its own as well as of the combination of 2 % MAT 7484 plus 0.1% cyfluthrin are presented and discussed.

INTRODUCTION

One of the most important aims of research on organophosphorus derivatives was to find and develop highly effective contact insecticides specifically for the control of soil insects.

Among the organophosphorus derivatives synthesized, MAT 7484 stood out right from the outset, due in particular to its very good soil-insecticidal activity even at very low doses not previously observed in this chemical group.

The present paper describes the technical properties of MAT 7484, its biological properties under laboratory and greenhouse conditions, and the corresponding efficacy under field conditions.

CHEMICAL AND PHYSICAL PROPERTIES

Chemical name:	O-2-tert-butylpyrimidin-5-yl O-ethyl O-isopropyl phosphorothioate
Family:	Organophosphorus pesticide
Code numbers:	MAT 7484, BAY MAT 7484,

Molecular formula: $C_{13}H_{23}N_2O_3PS$

Structural formula:

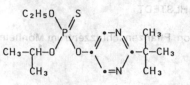

Molecular weight:	318.4
Appearance:	Colourless to amber liquid
Vapour pressure:	3.8 mPa at $20°C$
Melting point:	Not established
Boiling point:	$135°C$ at 2 mb
Stability:	Hydrolysis under alkaline conditions
Solubility:	5.5 mg AI / l in water at $20°C$ (pH 7), soluble in most organic solvents like alcohols, ketones, and toluene
Octanol/water partition coefficient:	85000 at $22°C$
Formulation:	2 GR
Combination:	MAT 7484 2% plus cyfluthrin 0.1% (= 2.1 G)

TOXICOLOGICAL AND ECOBIOLOGICAL CHARACTERISTICS

Mammalian toxicity MAT 7484   active ingredient: 2. G:

Acute oral	LD_{50}	rat	male (fasted)	2.9 - 3.6 mg/kg	163
			female (fasted)	1.3 - 1.8 mg/kg	70
		mouse	male	14.0 mg/kg	
			female	9.3 mg/kg	

Acute dermal	24 h LD_{50}	rat	male	31.0 mg/kg	>5000
			female	9.4 mg/kg	3216

Mutagenicity/Genotoxicity	Negative in vitro and in vivo
Embryotoxicity /Teratogenicity	No embryotoxic and no teratogenic effects, neither in rats nor in rabbits
Oncogenicity	No carcinogenic potential
Neurotoxicity	No indication of a delayed neurotoxic potential

Aquatic toxicology MAT 7484		active ingredient:
Rainbow trout	96 h LC_{50}	2250 $\mu g/l$
Golden orfe	96 h LC_{50}	2550 $\mu g/l$
Daphnia magna	48 h LC_{50}	0.078 $\mu g/l$

Additional and extensive testing confirms that MAT 7484 plus cyfluthrin (2.1 G) has no acute risk to fish and minimal risk to aquatic environments and organisms.

Avian toxicity MAT 7484   active ingredient:

Mallard duck	5 day LC_{50}	577 mg/kg
Bobwhite quail	5 day LC_{50}	191 mg/kg
	LD_{50}	20.3 mg/kg

MAT 7484 plus cyfluthrin (2.1 G) poses a low risk to birds, in particular when compared to other registered soil insecticides.

BIOLOGICAL PROPERTIES — LABORATORY STUDIES

Material and methods

To determine the biological efficacy, MAT 7484 and in comparison different commercial standards were incorporated homogeneously into soil. The soil either already contained the test organisms or was artificially infested with them immediately after the application of the respective active ingredient. Efficacy against soil insects was generally determined by establishing the mortality 1 week after the soil had been infested with insects. Investigations of root-systemic efficacy were performed with insects caged on the leaves of host plants. Nematicidal investigations were performed with natural soil populations. The degree of efficacy was measured by assessment of the symptoms or by count of nematodes which had penetrated the root.

Spectrum of activity

Control by contact action against the larvae of Coleoptera such as *Diabrotica balteata* or *Agriotes sp.* was achieved with extremely low concentrations of MAT 7484 (Table 1). Good control of Diptera maggots was achieved with the product, but only marginal initial action against the Lepidoptera representative *Agrotis segetum*. Root systemic uptake and activity against *Myzus persicae* and *Phaedon cochleariae* was not observed. MAT 7484 had a side effect against certain nematode species such as *Globodera rostochiensis* or *Radopholus similis*.

Table 1. Acute toxicity of MAT 7484 and standard soil insecticides (EC95, mg AI / I) following soil application in greenhouse and laboratory studies (sandy loam soil).

Species	MAT 7484	terbufos	carbofuran	tefluthrin	chlorpyrifos	fonofos
Diabrotica balteata	0.03	0.15	0.6	0.07	0.6	2.5
Agriotes sp.	<0.15	0.6	2.5	2.5	2.5	1.25
Agrotis segetum	10	>20	20	0.3	5	20
Phorbia antiqua	2.5	2.5	1.25	2.5	2.5	5
Myzus persicae	>20	<1.25	2.5	>20	>20	>20
Phaedon cochleariae	>20	1.25	2.5	>20	>20	>20
Meloidogyne incognita	20	5	20	>20	10	5
Globodera rostochiensis	5	1.25	2.5	>20	10	5
Pratylenchus sp.	>20	1.25	1.25	—	20	20
Radopholus similis	20	2.5	2.5	—	—	—

Residual activity

After application even at low dosage, MAT 7484 has a sufficient long residual activity. With *Diabrotica balteata*, for an example (Table 2), a residual activity of 4 weeks was achieved even with a concentration as low as 0.15 mg Al/ l (EC$_{90}$). This extended activity was demonstrated on all soil types (Table 3). As with other organophosphorus compounds and carbamates, the residual activity was only shortened if the organic material content of the soil was extremely high. No appreciable dependence of the residual activity on the soil moisture content was observed.

Table 2. Residual activity of MAT 7484 against *Diabrotica balteata* after incorporation into sandy loam soil.

	dosage mg Al /l	activity (% Abbott) after....weeks					
		2	4	6	8	10	12
MAT 7484	0.6	100	100	100	100	100	98
	0.3	100	93	85	82	70	63
	0.15	100	90	72	70	52	50
terbufos	2.5	100	100	100	100	100	100
	1.25	100	100	95	90	60	36
	0.6	51	23	13	0	0	0
chlorpyriphos	2.5	100	100	100	100	94	50
	1.25	100	100	95	60	0	0
	0.6	50	0	0	0	0	0

Table 3. Influence of soil type on the residual activity of MAT 7484 (test insect: *Diabrotica balteata*).

	dosage mg Al /l	residual activity (LC 95) in weeks			
		sand soil	loamy sand	loam	humus soil
MAT 7484	0.6	>8	>8	>8	8
	0.3	7	6	7	2-6
	0.15	6	4	6	1
	0.07	4	1	4	0
terbufos	5	>8	>8	>8	7
	2.5	6	6	>8	4
	1.25	5	4	4	2

Mobility in soil

Based on adsorption studies with various types of soil, the active ingredient can be classified as immobile. The low translocation capacity can be illustrated with a biotest (Table 4). In this biotest no significant activity was found in soil layers below 5 cm even after 60 days.

Table 4. Vertical soil penetration of MAT 7484 in micro - block trials; average from 7 trials. (Granules at a rate of 125 g AI/ha were incorporated into sandy soil. 6" soil cores were taken at periodic intervals and sectioned for laboratory bioassay with *Diabrotica balteata*.).

		days after treatment			
		7	15	30	60
Average % mortality	0 - 2.5 cm	100	100	100	97
of *Diabrotica balteata*	2.5 - 5 cm	9	18	24	22
larvae in soil	5 - 10 cm	3	3	3	7
from different depths	10 - 15 cm	3	0	5	5
Average cumulative rainfall / irrigation in mm		59	115	191	364

Accelerated microbial degradation

Repeated application of a soil insecticide to the same site may result in accelerated microbial degradation and hence to an inadequate residual activity under field conditions.

Studies with MAT 7484, however, performed at Vero Beach (Miles Research Station) and Monheim (Bayer Crop Protection Centre) showed a high degree of product stability to accelerated microbial degradation. Despite repeated treatment of a soil with MAT 7484, there was no discernible reduction of the residual activity (Fig. 1). In contrast, the residual activity of terbufos decreased slightly after each application. The large reduction in the efficacy of carbofuran after repeated application indicates accelerated microbial degradation.

BIOLOGICAL PROPERTIES — FIELD STUDIES

Worldwide field studies performed over several years have confirmed MAT 7484's spectrum of activity against the most important soil insects and all important species of *Diabrotica* (viz *D. virgifera virgifera, D. barberi*), wireworms, and Diptera maggots. Exceptionally low application rates were sufficient to control the above mentioned species. Most of the field studies were performed with the combination of 2 % MAT 7484 and 0.1% cyfluthrin. By the addition of 0.1% cyfluthrin to a 2% MAT 7484 granule it was possible to extend the spectrum of activity to cutworms (e.g. *Agrotis ypsilon*).

Figure 1. Stability to accelerated microbial degradation in sandy loam soil; test insect in biotests: *Diabrotica balteata*.

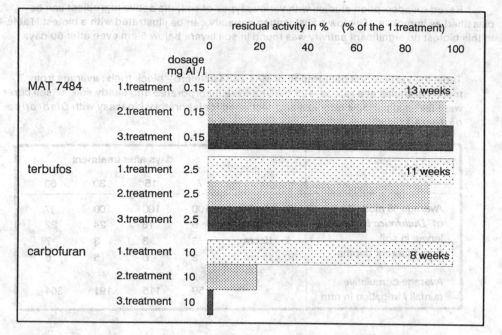

Maize - Diabrotica control

Extensive field studies since from 1984 until today and performed mainly in the USA, have proven MAT 7484 plus cyfluthrin (2.1 G) to provide a consistently reliable control of *Diabrotica sp.* with application rates of only 0.0131g AI / m (Table 5). The levels of efficacy were comparable to those achieved with 0.1 g AI / m terbufos. Even in the dry year 1988, an average root rating value of 2.4 was achieved. All important forms of application, band and in-furrow application (Table 6) and also T-band application provide very good field performance.

Table 5. Control of *Diabrotica sp.* in maize with MAT 7484 plus cyfluthrin (2.1 G) at a rate of 0.0131 g AI / m since 1984 (root rating 1-6, Hills and Peters, 1971).

	untreated	MAT 7484 & cyfluthrin	terbufos	number of tests
1984	4.0	2.5	2.6	13
1985	4.1	2.4	2.5	18
1986	4.1	2.3	2.4	14
1987	4.4	2.4	2.6	10
1988	4.3	2.4	2.9	7
1989	3.8	2.2	2.3	9
1990	4.5	2.7	2.5	13
1991	4.1	2.6	2.6	5

Table 6.   Control of *Diabrotica sp.* in maize with MAT 7484 ;
comparison of infurrow application with band application (1991
trial results from University Cooperators, USA).

	rate g Al / m	band		infurrow	
untreated	—	4.2	(15)	4.3	(14)
MAT 7484 & cyfluthrin	0.0131	2.1	(15)	2.2	(13)
terbufos	0.10	2.0	(15)	2.3	(14)
tefluthrin	0.011	2.4	(11)	2.5	(9)
chlorpyrifos	0.10	2.3	(15)	2.3	(7)

Other pests

The control of seedcorn maggot *Hylemyia platura* and *Phyllophaga polyphylla*
demonstrates as an example, the usefulness of MAT 7484 plus cyfluthrin (2.1 G) against other
important soil insects. The germination of maize in areas with infestation of *H. platura* was
promoted by the same order of magnitude with 0.0131 g Al / m (MAT 7484 plus cyfluthrin) as
with 0.1 g Al / m terbufos (Fig. 2). A study in Mexico demonstrates the good efficacy achieved
against *P. polyphylla* up to 94 days after planting with 0.0168 g Al/ m (Fig. 3).

Figure 2.   Control of *Hylemyia platura* in maize.

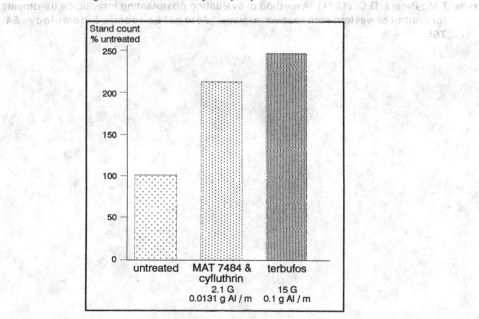

Figure 3.   Control of *Phyllophaga polyphylla* in maize.

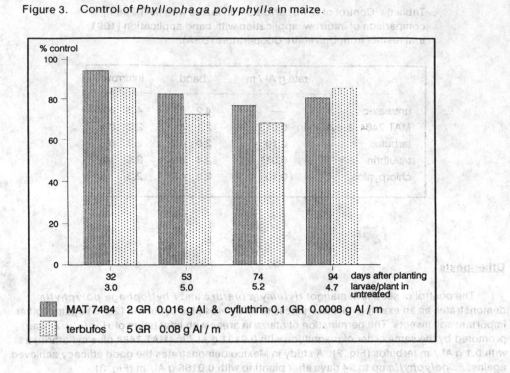

% control

| | MAT 7484   2 GR 0.016 g AI & cyfluthrin 0.1 GR 0.0008 g AI / m |
| | terbufos   5 GR 0.08 g AI / m |

| days after planting | 32 | 53 | 74 | 94 |
| larvae/plant in untreated | 3.0 | 5.0 | 5.2 | 4.7 |

REFERENCE

Hills, T.M.; Peters, D.C. (1971)   A method of evaluating postplanting insecticide treatments for control of western corn rootworm larvae. *Journal Economic Entomology.* **64**:764 - 765

CGA 215'944 - A NOVEL AGENT TO CONTROL APHIDS AND WHITEFLIES

C. R. FLÜCKIGER, H. KRISTINSSON, R. SENN, A. RINDLISBACHER, H. BUHOLZER,
G. VOSS

Plant Protection Division, Ciba-Geigy Ltd., CH-4002 Basel, Switzerland

ABSTRACT

CGA 215'944 is a new insecticide with a unique mode of action,
representing a novel class of insect control agents. It was discovered by
Ciba-Geigy and is now being developed worldwide. It is highly active against
susceptible and resistant aphids and whiteflies in vegetables, ornamentals,
cotton, field crops, deciduous fruits and citrus. The compound affects the
behaviour of homopterous insects and causes them to stop feeding before
they die. CGA 215'944 saves beneficials and is therefore especially useful
in IPM programmes. The recommended rate of application is 10 - 30 g AI /
100 l depending on the pest and crop. The compound is of low acute toxicity
to mammals, terrestrial and aquatic wildlife and has favourable ecochemical
properties.

INTRODUCTION

The need for a specific compound against aphids and whiteflies is becoming
more and more important as IPM is implemented on a wide scale and as plant protection
becomes more sophisticated. Aphids have several natural enemies; these should be
preserved because in addition they assist in controlling many other pests. Using a broad
spectrum insecticide just for aphids or whiteflies is not recommended, because it would
affect the predator/prey balance of other insects, resulting in the need for an extensive
insecticide spray programme later in the season. In addition, many established products
that are currently used to control aphids and whiteflies encounter resistance problems in
many countries (Voss, 1988).

CHEMICAL AND PHYSICAL PROPERTIES

Code number   :   CGA 215'944

Structural formula   :

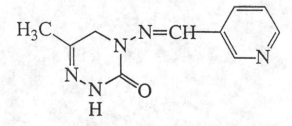

Chemical name	:	4,5-dihydro-6-methyl-4-(3-pyridyl-methyleneamino)-1,2,4-triazin-3(2H)-one
Molecular formula	:	$C_{10}H_{11}N_5O$
Molecular weight	:	217.23
Melting point	:	234.4° C
Physical state at 20° C	:	crystalline
Vapour pressure at 20° C	:	$\leq 9.7 \times 10^{-8}$ Pa
Solubility (g/l at 20° C)	:	water 0.270
		ethanol 2.25
		hexane < 0.001
Partition coefficient n-octanol / water (Log P)	:	0.2 (RP-TLC-method)
Formulation	:	25 % wettable powder (WP 25)

CGA 215'944 represents a new insecticide of unprecedented chemical structure. It can be synthesized in only few steps and with high yields from easily accessible starting materials (Kristinsson, 1988).

SAFETY

Based on toxicity data, available so far, CGA 215'944 is unlikely to present any acute hazard in normal use (WHO Class III), (Table 1).

TABLE 1. Acute toxicity of technical CGA 215'944

Acute oral LD 50	:	= 5820 mg / kg
Acute dermal LD 50 (24 h)	:	> 2000 mg / kg
Acute inhalation LC 50 (4 h)	:	> 1800 mg / m³ air
Eye irritation (rabbit)	:	none
Skin irritation (rabbit)	:	none
Skin sensitation (guinea pig)	:	none

No mutagenicity was detected in 5 different assays including the Ames test.

CGA 215'944 is practically non-toxic to birds, fish and bees and slightly toxic to Daphnia.

The compound is moderately mobile in soils (RMF approx. 1.0) and rapidly degraded (T 1/2 approx. 5 days).

BIOLOGICAL PROPERTIES UNDER LABORATORY AND GREENHOUSE CONDITIONS

Spectrum of activity

CGA 215'944 is a selective compound active against Homoptera. It does not control dipteran, coleopteran and lepidopteran insects and mites at recommended rates (Table 2). Both juvenile and adult stages of aphids and whiteflies are susceptible to CGA 215'944.

TABLE 2. CGA 215'944's spectrum of activity

PEST	ORDER	LC50 (mg / l)
Myzus persicae (N1)* (Green peach aphid)	Homoptera	0.2
Bemisia tabaci (N1) (Sweet potato whitefly)	Homoptera	0.9
Nilaparvata lugens (N2) (Brown Planthopper)	Homoptera	2.8
Musca domestica (L1) (House fly)	Diptera	> 1000
Diabrotica balteata (L1) (Cucumber beetle)	Coleoptera	> 1000
Heliothis virescens (L1) (Tobacco budworm)	Lepidoptera	> 1000
Spodoptera littoralis (L1) (Egyptian Cotton Leafworm)	Lepidoptera	> 1000
Tetranychus urticae (L1) (Two spotted spidermite)	Acarina	> 1000

* (L1) First instar larval stage ; (N1) First nymphal stage ; (N2) Second nymphal stage.

Selectivity versus beneficial arthropods

CGA 215'944 is safe to all tested beneficials in the laboratory (Table 3). This outstanding selectivity could also be demonstrated for various natural enemies in the field.

TABLE 3. Selectivity versus beneficial arthropods in the laboratory.

Beneficial	LC 50 values (g AI / 100 l)		
	CGA 215'944	pirimicarb	dimethoate
Orius majusculus	>810	16	3
Chrysoperla carnea	>810	>270	30
Coccinella septempunctata	>810	45	3
Amblyseius fallacis	>100	>100	0,3

Pirimicarb is the most selective aphicide presently on the market. Our data available indicate that the selectivity of CGA 215'944 is even more pronounced. This makes our compound especially useful in IPM programmes. It finally allows the implementation of a concept in pest control that was demanded many years ago in which natural enemies are preserved, so they can assist in controlling problem pests.

Behaviour in plants

In addition to its contact activity, CGA 215'944 also acts systemically. Field trials have shown that application of the compound as a soil drench controls aphids on the foliage of plants. The compound also has a translaminar activity causing aphids on the underside of the leaf to die when leaves are treated on the upper surface (Table 4).

TABLE 4. Mortality of *Aphis fabae* on the underside of leaves after treatment of the upper leaf surface only

INSECTICIDE	LC 50 (g AI / l)
CGA 215'944	0.7
pirimicarb	1.6
cypermethrin	>100

Resistance

CGA 215'944 does not have any of the known mode of actions for insecticides. In the field it controls strains of green peach aphids (*Myzus persicae*) that are resistant to OP and carbamate insecticides.

Antifeedant activity

Although aphids which are treated with CGA 215'944 need some time to die, their sucking activity is reduced shortly after application (Table 5).

TABLE 5. Antifeedant activity observed on *Aphis craccivora*

	Hours after application			
	0 - 3	3 - 6	6 - 24	24 - 48
% feeding reduction[1]	88	85	85	--
% control of aphids[2]	10	27	92	100

Concentration of CGA 215'944: 1 g AI / l
[1] feeding reduction is evaluated by comparing honeydew production per living individual with untreated check
[2] mortality of aphids compared with untreated check

BIOLOGICAL PERFORMANCE UNDER FIELD CONDITIONS

Vegetables

CGA 215'944 exhibited excellent activity against different aphids *(Myzus persicae, Aphis gossypii, Aphis fabae, Brevicoryne brassicae, Acyrthosiphon pisum)* and whiteflies *(Trialeurodes vaporariorum, Bemisia tabaci)* in different vegetables such as tomatoes, peppers, cucumbers, eggplants, peas and cole crops. Figure 1 demonstrates an example of the efficacy against aphids and figure 2 against whiteflies. The efficacy against *M. persicae* is remarkable in this trial, with only one application necessary with CGA 215'944 vs. 4 applications with pirimicarb. For more information about the potential of CGA 215'944 in vegetables, refer to Flückiger *et al.*, 1992.

Figure 1: Control of *Myzus persicae* on eggplant (Spain, 1991)

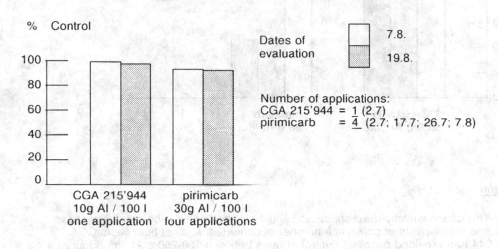

Figure 2: Control of *Trialeurodes vaporariorum* on tomatoes (Spain, 1990)

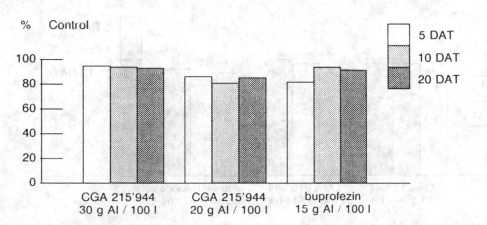

Potatoes

CGA 215'944 performs very well against the green peach aphid *(M. persicae)* and the potato aphid *(Macrosiphum euphorbiae)* at the rate of 200 g AI / ha (Figure 3).

Figure 3: Control of a mixed population of *Myzus persicae* and *Macrosiphum euphorbiae* on potatoes (Italy 1989)

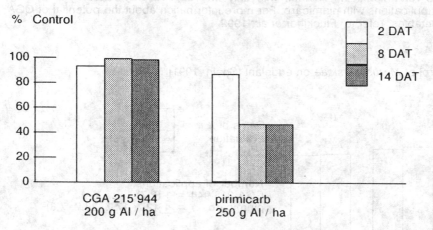

Cotton

The cotton whitefly *(Bemisia tabaci)* and the cotton aphid *(Aphis gossypii)* have become major pests of cotton in a number of countries. Against both pests CGA 215'944 has provided excellent control at rates between 150-200 g AI / ha (Figures 4 and 5).

Figure 4: Control of *Aphis gossypii* on cotton (average of 3 trials, Egypt, 1991)

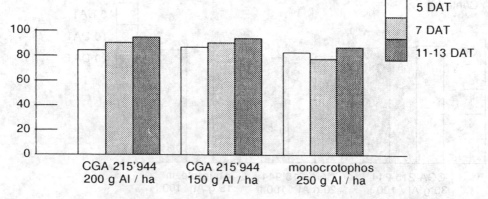

Figure 5: Control of *Bemisia tabaci* on cotton (Guatemala, 1991)

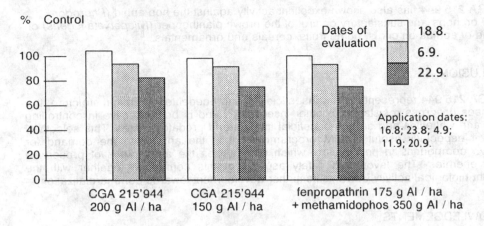

Peach

A remarkable feature of CGA 215'944 against the green peach aphid *(M. persicae)* on peach is its long residual activity. Small peach shoots that are treated will be protected from aphid infestations on their new growth for more than three weeks (Figure 6).

Figure 6: Control of *Myzus persicae* on peach (Spain, 1991)

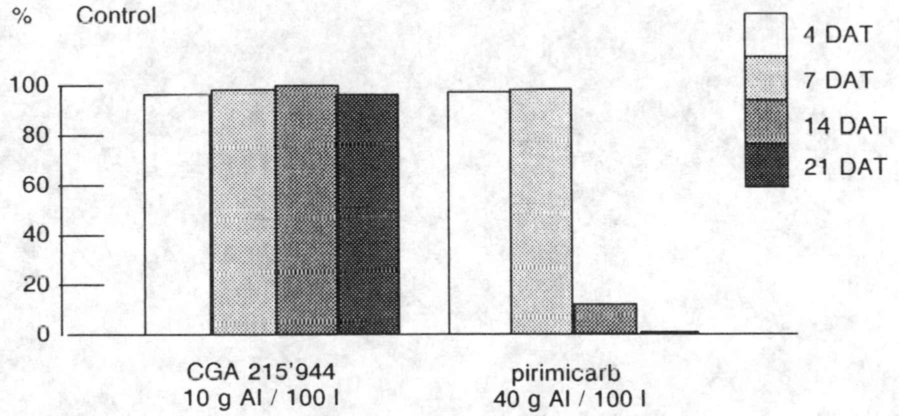

% Control

4 DAT
7 DAT
14 DAT
21 DAT

100
80
60
40
20
0

CGA 215'944
10 g AI / 100 l

pirimicarb
40 g AI / 100 l

Other crops

CGA 215'944 has also shown excellent activity against the hop aphid *(Phorodon humuli)* on hops and satisfactory control of the brown planthopper *(Nilaparvata lugens)* on rice and of aphids on citrus, pome fruits, cereals and ornamentals.

CONCLUSION

CGA 215'944 represents a new insecticide of unprecedented chemical structure. It possesses no cross resistance to other insecticides and is both effective in controlling aphids and whiteflies and safe to beneficial insects and predatory mites. This selectivity makes it especially useful in IPM programmes. It is the answer to the demand for selective compounds in pest control which emphasizes the advantages of preserving natural enemies. The favourable safety aspects of this compound together with the excellent biological activity warrants its further development towards commercialization.

ACKNOWLEDGEMENTS

The authors like to thank all of their collegues in Basel and many countries who have contributed to research and development. Without their dedicated assistance this paper would not have been possible.

REFERENCES

Flückiger, C.R.; Senn, R.; Buholzer, H. (1992) CGA 215'944 - Opportunities for use in vegetables. *Brighton Crop Protection Conference - Pests and Diseases 1992*, **1** (In Press).

Kristinsson, H. (1989) *European Patent Application* No 314'615, May 3.

Voss, G. (1988) Insecticide/acaricide resistance: Industry's effort and plans to cope. *Pesticide Science* **23**, 149-156.

FENAZAQUIN, A NOVEL ACARICIDE FOR THE MANAGEMENT OF SPIDER MITES IN A VARIETY OF CROPS

C. LONGHURST

DowElanco Europe, Research and Development Laboratory, Letcombe Regis, Wantage, OX12 9JT.

L. BACCI

DowElanco Italia S.R.L., Via d'Azelglio, 25, 40123 Bologna, Italy.

J. BUENDIA

DowElanco Iberica S.A., Josefa Valcarcel, 24, 28027 Madrid, Spain.

C. J. HATTON

DowElanco, 2800 Mitchell Drive, Walnut Creek, California 94598, USA.

J. PETITPREZ

DowElanco S.A., Domaine de la Bastide, Route de Generac, 30900 Nimes, France.

P. TSAKONAS

DowElanco S.A., 5 Voulgari Street, 54655 Thessaloniki, Greece.

ABSTRACT

Fenazaquin is a novel quinazoline acaricide discovered and developed by DowElanco for mite control in a range of crops. The compound has a good toxicological and environmental profile. Fenazaquin has a novel mode-of-action. It shows no cross-resistance with currently commercialised acaricides.

Fenazaquin shows excellent activity at low rates against eggs and motile forms of a number of mite genera including Panonychus, Tetranychus and Eotetranychus. Proposed field use rates are as low as 1.5 gAI/hl for the control of P.citri. Fenazaquin has outstanding knockdown activity providing a long persistence of effect. In contrast its short period of bioavailability on crops reduces its impact on beneficial arthropods immigrating into the crop and minimises resistance risk by providing only a short period of selective pressure.

In trials on a wide variety of crops, including sensitive apple cultivars such as Golden Delicious, fenazaquin has shown no injury at rates well in excess of proposed field rates.

INTRODUCTION

Fenazaquin (EL-436, DE-436) is a new quinazoline acaricide

discovered by DowElanco. This paper describes the properties and performance of fenazaquin, under both laboratory and field conditions, against a range of phytophagous and predatory mites.

Fenazaquin has been demonstrated to be a contact poison with good knockdown activity on motile forms as well as true ovicidal activity, preventing eclosion of mite eggs (Dreikorn et al. 1991). The compound affects metabolism, inhibiting the mitochrondrial electron transport chain by binding with Complex I at Co-enzyme site Q (Hollingworth et al. 1992).

Fenazaquin is not cross-resistant with a range of conventional acaricides such as dicofol, bifenthrin, amitraz and carbophenothion; under field conditions fenazaquin has not shown cross resistance to hexythiazox - resistant Panonychus citri (Hatton et al., 1992).

CHEMICAL AND PHYSICAL PROPERTIES

Chemical name: 4-tert-butylphenylethyl quinazolin-4-yl ether

Structural formula:

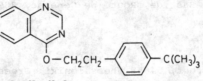

Molecular formula: $C_{20}H_{22}N_2O$

Molecular weight: 306.4

Other Properties:
water solubility: 0.1 mg/litre at 20°C
vapour pressure: 1.6×10^{-4} Pa at 25°C
octanol-water partitioning coefficient (logP):
5.51 at 25°C photolytic half-life: 15 days

Formulations: 200 g/litre Suspension Concentrate,
100 g/litre Emulsifiable Concentrate

TOXICOLOGICAL PROPERTIES

Technical material - Mammalian toxicity.

Acute oral - rat (male)   Median Lethal Dose 134 mg/kg
Acute oral - mouse (female) Median Lethal Dose 1480 mg/kg
Acute dermal - rabbit   Median Lethal Dose >5000 mg/kg

Eye irritation: slight
Skin sensitisation: none
Skin irritation: none
Mutagenicity: not genotoxic
Tetratology - rat, rabbit: No evidence of teratogenicity
Long term toxicity: no evidence of carcinogenic or reproductive effects

Acute oral - bobwhite quail, Median Lethal Dose 1747 mg/kg
         - mallard   Median Lethal Dose >2000 mg/kg
Acute dietary - bobwhite quail,
            mallard   Median Lethal Concentration >5000 ppm
Acute contact - bee   Median Lethal Dose 8.18 µg/bee
Acute 14 day - earthworm   Median Lethal Concentration 1.93 mg/kg
                                       soil
Acute 96 hour - bluegill   Median Lethal Concentration 34.1 µg/l
Acute 96 hour - trout   Median Lethal Concentration 3.8 µg/l

BIOLOGICAL PROPERTIES

Activity under Laboratory Conditions

When applied to pre-infested leaves, technical fenazaquin sprayed
to run-off on squash cotyledons showed activity against both motile forms
(larvae, nymphs and adults) and eggs (Table 1).

TABLE 1. Comparative toxicity of fenazaquin and competitors
to eggs and motile forms of Tetranychus urticae.*

| Life Stage | LC50 (mg/l) at 24 hours | | | |
	fenazaquin	fenbutatin oxide	dicofol	clofentezine
Motiles*	2.3	21.5	6.2	> 800
Eggs	2.8	24.9	10.0	0.1

* mixed age population on squash cotyledons.

The activity of fenazaquin was not affected by temperature. The
LD50 and LD90 values for fenazaquin and the pyrethroid, bifenthrin, were
determined by infesting pre-treated plants with Tetranychus urticae and
holding the plants at 12.6°C, 23.9°C or 35°C. Fenazaquin showed a slight
increase in activity with increasing temperature (Table 2) compared with
a large decrease in activity for bifenthrin. The relative insensitivity
of fenazaquin to changes in temperature allows it to be used under a wide
range of conditions.

TABLE 2. Effect of temperature on the toxicity of fenazaquin
and bifenthrin to Tetranychus urticae on Phaseolus vulgaris.

| Treatment | LC50 (mg/l) at 24 hours for 3 temperatures | | |
	12.6°C	23.9°C	35.0°C
fenazaquin	6.4	5.4	4.2
bifenthrin	0.9	3.8	36.9

The residuality of fenazaquin on crop surfaces was dependent on the
crop being investigated. In a series of linked field/laboratory

bioassays fenazaquin was sprayed onto crops under field conditions and excised leaves taken into the laboratory at prescribed intervals and assayed against T.urticae. Persistence of activity of a SC formulation to T.urticae was greatest on apple leaves, intermediate on almond leaves and shortest on cotton leaves (Table 3).

TABLE 3. Effect of crop type on the LC50's to Tetranychus urticae of fenazaquin with time (linked field treatment/laboratory bioassay).

| Crop | LC50 (mg/l) at days after treatment | | | |
	1	2	4	8
Cotton	197.0	>800	>800	-
Almond	18.0	43.0	125.0	>800
Apple	18.5	34.	67.0	571.0

The residuality of fenazaquin on apple (cv Golden Delicious) was compared with two reference acaricides, fenpropathrin (10%EC) and dicofol (18.6%EC) in a linked field/laboratory bioassay. The short persistence of fenazaquin is to be regarded as a positive benefit. It has no effect on its field performance (Tables 6 & 7) and will permit the immigration of beneficials into the treated crop and have a good impact on resistance management by reducing the period of selection pressure.

TABLE 4. Comparative residuality of fenazaquin, fenpropathrin and dicofol against Tetranychus urticae on apple leaves.

| Treatment | LC50 (mg/l) at days after treatment | | |
	1	3	7
fenazaquin	16.4	52.7	119.7
fenpropathrin	<12.5	24.8	40.6
dicofol	23.6	35.3	57.3

FIELD PERFORMANCE

The field performance of fenazaquin on a global basis has been reviewed by Dreikorn et al. (1991) and Hatton et al. (1992); in this paper the performance of the product in Europe is summarised.

Apple

Field trials were conducted throughout Europe with a 200 g/l SC formulation of fenazaquin. Replicated trials were sprayed to run-off with either a back-pack mistblower or hand lance. Volume rates ranged from 500 - 2000 l/ha, as appropriate to ensure adequate coverage. Counts were made of mite numbers before application and at prescribed intervals throughout the trials.

Fenazaquin at 10 - 15 gAI/hl (100 - 150 mgAI/l) provided
outstanding 'knockdown' of the European Red mite (Panonychus ulmi)
as well as providing excellent residual control (Table 5) to a
threshold of 5 mites/leaf for 42 days. Although fenazaquin will
normally be used against populations of low numbers of mites in
accordance with local Advisory recommendations it is capable of
bringing under control very high summer populations of P.ulmi (Table 6).

TABLE 5. Activity of fenazaquin 200 g/l SC against the European
red mite, Panonychus ulmi, in apple.

| Treatment | Rate gAI/hl | Average Number of mites/leaf (Range)[1] | | |
		7 days	28 days	42 days
Fenazaquin	5	0.4(0-1.8)	4.4(0-14.6)	14.9(0.2-57.8)
Fenazaquin	10	0.2(0-1.4)	1.7(0-5.0)	5.0(0.2-12.1)
Fenazaquin	15	0.2(0-0.5)	0.8(0-2.1)	2.4(0-9.3)
Dicofol[2]	40	3.0(0.1-13.4)	5.6(0.2-28.3)	40.3(17.6-82.0)
Propargite[2]	57	1.2(3.7)	14.9(1.1-95.1)	34.2(1.7-121.0)
Hexythiazox[2]	5	-	12.8(0-134.0)	9.7(0.2-57.0)

1. Average of 28 trials in Spain, France, Italy, U.K. and
Greece; initial populations ranged from 1.5 to 27.0 mites/leaf.
2. Dicofol as 48%EC, propargite as 57%EC, hexythiazox as 10%WP.

TABLE 6. Activity of fenazaquin 200 g/l SC against established
summer populations of the European red mite, Panonychus ulmi, in
apple[1].

| Treatment | Rate gAI/hl | Initial Population | Number of mites/leaf | |
			14 days	28 days
Fenazaquin	10	27	0.7	5.0
		99	3.5	12.8
Fenazaquin	15	27	0.1	2.1
		99	3.1	4.1
Dicofol[2]	40	27	1.2	46.1
Fenpropathrin[2]	20	99	13.0	32.7
Untreated		27	38.0	165.0
		99	87.0	100.0

1. Individual trials in France.
2. Dicofol as 48%EC, fenpropathrin 10%EC.

In addition to its activity against P.ulmi fenazaquin at 5 - 15 g/hl
has proven to be effective in controlling both T.urticae and T.viennensis
in apple in trials carried out in Greece and Turkey.

Fenazaquin has proven to be very safe on all cultivars of apple. No crop injury or russeting has been recorded in evaluation trials over five years. In a specific programme to evaluate the safety of fenazaquin 200 g/l SC to the sensitive cultivar, Golden Delicious, the product was sprayed three times at elevated rates at a period when developing fruit is sensitive to russet damage. No adverse reactions were recorded (Table 7).

TABLE 7. Safety of fenazaquin 200 g/l SC to the apple cultivar 'Golden Delicious' when sprayed 3 times on a 14 day schedule[1].

Treatment	Rate gAI/ha	% Russet at Harvest
Fenazaquin	10	24.0 ab
Fenazaquin	20	31.9 ab
Fenazaquin	40	30.5 ab
Dicofol[2]	50	41.9 a
Untreated		30.1 ab

ANOVA at p = 0.05
1. Applications on 18 April (petal fall), 3 May and 17 May.
2. Dicofol as 36%EC, fenpropathrin 10%EC.

The selectivity of acaricides under field conditions to beneficial mites is an important part of their evaluation. In a trial conducted by the Institute of Horticultural Research, U.K., fenazaquin was sprayed onto a mixed population of P.ulmi and Typhlodromus pyri (Solomon et al 1992). Although populations of T.pyri were initially reduced by 10 and 15 g/hl of fenazaquin 200 g/l SC, predators recovered over the duration of the trial in contrast to the populations treated with dicofol or fenpropathrin which were still significantly reduced 45 days after treatment (Table 8).

TABLE 8. Activity of fenazaquin 200 g/l SC to motile forms of the predatory Typhlodromus pyri in apple.

Treatment	Rate gAI/hl	Average Number of mites/25 leaves		
		6 days	19 days	45 days
Fenazaquin	5	10.8	21.9	15.0
Fenazaquin	10	6.3*	10.5*	12.9
Fenazaquin	15	2.6*	6.2*	14.0
Dicofol[1]	40	2.4*	2.7*	3.9*
Fenpropathrin[1]	5	0.4*	1.1*	0.3*
Untreated		26.4	36.7	12.7

* significantly different from untreated (analysis $\log_e$ n+1)
1. Dicofol as 18.6%EC, fenpropathrin as 10%EC.

Citrus

Fenazaquin, as a 100 g/l EC, was evaluated in a series of replicated trials in Spain against both Panonychus citri and T.urticae. Plots were sprayed to run-off with a hand-lance sprayer; volume rates were 2000 - 5000 l/ha depending on the size of the trees. Counts were made of mites before application and at prescribed intervals throughout the trial.

The citrus red mite, P.citri, was controlled by rates as low as 1.5 gAI/hl (Table 9). The two spotted mite, T.urticae, required slightly higher rates (2.5 gAI/hl) to achieve high levels of control.

TABLE 9. Activity of fenazaquin 100 g/l EC against the red mite, Panonychus citri, in citrus.

Treatment	Rate gAI/hl	Average Number of mites/leaf[1] (Range)
Fenazaquin	1.0	5.3 (0 - 11.7)
Fenazaquin	1.5	0.8 (0 - 2.0)
Fenazaquin	2.5	0.3 (0 - 0.6)
Fenbutatin[2] oxide	40.0	5.0 (0.7 - 12.1)
Dicofol[2]	60.0	10.5 (0.6 - 27.0)

1. Average of six trials, assessed between 21 and 35 days after treatment. 2. Dicofol as 48%EC, fenbutatin oxide as 50%WP

The activity of fenazaquin on predatory mites in citrus followed a similar pattern to that seen in apple. In a trial conducted at the University of Valencia, Spain, applications were made to trees with established Euseius stipulatus populations. Although the predators were initially reduced they showed good recovery with time. This was in contrast to the reference material, a mixture of tetradifon and dicofol; predator populations were dramatically reduced and did not recover during the duration of the trial (Table 10).

TABLE 10. Activity of fenazaquin 100 g/l EC against the predatory phytoseid mite, Euseius stipulatus in citrus.

Treatment	Rate gAI/hl	Average number of mites/20 leaves for days after treatment.				
		0	7	15	30	60
Fenazaquin	1.5*	25	18	19	23	21
Fenazaquin	2.5*	28	13	18	23	24
Fenazaquin	5.0	24	3	3	13	18
Tetradifon + dicofol[1]	15 + 40	29	1	5	0	0
Untreated		29	38	25	24	40
LSD (p=0.05)			9.1	1.0	8.2	11.6

* - proposed use rates - Spain. 1. Tetradifon+dicofol as 6%+16%EC

Other crops

Spider mites attack a wide range of crops in addition to apples and citrus. Fenazaquin has been evaluated in food crops such as grapevine, vegetables (eg cucurbits, tomatoes), soft fruit (eg strawberries) and cotton as well as a representative selection of ornamentals (Pollak et al. 1992). In grapes for example the yellow mite, Eotetranychus carpini, was controlled by 5 - 10 gAI/hl of fenazaquin. Over the range of pest species and crops tested 5 - 20 gAI/hl of fenazaquin gave excellent control of pest mites.

CONCLUSIONS

Fenazaquin is a new acaricide with an unique mode-of-action. It has an excellent toxicological and environmental profile; this coupled with low use rates and compatibility with beneficial mites offers a powerful new tool for pest management in a wide range of crops.

ACKNOWLEDGEMENTS

The development of a new product is a team effort and the efforts of all of our colleagues is gratefully acknowledged. I would like to especially thank G.D. Thompson for his pioneering work with fenazaquin and along with T. Worden and C. Mosberg for providing laboratory data. I should also like to thank M. Solomon (IHR, UK) and F. G. Mari (University of Valencia) for providing data on beneficial mites.

REFERENCES

Dreikorn,B.A.; Thompson,G.D.; Suhr,R.G.; Worden,T.V.; Davis,N.L. (1991) The discovery and development of fenazaquin (EL-436), a new broad spectrum acaricide. Seventh International Congress of Pesticide Chemistry, Hamburg 1991. Abstract 01A-33. Proceedings edited by H.Frehse, E.Kesseler-Schmitz and S.Conway.

Hollingworth,R.M.; Ahammad-Sahib, K.I.; Gadelhak, G.G.; McLauglin, L. (1992) Complex I of the Mitochrondrial Respiratory Chain: a target for pesticide development by both man & nature. American Chemical Society. New Pest Control Agents and Technologies with Reduced Environmental Impact - Insecticides. Proceedings of the San Francisco meeting. April 1992 (In Press)

Hatton, C.J; Babcock, J.M.; Schoonover, J.R.; Dripps, J.E. (1992) Fenazaquin, a new acaricide/insecticide. Proceedings of the XIXth International Congress of Entomology, Beijing, XIII S-35, June 1992, P.35.

Pollak, R.T., Butler, D.W.F.; Blackburn, P. (1992) Fenazaquin for the control of two spotted spider mite in ornamentals. Brighton Crop Protection Conference - Pests and Disease 1992 (In Press)

Solomon, M.G.; Fitzgerald J.D.; Ridout, M.S. (1992) Fenazaquin, a new acaricide for use in IPM in apple orchards in the U.K. Crop Protection (in Press).

FIELD EVALUATION OF RH 5992 ON LEPIDOPTEROUS PESTS IN EUROPE

JJ. HELLER, H. MATTIODA
Roussel Uclaf - 163 Avenue Gambetta 75980 Paris, Cedex 20 France
Procida/Roussel Uclaf, Saint Marcel, 13011 Marseilles, France

E. KLEIN, A. SAGENMÜLLER
Hoechst AG, K 607, P.O. Box 80 03 20, D-6230 Frankfurt am Main 80

ABSTRACT

RH 5992 is a novel insecticide discovered by Rohm & Haas. It acts as an ecdysone agonist and is highly specific to lepidopterous insects. The compound binds to the ecdysone receptor which in turn induces a premature lethal moult. Within a short time after uptake it causes feeding to cease. The selectivity to lepidopterous pests makes RH 5992 an excellent IPM tool. The product has some effects on selected Diptera and scales. RH 5992 has so far been found safe to bees and other beneficial insects.

In trials carried out by Hoechst and Roussel Uclaf since 1988, RH 5992 has provided excellent control of key lepidopterous pests in orchards, vine, vegetables and forestry. The results suggest a dosage range from 9.6 to 19.2 g Al/hl, depending on the target pest and crop. Applications of RH 5992 in deciduous fruits and vine should be made at egg hatching in order to optimize the performance.

INTRODUCTION

RH 5992 is a novel insecticide discovered by Rohm & Haas. It is highly specific to lepidopterous insects and acts on larvae. The product belongs to a new class of selective and safe insecticides acting as an ecdysone agonist (Robins et al., 1970). RH 5992 has been jointly developed by Hoechst and Roussel Uclaf in Europe since 1988. The paper describes the properties and performance of the product under field conditions.

RH 5992 PROPERTIES

Chemical and physical properties

Structural formula :

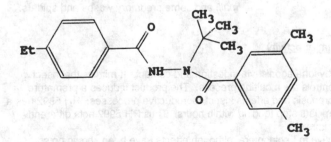

Molecular formula	:	$C_{22} H_{28} N_2 O_2$
Chemical name	:	3,5-dimethylbenzoic acid 1-(1,1-dimethylethyl)-2-(4-ethylbenzoyl) hydrazide
Melting point	:	191°C
Stability	:	stable at 25°C
Vapour pressure	:	3×10^{-8} mm Hg at 25°C

Toxicology (technical AI)

Acute oral LD50	:	rat, mouse	> 5000 mg/kg
Acute dermal LD50	:	rat	> 5000 mg/kg
Eye irritation	:	rabbit	inconsequentially irritating
Skin irritation	:	rabbit	practically non irritating
Sensitization	:	guinea pig	not a sensitizer
Inhalation LC50	:	rat	slightly toxic (> 4.4 mg/l)
Mutagenicity	:		negative

Ecotoxicity

Mallard duck 8-day dietary LC50	:	> 5000 mg/kg
Rainbow trout 96-h LC50	:	5.7 mg/l
Daphnia 48-h EC50	:	3.8 mg/l
Honey bees 96-h contact LD50	:	> 234 µg/bee no effects on larval development
Beneficial arthropods	:	no adverse effects under lab conditions on predatory beetles (*Stethorus punctum*), predatory mites (*Typhlodromus* spp., *Zetzellia mali*) and some predatory wasps and spiders.

Mode of action and spectrum of activity

RH 5992 acts as an ecdysone agonist via ingestion and contact. It mimics the insect hormone ecdysone which controls the moulting process. The product induces a premature lethal moult, inhibits metamorphosis and affects insect reproductive processes. RH 5992 has a fairly rapid action. The caterpillars stop feeding within hours. Thus RH 5992 acts differently from chitin biosynthesis inhibitors.

RH 5992 is highly selective to Lepidoptera, although effects have been shown on some selected Diptera and scale insects. A high level of activity has been proved on most of the lepidopterous families of importance such as Geometridae, Lymantriidae, Noctuidae, Pieridae, Pyralidae, Thaumetopoeidae and Tortricidae.

BIOLOGICAL ACTIVITY UNDER FIELD CONDITIONS

Materials and methods

Field trials aiming at insect pests were laid out to a randomized block design, and replicated 4 times. Plot sizes varied for different crops : apple 2 trees, peach 12 trees, vine 10 - 16 plants, sweet pepper 30 m². Bee trials were carried out according to German official recommendations (BBA guidelines 1991) : in a small hive per tent of 48 m², the product was sprayed when bees were actively foraging on flowering plants. Selectivity to predatory mites was assessed in trials aiming at vine moths.

In all trials a suspension concentrate formulation containing 240 g AI/l was used. RH 5992 was compared to commercial products applied at their registered doses. In bee trials, fenoxycarb was chosen as reference to investigate the effects on egg and larval development (Gerig, 1990).

Number and dates of treatment, volume of water sprayed and application timing are shown on the tables of results. Assessments were done according to local recommended methods. Significant treatment differences were established by analysis of variance.

Results

Insect pests

Laspeyresia pomonella on apples : under Mediterranean conditions RH 5992 gave outstanding control of the codling moth at dosages from 144 g AI/ha. In the French trial, with a very heavy pest pressure monitored by pheromone traps, the first application was done at the first egg hatching, followed by 6 applications until end of pest flight (Table 1). RH 5992 provided at least as good results as the standard and did not induce russeting in the cultivar Golden Delicious even after 7 applications with the highest tested rate of 192 g AI/ha.

TABLE 1 : CONTROL OF *LASPEYRESIA POMONELLA* ON APPLES (BOULBON - FRANCE 1991)

Product	Dose g AI/ha	% of attacked fruits	% of marketable fruits	% of fruits with russeting
RH 5992	96	33.7 b	65.7 a	5.6 a
RH 5992	120	26.3 b	72.5 a	8.6 a
RH 5992	144	11.9 a	86.2 a	5.9 a
RH 5992	192	8.1 a	91.2 a	8.5 a
Phosalone	600	14.3 a	60.4 a	7.8 a
Untreated		87.1 c	11.7 b	7.1 a

- 7 treatments from May 24 (first egg hatching) to August 13 (end of pest flight), 350 l/ha for the first and second applications then 400 l/ha.
- Values followed by the same letter are not significantly different at P = 0.05.

Laspeyresia molesta on peaches : in Italy RH 5992 gave good control of oriental fruit moth at rates from 14.4 g Al/hl. Three applications, done from the beginning of egg hatching to one week before harvest at 14-day intervals, were sufficient to ensure good protection of the fruits (Table 2).

TABLE 2 : CONTROL OF *LASPEYRESIA MOLESTA* ON PEACHES (PORPORANA - ITALY 1991)

Product	Dose g Al/hl	% of damaged fruits at harvest	
		with larvae	without larvae
RH 5992	9.6	3.2 a	3.6 a
RH 5992	14.4	2.0 a	2.2 a
RH 5992	19.2	1.3 a	1.8 a
Azinphos-Methyl	40	1.6 a	2.4 a
Untreated		9.5 b	6.8 b

- 3 treatments from June 27 (first egg hatching) to July 16 (1 week before harvest), 1000 l/ha
- Values followed by the same letter are not significantly different at P = 0.05.

Lobesia botrana on vine : in France RH 5992 provided excellent control of the vine moth at dosage as low as 96 g Al/ha when the product is applied at the beginning of egg hatching. The timing of the first application is crucial to ensure a high level of efficacy. The results were better than those for the reference product fenvalerate which is also intended for use at the same point of time. Sprayed one week later, RH 5992 can still show a good efficacy on larvae at higher dosages, but the delayed application led to more damage to the crop (Table 3). Other trials carried out in Germany, Italy, Spain and Switzerland confirmed these results.

TABLE 3 : CONTROL OF LOBESIA BOTRANA ON VINE (MONTADY - FRANCE 1991)

Product	Dose g Al/hl	Date of application	No. of larvae/cluster ( ) = % efficacy	No. of holes/cluster ( ) = % reduction
RH 5992	96	July 5	0.18 (97) bc	1.9 (90) ab
RH 5992	120	July 5	0.13 (98) ab	1.2 (94) a
RH 5992	144	July 5	0.06 (99) a	1.2 (94) a
Fenvalerate	75	July 5	1.32 (76) e	5.1 (75) b
RH 5992	96	July 12	0.91 (83) de	6.1 (70) b
RH 5992	120	July 12	0.45 (92) d	4.2 (79) b
RH 5992	144	July 12	0.35 (93) cd	2.5 (88) ab
Methyl-Parathion	300	July 12	0.63 (88) de	6.0 (70) b
Untreated			5.42 f	20.1 c

- Treatment at the beginning of egg hatching (July 5) or at the first penetrations (July 12), 400 l/ha.
- Assessments on July 26.
- Values followed by the same letter are not significantly different at P = 0.05.

Clysia ambiguella on vine : in Germany RH 5992 also achieved good control of the grape berry moth (Table 4). Application timing follows the same recommendations as for *L. botrana*.

TABLE 4 : CONTROL OF CLYSIA AMBIGUELLA ON VINE (BODENHEIM - GERMANY 1991)

Product	Dose g Al/ha	Date of application	No. of larvae/100 inflorescences ( ) = % efficacy
RH 5992	10	May 24/June 5	2.5 (94) a
RH 5992	15	May 24/June 5	3.3 (93) a
Fenoxycarb	10	May 24/June 5	18.5 (58) b
Untreated			44.0 c

- First treatment one week after the peak of flight, second treatment 12 days later, 600 l/ha.
- Values followed by the same letter are not significantly different at $\underline{P}$ = 0.05.

Spodoptera exigua on sweet pepper : in Spain excellent efficacy on beet armyworm was achieved with dosages from 96 g Al/ha onwards. RH 5992 controlled the pest for two to more than three weeks, depending on the dosage (Table 5).

TABLE 5 : CONTROL OF *SPODOPTERA EXIGUA* ON SWEET PEPPER (PARADAS - SPAIN 1991)

Product	Dose g Al/ha	Pre-count	% control at days after treatment* : 3		12		21	
RH 5992	96	-	87	a	100	a	79	a
RH 5992	192	-	100	a	98	a	93	a
RH 5992	288	-	100	a	100	a	95	a
Deltamethrin	12.5	-	58	b	98	a	72	a
Untreated		(13.7)	(12.0)	b	(22.5)	b	(19.5)	b

* Treatment on May 17, 1000 l/ha.
( ) = No of larvae/10 plants.
- Values followed by the same letter are not significantly different at $\underline{P}$ = 0.05.

Pollinators and beneficials

As RH 5992 is highly specific to lepidopterous insects, the product was expected to be selective to numerous beneficial arthropods. In the first step of its evaluation, special attention was paid to determine precisely its potential effects to bees and predatory mites which are among the most important beneficials in European vineyards and orchards.

Apis mellifera : Tent trials carried out in Germany confirmed the selectivity of RH 5992 to adult bees as indicated previously by laboratory tests. More, this evaluation showed that the product applied at dosages up to ten times higher than that recommended for field uses had no effect on either egg hatching or larval development (Table 6).

TABLE 6 : SELECTIVITY TO *APIS MELLIFERA* IN TENT TRIALS (GERMANY 1991)

Product	Dose g Al/hl	No of foraging bees/m² at day of treatment		Dead adults		Dead pupae	
		Trial 1	Trial 2	Trial 1	Trial 2	Trial 1	Trial 2
RH 5992 *	300	38-43	14-18	777	373	39	7
Fenoxycarb	40	30-35	20-25	637	385	105	12
Untreated		35-40	14-16	670	535	51	7

Product	Dose	No of hatched bees		Average weight in mg		Hatching rate in %		Observation
		Trial 1	Trial 2	Trial 1	Trial 2	Trial 1	Trial 2	
RH 5992 *	300	700	390	100	110	100	98	No abnormal bees
Fenoxycarb	40	0	413	-	99.4	-	60	Death due to growth abnormalities; pupae with white eyes
Untreated		1061	450	108	109	100	98	No abnormal bees

* Mean of 2 replications. RH 5992 applied at about 10 times the recommended dose/ha.
- Products sprayed when bees were actively foraging on *Phacelia*, 400 l/ha.
- Treatment on June 2 - 21˚C (Trial 1) and July 2 - 30˚C (Trial 2).

Typhlodromus pyri : In most of the vine moth trials carried out in Germany, the influence of RH 5992 on *T. pyri* was assessed. At the highest tested dosages, no adverse effects were observed (Table 7). These results were confirmed in experiments conducted in France and Italy.

TABLE 7 : SELECTIVITY TO *TYPHLODROMUS PYRI* IN VINE MOTH TRIALS
(GERMANY 1991)

Product	Dose g Al/hl	No. of *Typhlodromus pyri*/leaf at ....days after 2nd application		
		14 DAT 2 HOCHHEIM*	9 DAT 2 MUSSBACH **	13 DAT 2 OESTRICH ***
RH 5992	10	8.8 a	7.2 a	7.7 a
RH 5992	15	7.9 a	6.3 a	6.1 a
Fenoxycarb	10	5.5 a	6.1 a	5.5 a
Untreated	-	7.1 a	7.8 a	9.4 a

- Dates of treatment : * July 26, August 2; ** July 20, 26; *** July 23, August 2.
- Products sprayed twice against the 2nd generation of vine moths, 600 l/ha.
- Values followed by the same letter are not significantly different at $\underline{P}$ = 0.05.

<u>Crop tolerance</u>

In all trials, whatever the tested dosages, RH 5992 was not phytotoxic to leaves or fruits of the treated crops.

CONCLUSIONS

In the field trials carried out by Hoechst and Roussel Uclaf since 1988, RH 5992 provided outstanding control of key pests in orchards (*L. pomonella, L. molesta*), vine (*L. botrana, C. ambiguella*) and vegetables (*S. exigua*) at dosages ranging from 9.6 to 14.4 g AI/hl. Further experiments have also given promising results of *Laspeyresia funebrana* on plums, *Capua reticulana* on apples, *Sparganothis pilleriana* on vine, as well as *Pieris* spp and *Mamestra brassicae* on vegetables. Recent laboratory and field trials carried out in Germany and Spain have given very promising results against forestry pests such as *Thaumetopoea pityocampa, Lymantria monacha, Sphinx pinastri*.

Application timing appears to be crucial for success. In orchards and vine RH 5992 should be sprayed at egg hatching in order to optimize performance. In most situations the use of pheromone traps to monitor the pest flight can make it easier to determine the most suitable time for application.

The original mode of action together with a good toxicological and ecotoxicological profile suggest that RH 5992 will be a valuable tool, as a suitable selective insecticide for IPM, for the protection of perennial crops, row crops and forests.

ACKNOWLEDGEMENTS

We would like to express our thanks to all our colleagues who have contributed to the field evaluation of RH 5992 in Europe.

REFERENCES

BBA Guidelines : Prüfungsrichtlinie VI, 23 - 1 June 1991 (Evaluation of product selectivity to bees). Gerig, L. (1990) News about the use of Insegar (Fenoxycarb) in Switzerland *4th International Symposium on the harmonization of methods for testing the toxicity of pesticides to bees*. Prague, May 1990, 74 - 75.
Robbins, W.E. *et al* (1970). *Steroids* **16**,105

ACTIVITY OF THE NATURAL PLANT PRODUCT (2R, 3R, 4R, 5R)-2,5-BIS (HYDROXYMETHYL) PYRROLIDINE-3,4-DIOL (DMDP) AS AN ANTI-NEMATODE AGENT

A.N.E. BIRCH, W.M. ROBERTSON, I.E. GEOGHEGAN, W.J. McGAVIN, T.J.W. ALPHEY

Scottish Crop Research Institute, Invergowrie, Dundee DD2 5DA

L.E. FELLOWS, A.A. WATSON, M.S.J. SIMMONDS, E.A. PORTER

Royal Botanic Gardens, Kew, Richmond, Surrey TW9 3AB

ABSTRACT

The plant-derived sugar analogue (2R, 3R, 4R, 5R)-2,5-bis (hydroxymethyl) pyrrolidine-3,4-diol, also known as DMDP, from tropical legumes was found to have a range of activities against several plant parasitic nematode species. As a foliar spray, soil drench or seed dressing DMDP reduced root galling of tomato by *Meloidogyne* spp. At 30 mg/l soil drench it also inhibited virus acquisition, transmission and root galling by *Xiphinema diversicaudatum* on *Petunia*. At 100 mg/l DMDP enhanced the control of potato cyst nematodes *Globodera rostochiensis* on the partially resistant potato cv. Heather.

INTRODUCTION

Because of the inherent toxicity of most existing synthetic pesticides to non-target organisms and because of their persistence in the environment there is increasing pressure on the agricultural industry to find more acceptable alternatives. A number of unusual polyhydroxy alkaloids have recently been isolated from plants (Fellows & Nash, 1990). Many are sugar analogues with a range of interesting biological activities and are now known as alkaloidal glycosidase inhibitors (AGIs). One AGI incorporating a five-sided ring, (2R, 3R, 4R, 5R)-2,5-bis (hydroxymethyl) pyrrolidine-3,4-diol (DMDP, Fig. 1) is of particular interest in crop protection because of its activity as a potent insect feeding deterrent (reviewed in Fellows *et al.*, 1992). DMDP is also a powerful inhibitor of insect gut alpha-glucosidase enzymes including trehalase. However, DMDP is relatively inactive against mammalian gut alpha-glucosidases and is considered to have low mammalian toxicity. The present paper reports for the first time the activity of DMDP against several plant parasitic nematode species. A range of sensitive bioassays developed at SCRI were used to screen DMDP and other natural plant products isolated by collaborating phytochemists at the Royal Botanic Gardens, Kew.

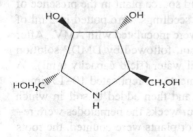

Fig. 1. DMDP

MATERIALS AND METHODS

Drench application tests

Glass tubes (7.5 cm x 2.5 cm) were filled with 24.5 g of sieved, dried sand. To this was added 5 ml of water containing c. 350 juveniles of the root–knot nematode *Meloidogyne javanica* and DMDP solutions to produce final concentrations of 0, 1, 10, 25 or 50 mg/l. A two week old tomato seedling (cv. Moneymaker) was planted in each tube. After 14 days in a greenhouse at 22–27°C the roots were washed and gall counts compared with a water control. Each treatment was replicated 10 times. The test was repeated using five week old plants in 2.5 cm diameter pots filled with 75 g of Levington Universal compost mixed with sand in a 3:1 ratio.

Foliar application tests

Five week old tomato (cv. Moneymaker) seedlings were transferred to 6 cm pots filled with 3:1 Levington Universal compost:sand mixture. Non–absorbent cotton wool was placed around the base of each seedling to protect the soil during foliar application. Each plant was carefully sprayed with 0.3 ml of water or DMDP in water at 1, 10, 35, 75 or 150 mg/l using an air brush. On the following day, 1 ml of water containing c. 350 *M. javanica* larvae was added to each pot. After 14 days the roots were assessed for root galls.

Seed treatment tests

Batches of 30 uniform seeds of tomato (cv. Moneymaker) were placed in glass dishes. Water or aqueous DMDP (0.6 ml) at 0.1, 1, 10, 100 or 1000 mg/l was added. After 24 hours soaking each seed was air–dried and individually planted in a 6 cm diameter pot containing 75 g of 3:1 Levington Universal compost:sand mixture. After germination, 10 uniform seedlings at the cotyledon stage from each DMDP seed treatment were each inoculated with c. 350 *M. incognita* juveniles in 1 ml of water. Six days later a further 10 seedlings from the original seed treatments, now at the 2–3 true leaf stage, were also each inoculated with c. 350 juveniles. After 14 days roots were assessed for root galls.

Virus acquisition and transmission

The effect of DMDP was tested on the nematode *Xiphinema diversicaudatum*, a vector of Arabis Mosaic Virus (AMV). In this experiment, effects on virus acquisition were tested by exposing virus–free nematodes to a virus–infected source plant in the presence of DMDP, applied as a soil drench. Three week old *Petunia* seedlings were potted in 2 ml of 3:1 sand:loam mixture. Forty–eight hours later the plants were inoculated with AMV. After a further 24 h, five adult nematodes were added to each pot, followed by DMDP solution to produce final concentrations of 15 or 30 mg/l in the soil water (field capacity 6 ml). A control of oxamyl at 7 mg/l was also included. Each treatment was replicated 10–15 times. After four weeks the nematodes were carefully extracted and then added to soil in which virus–free receptor plants were growing. After a further four weeks the nematodes were re-extracted and counted. The galls on the roots of the receptor plants were counted, the roots macerated and the sap applied to leaves of virus indicator plants (*Chenopodium quinoa*).

Interactions of DMDP with PCN resistant potato

Plastic pots (10 cm diameter) were filled with 600 g 3:1 sterilised sieved loam: dried sand mixture with a field capacity of 150 mls. Five PCN (*Globodera rostochiensis*) cysts held in a small terylene voile bag were placed in the middle of the soil. Single sprouts of equal size removed from potatoes by a small scoop were planted, sprout down, in the soil above the bag containing the cysts. The susceptible cv. Desiree and the partially resistant cv. Heather were used. The pots were placed in polythene bags and their positions randomised on a sand bed in a glasshouse kept at 22°C. DMDP at 1, 10 or 100 mg/l was applied to soil to field capacity. After 10 weeks the roots and soil were examined and the numbers of new cysts counted.

TABLE 1. Effect of DMDP drench treatment on root galling by *Meloidogyne javanica* on tomatoes grown in sand or compost:sand mix.

Treatment/Final Conc. (mg/l)	Sand grown % gall reduction	Compost:sand grown % gall reduction
Water (control)	0 a	0 a
DMDP/1	73 c	40 c
DMDP/10	68 b	34 c
DMDP/25	56 b	21 b
DMDP/50	53 b	20 b

Means with differing letters are significantly different (P<0.05).

RESULTS

DMDP applied as a drench

Experiments demonstrate that DMDP applied as a drench to roots reduced root galling by *M. javanica* attacking tomato. When sand was used as the growing medium, up to 73% control of root galling at 1 mg/l was achieved. Better control was found using DMDP at lower rather than higher concentrations (Table 1). When the growing medium was 3:1 compost:sand, DMDP significantly decreased galling, but the percent reduction was less (maximum of 40% at 1 mg/l) than found in sand (Table 1). However, it was again more effective at the lower than at the higher concentrations.

DMDP applied as a foliar spray

When DMDP was sprayed onto leaves of tomato plants grown in compost:sand mix a significant reduction in root galling was found for all concentrations of DMDP tested, with a maximum of 61% at 1 mg/l (Table 2).

TABLE 2. Foliar application of DMDP to control root galling by *Meloidogyne javanica* on tomato plants grown in compost:sand.

Treatment/Conc. (mg/l)	Mean galls/root	% gall reduction
Water (control)	99.9 a	0 a
DMDP/1	39.4 d	61 c
DMDP/10	43.0 c	57 c
DMDP/35	43.1 c	57 c
DMDP/75	55.5 b	45 b
DMDP/150	60.2 b	40 b

Means with differing letters are significantly different (P<0.05).

Seed treatments with DMDP

Soaking seeds in solutions of DMDP for 24 h prior to planting gave useful levels of protection to the seedlings against root galling by *M. incognita*. When the seedlings were inoculated at the cotyledon stage 10, 100 and 1000 mg/l seed treatments resulted in significantly (P<0.001) decreased galling, with a maximum of 38% reduction at the highest concentration tested (Table 3). Delaying inoculation until the plants had reached the 2–3 true leaf stage further increased the effectiveness and a significant effect was found even at 1 mg/l.

TABLE 3. Seed treatments with DMDP to control root galling by *Meloidogyne incognita*.

Treatment/Conc. (mg/l)	% gall reduction (cotyledon stage)	% gall reduction (2–3 true leaf stage)
Water (control	0 a	0 a
DMDP 0.1	4 a	6 a
DMDP 1	8 a	25 b
DMDP 10	25 b	53 c
DMDP 100	34 b	55 c
DMDP 1000	38 b	58 c

Means with differing letters are significantly different (P<0.05).

Virus acquisition and transmission

DMDP applied as a drench during the acquisition stage significantly (P<0.05) decreased root galling on the receptor plants, compared with the control (Table 4). The percent control of galling at 15 and 30 mg/l (66% and 73% respectively) was not significantly less than that for oxamyl at 7 mg/l. The analysis of virus acquisition and transmission was complicated by the fact that the numbers of nematodes transferred to receptor plants differed. Treatment comparisons were made by estimating the probability of a single nematode acquiring or transmitting the virus. These probabilities and a standard error were calculated for each treatment using the maximum likelihood estimator (Walter et al., 1980). Pairwise comparisons of these probabilities revealed that DMDP at 15 and 30 mg/l decreased acquisition and transmission of AMV but was less effective than oxamyl at 7 mg/l (Table 4).

TABLE 4. Effect of DMDP and oxamyl on galling and transmission of Arabis Mosaic Virus by *Xiphinema diversicaudatum*.

Treatment/Conc. (mg/l)	% mean reduction of galling, compared with controls	Probability of acquisition
Control	0 a	0.34 a
DMDP/15	66 b	0.9 b
DMDP/30	73 b	0.22 c
Oxamyl/7	80 b	0 c

Means with differing letters are significantly different (P<0.05).

Interactions of DMDP with PCN resistant potato

The number of cysts per root and the number of eggs per g soil were analysed using ANOVA. DMDP at concentrations between 1 and 100 mg/l had no significant effect on the number of cysts of *G. rostochiensis* which developed on roots of the PCN susceptible cv. Desiree. However, the compound did significantly decrease the number of eggs per g soil on this cultivar, a maximum of 53% decrease being achieved by DMDP at 10 mg/l. The cv. Heather is partially resistant to PCN, and the mean number of cysts on the water−treated roots of this cultivar was 81% less than on the roots of water−treated susceptible cv. Desiree. When DMDP was applied as a drench at 100 mg/l to Heather, the number of cysts which developed decreased by 61% compared with its water−treated control. In addition, the mean number of eggs per g soil on Heather treated with 100 mg/l DMDP decreased by 79% compared with the control (Table 5).

TABLE 5. Interaction of DMDP with PCN–susceptible and partially–resistant potato cultivars.

Cultivar/ DMDP conc. (mg/l)	Cysts per root		Eggs/g soil	
	Mean number	% reduction within cultivar	Mean number	% reduction within cultivar
Desiree/0	196 a	0 a	112.4 a	0 a
Desiree/1	182 a	7 a	72.3 b	36 b
Desiree/10	149 a	24 a	53.3 b	53 b
Desiree/100	222 a	0 a	72.3 b	36 b
Heather/0	37.2 b	0 b	21.2 c	0 c
Heather/100	14.4 c	61 c	4.4 d	79 d

Means with differing letters are significantly different ($P<0.05$).

DISCUSSION

From these studies we have demonstrated that the plant–derived sugar analogue, DMDP, has a range of activities against plant parasitic nematodes. Our results indicate that DMDP, has sub–lethal effects on nematodes, has useful systemic activity and has a considerable potential in future integrated control strategies whilst minimising undesirable effects on the environment.

ACKNOWLEDGEMENTS

This research was funded by a contract from the British Technology Group to the Scottish Crop Research Institute and the Royal Botanic Gardens, Kew.

REFERENCES

Fellows, L.E.; Kite, G.C.; Nash, R.J.; Simmonds, M.S.J.; Scofield, A.M. (1992) Distribution and biological activity of alkaloidal glycosidase inhibitors from plants. In: *Nitrogen Metabolism of Plants*, K. Mengel & D.J. Philbean (eds). Proceedings of the Phytochemical Society of Europe. Oxford, Clarendon Press.

Fellows, L.E.; Nash, R.J. (1990) Sugar shaped alkaloids. *Science Progress Oxford*, **74**, 245–255.

Walter, S.D.; Hildreth, S.W.; Beaty, B.J. (1980) Estimation of infection rates in populations of organisms using pools of variable size. *American Journal of Epidemiology*, **112**, 124–128.

STEINERNEMA B-326 AND B-319 (NEMATODA): NEW BIOLOGICAL SOIL INSECTICIDES

R. GEORGIS, C.T. REDMOND AND W.R. MARTIN

BIOSYS, 1057 East Meadow Circle, Palo Alto, California, 94303 USA

ABSTRACT

Under the code names B-326 and B-319, two biological soil insecticides based on the insect-parasitic nematodes *Steinernema glaseri* and *S. scapterisci* were developed for the control of white grubs (Scarabaeidae) and mole crickets (Gryllotalpidae), respectively. Progress achieved in liquid fermentation (up to 60,000 litre) and flowable formulation as well as generating field efficacy comparable to standard insecticides will allow these products to become competitive in the market place.

INTRODUCTION

Nematodes in the genera *Steinernema* and *Heterorhabditis* are effective against a wide range of soil-inhabiting insects and insects occupying cryptic habitats (Georgis, 1992). Recent developments in production through liquid fermentation and exemption from registration requirements in most countries have favoured their commercial development by industrial companies. These efforts have led to a successful introduction of a number of products into various markets (e.g. **Exhibit®**- Ciba-Geigy, **BioSafe®** - Ortho Chevron, **BioVector®** - biosys, **Nemasys®** - Agricultural Genetic Company and **Sanoplant®** - Dr. R. Maag). However, these products are not equally effective against all soil insects and there is continuous research for other nematode species. Two species offering potential against white grubs and mole crickets were isolated from soil in New Jersey, USA and Colon, Argentina, respectively. They were identified as *Steinernema glaseri* (B-326) and *S. scapterisci* (B-319).

ACTIVE INGREDIENT AND MODE OF ACTION

The active ingredient of B-326 and B-319 is the third stage infective juvenile and its associated bacterium *Xenorhabdus* sp. The measurements of the infective juveniles for B-319 are 570 μm long and 24 μm wide and 1,100 μm long and 42 μm wide for B-326. The relationship between the nematode and the bacterium is symbiotic because the nematode cannot reproduce inside the insect without the bacterium and the bacterium cannot enter the insects hemocoel to cause infection without the nematode.

The free-living third infective stage of the nematode is ensheathed in a cuticle retained from the previous moult and carries the bacterium within its intestine. The infective stage locates insects in soil by detecting insect excretory products and carbon dioxide levels, initiates infection and is the only stage in the nematode's life cycle that survives outside the insect. The infective stage enters the insects via the mouth, anus or spiracles and penetrates mechanically into the body cavity where it releases the bacteria. The bacteria proliferate, cause septicaemic death of the insect within 24-72 h, establish an environment favourable to nematode reproduction, and inhibit the growth of many foreign micro-organisms. The nematodes feed on the multiplying bacteria and the host tissue, usually passing through two generations. Eventually when the available nutrients are depleted, the developing juveniles become the infective stage nematodes and exit the host. These infective juveniles then seek new healthy hosts. At 22-28°C the life cycle takes approximately 6 d for B-326 and 10 d for B-319 in most insects.

Xenorhabdus spp are medium to long motile rods with peritrichous flagellae. They are gram negative facultative anaerobes that form spheroplasts (x=2.6 μm diameter) in older cultures. They are nonspore formers and thus do not have an environmentally resistant stage. They are found only inside the nematodes and infected insect hosts.

PRODUCTION, FORMULATION AND PACKAGING

At present, consistent effective production of B-326 and B-319 is achieved in 30,000-60,000 litre fermenters with a yield capacity as high as 90,000 infectives/cm^3. Since distinct physiological differences exist between B-326 and B-319, the growing media vary considerably, but in general consist of an emulsifier, a yeast source, a vegetable oil and a source of protein.

The formulation is based on immobilizing the infective stages in a gel polymer and packing them in 45x45 cm special film material mounted on a frame. A 50x50x35 cm box can hold 10 frames which are enough to treat half a hectare (assuming 125x10^6 infectives/ frame and a rate of 2.5x10^9 infectives/ha). This formulation provides up to 3 months shelflife at room temperature and 12 months under refrigeration and is considered practical since the polymer containing the infective stage is dissolved immediately after placement in the sprayer.

B-326 and B-319 formulations can be applied with common agrochemical equipment and irrigation systems. They can withstand application pressures of 2068 kPa and can be delivered with all common nozzle type sprayers (e.g. "01" nozzles) with openings as small as 50 μm in diameter. Both products can be tank mixed with *Bacillus thuringiensis* - based products, pyrethroids, insect growth regulators and many organophosphate insecticides, fungicides, herbicides and fertilizers.

HOST PREFERENCE AND SAFETY

Once inside the hemocoel of an insect, infective nematodes can kill and reproduce, but not all insects are equally susceptible to the nematode-bacterium complex. Various physical and chemical factors influence the host preference.

Host preference studies were performed in the laboratory using 9 cm petri dishes filled with sandy soil (moisture content about 15%, based on volumetric measurements). Each dish was treated with 200 infective stages in 2ml of water and was immediately inoculated with one insect of a particular stage. There were 3 trials/insect and 10 replicates/ trial. The mortality was recorded after 96 h. The results showed that the insects in the order Orthoptera and Coleoptera are the preferred host for B-319 and B-326, respectively (Table 1).

B-326 and B-319 are highly sensitive to u.v. light and desiccation, with significant mortality 15-30 min after application in exposed environments. In aquatic habitats, nematode survival is poor due to the low oxygen level (nematodes settle quickly to the bottom). Therefore, no impact on beneficial arthropods is expected with nematodes in exposed and aquatic environments.

TABLE 1. Host preference of *Steinernema* B-326 and B-319.

Insect Host	Insect Stage	% Mortality (± SEM) B-326	B-319
Blattella germanica (German cockroach)	males	17.6 ± 4.1 de	72.3 ± 9.2 a
Scapteriscus vicinus (Mole cricket)	males	34.4 ± 6.3 d	77.0 ± 4.3 a
Schistocerca nitens (Vargant grasshopper)	females	39.1 ± 5.4 d	57.2 ± 6.4 b
Musca domestica (House fly)	second stage larvae	5.7 ± 3.2 e	18.1 ± 7.2 d
Diabrotica sp. (Southern corn rootworm)	third stage larvae	65.4 ± 5.3 bc	40.3 ± 8.1 b
Cyclocephala borealis (Northern masked chafer)	third stage larvae	76.9 ± 3.8 b	31.5 ± 6.6 bcd
Rhizotrogus majalis (European chafer)	third stage larvae	58.6 ± 9.2 bc	28.4 ± 3.6 d
Phyllophaga sp. (May beetles)	third stage larvae	55.3 ± 8.4 c	46.5 ± 4.5 b
Otiorhynchus sulcatus (Black vine weevil)	late stage larvae	93.1 ± 3.9 a	39.7 ± 6.3 bc
Spodoptera exigua (Beet armyworm)	pupae	58.6 ± 7.0 bc	3.4 ± 2.2 e
Trichoplusia ni (Cabbage looper)	pupae	14.3 ± 8.2 de	2.3 ± 2.7 e

Means (± SEM) within each column followed by the same letters are not significantly different at P = 0.05 using Kruskal-Wallis test (Hollander and Wolfe, 1973). No significant insect mortality recorded in the control.

Field applications of steinernematid nematodes in Japan, Western Europe and the United States showed no detrimental effects on predatory insects, predatory mites and earthworms (see Georgis, 1992). Moreover, tests conducted on rats, mice, chicks, rabbits and pigs showed no symptoms or mortality caused by nematodes and their associated bacteria by oral, intradermal, subcutaneous and interperitoneal inoculation. In mammals and birds, the nematode – bacterium complex cannot survive the high body temperature (37° C) and is eliminated by the immune system upon injection. Additionally, the thickened gut of these animals prevents nematode penetration to the blood stream, resulting in elimination of the ingested nematodes with the faeces (Poinar, 1989).

B-326 and B-319 and their symbiotic bacteria, are exempt from the registration requirements of the Federal Insecticide, Fungicide, Rodenticide Act (FIFRA) in the United States. Thus far, no standard laws and regulations have been enacted in any other countries governing the field release of insect-parasitic nematodes.

TEMPERATURE/PATHOGENICITY RELATIONSHIP

The pathogenicity of B-326 and B-319 at various temperatures was studied under laboratory conditions using the methodology described in host preference experiment. After the nematodes were added to the sand, the dishes were wrapped with parafilm to maintain the moisture level of soil. The nematodes were allowed to acclimate for 24 h at a particular temperature before the addition of the target insect. Insect mortality was recorded after 96 h exposure.

The effective temperatures for infectivity by both nematode products ranged between 15-35°C with the highest mortality occurring between 25-35° C (Table 2). Similar results were reported by Nguyen and Smart (1990) and Parawinder *et al.* (1992) with the Uruguayan strain of *S. scapterisci*.

TABLE 2. Effect of temperature on the effectiveness of *Steinernema* B-326 against the northern masked chafer and *Steinernema* B-319 against the tawny mole cricket.

Temperature (C°)	% Insect Mortality (± SEM)[a]	
	B-326	B-319
10	0.0 d	0.0 e
15	11.2 ± 5.1 c	4.3 ± 2.6 d
20	52.6 ± 6.4 b	19.0 ± 3.3 c
25	76.1 ± 4.2 a	65.5 ± 2.9 b
35	71.8 ± 4.3 a	82.6 ± 5.2 a
40	0.0 d	0.0 e

[a] Means (± SEM) within each column followed by the same letters are not significantly different at P = 0.05 using Kruskal-Wallis test (Hollander and Wolfe, 1973). No significant insect mortality was recorded in the control.

VERTICAL MOVEMENT

Under greenhouse conditions (25±2°C), potting soil (moisture content about 26%, based on volumetric measurements) was added to 3.78 litre pots covered with St. Augustine grass (mole cricket test) or Kentucky bluegrass (northern masked chafer test). Five late instars of the mole crickets *Scapteriscus vicinus* or the northern masked chafer *Cyclocephala borealis* were placed 5 cm and 10 cm below the soil surface in a mesh screen cage (8 cm in diameter and 1 cm high) to restrict their movement. Food was mixed with soil in the cage. To the surface of each pot were added uniformly O (control) or 25,000 infective stages in 200 ml water (equivalent to 2.5×10^9 infectives in 1,800 litre spray/ha). All treatments were replicated four times and the evaluation was made 10 d after the application.

The results showed that B-326 and B-319 have the ability to move 5 cm and 10 cm, respectively, and to cause high infection (Table 3). Similar conclusions were reached by Nguyen and Smart (1990) and Parawinder *et al.* (1992) working with the Uruguayan strain of *S. scapterisci.*

TABLE 3. Vertical movement and effectiveness of *Steinernema* B-326 against the northern masked chafer and *Steinernema* B-319 against the tawny mole cricket.

Depth	% Insect mortality (± SEM)[a]	
	B-326	B-319
5 cm	82.6 ± 9.2 a	72.9 ± 10.8 a
10 cm	76.1 ± 5.3 a	24.5 ± 7.1 b

[a] Means (± SEM) followed by the same letter are not significantly different at P = 0.05 using Kruskal-Wallis test (Hollander and Wolfe, 1973). No significant insect mortality was recorded in the control.

FIELD TRIALS AND PERSISTENCE

During 1988-1990, over 100 trials were conducted to define the most effective application strategy for B-326 and B-319. The generated data were used in 1990 and 1991 trials as described below.

Tests were conducted in turfgrass against the second and third instars of the Japanese beetle *Popillia japonica* (with B-326) or against mid-later instars (pronotal length from 5mm to 8mm) and adults of the mole cricket *Scapteriscus vicinus* (with B-319). Experimental design was a randomized complete block with three to five replicates; plots ranged in size from 6 to 9 m² for B-326 and from 85 - 250 m² for B-319. Larval density of the Japanese beetle before treatment ranged from 174-398/m².

Treatments were applied between 0600 and 0800 or 1600 and 1800 hour. Applications were made using an 8-12 litre back pack sprayer or a 100-400 litre ground sprayer at 1,500-2,400 litre of spray volume/ha. Test plots received approximately 1 cm irrigation before (unless soil was already moist) and after application. Thereafter, the plots were irrigated at 2-3 d intervals unless rainfall occurred earlier in the day. At least one insecticide was used as a standard in each trial.

Treatment effectiveness for B-326 was determined 4-5 weeks after treatment by counting the number of live larvae in 4-5 soil samples (18 x 18 x 7cm/m^2) taken from each plot replicate. For B-319, pre- and post - treatment (after 2-4 weeks) evaluations of mole cricket damage were made using a 0.6m frame divided into nine equal sections. In each plot, the frame was positioned at four to ten locations (at least 30 cm from borders and other samples) and the number of sections in which damage was present was counted each time. Consequently, damage could range from zero (no damage present in any of the nine sections) to nine (all sections contained mole cricket mounds and/or tunnels). These counts were compared with untreated control plots.

The mean soil temperature at 5 cm depth ranged from 10-27°C (mean 23°C) for B-326 trials and from 26-32°C (mean 28° C) for B-319 trials.

The results against the Japanese beetle and the tawny mole cricket were successful and comparable to the standard insecticides (Tables 4,5).

The post-application persistence of both products were determined from 10 field trials by taking two core samples randomly (5cm diameter, 10cm deep) from each plot at one week intervals for 8 weeks. Each sample was divided into two parts, placed in plastic containers and immediately inoculated with 10 last instars of *Galleria mellonella*. This insect is known to be highly susceptible to insect-parasitic nematodes. The number of infected larvae was recorded after 4 d (25 ± 1°C). At 8 weeks post treatment, the *G. mellonella* mortality ranged between 0-12% for both products. Immediately after application, insect mortality was 88-100%. The mortality declined to 33-71% (B-319) and 42-66% (B-326) 4 weeks post treatment.

TABLE 4. Summary of field efficacy of *Steinernema* B-326 against the Japanese beetle *Popillia japonica* compared with insecticidal treatments in 1990 and 1991.

Treatment	Rate[a]	No. of Tests	% reduction (± SEM)[b]
B-326	2.5x10^9	12	79.4 ± 11.5
Isofenphos	2.50 kg	10	75.0 ± 9.2
Diazinon	2.25 kg	4	66.5 ± 6.1
Bendiocarb	2.50 kg	9	83.2 ± 12.6

[a] Number of infective juveniles and AI for chemical treatment per hectare.
[b] Significant differences (P>0.05) between treated and untreated plots using Kruskal-Wallis test (Hollander and Wolfe, 1973).

TABLE 5. Summary of field efficacy of *Steinernema* B-319 against the tawny mole cricket *Scapteriscus vicinus* compared with insecticidal treatments in 1990 and 1991.

Treatment	Rate[a]	No. of Tests	Mean Damage Rating[b]	
			Pre Treatment	Post Treatment
B-319	2.5×10^9	13	4.8 ± 1.3 a	2.0 ± 0.8 a
Isofenphos	2.25 kg	7	5.1 ± 2.5 a	1.6 ± 1.0 a
Acephate	1.8 kg	9	4.5 ± 1.6 a	1.7 ± 0.7 a
Ethoprop	4.5 kg	2	5.9 ± 1.1 a	1.2 ± 0.7 a
Control	--	13	5.1 ± 2.9 a	3.9 ± 1.3 b

[a] Number of infective juveniles and AI for chemical tratments per hectare.
[b] Damage rate scale is 0-9 (non-most). Means (± SEM) within each column followed by the same letters are not significantly different at P = 0.05 using Kruskal-Wallis test (Hollander and Wolfe, 1973).

CONCLUSION

A comparable cost/effectiveness ratio to chemical insecticides is critical for the successful introduction of *Steinernema* B-326 and B-319 to the market. Liquid fermentation, formulation and field efficacy is making significant progress towards this goal.

REFERENCES

Georgis, R. (1992) Present and future prospects for entomopathogenic nematode products. *Biocontrol Science and Technology*, **2**, (in Press).

Hollander, M. Wolf, O.A. (1973) *Nonparametric Statistical Methods*. New York: Wiley

Nguyen, K.B.; Smart, G.C. (1990) Vertical dispersal of *Steinernema scapterisci*. *Journal of Nematology*, **22**, 574-578.

Parawinder, S.G.; Gaugler, R.; Kaya, H.K.; Wusaty, M. (1992) Aspects of infectivity of the entomopathogenic nematode *Steinernema scapterisci* (Nematoda: Steinernematidae). *Journal of Invertebrate Pathology*, (in press).

Poinar, G.O. (1989) Non-insect hosts for the entomogenous rhabditid nematodes *Neoaplectana* (Steinernematidae) and *Heterorhabditis* (Heterorhabditidae). *Revue de Nematologie*, **12**, 423-428.

ACKNOWLEDGMENTS

The authors thank Dr. Harry Kaya (University of California, Davis) and Dr. Stephen Manweiler (biosys) for their critical review of the manuscript.

FLUFENPROX - A NEW INSECTICIDE FOR RICE

R. F. S. GORDON, M. J. BUSHELL

ICI Agrochemicals, Jealott's Hill Research Station, Bracknell, Berks,
RG12 6EY

R. PASCOE

ICI Agrochemicals, Fernhurst, Haslemere, Surrey, GU27 3JE

T. ENOYOSHI

ICI Japan Ltd., Agricultural Research Station, 780 Kunocho, Ushiku-shi,
Ibaraki-ken 300-11, Japan

ABSTRACT

Flufenprox (ICIA5682) is a new bis-aralkyl ether insecticide
which provides broad-spectrum insect control combined with
relatively low toxicity to spiders and predaceous mites.
Granular, dust and liquid formulations have been developed and
the compound has applicability both alone and in mixture with
other insecticides or fungicides, especially in rice.
Flufenprox is not affected by the major mechanisms of
resistance in leaf- and plant-hoppers. Its selectivity to
spiders at field use rates is an advantage in integrated pest
management programmes and reduces the risk of hopper
resurgence in rice. It is of low hazard to users, fish,
mammals and earthworms.

INTRODUCTION

Flufenprox ([3-(4-chlorophenoxy)benzyl](RS)-2-(4-ethoxyphenyl)
-3,3,3-trifluoropropyl ether) was first synthesised by chemists at ICI
Agrochemicals Jealott's Hill Research Station. The invention of
flufenprox was the result of research targeted at low levels of fish
toxicity and applicability to pest management programmes where greater
selectivity is required in favour of beneficial insects, spiders and
mites. Flufenprox, a novel bis-aralkyl ether insecticide, combines
those characteristics with fast action and residual efficacy against a
range of insect pests.

CHEMICAL STRUCTURE

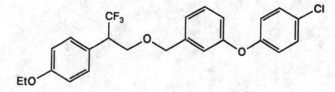

CHEMICAL AND PHYSICAL PROPERTIES OF THE TECHNICAL MATERIAL

Common Name	:	Flufenprox
Appearance	:	Odourless, transparent pale yellow-green liquid, mobile at ambient temperature.
Density	:	1.25g cm^{-3} at 25° C
Boiling Point	:	204° C at 0.2mm Hg
Vapour Pressure	:	1×10^{-9}mm Hg at 20° C
Water Solubility	:	2.5 ug/l in pH 7.0 buffered water.
Solubility	:	Soluble (>500g/l) in hexane, toluene, acetone, dichloromethane, ethyl acetate, octan-1-ol, acetonitrile and methanol.

CHEMISTRY

There are several good synthetic routes to flufenprox (Bushell et al., 1987). Details of some of these approaches have been published (Bushell, 1990). Flufenprox contains one chiral centre. Biological testing of the individual isomers found that the majority of insecticidal activity resides in one of the enantiomers (probably the R-isomer (Tsushima et al., 1988; Bushell, 1990)). Several processes have been devised to prepare individual isomers but none of these is suitable for large scale manufacture.

FORMULATIONS

Technical grade flufenprox is a stable, non volatile oil with no major handling problems. It has therefore been possible to present the compound in a wide range of formulation types, to suit many different methods of application.

Formulations have been devised which meet the exacting standards of the Japanese market. They include a 5 g/kg Driftless Dust (DL), a 10 g/kg Granule (GR), and a 150 g/kg Emulsion (EW). Other formulations currently available include a 100 g/l Emulsifiable Concentrate (EC), a 7.5 g/kg GR and a 200 g/l EW. A special type of granule has been developed for the rice market (patent pending) which gives excellent distribution of active ingredient in flooded rice.

BIOLOGY

Flufenprox is highly active against insects in the orders Homoptera, Heteroptera, Lepidoptera and Coleoptera. Activity has also been shown against cockroaches and termites. Applied at recommended doses, flufenprox has caused no phytotoxic symptoms in major crops such as rice, cotton, soya, potato and brassicae. Flufenprox has shown particular value in rice and a range of formulations has been developed which covers the major application types. Development has been conducted both as flufenprox alone and in mixture with other insecticides, such as buprofezin or sumithion, and with fungicides such as fthalide and isoprothiolane.

Rice Hoppers

Flufenprox shows excellent activity against a range of hopper species, notably Brown planthopper (Nilaparvata lugens), Green leafhopper (Nephotettix spp.), White backed planthopper (Sogatella furcifera), Smaller brown planthopper (Laodelphax striatellus) and Zigzagged leafhopper (Recilia dorsalis). DL, EC and EW formulations have provided fast action and residual efficacy as shown in Table 1.

The activity of flufenprox did not differ significantly between organophosphate/carbamate resistant and susceptible strains of N. lugens in laboratory tests. This indicates that flufenprox is not affected by the major types of rice hopper resistance - altered acetyl cholinesterase and increased esterase levels.

TABLE 1. Control of Nilaparvata lugens (nymph) in rice with a DL formulation of flufenprox. Japan 1989.

TREATMENT	DOSE	Corrected Density Index		
	g AI/ha	1	7	28
Flufenprox	200	4	11	6
Etofenprox	200	52	48	198
Buprofezin/Fenobucarb	400/800	11	23	12
Untreated		100	100	100

Source : Kyushu Agricultural Experiment Station.
Corrected density index : hopper numbers per 10 sweeps expressed as:

$$\frac{\text{Untreated 0 DAT}}{\text{Untreated n DAT}} \times \frac{\text{Treatment n DAT}}{\text{Treatment 0 DAT}} \times 100$$

Resurgence Potential

Flufenprox shows valuable selectivity in favour of spiders (see ECOLOGY, below) and this feature is believed to contribute to a low resurgence potential during field use against rice hoppers (Table 2).

TABLE 2. <u>Nilaparvata</u> <u>lugens</u> resurgence potential following treatment with different insecticides, Philippines, 1987.

| TREATMENT (EC) | DOSE g AI/ha | Number of hoppers per 10 rice hills | | | | | |
		Pre-spray	6 DAT 1	6 DAT 2	6 DAT 3	6 DAT 4
Flufenprox	75	67.3	38.3	21.3	10.5	2.8
Deltamethrin	6.25	67.5	81.3	166.0	216.3	81.0
Untreated		70.4	89.6	80.7	65.6	17.7

Source: ICI Agrochemicals Research Station, Cabanatuan.
Treatments made at 7 day intervals from 25 days after transplanting.

Rice Bugs

This category comprises various species of Heteroptera in rice and is of increasing importance to rice grain quality, especially in Japan. Flufenprox provides good control of a broad spectrum of rice bug species when applied as either DL or EW formulation (Table 3).

TABLE 3. Reduction of bug damage in rice by flufenprox, Japan 1989.

TREATMENT	DOSE g AI/ha	Damaged rice grains Percent	Japanese rice quality grade
Flufenprox	200	0.04	1st
Fenobucarb/ Fenthion	800/800	0.24	2nd
Untreated		0.9	under

Source : Chiba Prefectural Plant Protection Office.
Principal targets : Rice bug : <u>Leptocorisa</u> <u>chinensis</u>
                     Stink bug : <u>Cletus</u> <u>punctiger</u>
Japanese rice quality grades : 1st grade, up to 0.1% damage;
                     2nd grade to 0.3%; 3rd grade to 0.7%;
                     thereafter rice is graded as "under". The
                     grade is reflected in the market price.

Coleoptera

Both foliar-applied dust (DL) and water-applied granular (GR) treatments of flufenprox have given good control of Rice water weevil <u>Lissorhoptrus</u> <u>oryzophilus</u> (Table 4) and Rice leaf beetle <u>Oulema</u> <u>oryzae</u> (Table 5). In the case of L. <u>oryzophilus</u>, the adults are susceptible to the floating active ingredient released from the flufenprox GR formulation.

TABLE 4. Control of Rice water weevil with a GR formulation of flufenprox. Japan 1991.

TREATMENT (see note 1)	DOSE	No. of larvae/4 hills (DAT) 20	27	35
Flufenprox	450g AI/ha	0.2 b	0.5 c	3.1 c
	300g AI/ha	0.0 b	2.5 c	6.9 bc
	200g AI/ha	0.0 b	1.3 c	10.8 b
Carbosulfan	2.5g AI/ nursery box	0.0 b	10.6 b	10.4 b
Untreated		8.2 a	41.4 a	43.6a

Source : ICI Japan Agricultural Research Station.
1. Flufenprox applied to the paddy 14 days after transplanting. Carbosulfan granules applied to the nursery box just before transplanting.
   Treatment means with no letter in common are significantly different at the 5.0% probability level.

TABLE 5. Control of Rice leaf beetle in rice with a DL formulation of flufenprox. Japan 1989.

TREATMENT	DOSE g AI/ha	No. of larvae/100 hills (DAT) 0	2	14
Flufenprox	150	245.0	0.0	3.0
Fenobucarb	600	287.0	0.0	50.0
Untreated		210.0	224.0	182.0

Source : Ishikawa Prefectural Plant Protection Association.

Lepidoptera

Good control of Rice leaf folder, Cnaphalocrocis medinalis, has been achieved by flufenprox (Table 6). Good control has also been achieved of Rice stem borer, Tryporyza incertulas and Chilo suppressalis, from applications of flufenprox DL at 200 g AI/ha at a preventive timing.

TABLE 6. Control of Rice leaf folder in rice with a DL formulation of flufenprox, Japan 1991.

TREATMENT	DOSE g AI/ha	No. of damaged leaves/30 hills (DAT) 0	12	19	27
Flufenprox	200	0.0	0.0	0.0	0.5
Cartap	1600	0.0	0.0	0.5	8.0
Untreated		0.0	47.5	104.0	134.0

Source : Ishikawa Prefectural Plant Protection Association.

ECOLOGY

Flufenprox has been tested in the laboratory against a number of terrestrial species. This work demonstrates that flufenprox is remarkably safe to many predatory arthropods, including spiders and earthworms.

Flufenprox is about two orders of magnitude less toxic to spiders than to N.lugens, on a weight to weight basis (Table 7). In the field, an additional safety margin will arise from the larger size of the spider compared to N. lugens. These results were not significantly different from etofenprox, known to be safe to lycosid spiders in the field (Untung, 1991).

TABLE 7. Selectivity of flufenprox to the lycosid spider Pardosa spp in the laboratory.

72 h LD50 to N. lugens (ug AI/g)	72 h LD50 to Pardosa spp (ug AI/g)
2.4	200

A series of selectivity field studies was conducted in rice during the wet season in Indonesia (Table 8). Four sprays of flufenprox were made at 10-14 day intervals when N.lugens numbers reached 10-20 per hill. Assessments made on the day following the final spray showed that there had been no effects on Paederus spp, Lycosa spp or Cyrtorhinus lividipennis.

TABLE 8. Selectivity of flufenprox to spiders in the field. Indonesia, 1990.

TREATMENT	DOSE g AI/ha	Mean Number of Predators per 10 Rice Hills		
		Paederus spp	Lycosa spp	Cyrtorhinus lividipennis
Untreated		14	32	5.1
Flufenprox 10% EC	50	12	38	4.7
Flufenprox 10% EC	75	13	36	4.4
Flufenprox 10% EC	100	14	38	5.1

Source : ICI Pesticida
Mean of two trials, wet season.
Assessment made on the day following the final application.

A laboratory experiment with the predatory mite <u>Typhlodromus</u> <u>pyri</u> showed that flufenprox had an LC50 at 48h in the region of 100 mg/l, which is in excess of a typical use rate of 50 mg/l.

In the laboratory, flufenprox has a similar acute toxicity to the honey bee as the pyrethroid insecticides, the LD50 being 0.03 ug AI/bee and the no-observed-effect-level (NOEL), 0.002 ug AI/bee.

Flufenprox is not toxic to the earthworm <u>Eisenia</u> <u>foetida</u>. The laboratory LD50 is in excess of 1000 mg/kg, with the NOEL between 100 - 1000 mg/kg.

TOXICOLOGY

<u>Mammals</u>

Flufenprox is of low acute, systemic toxicity to rats. The acute oral median lethal dose (rat) is greater than 5000 mg/kg while the acute dermal MLD (rat) is greater than 2000 mg/kg. Flufenprox is a mild skin and eye irritant in rabbits and a skin sensitizer in guinea pigs. It was not genotoxic in any of the <u>in vitro</u> assays (Ames and Cytogenetic test in human cells) or <u>in vivo</u> assays (mouse micronucleus and unscheduled DNA synthesis) conducted on the compound. It is not teratogenic in rats or rabbits at maternally toxic doses and, to date, has shown no effects on other reproductive parameters in an on-going multigeneration study. There is no major adverse toxicity in the sub-chronic studies in either rats or dogs.

<u>Fish</u>

Flufenprox has low toxicity to fish when tested under static test conditions. As the technical material, with results based on nominal concentrations, the 96 hour LC50 to carp (<u>Cyprinus</u> <u>carpio</u>) is > 10 mg AI/l and formulated as a 20% EW the 96 hour LC50 is > 25 mg AI/l. Formulated as a 0.5% dust or granule, the 96 hour LC50s to red killifish (<u>Oryzias</u> <u>latipes</u>) and Asian pond loach (<u>Misgurnus</u> <u>anguillicaudatus</u>) are both > 10 mg AI/l.

<u>Aquatic Invertebrates</u>

Flufenprox, as would be expected of a highly active insecticide, is of relatively high toxicity to aquatic invertebrates in laboratory studies carried out in clean water systems, with 48 hour LC50 of the technical material to <u>Daphnia</u> <u>pulex</u> of 0.00035 mg/l and a 96 hour LC50 of 0.5% DL formulation to <u>Procambarus</u> <u>acutus</u> <u>acutus</u> (freshwater crayfish) of 0.00038 mg AI/l, based on nominal concentrations. In the field situation, toxicity would be greatly reduced since the extremely low water solubility of flufenprox ensures rapid adsorption to suspended and bottom sediments.

CONCLUSIONS

Flufenprox is a novel bis-aralkyl ether insecticide which offers significant benefits to the farmer, notably:

- Control of a wide range of homopteran, heteropteran, coleopteran and lepidopteran pests with rapid and residual action.

- Selectivity in favour of spiders and predacious mite species which is valuable in IPM programmes and in the avoidance of hopper resurgence.

- Flexibility in mode of application in rice, including granules for nursery box or field application, dust and liquid formulations for foliar spray.

- Relatively low toxicity to the user, to fish and to earthworms.

ACKNOWLEDGEMENTS

The authors gratefully acknowledge the permission to publish data from the Kyushu and Ishikawa Prefectural Agricultural Experiment Stations and the Chiba Prefectural Plant Protection Office, Japan, and also the contributions of many staff throughout the ICI network, notably Dr R A Brown, Mr S Chart, Mr P W Ewens, Mr M Hamer, Mr T Koike, Dr J P Leahey, Mr G J Marrs, Mr T Nakahara, Mr N Ohsaki and Mr Flor Pangilan who have contributed directly to this paper.

REFERENCES

Bushell, M.J.; Whittle, A.J.; Carr, R.A.E. (1987) Insecticidal Ethers. UK Patent No. GB2178739.
Bushell, M.J. (1990) Synthesis of some fluorinated non-ester pyrethroids. In : Recent Advances in the Chemistry of Insect Control II, ed. Crombie L. pp. 125-141.
Tsushima K.; Yano, T.; Takagaki, T.; Matsuo, N.; Hirano, M.; Ohno, N. (1988) Preparation and insecticidal activity of optically active 3-phenoxybenzyl 3,3,3-trifluoro-2-phenylpropyl. Agricultural and Biological Chemistry, 52, 1323-1325.
Untung, K. (1991) Efficacy of etofenprox for controlling Brown Plant Hopper and the effect on the Wolf Spider (Lycosa pseudannulata), a natural enemy of the hopper. Proceedings of the 11th International Congress of Plant Protection, Manila, Philippines, October 5-9, 1987. pp 350-354.

NI-25, A NEW TYPE OF SYSTEMIC AND BROAD SPECTRUM INSECTICIDE

H. TAKAHASHI, J. MITSUI, N. TAKAKUSA, M. MATSUDA,
H. YONEDA, J. SUZUKI, K. ISHIMITSU, T. KISHIMOTO

Odawara Research Center, Nippon Soda Co., Ltd., 345, Yanagi-machi, Takada,
Odawara-city, Kanagawa Pref., 250-02, Japan

ABSTRACT

NI-25 is a novel broad spectrum insecticide having an amidine
structure. It shows high activity against Hemiptera, Thysanoptera
and Lepidoptera. This compound is also effective against fruit
moths with its ovicidal activity. In addition to high activity by
foliar application, NI-25 possesses systemic activity. Therefore,
the product is useful for soil application. Field trials have
demonstrated the excellent efficacy of NI-25.

INTRODUCTION

NI-25 is a novel insecticide invented by Nippon Soda Co., Ltd. This
compound was found in our research of the nitrometylene derivatives (Soloway
et al., 1979), but the chemical structure and the biological properties are
well characterized compared with other compounds of the group. NI-25 is
under development by Nippon Soda Co., Ltd. The present paper describes its
chemical properties and biological activities in laboratory and field tests.

CHEMICAL AND PHYSICAL PROPERTIES

Chemical name   : N^1-[(6-chloro-3-pyridyl)metyl]-N^2-cyano-N^1-
                       metylacetamidine
Code number   : NI-25
Molecular formula   : $C_{10}H_{11}ClN_4$
Structural formula   :

Molecular weight   : 222.68
Physical appearance : White crystals
Melting point   : 101.0-103.3°C
Vapour pressure   : <1×10⁻⁶Pa (<1×10⁻⁸mmHg) at 25°C
Solubility at 25°C   : 4200 mg/l in water
                       Soluble in acetone, methanol, ethanol,
                       dichloromethane, chloroform, acetonitrile,
                       tetrahydrofuran

Hydrolytic stability	: Stable in buffer solutions at pH 4, 5, 7
	Degraded gradually at pH 9 and $45°C$
Photostability	: Stable under sunlight
Formulations	: 20% SP (W/W)
	2% G (W/W)

TOXICOLOGY

Acute oral LD_{50}	: Rat male 217 mg/kg female 146 mg/kg
	Mouse male 198 mg/kg female 184 mg/kg
Skin and eye irritation	: Non irritating (rabbit)
Mutagenicity	: Negative (Ames test)

BIOLOGICAL ACTIVITIES

Laboratory studies

Insecticidal spectrum

NI-25 possesses a broad insecticidal spectrum. It shows excellent activity on Hemiptera, especially on aphids, and also on Thysanoptera and Lepidoptera. NI-25 exhibits high activity on pests resistant to conventional insecticides as well as susceptible strains (Table 1).

TABLE 1   Insecticidal spectrum of NI-25

Species	Stage	Method	LC_{50} (mg/l)		
			NI-25	acephate	cypermethrin
Aphis gossypii (S)	L_1	Spr	0.056	8.2	0.21
Aphis gossypii (R)	L_1	Spr	0.069	>125	>125
Myzus persicae (S)	L_1	Dip	0.21	15.8	0.47
Myzus persicae (R)	L_1	Dip	0.29	125	140
Rhopalosiphum padi	Mix	Spr	0.32	–	–
Aphis fabae	Mix	Spr	0.19	–	0.27
Aulacorthum solani	Mix	Spr	0.20	–	0.29
Plutella xylostella (S)	L_1	L.D.	4.4	11.1	0.05
Plutella xylostella (R)	L_1	L.D.	13.4	132	54.8
Spodoptera litura	L_1	L.D.	9.6	14.0	0.21
Mamestra brassicae	L_2	L.D.	13.4	36.8	1.6
Grapholita molesta	E	Spr	3.1	–	0.62
Carposina niponensis	E	Spr	2.8	–	<0.78
Bemisia tabaci	E	Spr	4.8	–	5.9
Thrips palmi	A	Spr	3.4	–	18.5

S : susceptible strain
R : organophosphorus and/or pyrethroid-resistant strain
E : eggs L_1, L_2 : 1st, 2nd-instar larvae   A : adults
Mix : larvae & adults
Spr : spraying   Dip : insects and leaf dipping
L.D. : leaf dipping

Systemic activity

NI-25 exhibits high systemic activity in vegetables. It shows efficacy on the green peach aphid (Myzus persicae) at low concentrations (LC$_{50}$ 0.031 mg/l) by a root dipping method. NI-25 is also effective against the diamondback moth (Plutella xylostella) systemically (Table 2).

TABLE 2   Systemic activity of NI-25 against M. persicae and P. xylostella

| Species | Stage | Method | LC$_{50}$ (mg/l) | |
			NI-25	acephate
Myzus persicae (S)	L$_1$	R.D.	0.031	0.71
Plutella xylostella (S)	L$_1$	R.D.	0.31	1.8

S : susceptible strain   L$_1$: 1st-instar larvae
R.D. : root dipping

Residual activity

NI-25 shows residual activity on A. gossypii and P. xylostella for 2 weeks in greenhouse tests. It possesses long residual activity also on Carposina niponesis (Fig. 1).

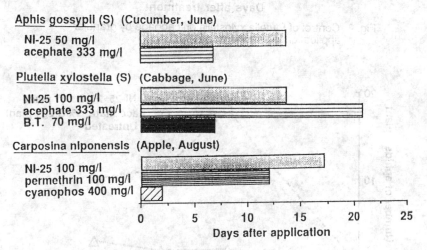

Aphis gossypii (S) (Cucumber, June)

NI-25 50 mg/l
acephate 333 mg/l

Plutella xylostella (S) (Cabbage, June)

NI-25 100 mg/l
acephate 333 mg/l
B.T. 70 mg/l

Carposina niponensis (Apple, August)

NI-25 100 mg/l
permethrin 100 mg/l
cyanophos 400 mg/l

0   5   10   15   20   25
Days after application

Fig. 1   Residual activity (≥90% control) of NI-25 by foliar application against
A. gossypii, P. xylostella and C. niponensis.

Field trials

The effects of NI-25 against economically important pests of many crops were evaluated in the field. This report focuses on the results of trials on vegetables, fruit and tea.

Vegetables

There are many important pests in vegetables. P. xylostella is widespread on many vegetables. Resistance of this pest to conventional insecticides has developed and has become a serious problem in South East Asia. Thrips palmi and aphids are also serious pests in many countries. NI-25 is very effective against these pests by foliar and granular soil application.

NI-25 shows good efficacy against P. xylostella and M. persicae by granular application to planting hole (Figs. 2 and 3).

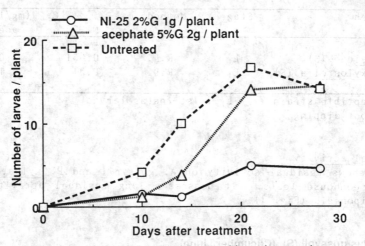

Fig. 2 Control of Plutella xylostella on cabbage by granular application to planting hole (1991).

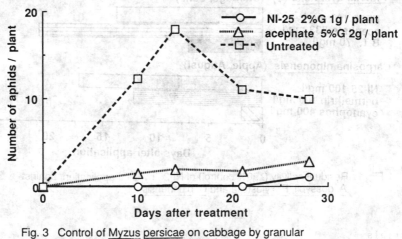

Fig. 3 Control of Myzus persicae on cabbage by granular application to planting hole (1991).

NI-25 shows high activity against T. palmi at a concentration of 50 mg/l. The compound appears to be more active against this pest than cypermethrin and sulprofos (Fig. 4).

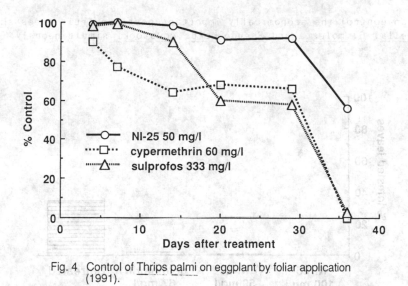

Fig. 4   Control of Thrips palmi on eggplant by foliar application
(1991).

Fruit

NI-25 shows excellent activity against the leaf mining pests such as
the apple leafminer (Phyllonorycter ringoneella) and the citrus leafminer
(Phyllocnistis citrella) mainly by its translaminar activity. In addition,
the compound is active against fruit moths such as the oriental fruit moth
(Grapholita molesta) and the peach fruit moth (Carposina niponensis) by both
ovicidal and larvicidal activities. NI-25 is also useful for the control of
scales and aphids. This product is active against these pests at the
concentrations of 50 to 100 mg/l. NI-25 shows high activity on the apple
aphid (Aphis spiraecola) and suppresses the pest for 3 to 4 weeks (Fig. 5).

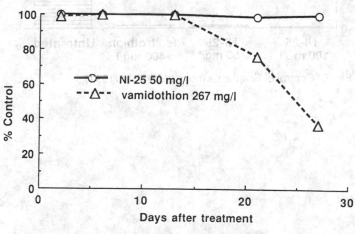

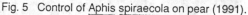

Fig. 5   Control of Aphis spiraecola on pear (1991).

NI-25 can control the economically important pests on fruit trees such as P. ringoneella, G. molesta and Pseudococcus comstocki simultaneously (Figs. 6-8).

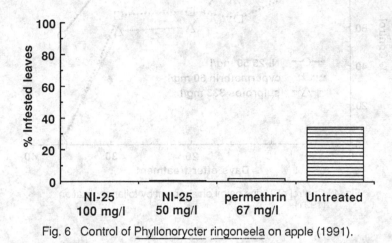

Fig. 6   Control of Phyllonorycter ringoneela on apple (1991).

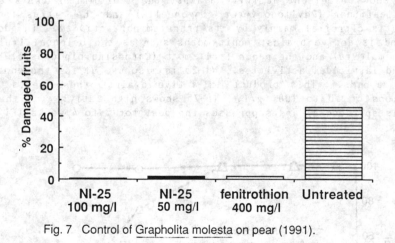

Fig. 7   Control of Grapholita molesta on pear (1991).

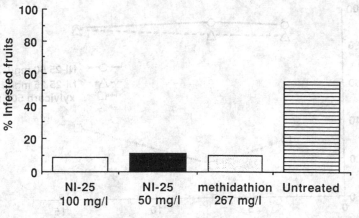

Fig. 8   Control of <u>Pseudococcus</u> <u>comstocki</u> on pear (1991).

<u>Tea</u>
NI-25 shows good efficasy against the tea leafroller (<u>Caloptilia</u> <u>theivora</u>), the green leafhopper (<u>Empoasca</u> <u>onukii</u>) and the yellow tea thrips (<u>Scirtothrips</u> <u>dorsalis</u>) (Figs. 9-10).   These insects emerge almost at the same period and so the product can control these pests simultaneously.   The formulation of NI-25 (20% SP) does not leave any stain nor odour on the leaves after treatment.   Therefore, NI-25 is an appropriate insecticide for the control of tea insect pests.

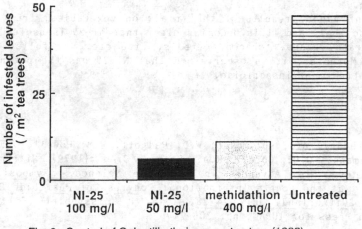

Fig. 9   Control of <u>Caloptilia</u> <u>theivora</u> on tea tree (1992).

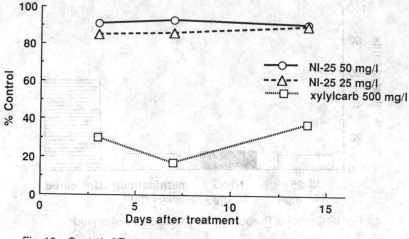

Fig. 10 Control of Empoasca onukiii on tea tree (1991).

CONCLUSION

NI-25 is a promising novel insecticide. The compound is useful for the control of the pests on vegetables, fruit and tea. NI-25 exhibits high activity against Hemiptera, Thysanoptera and Lepidoptera. This product is effective on the vegetable pests by foliar and soil application. It shows good efficacy against resistant pests to conventional insecticides as well as susceptible strains owing to a novel chemical structure and biological mode of action.

In the present paper, results of the trials on vegetables, fruit and tea are mainly described, and it is becoming clear that NI-25 is useful for pest control on potato, beans, tobacco, cereals, rice etc., by foliar and soil application. Moreover, it is ascertained that NI-25 has the potential for use as a seed treatment insecticide.

REFERENCE

Soloway, S.B; Henry, A.C; Kollmeyer, W.D; Padgett, W.M; Powell, J.E; Roman, S.A; Tiemans, C.H; Corey, R.A; Horne, C.A. (1979) Nitromethylene Insecticides. In: Advances in Pesticide Science. Symposia Papers presented at the Fourth International Congress of Pesticide Chemistry Zurich, Switzerland, July 24-28, 1978, H Geissbuhler (Ed), Oxford: Pergamon Press for IUPAC, pp. 206-217

SESSION 3A

SCLEROTINIA: ITS BIOLOGY AND IMPLICATIONS FOR DISEASE CONTROL

CHAIRMAN   DR J. T. FLETCHER

SESSION
ORGANISER   DR T. LOCKE

INVITED PAPERS   3A-1 to 3A-4

THE EFFECTS OF ROTATION AND OTHER CULTURAL FACTORS ON SCLEROTINIA IN OILSEED RAPE, PEAS AND POTATOES.

S.A. ARCHER, S.J. MITCHELL & B.E.J. WHEELER

Imperial College, Silwood Park, Ascot, Berks SL5 7PY.

ABSTRACT

Field surveys and small plot trials have been used to assess the risk from Sclerotinia posed by a range of crop management practices. Populations of sclerotia in soil increase substantially following severe infections of susceptible crops, and in the absence of replenishment, decline with a half-life of c. 2.5 year. Apothecial production in autumn-sown crops is greatest where crop residues are burnt or chopped the previous season; and productivity is brought forward following minimal cultivations, and is delayed by spring nitrogen. In Britain two distinct epidemiological phases of the disease are seen, the first in May associated with winter crops, and the second 4-6 weeks later associated with spring-sown crops.

INTRODUCTION

Although widely recognised as a major pathogen overseas, especially in North America (Purdy, 1979; Dueck et al.,1983), Sclerotinia sclerotiorum has not, at least until recently, been regarded as a serious threat to crop production in Great Britain. Progressive post-war economic and technological changes in British agriculture resulted in a steady decline in the acreage of susceptible crops up to the late 1970s, and the threat presented by Sclerotinia accordingly declined in the increasingly cereal and grass dominated countryside. However, the last decade has seen a substantial reversal of the situation, necessitating a reappraisal of the risk from Sclerotinia posed by the cultivation of a wider range of potential hosts (Price & Colhoun, 1975; Purdy, 1979) over a greater area and often with shortened rotations (Jellis et al.,1984).

The current investigation was prompted by the factors above and the need to study the epidemiology of the pathogen under changing patterns of management, many of which threatened to transform Sclerotinia disease from a local to a national problem, a prediction finally borne out in 1991. Two main approaches to the investigation have been followed. Firstly, field surveys have been undertaken in known Sclerotinia "hot-spots" in an attempt to correlate disease outbreaks with particular combinations of husbandry or climatic factors. The second approach has been to use small-plot field trials to reproduce model systems of rotation and cultivation, and to examine the effects of these on pathogen survival, sporulation and infection.

FIELD SURVEYS 1988-1990

Farms on the Chichester plain and in the Romney Marsh area, selected on the basis of advice from local crop protection consultants, were visited regularly during the 1988, 1989 and 1990 growing seasons. These areas have a lengthy history of <u>Sclerotinia</u> disease fostered by a favourable local climate and rotations which historically have included a high frequency of susceptible crops. Typically these include oilseed rape (OSR), peas, potatoes, horticultural Brassicas, field bean, in recent years linseed, and formerly <u>Phaseolus</u> bean.

The survey extended to some 35 fields over seven farms in the Chichester area and six fields on a single farm in Kent. The survey included assessments of sclerotial numbers in soil before and after cropping; apothecial production during the growing season; ascospore inoculum caught on rod spore traps (Jenkyn, 1974) or on petals detected by plating onto potato dextrose agar; and disease incidence estimated at a suitable stage prior to harvest. Fields received fortnightly visits between late March and the end of July, with weekly monitoring during part of April and May, which is the main infection period for winter OSR, the major crop in the survey.

Weather during the three years of the survey differed from the long term mean and was characterised by mild dry winters, dry springs and summers (not 1988) with periods of exceptional heat and drought. Crop growth stages were at times several weeks ahead of the long term average and ripening of some crops was up to a month early. Flowering of winter OSR was on average 12-14 day earlier than in a previous study in 1981-1983. These factors tended to restrict the incidence of <u>Sclerotinia</u>, especially on spring-sown crops and flushes of apothecial production tended to be short. Severe infection was restricted to lodged crops, and where isolated showers had provided surface moisture at a critical period. The following presents a summary of the main conclusions, supplemented by additional observations during 1991-92.

Survival of sclerotia

Numbers of sclerotia in field soils varied from zero up to 6.2 kg^{-1} air-dried soil (potatoes, Kent, 1990). In general, numbers declined under non-host or spring-sown crops without irrigation in the seasons of low rainfall. Numbers increased where disease occurred in the preceding crop. However the greatest increases were observed in the second crop following sowings in 1988 of pea, potato and sunflower (table 1). This delay reflects shallow sampling (designed to detect only sclerotia of significance in the current season) and the effect of soil inversion by ploughing.

TABLE 1. Numbers of sclerotia in air-dried soil following infection of a susceptible crop in the 1988 growing season

Crop	Location	Sclerotia kg^{-1} following cropping in			
		1987[a]	1988	1989[b]	1990
Pea	Chichester	0.80	1.20	3.0	2.57
Potato	Kent	1.20	0.80	1.51	-
Sunflower	Kent	-	2.60	3.60	1.60

a measured before cropping in spring 1988
b 1989 crops were non-susceptible

One site at Chichester at which no infection was seen in the only susceptible crop (peas, 1989) maintained high, though decreasing levels of sclerotia throughout (5.7 - 4.4 - 2.0 - 2.7 kg^{-1} soil). Other fields from the same farm where numbers of sclerotia were lower (c. 0.4 kg^{-1}) contained <u>Coniothyrium</u> <u>minitans</u>, a mycoparasite which attacks and degrades sclerotia.

Size of sclerotia varied widely between 1-3 mm from diseased linseed and OSR pods, up to walnut-sized (15-20 mm) in the case of sunflower. Sclerotial returns to soil are typically 5-7 per plant for OSR, and in the range 5-15 for potato. A severely infected (50% incidence) crop of vining peas in Norfolk was responsible for a mean sclerotial return of 88 m^{-2} (178 m^{-2} if the haulm was included), which in turn raised the soil reservoir to 1.20 kg^{-1} from an unknown baseline. Stems of single, severely infected sunflower plants (table 2) yielded up to 90 sclerotia, and a similar number, sometimes fused in groups, could be recovered from head lesions.

Incidence of apothecia

Numbers of apothecia under crops varied widely from zero to 89.3 m^{-2} (winter wheat, after sunflower). The average productivity at the peak over the years 1988-90 was 4.5 m^{-2}. In general, apothecial production was proportional to sclerotial load in soil, but with much weather-induced variation. The peak of apothecium production under winter OSR occurred seven days either side of mid-flowering, but apothecia tended to peak higher and be present for longer under winter cereals. The earliest apothecia were usually detected in winter wheat in late March/early April, although excavation of sclerotia in depots sometimes revealed stipes in January.

Apothecia under spring crops always appeared later, never before June, reflecting a requirement for a minimum period without soil disturbance of 6 8 weeks, and for a crop canopy to slow drying of the surface layers of the soil. This fortuitous delay ensures reasonable synchrony between ascospore release and the start of the susceptible period for spring crops.

The smallest sclerotia can support the production of only a single apothecium and must be in the surface 1-2 cm layer of soil for successful fruiting. In contrast those from sunflower may subtend up to 15 apothecia and stipes can reach the surface from a depth of 10-12 cm.

Ascospore dispersal

Ascospores were readily trapped on sticky rods and on petals of OSR. Although less quantitative, the latter were generally preferred for ease of use and for relevance to infection on OSR. Most spores were trapped at the peak of apothecium production, and fewest were seen on petals collected after fungicide sprays. However, these results could not be linked quantitatively to the potential for infection in the field. In some cases spores were trapped in fields, both cropped and fallow, in which no apothecia were seen, providing clear evidence for wind dispersal. <u>Sclerotinia</u> was rarely detected on petals of other crop hosts.

Disease incidence

In each year outbreaks of winter-kill by <u>Sclerotinia</u> on OSR were evident, but could not be ascribed with certainty either to mycelial or ascosporic infection in any year. It tended to occur in thick crops following lush growth in the mild autumns. Treatment with a benzimidazole fungicide prevented inter-plant spread of mycelium.

Summer infections over the three years 1988-90 were mostly at a low level, the mean incidence over all fields being 1.1% (sprayed winter OSR), 6.6% (unsprayed winter OSR), 1.7% (pea), 7.9% (potato), and 1.9% (spring OSR). The maximum levels seen in individual crops were very much greater (table 2), especially in 1991 when a wetter season provided greater opportunity for infection.

TABLE 2. Maximum disease incidence (percentage of plants with at least one lesion) seen in field surveys 1988-1992.

Year	Crop	Location	Disease incidence	Notes
1988	Winter OSR	Chichester	6.3	Sprayed
1988	Winter OSR	Chichester	16.7	Unsprayed
1988	Sunflower	Kent	17.9	-
1988	Pea	Norfolk	>50.0	Vining cv.
1988	Pea	Chichester	80.8	Combining cv.
1989	Potato	Kent	28.1(10.6)*	Main crop
1990	Potato	Kent	60.0(16.0)*	Main Crop
1990	Winter OSR	Chichester	47.1	#
1991	Winter OSR	Chichester	35.0	Unsprayed
1991	Spring OSR	Chichester	20.0	Unsprayed
1991	Linseed	Chichester	8.0	Dense crop
1992	Spring OSR	Chichester	15.0	Dense Crop

* figure in parenthesis is based on stems, not plants
# localised infection following thunderstorm

A feature evident in each season was the presence of disease in crops of OSR in which apothecia were never seen despite considerable searching. After allowing for sampling errors it is clear that such crops could not generate sufficient inoculum internally to account for the disease levels seen, up to 20% in 1991. Additionally, some crops exhibited a disease gradient indicating the likely source of inoculum which in some cases must have carried up to 200m.

Except on sunflower where stem base infections from sclerotia were reasonably common, virtually all other summer infections clearly originated from wind-dispersed ascospores. On OSR, infections could invariably be traced to abcissed petals attached to petioles and stems (Kruger, 1974; McLean, 1958). Save for head infection of sunflower via senescent ray florets, floral organs seem to be less important in other crops. Peas can become infected via petals, but senescent lower foliage is also much involved. Petals of linseed are ephemeral and show little tendency to lodge on the plant: most infections originate at the axils of senescent lower leaves or are attributable to mechanical damage. Lesions on potato mostly originate from senescent leaflets and petioles.

Attempts to link disease incidence with pre-determinable risk factors have been thwarted by the generally low levels of infection of the first three years. Disease incidence in winter OSR and the sclerotial load in fields were not (1988-89) or were only weakly (1990) correlated. Similarly the association between infection and the Sclerotinia load on petals was weak except in 1990 when a correlation (r=0.89) was found across a sample of nine fields.

Alternative sources of inoculum

Although Sclerotinia was noted on a range of common weed species in surveyed crops, at no time was infection above trace levels. The only exception was infection of nettles (Urtica urens) in potato in 1990 and in a dense crop of linseed in 1991. Further, infection has rarely been seen on plants on field margins or in hedgerows. The overwhelming conclusion is that wild plants are an insignificant source of Sclerotinia inoculum: at best the have a role in perpetuating the pathogen at a low level.

On a single farm, a field margin strip of Jerusalem Artichoke (Helianthus tuberosus) grown as game cover was found carrying significant infection (lesions on 10% of plants). This was possibly the source of inoculum for a severe disease outbreak on peas in an adjacent field. Such specialist crops and horticultural holdings can locally provide inoculum, as more generally can contamination of seed stocks by sclerotia for all crops except potato.

FIELD TRIALS 1988-91

A number of small-plot trials was established during this period at Silwood Park, Berkshire to examine the effects of different regimes of crop management on Sclerotinia survival and development. Soils were infested with sclerotia either produced in vitro (Mylcreest & Wheeler, 1987) or recovered from infected crop debris from commercial farms. Never, in any of these trials was there any evidence of host specificity: infection of any of the crop hosts, or weeds, seemed to be achieved as readily by one isolate as another. Occasionally differences were seen between isolates in the time of apothecial production, but this seemed to be random inter-strain variability as much as any genuine crop specificity.

Trials established in 1988 and 1989 suffered severely from drought conditions and because of this a number of aims were not realised. The major conclusions of the trials are summarised below.

Sclerotial returns and survival in soil

Separate trials of combinable pea, cv Solara became severely infected during the 1988 growing season. Disease incidence ranged up to 41.5% (table 3). After harvest the haulm was chopped, the debris returned to the soil surface and sclerotia in random quadrats counted. Table 3 also records the resulting sclerotial load in soil sampled from the seedbed of the following crop (winter OSR or winter wheat). Also shown are the calculated sclerotial return to the soil surface for each 1% infection (pea only) and the sclerotial numbers in surface debris needed to load the cultivated layers of the soil by 1 propagule per kg.

Yields of sclerotia from individual pea plants in Trial 1 averaged 6.3, rather more than was typical of individual lesions on OSR (4.5). Averaged over all trials peas gave an increase in sclerotia of 52.0% over those present at drilling and OSR an increase of 31.2%.

When investigating the effect of management practices, greater numbers of sclerotia were detected in the seedbed of the following crop where rape straw was chopped prior to ploughing and where wheat straw or stubble was unburnt prior to incorporation by ploughing or minimal cultivation.

TABLE 3. Sclerotial returns to soil from infected crops of pea.

Trial	Disease[a]	Soil surface[b]	Bulk soil[c]	D	E
I	41.5	92.0	2.50	2.2	36.8
III	25.4	44.0	2.02	1.7	21.8
IV	25.4	48.0	1.63	1.9	29.4
Mean				1.9	29.3

a percentage disease incidence
b soil surface sclerotial numbers after harvest (m^{-2})
c sclerotia per kg air-dried soil in subsequent samples
D sclerotial return to soil surface for each 1% infection
E calculated sclerotial load on soil surface needed to raise
   bulk soil population by 1 sclerotium per kg

Longevity of sclerotia in soil has been examined over the medium term by soil sampling: table 4 shows representative data. Over the shorter term sclerotia buried in nylon mesh bags have been recovered from soils and assessed for viability. Both numbers recovered, and the capacity for myceliogenic germination of those remaining, typically decline by about 10% over six months. However in two trials capacity for carpogenic germination dropped much more rapidly, typically showing declines of 50% over the same period.

TABLE 4. Numbers of sclerotia sampled from trial plots.

Year	Trial 1		Trial III	
	sclerotia kg^{-1}	after	sclerotia kg^{-1}	after
1988	2.45	pea	1.83	pea
1989	1.49	WW	2.60	WOSR
1990	1.02	WOSR*	0.94	WW
1991	-		2.61	pea

* no infection
WW winter wheat
WOSR winter oilseed rape

Apothecial production in relation to management practices

Averaged over all trials there was a broad positive correlation between numbers of sclerotia in soil and ensuing apothecial production. Table 5 shows examples of apothecial productivity and also reveals that winter wheat provides a better cover crop than rape for early season apothecia. This was a general observation made over several years: compared with OSR, under winter wheat apothecia tended to be more prolific, first appeared up to two weeks earlier, and the peak in production was also earlier.

Apothecium production was also influenced by the way in which previous crops residues were treated. In 1990 OSR plots, productivity was greatest where wheat straw had been burnt the previous season, and earliest where minimal cultivations, not ploughing, had been used to prepare the seedbed. Wheat following OSR had higher numbers of apothecia where straw had been chopped, a distribution also reflected in numbers of sclerotia, suggesting that chopping was liberating sclerotia from crop debris and possibly bringing forward fruiting by one season.

TABLE 5. Sclerotia in soils and apothecial productivity.

Sclerotia in soil[a]	Cover crop[b]	Peak apothecia[c]	Mean apothecia[d]
2.50	WOSR	5.30	1.47
2.50	WW	20.31	5.73
2.02	WOSR	6.70	0.54
1.63	WW	8.01	3.85

a number of sclerotia per kg soil
b for key see table 4
c apothecia m^{-2} recorded at the peak of production
d apothecia m^{-2} averaged over entire span of production

In one trial in 1988 apothecium production in OSR was delayed by high spring nitrogen, confirming earlier observations of Mylchreest (1985).

Infection of weeds by Sclerotinia

In 1988 a trial area was seeded with sclerotia and allowed to develop natural weed cover over the growing season. Apothecia were found first at the end of May and were present in large numbers through to July 5th. Despite the rapid development of ground cover and generally suitable conditions for infection (disease incidence in a nearby pea crop was 41.5%) little disease developed. Of the 20 plant species recorded in the 135 m^2 trial only six became infected, and the majority of lesions were accounted for by a single species (wild radish, Rhaphanus raphanistrum: 64 infected plants). Other hosts, in declining frequency of infection were Chamomilla recutita, Conyza canadensis, Cirsium arvense, Capsella bursa-pastoris and Polygonum aviculare (single plant). Sclerotial returns to soil were minimal, the smaller hosts averaging one to two per plant, and Cirsium and Conyza no more than four.

On separate occasions at Silwood Park, wild radish, mayweeds and cudweed (Gnaphalium sylvaticum) were found infected, but despite considerable searching, Sclerotinia was never observed on larger members of the Compositae or Umbelliferae, such as burdock and hogweed, which would have the capacity for larger scale production of sclerotia.

DISCUSSION

In several respects the results of the field survey and small plot experiments reinforce each other, and a number of general conclusions can be drawn. Numbers of sclerotia in soils generally changed in a predictable way provided due allowance was made for the irregularities introduced by sampling variation. Infected pea crops in particular, caused a marked increase in soil population levels (table 3), the trial data providing two guideline figures; that each 1% infection will contribute approximately two sclerotia m^{-2}, and that to raise the bulk soil population by one sclerotium kg^{-1} approximately 30 sclerotia m^{-2} are needed on the surface. Sclerotial returns to soil of this magnitude are in line with field experience, for example Norfolk 1988, and with rises in the soil population seen on commercial farms (table 1). The highest farm figure of 6.2 sclerotia kg^{-1} must reflect the accumulated residue of many years of serious disease.

The high degree of gearing implicit in the ratio between soil surface and bulk soil numbers of sclerotia highlights the risks of relying too greatly on the error-prone and laborious task of washing soil through sieves. Using the ratio of table 5, an error of one sclerotium either way in a count could cover a range of nil to 50 in terms of the soil surface population.

Both trials and surveys indicate that infected crops of OSR return rather fewer sclerotia to soils than do peas, although maximum levels can be similar, for example Mylchreest (1985) reported a 38%-infected crop of cv. Bienvenue which returned 75 sclerotia m^{-2} to the soil surface. Of those crops less widely grown or less commonly infected, sunflower and potato can provide the greatest sclerotial returns. Given equivalent levels of infection, we believe the risk to succeeding crops is of the order; sunflower > potato = pea > winter OSR > spring OSR > linseed.

As would be expected, numbers of sclerotia in soils declined in the absence of disease or in sequences of non-host crops. The general trend was for numbers to halve approximately every 2.5 year. This crude measurement of numbers gives no indication of viability which may decline more rapidly. We have preliminary evidence that capacity to undergo carpogenic germination, a key factor in epidemiology, may be lost more quickly than would be suggested by cruder measures of viability. This phenomenon requires verification and the whole topic of sclerotial degradation in soils is a fruitful one for further study.

Under British conditions apothecial production occurs in two main flushes. The first in autumn-sown crops covers the period April-May, and the second, mostly taking place in June and July takes place in spring-sown crops. There are thus two distinct epidemiological phases which overlap only slightly, and there are obvious combinations of donor and receptor crops for inoculum. Winter wheat is an obvious source of spores for winter OSR and potentially for winter beans, although these are rarely if ever seen infected with S. sclerotiorum (Jellis et al., 1990). Evidence from both survey and trial all indicates that winter wheat is a marginally better cover crop than OSR for sporulation of Sclerotinia; and such crops, on land that has a history of the disease should always be considered a risk factor for nearby winter OSR. Not only are apothecia seemingly earlier and more abundant in winter wheat (table 5), but the short and, prior to flag leaf emergence, relatively open crop canopy is conducive to efficient spore dispersal. Likewise, spring cereals are a potential source of inoculum to spring-sown host crops.

In field surveys clear evidence was seen for infections resulting from both internally and externally generated inoculum. Wind dispersal was also a factor in trials and it repeatedly confounded attempts, when using small plots, to correlate apothecium productivity with spore trapping data, with disease incidence or with yield. It is our experience that ascospores can be dispersed in infective quantities certainly in the range up to 200 m, a view that broadly parallels North American experience (Abawi & Grogan, 1979; Williams & Stelfox, 1979).

Attempts to correlate petal infestation by Sclerotinia in OSR with the resulting levels of disease have been only partially successful in these studies, and we doubt that it could be used alone as the basis of a forecasting system as is proposed in Canada (Turkington et al., 1991). Certainly it is a more reliable guide to OSR crops immediately at risk than counting apothecia or sclerotia, but overriding all other factors is the effect of weather. In each of the three years under study crops escaped infection because the warm dry conditions prevented the substantial period of surface wetness needed for infection by Sclerotinia (Abawi & Grogan, 1975).

There is little evidence from our studies that infection of weed or hedgerow plants provides other than an incidental source of inoculum. Notwithstanding isolated observations to the contrary (Hims, 1979), it would seem that non-cultivated plants are not a major reservoir of the disease in Britain, and the results of the natural infection trials provide little encouragement for those who advocate the use of Sclerotinia for the biological control of weeds (Riddle et al., 1991).

Experiments designed to investigate the effects of various post-harvest treatments have been rendered somewhat academic now that stubble burning is no longer an option. Broadly, the choice should be between attempting to exhaust the pathogen as quickly as possible, and trying to bury it. For the former approach, applicable in the absence of nearby susceptible crops, we would recommend if practicable, chopping the straw of any infected crop, followed by minimal cultivation, and sowing to winter cereals which are both resistant to the disease and very conducive to apothecium formation. In the second approach deep ploughing in the first year, followed by minimal cultivations for as many years as soil conditions allow, should be the goal. Neither approach is likely to be wholly successful however due to the incomplete nature of soil inversion during ploughing and the essentially random nature of sclerotial decline. In the special case of severe infection on sunflower the potential for return of inoculum to the soil is so great that cutting and removal of individual plants is probably warranted despite the expense.

ACKNOWLEDGMENTS

This work was supported by MAFF research contract CSA 1226. We are grateful to Dr. M.P. McQuilken and Dr. G.E. Jackson for assistance with data collection, and Mr. R. Cartwright and Mr. H. Overman for helpful discussions and assistance with the selection of survey sites.

REFERENCES

Abawi, G.S.; Grogan, R.G. (1975) Source of primary inoculum and effects of temperature and moisture on infection of beans by Whetzelinia sclerotiorum. Phytopathology, 65, 300-309.

Abawi, G.S.; Grogan, R.G. (1979) Epidemiology of diseases caused by Sclerotinia species. Phytopathology, 69, 899-903.

Dueck, J.; Morrall, R.A.A.; McKenzie, D.L. (1983) Control of Sclerotinia sclerotiorum in rapeseed with fungicides. Canadian Journal of Plant Pathology, 5, 289-293.

Hims, M.J. (1979) Wild plants as a source of Sclerotinia sclerotiorum infecting oilseed rape. Plant Pathology, 28, 197-198.

Jellis, G.J.; Davies, J.M.L.; Scott, E.S. (1984) Sclerotinia on oilseed rape: implications for crop rotation. 1984 British Crop Protection Conference - Pests and Diseases, 2, 709-715.

Jellis, G.J.; Smith, D.B.; Scott, E.S. (1990) Identification of Sclerotinia spp. on Vicia faba. Mycological Research, 94, 407-409.

Jenkyn, J.F. (1974) A comparison of seasonal changes in deposition of spores of Erysiphe graminis on different trapping surfaces. Annals of Applied Biology , 76, 257-267.

Kruger, W. (1974) Untersuchungen uber die epidemiologie des Rapskrebs verursacht durch Sclerotinia sclerotiorum (Lib.) de Bary. Proceedings of the International Rapeseed Conference, Giessen, Germany, 595-603.

McLean, D.M. (1958) Role of dead flower parts in infection of certain crucifers by Sclerotinia sclerotiorum (Lib.) de Bary. Plant Disease Reporter, 42, 663-666.

Mylchreest, S.J. (1985) Development of Sclerotinia stem rot on cultivars of oilseed rape. Ph.D. Thesis, University of London.

Mylchreest, S.J.; Wheeler, B.E.J. (1987) A method for inducing apothecia from sclerotia of Sclerotinia sclerotiorum. Plant Pathology, 36, 16

Price, K.; Colhoun,J. (1975) Pathogenicity of isolates of Sclerotinia sclerotiorum (Lib.) de Bary to several hosts. Phytopathologische Zeitschrift, 83, 232-238.

Purdy, L.H. (1979) Sclerotinia sclerotiorum: History, Diseases and Symptomology, Host Range, Geographic Distribution and Impact. Phytopathology, 69, 875-880.

Riddle, G.E.; Burpee, L.L.; Boland, G.J. (1991) Virulence of Sclerotinia sclerotiorum and S. minor on dandelion (Taraxacum officinale). Weed Science, 39, 109-118.

Turkington, T.K.; Morrall, R.A.A.; Gugel, R.K. (1991) Use of petal infestation to forecast Sclerotinia stem rot of canola: evaluation of early bloom sampling, 1985-1990. Canadian Journal of Plant Pathology, 13, 50-59.

Williams, J.R.; Stelfox, D. (1979) Dispersal of ascospores of Sclerotinia sclerotiorum in relation to Sclerotinia stem rot of rapeseed. Plant Disease Reporter, 63, 395-399.

RELEASE AND DISPERSAL OF *SCLEROTINIA* ASCOSPORES IN RELATION TO INFECTION

H. A. McCARTNEY, MAUREEN E. LACEY

AFRC Institute of Arable Crops Research, Department of Plant Pathology, Rothamsted Experimental Station, Harpenden, Herts. AL5 2JQ

ABSTRACT

From 1988 to 1991 a plot of sunflower plants (cv. Sunbred 246) was inoculated with sclerotia of *Sclerotinia sclerotiorum* in February or March and disease development was monitored on each plant during the summer. The concentration of airborne ascospores corresponded roughly to the number of apothecia but the relationship differed between years. The seasonal timing of ascospore production and the concentrations found also varied between years. Ascospores were released predominantly during the day, mostly around 1200 BST. Disease symptoms were observed, between 25 and 40 days after ascospores were first found. In 1988 the number of plants per week with new symptoms was roughly proportional to the average ascospore concentration measured 5 weeks previously. Laboratory studies suggested that ascospores were released in response to decreases in relative humidity. The observations suggest that severity of disease may be related to ascospore concentration during the infection period.

INTRODUCTION

Oilseed crops have become more important in U.K. agriculture over the last few years, for example oilseed rape (*Brassica napus* var. *oleifera*) is now the third largest arable crop grown. Interest in other oilseed crops, such as linseed (*Linum usitatissimum*) and sunflowers (*Helianthus annuus*), is also increasing. All three oilseed crops are hosts to the pathogen *Sclerotinia sclerotiorum* which can cause several yield reducing diseases.

Although much is known about the environmental conditions required for sclerotia survival and apothecial development in *S. sclerotiorum* (eg. Coley-Smith & Cook, 1971; Mitchell & Wheeler, 1990) there appears to be little information available on ascospore release and dispersal and the relationship between ascospore production and potential disease development. In this paper we report some results of a four year study of ascospore release and disease progress in a sunflower plot at I.A.C.R., Rothamsted.

METHODS

Field experiments

Experiments were done in an 8 x 8.8m plot enclosed by concrete walls sunk 2m into the ground (McCartney & Lacey 1991). The plot was divided into 32 sub-plots, 1.0 x 2.2m each separated from its neighbour by a concrete or wooden partition also sunk 2m into the soil. The sub-plots were arranged in four rows of eight, with the short side of each sub-plot parallel to rows and orientated North-South. In February or March in each year sclerotia of *S. sclerotiorum* were planted about 1cm deep in the central eight sub-plots (Table 1). In early May (Table 1) each sub-plot was planted with sunflower seedlings (cv Sunbred 246), about 30cm apart, in a 3 x 7 grid pattern. During periods of dry weather in May and June overhead irrigation was used to prevent the surface soil drying out.

The numbers of apothecia of *S. sclerotiorum* in each sub-plot were counted at weekly intervals during June and July. From June onwards, every week each plant in the plot was assessed for the presence of lesions caused by infection of *S. sclerotiorum*. Collapsed plants were removed from the plot and sclerotia formed within the plant collected. In September all remaining diseased plants were harvested, allowed to dry and sclerotia collected.

Concentrations of airborne ascospores were monitored in the centre of the plot using a seven day recording volumetric spore trap (Burkard Manufacturing Co. Ltd, Rickmansworth, UK.). The trap was operated from late May until the end of August in all four years (Table 1). The ascospore deposit on the trapping surface was counted using a light microscope and 24h average concentrations of ascospores estimated (McCartney *et al.*, 1986). Hourly average ascospore concentrations were also assessed on selected days.

On occasion, ascospore concentration was measured, at different heights above the ground, using roto-rod spore samplers (McCartney *et al.*, 1986).

Hourly average values of soil temperature, air temperature and humidity were recorded within the plot and air temperature, solar radiation and wind speed at 2m above the ground and rainfall were measured about 10m from the plot edge.

Laboratory experiments

The effect of changes in humidity on ascospore release was studied in a miniature wind tunnel 56cm long with 8x3cm cross section (McCartney & Lacey, 1990). Air was drawn through the tunnel using a Burkard spore trap, which also trapped spores released in the tunnel. Apothecia were placed in the wind tunnel for periods of up to a week and exposed to different sequences of "high" (close to saturation) and "low" (between 60 and 70%) relative humidity.

RESULTS

Ascospore release

The miniature wind tunnel experiments showed that ascospores were discharged in response to decreases in relative humidity. Very few ascospores were discharged when apothecia were exposed in air close to saturation. Apothecia were placed in the wind tunnel and exposed to alternating periods of "high" (>98%) and "low" (about 70%) relative humidity. The lengths of the periods of each were the same and lasted from 1 to 6 hours. After about a week the tunnel was opened to ambient air and the apothecia allowed to dry. In these experiments ascospores were usually discharged at the onset of the drying periods with very few ascospores caught during periods of high humidity. This pattern was found with "high" and "low" humidity cycles of 1 to 6 hours duration. Ascospore discharge continued for periods of up to 72h. Large numbers of ascospores were often discharged at the end of the test as the apothecia dried. Similar patterns of discharge were found when the periods of low humidity were reduced to about 10 min. Apothecia were exposed to changes in periods of light and dark (12h light, 12h dark) in addition to changes in humidity. Light (artificial fluorescent tubes) appeared to have little effect on ascospore discharge.

Ascospore discharge was also observed in the field. Laboratory grown apothecia were placed in the field plot overnight and ascospore discharge monitored by collecting ascospores on microscope slides held over the apothecia. The slides were change at hourly intervals or after a "puff" of ascospores was observed. Apothecia were observed to discharge ascospores in "puffs" and most were discharged between 1000 BST and 1300 BST. Individual apothecia continued to release ascospores for up to six hours. The time between "puffs" was variable but could be as short as 10min.

TABLE 1. Sclerotia sowing dates, crop planting date, trapping dates, apothecia numbers, average weather parameters and total numbers of infected plants for 1988, 1989, 1990 and 1991.

	1988	1989	1990	1991
Sclerotia sowing date	16/2	28/2	18/3	29/3
Weight of sclerotia (g)	416	503	205	278
Planting date	13/5	3/5	9/5	15/5
Ascospore trapping dates	27/5-6/9	25/5-17/6	25/5-19/8	30/5-13/8
Maximum number of apothecia (date)	860 (6/7)	74 (22/6)	460 (24/7)	1500 (16/7)
Mean air temperature* (°C)	14.5	16.0	15.9	17.2
Mean soil surface temperature* (°C)	15.4	15.6	15.4	16.6
Total rainfall, including irrigation* (mm)	167	157	136	192
Mean daily radiation total* (MJ m^{-2})	15.1	19.6	18.6	16.7
Infected plants (total)	449	93	33	46
Infected heads (total)	6	0	7	30

* Averaged over ascospore production period.

Ascospore dispersal

Apothecia were found in the central eight sub-plots by the first half of June in all four years. The numbers of apothecia increased rapidly reaching a maximum by late June or mid July (Table 1) after which they declined. Apothecia numbers differed between years the largest number recorded was in 1991 (1500) and the smallest in 1989 (74).

The seasonal pattern ascospore release was similar for all four years (Fig 1). Although there was considerable day to day variation in ascospore numbers, concentrations tended to increase with time reaching a maximum and then declining. The highest 24h average spore concentration (about 7000 m^{-3}) was measured in 1988, but, in the other years were much lower (Fig. 1) The timing of spore release also varied from season to season; peak concentrations were measured in late June in 1989, mid July in 1988 and late July in 1990 and 1991. In 1988 spores were produced for about 55 days compared with between 40 and 45 days in 1990 and 1991, while in 1989 ascospore production lasted only about 25 days.

Ascospore concentrations appeared to follow the increase and decline in apothecia numbers. In 1988 and 1990 ascospore concentration was roughly proportional to the number of apothecia found in the plots when averaged over a week: concentration increased by about 4 ascospores m^{-3} per apothecium. In 1989 apothecia numbers were low and although ascospore concentrations were also small there were about 13 ascospores per apothecium. In contrast in 1991 when apothecia numbers were large ascospore concentrations were similar to those found in 1989.

Hourly average ascospore concentrations in the centre of the plot showed a marked diurnal periodicity with the largest concentrations found around midday (see McCartney & Lacey, 1991). Generally few ascospores were caught during the night, although occasional peaks were found at night, often following rain. Ascospore concentration usually increased sharply after about 0800 BST and had decline again by 1600 BST.

Several measurements of ascospore concentration at different heights above the ground were made at the downwind edge of the plot during the period of peak spore production. The spore traps were exposed for about 4 hours in the morning and early afternoon. Ascospore concentrations decreased with height above the ground. The rate of decrease depended on crop height: for example in 1988, the concentration at crop height (between 0.6 and 0.8m) was about 0.4 of the value near the ground, while in 1991 it was about 0.1 when the crop was about 1m tall.

Disease development

The relationship between ascospore concentration and subsequent disease for 1988 and 1989 seasons has been discussed elsewhere (McCartney & Lacey, 1991). The results for 1990 and 1991 confirmed some of the earlier observations: the first disease symptoms were found between 25 and 40 days after ascospore concentration exceeded about 50m^{-3}; no new diseased plants were found about 40 to 50 days after ascospore production had effectively stopped. The total number of diseased plants which developed in the plot depended roughly on the number of ascospores released. Disease was severest in 1988 with about 67% of the 672 plants in the plot infected. In 1989, 1990 and 1991 only 14,

5 and 7% of the plants developed disease. In 1988 and 1989 few sunflower heads became infected (Table 1) while in 1990 and 1991 the proportion of infections found on heads was larger (21 and 86% respectively) although the total number of plants infected was small. In 1990 and 1991 the peak in spore production occurred in late July when the crop had reached full height (Fig. 1) and was in full flower. In contrast in 1988 and 1989 most of the ascospores were dispersed towards the end of June or early July before the crop had reached full height (Fig. 1). Indeed, in 1989 when ascospore dispersal was earliest no disease was found on the heads. In three of the four years (1988, 1989 and 1990) about 5% of the plants developed lesions near their base, which may also have been caused by mycelial infections. In 1990 only four plants developed base lesions.

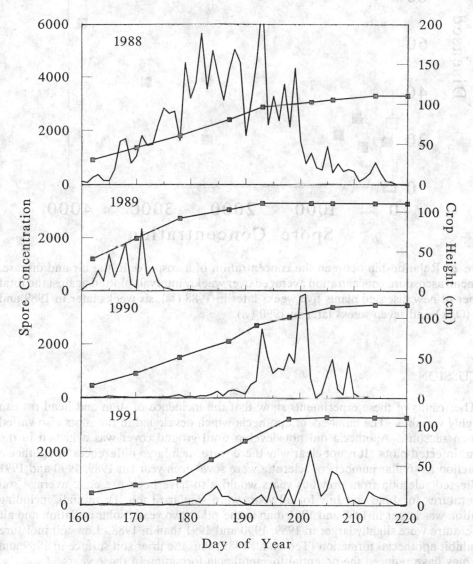

Figure 1. Twenty-four hour average concentration of ascospores measured in the centre of the plot from 9 June till 8 August for 1988 to 1991. Crop height (■) is also plotted.

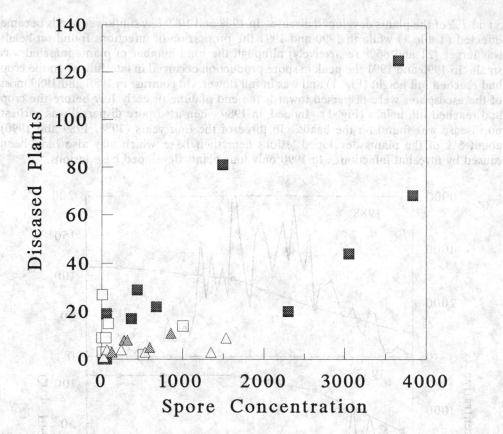

Figure 2. Relationship between the concentration of ascospores in the air and disease. 24h mean ascospore concentration averaged over weekly intervals plotted against the total number of new diseased plants five weeks later in 1988 (■), six weeks later in 1989 and 1991 (□, ▲) and seven weeks later in 1990 (△).

DISCUSSION

The results of these experiments show that the incidence of stem and head rot can be highly variable. The numbers of apothecia which developed in the plots also varied between seasons. Apothecia did not develop until ground cover was achieved in the central infected plots. It is not clear why there were such large differences in apothecia production as similar numbers of sclerotia were sown each year (in 1989, 1990 and 1991 uncollected sclerotia from previous years would also have been present): average soil temperatures for June and July for all years were similar (Table 1); rainfall, including irrigation was larger in 1988 and 1991 than in the other two years; solar radiation and air temperature were slightly larger in 1989, 1990 and 1991 than in 1988. Low soil moisture can inhibit apothecial formation (Teo et. al. 1989) thus the drier soil surface in 1989 and 1990 may have reduced the potential for apothecia formation in those years.

In three of the four years ascospore concentrations in the air within the crop appeared to be related more to the numbers of apothecia present than weather variables. However, the relationship between apothecia and ascospores was not consistent between years. Harthill (1980) found little relationship between weather variables and ascospore concentration above tobacco crops in New Zealand as long as there was sufficient rain to moisten the soil and promote apothecia formation.

The release of ascospore was more or less confined to the middle of the day; only a few spores were released at night or in the early morning. Harthill (1980) found a similar pattern in tobacco crops. Wind tunnel tests suggested that changes in humidity are implicated in ascospore discharge. Dijkstra (1964) observed puff discharge in response to exposure to gusts of cold air. In the field, Kruger (1975) found that airborne ascospores were more common when the weather was dry and windy than when it was wet. Decreases in relative humidity and increases temperature and wind speed were often observed within the plot in the morning which may have triggered ascospore discharge. Ascospore dispersal will be most effective if they are released during the middle part of the day, when wind speed and turbulence levels tend to be larger. The results of the roto-rod traps suggest that substantial numbers of ascospores may escape from the crop. *S. sclerotiorum* ascospores have been shown to be dispersed considerable distance by wind (Williams & Stelfox, 1979).

The first disease symptoms were found between 25 and 40 days after spore production began, suggesting that it takes between 30 and 40 days from initial infection before visible symptoms appear on the plants. The maximum number new infections per week occurred about five weeks after the highest spore concentrations were measured in 1988, six weeks in 1989 and 1991 and seven weeks in 1990. In 1988 the number of new diseased plants per week was roughly proportional to the average ascospore concentration measured five weeks before (Fig. 2). Because of the low levels of disease in the other years the relationship between spore concentration and subsequent disease was less clear. The 1988 results suggest that in years when the weather is favourable for infection airborne ascospore concentration may be a useful indicator of potential disease incidence. However, the variability in the efficiency of infection (ie the number of infections per unit of ascospore concentration) may make setting practical ascospore concentration thresholds difficult. Studies on other crops suggest that disease may not necessarily correlate well numbers of apothecia formed in the crop (Morrall & Dueck 1982, Boland & Hall 1988). However, Gugel & Morrall (1986) showed that, in oilseed rape crops in Canada, petal infestation by *S. sclerotiorum* ascospores, which may be closely related to ascospore concentration, was a good predictor of subsequent disease.

In 1988 and 1989, when ascospore release occurred largely before full flower, mostly stems became infected, whereas in the other two years a larger proportion of heads were infected when ascospore concentration peaked later. This suggest that sunflowers may be susceptible to attack throughout the growing season.

Severe attacks by *S. sclerotiorum* in sunflower and other oilseed crops can cause severe damage. Unfortunately, little can be done to save the crop after disease symptoms appear. Disease incidence varies greatly from year to year, therefore, it would be useful to be able to predict the potential of disease epidemics developing so that adequate control measures could be taken. These results suggests that apothecia production or ascospore concentration may be a useful indicator of disease potential. However, further work is needed to increase our understanding of the biological and environmental constraints governing the production of apothecia and ascospores in the field if practical methods of disease forecasting are to be developed.

ACKNOWLEDGEMENTS

The authors would like to thank Mr. Pere Kokoa for assisting with the ascospore discharge measurements.

REFERENCES

Boland, G. J.; Hall, R. (1988) Relationships between the spatial pattern and number of apothecia of *Sclerotinia sclerotiorum* and stem rot of soybean. *Plant Pathology*, **37**, 329-336.

Coley-Smith, J.R.; Cook, R. C. (1971) Survival and germination of fungal sclerotia. *Annual Review of Phytopathology*, **9**, 65-92.

Dijkstra, J. (1964) Inoculation with ascospores of *Sclerotinia sclerotiorum* for detection of clover rot resistant red clover. *Euphytica*, **13**, 314-329.

Gugel, R. K.; Morrall, R. A. A. (1986) Inoculum-disease relationships in sclerotinia stem rot of rapeseed in Saskatchewan. *Canadian Journal of Plant Pathology*, **8**, 89-96.

Harthill, W. F. T. (1980) Aerobiology of *Sclerotinia sclerotiorum* and *Botrytis cinerea* spores in New Zealand tobacco crops. *New Zealand Journal of Agricultural Research*, **23**, 259-262.

Kruger, W. (1975) Die Beeinflussung der Apothezien- und Ascosporen-Entwicklung des Rapskrebserregers *Sclerotinia sclerotiorum* (Lib) de Bary durch Umweltfaktoren. *Zietschrift für Pflanzenkrankheiten und Plfanzenschutz*, **82**, 101-108.

McCartney, H. A.; Lacey, M. E.; Rawlinson, C. J. (1986) Dispersal of *Pyrenopeziza brassicae* spores from an oil-seed rape crop. *Journal of Agricultural Science, Cambridge*, **107**, 299-305.

McCartney, H.A.; Lacey, M.E. (1990) The production and release of ascospores of *Pyrenopeziza brassicae* Sutton et Rawlinson on oilseed rape. *Plant Pathology*, **39**, 17-32.

McCartney, H.A.; Lacey, M.E. (1991) The relationship between the release of ascospores of *Sclerotinia sclerotiorum*, infection and disease in sunflower plots in the United Kingdom. *Grana*, **30**, 486-492.

Mitchell, S. J.; Wheeler, B. E. J. (1990) Factors affecting the production of apothecia and longevity of sclerotia of *Sclerotinia sclerotiorum*. *Plant Pathology*, **39**, 70-76.

Morrall, R. A. A.; Dueck, J. (1982) Epidemiology of sclerotinia stem rot of rapeseed in Saskatchewan. *Canadian Journal of Plant Pathology*, **4**, 161-168.

Steadman, J. R. (1983) White mould - a serious yield limiting disease of bean. *Plant Disease*, **67**, 346-350.

Teo, B. K.; Morrall, R. A. A.; Verma P.R. (1989) Influence of soil moisture, seeding date, and canola cultivars (Tobin and Westar) on the germination and rotting of sclerotia of *Sclerotinia sclerotiorum*. *Canadian Journal of Plant Pathology* **11**, 393-399.

Williams J. R.; Stelfox D. (1979) Dispersal of ascospores of *Sclerotinia sclerotiorum* in relation to sclerotinia stem rot of rapeseed. *Plant Disease Reporter*, **63**, 395-399.

RESISTANCE TO SCLEROTINIA SCLEROTIORUM IN LINSEED, OILSEED RAPE AND
SUNFLOWER CULTIVARS, AND ITS ROLE IN INTEGRATED CONTROL

J.B. SWEET, S.J. POPE AND J.E. THOMAS

National Institute of Agricultural Botany, Cambridge, CB3 0LE.

ABSTRACT

Artificial inoculation with mycelium and ascospores of
Sclerotinia sclerotiorum produced significantly different
levels of infection on linseed cultivars but not on oilseed rape
cultivars in NIAB tests. Field trials at different locations in
England developed different levels of disease on cultivars. The
differences in infection levels in linseed cultivars correlated
with those found in artificial inoculation. The levels of
disease in oilseed rape cultivars were correlated with
earliness of flowering and were inversely correlated with
cultivar height. The resistances found by other workers in
oilseed rape and sunflower are currently being developed in
breeding programmes. The prospects for exploiting resistance
and changes in morphological characters which reduce
susceptibility are discussed.

INTRODUCTION

Stem rot of oilseed rape caused by Sclerotinia sclerotiorum is a very
important disease in a few areas in the south of England and occurs
sporadically and occasionally at significant levels in other regions
(Jellis et al, 1984). The last two seasons in the UK have resulted in
widespread inspections at high levels due to the occurrence of warm
wet weather at the onset of flowering which favour apothecia
production and ascospore infection (Lamarque, 1983).

In Eastern and Southern Europe the incidence of S.sclerotiorum in
oilseed rape and sunflowers is high, resulting in extensive fungicide usage
to prevent crop losses (Regnault & Pierre, 1984). In linseed and flax,
stem rot incidence is generally low and crop losses have not been reported
(Mitchell et al., 1986).

This paper discusses studies of the resistance to stem rot in some
oilseed rape (Pope et al, 1992) and linseed cultivars (Pope & Sweet, 1991)
submitted to NIAB for National List and Recommended List testing in
1987-1991. Resistance studies in sunflowers, oilseed rape and linseed
conducted by other workers are reviewed and the prospects for exploiting
different types of resistance are discussed.

LINSEED

A range of linseed varieties entered for NIAB Descripive List trials
were tested in artificial inoculation tests and in field trials. The
incidence of infected stems two weeks after inoculation in 8 trials
inoculated with mycelium and two trials inoculated with ascospores is shown
in Table 1. In addition the length of the stem lesions was recorded on 25

infected plants per plot in two of the trials (Table 2). After 2 weeks secondary spread occurred to previously uninfected stems, and recording was terminated.

The inoculated tests consistently induced different levels of infection on cultivars and the severity of infection, recorded as stem lesion length, showed similar cultivar differences, suggesting that cultivars differ in both their resistance to primary infection and to the development of the disease. Artificial inoculation with ascospores demonstrated that S. sclerotiorum ascospores can infect linseed in the absence of applied exogenous organic material (ie. petals) under certain conditions of high humidity, in contrast to the normal requirements for infection by ascospores of oilseed rape (Lamarque, 1983).

A field trial at Chichester in 1990 developed appreciable levels of stem rot (Table 1) in early August, following flowering from the 22nd June. Very little stem rot was observed in other trials. Inoculation of field plots with mycelial suspension induced very little infection (below 0.1% infection) so that data from field trials are still very scarce. However the field trial result at Chichester produced similar results to the inoculated tests (Table 1) and it thus appears that inoculated tests produce results that indicate field resistance (Figure 1). However, additional field trials are required to confirm this finding.

Sclerotinia stem rot has only occasionally been reported in linseed, though as the crop is becoming more widely grown in both UK and mainland Europe, the disease may become of greater significance. Linseed is a crop which flowers in June and matures in July - September in the UK. It tends not to form a dense canopy and the combination of later growth and more open habit reduces the humidity within the crop in comparison with oilseed rape. The conditions favoured by Sclerotinia for infection thus occur less frequently than in rape (Lamarque, 1983).

Though the NIAB studies detected resistance in linseed, it is not thought likely that exploitation of this resistance by breeders will occur unless the increasing area of linseed becomes subject to greater levels of infection.

OILSEED RAPE

Inoculated tests using both mycelium and ascospores (Pope et al, 1992) produced high but similar levels of infection in all tested cultivars with no significant differences being apparent, so that current varieties appear to have little or no resistance to Sclerotinia.

Field trials had very variable levels of Sclerotinia stem rot at different sites in different seasons (Table 3), reflecting the influence of climatic conditions on disease incidence. In trials where appreciable levels of disease developed, significant differences in disease incidence were recorded between cultivars. Significant differences in height and time of flowering were also recorded. Correlation between height, and incidence of stem rot were $r = 0.41$ in all the trials, $r = 0.85$ in the 1989 trials (Figure 2) with higher levels of infection, and $r = 0.63$ in the Rosemaund 1991 trial. The correlation coefficient between earliness of

TABLE 1. The percentage infection of linseed plants following inoculation with mycelial suspension or ascospores of S. sclerotiorum and in a field trial in 1990.

Cultivar	Inoculated Mean Infection	No. of Experiments	Field Infection	
Amazon	46.79 a	10	2.00 a	
Blue Chip	35.15 ab	10	1.50 ab	
Vimy	34.95 abc	5	-	
Atlante	34.29 bc	5	1.50 ab	
Lidgate	32.06 bc	2	-	
Tadorna	31.67 bc	10	-	
McGregor	29.04 bcd	5	0.50	cde
Linda	28.00 bcd	5	0.75	cd
Beryl	27.03 bcd	5	1.00	bc
Norlin	23.23 cd	10	0.00	de
Antares	18.40 cd	5	0.25	de
Mean	30.96		0.94	
L.S.D. (P=0.05)	11.92		0.74	

All data angularly transformed. Cultivar means adjusted by fitted constants analysis and ranked.

Figures followed by the same letter cannot be separated statistically. (Duncans Multiple Range Test). LSD calculated from average S.E. (diff) = 5.93.

TABLE 2. Mean length of stem lesions on linseed cultivars inoculated with S. sclerotiorum.

Cultivar	Lesion length (mm)
Amazon	133.67
Blue Chip	100.59
Tadorna	98.86
McGregor	93.34
Atalante	92.84
Linda	60.50
Beryl	60.30
Norlin	50.06
Antares	37.73
Mean	80.88
SED	95.4

Fig. 1. Relationship between Sclerotinia infection levels in linseed
cultivars in inoculated tests and a naturally infected field
trial in 1990.

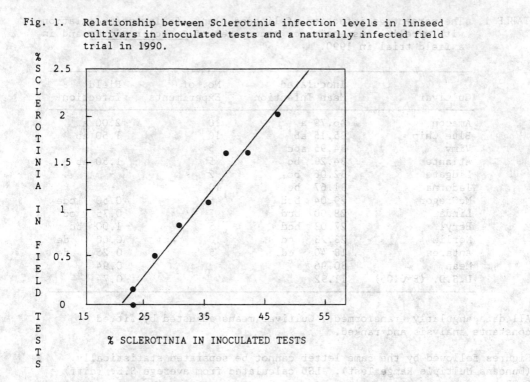

% SCLEROTINIA IN INOCULATED TESTS

Fig. 2. Relationship between Sclerotinia infection levels and height
of oilseed rape cultivars in 1989 trials.

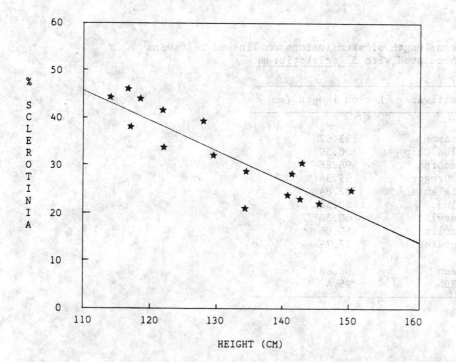

HEIGHT (CM)

TABLE 3. Sclerotinia stem rot incidence (%) and plant height at flowering in 6 oilseed rape trials in 1987, 1988 and 1989.

Cultivar	Mean % infection	Mean height (cm)
Rafal	21.7	118.3
Bienvenu	4.8	125.0
Ariana	17.6	141.8
Mikado	25.6	114.2
Pasha	18.6	120.0
Libravo	14.0	141.3
Cobra	16.9	137.1
Karma	5.7	133.0
Lictor	15.5	142.1
Liquanta	5.6	147.0
Doublol	8.9	133.0
Payroll	2.9	120.7
Corvette	23.9	118.5
Score	22.7	128.5
Capricorn	8.7	123.7
Susana	14.9	150.0
Link	2.8	153.7
Tapidor	30.7	116.6
Liborius	14.6	146.8
Semudnk 1023	16.0	139.4
Samourai	26.1	124.7
Falcon	23.7	132.5
Mean % plants affected	25.3	134.6
SED	4.5	3.8

Fig. 3. Relationship between Sclerotinia infection levels and time of flowering in oilseed rape cultivars in 1989 trials.

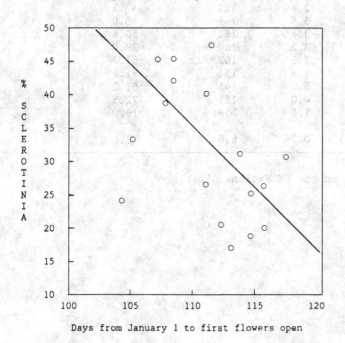

Days from January 1 to first flowers open

TABLE 4. Flowering, height and Sclerotinia stem rot incidence in winter
          oilseed rape trial, Rosemaund, 1991.

Cultivar*	Index of Flowering 1-9 (9=early)	Height at flowering (cm)	% Plants with Sclerotinia at pod ripening
Libravo	4.2	159	42.5
Cobra	3.8	155	50.5
Tapidor	4.4	139	98.7
Falcon	4.0	152	72.5
Lictor	2.9	162	39.2
Samourai	7.5	142	87.5
SE	3.1	156	53.0
Eurol	6.8	148	92.5
Idol	6.6	150	83.7
Envol	6.2	149	70.0
Aztec	4.1	143	53.2
Lincoln	4.0	159	40.0
Limerick	3.5	161	30.0
Rocket	5.4	140	75.0
Dragon	6.4	149	92.0
29	3.4	154	50.0
PR	5.1	152	58.7
AN	6.4	153	53.7
Bristol	5.7	150	71.2
AS	3.5	161	30.0
NP	4.5	146	55.0
LI	2.5	161	19.0
Lineker	2.8	165	30.7
B7	3.4	162	47.5
LD	3.6	144	48.0
AR	3.4	161	50.5
Cobol	3.2	160	28.0
DI	2.3	162	51.7
R9	5.8	151	51.2
IN	5.0	145	61.2
Apache	4.0	151	72.5
CP	1.5	159	18.0
LSD (P=0.05)	0.76	6.6	8.6

* Coded varieties are not on the UK National List.

flowering and stem rot incidence were -0.62 in the 1989 trials and -0.63 in the trial at Rosemaund in 1990. There was also a close negative correlation between height and earliness of flowering (r = 0.82 in the 1989 trials and r = 0.51 at Rosemaund).

Thus the incidence of infection in field trials varied between cultivars and appeared to be correlated with height and time of flowering of cultivars (Figs 2 and 3). Souliac (1991) demonstrated that incidence of Sclerotinia increased when oilseed rape was treated with growth regulators that reduced height without affecting flowering time. It could therefore by hypothesised that shorter cultivars are more susceptible due to their reduced height resulting in closer proximity of flower petals to ascospores released by apothecia on the ground. However, since most short cultivars are also earlier to flower, it could also be hypothesised that earlier flowering cultivars have more petals exposed to infection when ascospore production is at its greatest. Susceptibility of oilseed rape cultivars could thus be associated with a combination of reduced height and earlier petal exposure. Further studies are required which differentiate the effects of height from time of flowering.

Incidence of sclerotinia stem rot was correlated with yield (r=0.52) and reduction in yield (r=0.64) in the 1991 variety trial at Rosemaund (Figure 4, Table 5).

Where plots lodged or plants had been pushed down during tractor passes, stem contact occurred between lodged or flattened plants, allowing infection to spread by mycelial growth from stem to stem. This often resulted in very high levels of secondary infection.

Since time of flowering, lodging and height markedly influence levels of disease in oilseed rape and petals are a primary source of infection, plants that have significantly reduced petal and sepal sizes and duration of flowering, flower later and stand up well, but are of above average height, will have lowest levels of infection in many seasons. However, since Sclerotinia incidence is very dependent on the weather at the flowering period, high risk crops will often merit fungicide treatment to avoid potentially high yield losses.

Newman and Bailey (1987) described the resistance occurring in certain Japanese selections of spring rape and breeders have incorporated this resistance into winter oilseed rape breeding lines. Resistant cultivars are now being evaluated and will come into NIAB trials in the next two years.

SUNFLOWERS

Resistance to S. sclerotiorum in sunflower cultivars has been described in Europe (Tourvieille & Vear, 1986), North America (Gulya, et al, 1989) and many other parts of the world. Infection occurs at the stem base, in leaf axils, or in the flowering head, from early bud development to complete development of the capitulum post flowering. Individual tissues in a sunflower cultivar differ in susceptibility and tests have shown that inoculation of the different tissues will discriminate cultivars (Castano et al, 1989). Peres et al (1989) showed that ascospore inoculation of the terminal bud at the 5-12 leaf growth stage resulted in the most severe levels of infection.

TABLE 5. Effects of Sclerotinia stem rot on the yield of some oilseed
rape cultivars at Rosemaund compared with National average
yields in 1991.

Cultivar	Yield at Rosemaund t/ha	Mean yield over all sites t/ha	% Reduction in yield at Rosemaund	% Plants with Sclerotinia
Libravo	3.04	3.19	4.7	42.5
Cobra	2.60	3.35	22.0	50.5
Tapidor	1.28	3.19	60.0	98.8
Falcon	2.20	3.42	36.0	72.5
Lictor	2.84	3.32	14.0	39.2
Samourai	2.55	3.45	26.0	87.5
Eurol	2.08	3.48	40.0	92.5
Idol	2.42	3.39	29.0	83.7
Envol	2.77	3.49	21.0	70.0
Aztec	2.52	3.39	26.0	53.2
Lincoln	2.75	3.45	20.0	40.0
Limerick	3.03	3.26	7.0	30.0
Rocket	2.22	3.39	34.5	75.0
LSD (P=0.05)	0.24	0.16	–	8.6

Fig. 4.   Relationship between Sclerotinia infection and yield of oilseed
rape cultivars at Rosemaund in 1991.

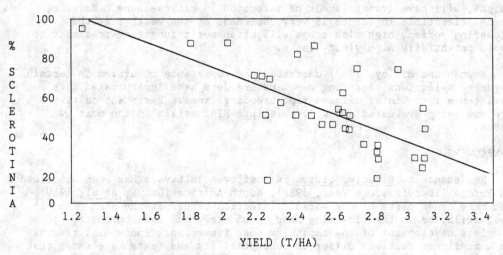

Studies of resistance mechanisms in sunflower have revealed that plants produce both phytoalexins (Martinson et al, 1988) and phenolic compounds (Bazzalo et al, 1985) in response to inoculation with S.sclerotiorum. In addition terpenoids with antifungal properties have been identified in sunflowers (Picman et al, 1990). Plant breeders are now selecting breeding material possessing enhanced levels of these compounds.

S. sclerotiorum produces oxalic acid from hyphae which assists with cell wall and membrane degradation and thus the necrotrophic development of the pathogen in the host. Oxalic acid acts as the elicitor for phytoalexin production and the subsequent production of phenolic compounds. Molecular markers that discriminate between resistant and susceptible sunflower cvs on the basis of their response to oxalic acid are being developed (Mouly & Esquerre-Tugaye, 1989) which can subsequently be used to assist with the selection of resistant material.

EXPLOITING RESISTANCE IN INTEGRATED CONTROL SYSTEMS

Resistance to Sclerotinia in all three crops appears to be multigenic, with resistance gene combinations occuring 'naturally' in some material. However, resistance is partial in the three crops, so that where environmental conditions favour severe epidemics, losses are still likely to occur. Thus at present, it appears that resistance will be sufficient in seasons of low inoculum potential or low risk, whereas additional strategies are required in high risk seasons. These could involve using growth regulators or lower seed rates to keep crops standing and to avoid secondary spread from stem contact and high humidity in the crop; use of cultivars with combinations of resistance and reduced petal size or petal numbers, and reduced length of flowering period to minimise disease levels. However, it seems likely that the use of fungicides applied at early and mid-flowering on sunflower and rape respectively will continue to provide cost effective disease control in high risk situations, and thus the present emphasis for good disease control is on environmental monitoring and risk evaluation, combined with the strategies described above.

ACKNOWLEDGEMENTS

The authors acknowledge the assistance of Mr R. Cartwright (consultant), Mr M. Gentle, Mr M. Johnstone (Farmers); Dr S.A. Archer and Dr B. Wheeler of Imperial College, and Dr P. Gladders of ADAS with their research programme, which was finanically supported by the Ministry of Agriculture, Fisheries and Food, Schering Agriculture and Ciba-Geigy Agrochemicals.

REFERENCES

Bazzalo, M.E.; Heber, E.M.; Del Peno Martinez, M.A.; Caso, O.H. (1985) Phenolic compounds in stems of sunflower plants inoculated with Sclerotinia sclerotiorum and their inhibitory effects on the fungus Phytopathologische Zeitschrift 112, 322-332.

Castano, F.; Vear, F.; Tourvieille, D. (1989) L'utilisation de plusiers tests simultanies dans la selection pour la resistance du tournesol vis-a-vis de Sclerotinia sclerotiorum. Informations Techniques Cetiom, 107, 14-20.

Gulya, T.J.; Vick, B.A.; Nelson, B.D.; (1989) Sclerotinia head rot of sunflowers in North Dakota: 1986 incidence, effect on yield and oil components, and sources of resistance. Plant Disease 73, 504-507.

Jellis, G.J.; Davies, J.M.L.; Scott, E.S. (1984). Sclerotinia on oilseed rape: Implications for crop rotations. Proceedings 1984 British Crop Protection Conference - Pests and Diseases 2, 709-715.

Lamarque, C. (1983). Conditions climatique qui favoriscent le processus natural de la contamination de colza par le Sclerotinia sclerotiorum. Proceedings of the 6th International Rape Seed Conference, 1038-1043.

Martinson, C.A.; Avila, F.J.; Yang Z.B.; Daugherty, C.J. (1988) Phytoalexin type response of sunflower stems to Sclerotinia sclerotiorum. Proceedings of the 12th International Sunflower Conference, Yugoslavia 25-29 July 1988, 582-586.

Mitchell, S.J.; Jellis, A.J.; Cox T.W.; (1986) Sclerotinia sclerotiorum on linseed. Plant Pathology 35, 403-405.

Mouly, A.; Esquerre-Tugaye, M-T (1989). Recherche de marquers moleculaires de la tolerance du tournesol à Sclerotinia sclerotiorum. Information Techniques Cetiom 108, 30-36.

Newman, P.L.; & Bailey, D.J. (1987). Screening for resistance to Sclerotinia sclerotiorum in oilseed rape in the glasshouse. Tests of Agrochemicals and Cultivars, 8. Annals of Applied Biology, 110 (Supplement).

Peres, A.; Regnault, Y.; Allard, L-M (1989) Sclerotinia sclerotiorum mise au point d'une mèthode de contamination artificielle sur bourgeon terminal du tournesol. Information Techniques Cetiom, 107, 3-6.

Picman, A.K.; Schneider, E.F.; Gershenzon, J. (1990) Antifungal activities of sunflowers turpenoids. Biochemical Systematics and Ecology 18, 325-328.

Pope, S.J.; Sweet, J.B. (1991). Sclerotinia stem rot resistance in linseed cultivars. Aspects of Applied Biology 28, 79-83.

Pope, S.J.; Sweet, J.B.; Thomas, J.E.; Varney, P.L. (1992). Studies of Sclerotinia sclerotiorum infection of linseed (Linum usitatissum) and oilseed rape (Brassica napus s.sp oleifera) cultivars. IOBC/WPRS Bulletin 15, in press.

Regnault, Y.; Pierre, J.G.; (1984). Control of Sclerotinia sclerotiorum Lib.) de Bary on oilseed rape in France. Aspects of Applied Biology, 6, 355-360.

Souliac L. (1991). Impact des regulators de croissance sur les epidemies de sclerotiniose du colza. Compte Rendu de la troisieme Conference Internationale sur les Maladies des Plantes, Bordeaux 1, 427-432.

Tourvieille D., Vear F. (1986). Sclerotinia: lutte par l'amelioration genetique, la resistance. La Defense des Vegetaux, 238 (40), 16-21.

BIOLOGICAL CONTROL OF *SCLEROTINIA SCLEROTIORUM* IN GLASSHOUSE CROPS

J.M. WHIPPS, S.P. BUDGE

Horticulture Research International, Worthing Road, Littlehampton, West Sussex BN17 6LP

ABSTRACT

Coniothyrium minitans and three *Trichoderma* isolates were examined for their ability to control Sclerotinia disease in sequential celery and lettuce crops over a six-year period. Depending on disease level, preplanting applications of *C. minitans* to soil naturally infested with *Sclerotinia sclerotiorum*, gave significant control of disease in lettuce but relatively poor control in celery. *C. minitans* decreased sclerotial survival over moist autumn fallow periods, survived for over one year and spread to infect sclerotia in other plots. The three *Trichoderma* isolates had little or no effect on disease or sclerotial viability, even though they survived in the soil.

INTRODUCTION

Sclerotinia sclerotiorum is a pathogen of more than 360 species of plants worldwide (Purdy, 1979). In the UK it regularly causes crop losses of between 1-10% in lettuce, celery, oil seed rape and potatoes but these can be considerably more. Losses in the glasshouse are generally kept low by prophylactic spraying with fungicides and, if the disease builds up, soils are fumigated with chemicals such as methyl bromide or sterilized with steam. However, some fungicides such as Ronilan (vinclozolin) have been withdrawn for use on glasshouse lettuce and soil sterilization is being carried out less frequently due to environmental concerns over the fumigants and the high cost of these treatments. Consequently, alternative disease control methods are urgently required.

Over the last six years at HRI-Littlehampton, biological methods of controlling Sclerotinia disease on celery and lettuce in the glasshouse, have been investigated using preplanting soil applications of fungal antagonists. Initial studies by Lynch & Ebben (1986) demonstrated that use of wheat grain inoculum of *Coniothyrium minitans* before each of three consecutive lettuce crops, gave 85% disease reduction or greater when 30-50% disease was present in control plots, comparable with fortnightly sprays of Ronilan. This paper reviews subsequent experiments involving the use of *C. minitans* and three *Trichoderma* isolates with proven biocontrol activity against sclerotial pathogens, in sequential celery and lettuce crops (Whipps *et al.*, 1989; Budge & Whipps, 1991) and indicates possible directions for future commercial development.

EXPERIMENTAL

Two series of glasshouse experiments were carried out using soil applications of maizemeal-perlite preparations of *C. minitans* and the *Trichoderma* isolates. Firstly, one summer crop of celery was followed by one winter crop of lettuce (Whipps *et al.*, 1989) and secondly, one summer crop of celery was followed by one winter-spring and one summer-autumn crop of lettuce (Budge & Whipps, 1991). In the first experiment, *C. minitans* and *T. harzianum* were applied before the celery crop but then no further additions were made and in the second experiment, *C. minitans*, *T. harzianum* HH3 and *Trichoderma* sp. B1 were applied before the celery and first lettuce crops only. Numbers of sclerotia present in the soil, their viability and infection by antagonists were assessed at harvest and following a three-month fallow period. Survival of the antagonists in the soil was also monitored.

RESULTS

In the celery crop in Experiment 1, *C. minitans* treatment resulted in 24% control of disease when 25% disease was present in the control plots but in Experiment 2, no control was found when 83% of plants in control plots were infected (Table 1). After application of *C. minitans* to the first lettuce crop in Experiment 2, 47% control of disease was obtained when 90% of control plants were infected, but there was no significant control in the lettuce crops with no preplanting application of *C. minitans*. None of the *Trichoderma* applications significantly controlled disease. Prophylactic sprays with Ronilan almost completely controlled disease in Experiment 1.

TABLE 1. Effect of *Coniothyrium minitans* and *Trichoderma* species on Sclerotinia disease in sequential celery and lettuce crops.

Treatment	Disease (%) and disease reduction (%)					
	Celery		1st Lettuce		2nd Lettuce	
	Disease[c]	Disease Red.	Disease	Disease Red.	Disease	Disease Red.
Experiment 1[a]						
Control	25^x		50^x		-	-
C. minitans	19^y	24	36^x	28	-	-
T. harzianum	23^x	8	47^x	6	-	-
Ronilan	1^z	96	1^y	98	-	-
Experiment 2[b]						
Control	83^x		90^x		59^x	
C. minitans	80^x	4	48^y	47	50^x	15
T. harzianum HH3	79^x	5	63^x	31	56^x	5
Trichoderma sp. B1	94^y	-13	77^x	14	46^x	22

[a] Values from 9 plots of 100 celery and 130 lettuce plants. Antagonists incorporated into soil before planting celery only.
[b] Values from 5 plots of 56 plants of celery and lettuce. Antagonists incorporated into soil before planting celery and 1st lettuce crops only.
[c] For each experiment, values in columns followed by different letters are significantly different at 5% level estimated from 2 x SED of plant data.

Following soil incorporation of *C. minitans*, sclerotial populations in the soil at harvest in both the celery and lettuce crops were significantly lower than in control plots, but not in lettuce crops where preplanting applications were not made (Table 2). *Trichoderma* sp. B1 in the first lettuce crop in Experiment 2 was the only other antagonist to achieve lower sclerotial populations at harvest. Following moist fallow periods in the celery and second lettuce crops in Experiment 2, there was a downward trend in numbers of sclerotia recovered in all plots. However, *C. minitans* was the only antagonist to reduce the number recovered significantly during these periods in both crops. There were no differences in the number of sclerotia recovered following the fallow period after either of the first lettuce crops when the soil was dry.

TABLE 2. Effect of *Coniothyrium minitans* and *Trichoderma* species on production and survival of sclerotia of *Sclerotinia sclerotiorum* in sequential celery and lettuce crops.

Treatment	Number of sclerotia[e,f]					
	Celery		1st Lettuce		2nd Lettuce	
	Harvest[a]	Fallow[b]	Harvest	Fallow	Harvest	Fallow
Experiment 1[c]						
Control	10.1[x]	ND[g]	82.1[x]	87.4[x]	-	-
C. minitans	3.1[y]	ND	84.6[x]	65.3[y]	-	-
T. harzianum	8.2[x]	ND	88.5[x]	79.6[x]	-	-
Ronilan	<0.1[z]	ND	<0.1[y]	<0.1[z]	-	-
Experiment 2[d]						
Control	31.6[x]	26.2[x]	84.8[x]	95.0[x]	48.6[x]	10.2[x]
C. minitans	14.9[y]	6.6[y]	24.4[y]	21.1[z]	54.0[x]	18.2[x]
T. harzianum HH3	44.8[x]	28.6[x]	64.2[x]	67.3[y]	60.4[x]	28.0[y]
Trichoderma sp. B1	20.4[x]	12.0[y]	34.9[y]	50.4[y]	36.8[x]	9.8[x]

[a] Sclerotia recovered at harvest
[b] Sclerotia recovered after 3-month fallow period
[c] Antagonists incorporated into soil before planting celery only
[d] Antagonists incorporated into soil before planting celery and 1st lettuce crops only
[e] Values are the mean number of sclerotia per 500 cm^{-2} except for lettuce in Experiment 1 where values are the mean number of sclerotia per plant
[f] For each experiment, values in columns followed by different letters are significantly different at the 5% level estimated from 2 x SED of log transformed data
[g] Not determined

C. minitans reduced viability of sclerotia at all sampling times, except harvest in the second lettuce crop (Table 3). There were no further significant reductions in viability after the fallow period. No *Trichoderma* isolate had any effect on sclerotial viability.

TABLE 3. Effect of *Coniothyrium minitans* and *Trichoderma* species on percent viability of sclerotia of *Sclerotinia sclerotiorum* in sequential celery and lettuce crops.

| Treatment | Viability (%) of sclerotia[f] | | | | | |
| | Celery | | 1st Lettuce | | 2nd Lettuce | |
	Harvest[a]	Fallow[b]	Harvest	Fallow	Harvest	Fallow
Experiment 1[c]						
Control	ND[e]	ND	98.9[x]	96.1[x]	-	-
C. minitans	ND	ND	82.8[y]	77.6[y]	-	-
T. harzianum	ND	ND	98.6[x]	96.4[x]	-	-
Experiment 2[d]						
Control	96.3[x]	97.7[x]	98.0[x]	92.0[x]	86.0[x]	92.9[x]
C. minitans	75.7[y]	82.9[y]	60.0[y]	48.3[y]	78.7[x]	78.5[y]
T. harzianum HH3	95.7[x]	96.0[x]	98.7[x]	95.0[x]	84.3[x]	94.6[x]
Trichoderma sp. B1	98.0[x]	96.3[x]	99.7[x]	97.0[x]	87.6[x]	89.5[x]

[a] Sclerotia recovered at harvest
[b] Sclerotia recovered after a 3-month fallow period
[c] Antagonists incorporated into soil before planting celery only
[d] Antagonists incorporated into soil before planting celery and 1st lettuce crops only
[e] Not determined
[f] Values derived from samples of 30 sclerotia per plot where possible. For each experiment, values followed by different letters are significantly different at the 5% level estimated from 2 x SED of logit transformed data.

C. minitans was recovered from sclerotia from all treatment plots, except the fallow sample of *Trichoderma* sp. B1 from celery in the second experiment, and increased with time in the control and *Trichoderma* treatments in Experiment 2, to maximum values of 67 and 53% infection respectively (Table 4). The highest levels of infection of sclerotia (86%) were in plots treated with *C. minitans*. *Trichoderma* isolates were detected in a maximum of only 5% of sclerotia from plots treated with *Trichoderma* isolates, even though all antagonists survived in the soil in treated plots at levels of 10^4 colony forming units (c.f.u.) cm^{-3} one year after incorporation. *Trichoderma* counts in control plots were generally about 10^2 c.f.u. cm^{-3}.

DISCUSSION

The *Trichoderma* isolates had relatively little effect on disease or sclerotial viability in comparison with *C. minitans*, even though they survived in soil and infected sclerotia in the laboratory (Davet, 1986; Davet & Camporota, 1986). The relatively high temperature (28°C) used for the original infection tests could explain part of this, as soil temperatures at 2 cm depth in the glasshouse rarely exceed 18°C during the summer. Subsequent laboratory experiments have shown poor infection by these *Trichoderma* isolates at 18°C, whereas *C. minitans* infects well (Whipps & Budge, 1990).

TABLE 4. Occurrence (%) of *Coniothyrium minitans* in sclerotia of *Sclerotinia sclerotiorum* from soil in sequential celery and lettuce crops.

Treatment	Celery		1st Lettuce[f]		2nd Lettuce	
	Harvest[a]	Fallow[b]	Harvest	Fallow	Harvest	Fallow
Experiment 1[c]						
Control	ND[e]	ND	1.0[x]	1.8[x]	-	-
C. minitans	ND	ND	46.2[y]	41.3[y]	-	-
T. harzianum	ND	ND	1.6[x]	6.0[z]	-	-
Experiment 2[d]						
Control	18.3[x]	9.0[x]	17.0[x]	22.3[x]	67.3[x]	35.0[x]
C. minitans	56.7[y]	39.2[y]	81.7[y]	86.7[y]	72.0[x]	74.0[y]
T. harzianum HH3	10.0[x]	7.0[x]	2.3[x]	12.7[z]	53.0[x]	23.6[x]
Trichoderma sp. B1	11.3[x]	0[z]	3.7[x]	16.0[x]	40.0[x]	29.0[x]

[a] Sclerotia recovered at harvest
[b] Sclerotia recovered after a 3-month fallow period
[c] Antagonists incorporated into soil before planting celery only
[d] Antagonists incorporated into soil before planting celery and 1st lettuce crops only
[e] Not determined
[f] Values derived from samples of 30 sclerotia per plot where possible. For each experiment, values followed by different letters are significantly different at the 5% level estimated from 2 x SED of logit transformed data.

Application of *C. minitans* before planting gave significant control of Sclerotinia disease on lettuce in these and previous experiments (Lynch & Ebben, 1986) but the longer cropping period of celery and its higher leaf canopy allowing greater dispersal of pathogen spores, may limit the use of *C. minitans* in this crop. At low disease levels, *C. minitans* can provide disease control in lettuce equivalent to prophylactic sprays of Ronilan (Lynch & Ebben, 1986) but this level of control cannot be maintained by *C. minitans* as the disease pressure increases, even though significant disease control is obtained. When used, Ronilan has always given disease control greater than 95% in all our experiments. However, *C. minitans* was able to survive and infect sclerotia at all times of the year, decreasing sclerotial numbers when the soil was moist and inhibiting viability and apothecial production (see Whipps *et al.*, 1989 for latter data). It was also able to infect sclerotia at a distance from application and consequently shows potential for long term efficacy.

Taken together, these experiments and those of Lynch & Ebben (1986) show that only when there is more than 40% disease in untreated naturally infected plots does *C. minitans* fail to give control of Sclerotinia disease equivalent to fungicide treatments. This is a far higher disease level than commercial growers would accept before steaming or sterilizing the soil. Consequently, preplanting applications of *C. minitans* appear to be a realistic proposition for control of Sclerotinia disease in the glasshouse. However, there are still problems to overcome. For example, the bulky solid substrate treatments may be too expensive or inconvenient to use in the existing growing systems, therefore other culture and application systems need to be investigated. Further, because of the risk of *Botrytis cinerea* or other diseases, prophylactic fungicide sprays may still be required. A search for strains of *C. minitans* compatible with these and other chemicals routinely used in the glasshouse would seem of value. Similarly, if more active isolates could be obtained at the same time, the period to commercial trials could be reduced.

ACKNOWLEDGEMENTS

This work was funded by the Ministry of Agriculture, Fisheries and Food.

REFERENCES

Budge, S.P.; Whipps, J.M. (1991) Glasshouse trials of *Coniothyrium minitans* and *Trichoderma* species for the biological control of *Sclerotinia sclerotiorum* in celery and lettuce. *Plant Pathology*, **40**, 59-66.

Davet, P. (1986) Activité parasitaire des *Trichoderma* vis-à-vis des champignons à sclérotes; corrélation avec l'aptitude à la competition dans un sol non stérile. *Agronomie*, **6**, 863-867.

Davet, P.; Camporota, P. (1986). Etude comparative de quelques méthodes d'estimation de l'aptitude à la compétition saprophytique dans le sol des *Trichoderma*. *Agronomie*, **6**, 575-581.

Lynch, J.M.; Ebben, M.H. (1986) The use of micro-organisms to control plant disease. *Journal of Applied Bacteriology Symposium Supplement*, **61**, 115S-126S.

Purdy, L.H. (1979) *Sclerotinia sclerotiorum*: history, diseases and symptomology, host range, geographic distribution and impact. *Phytopathology*, **69**, 875-880.

Whipps, J.M.; Budge, S.P. (1990) Screening for sclerotial mycoparasites of *Sclerotinia sclerotiorum*. *Mycological Research*, **94**, 607-612.

Whipps, J.M.; Budge, S.P.; Ebben, M.H. (1989) Effect of *Coniothyrium minitans* and *Trichoderma harzianum*, on *Sclerotinia* disease of celery and lettuce in the glasshouse at a range of humidities. In: *Integrated Pest Management in Protected Vegetable Crops*. Proceedings of CEC-IOBC Joint Experts Meeting, Cabrils 27-29 May 1987, R. Cavalloro and C. Pelerents (Eds), Rotterdam, Balkema, pp. 233-243.

SESSION 3B

TOXICOLOGY: MODERN METHODS FOR RISK ASSESSMENT

CHAIRMAN   PROFESSOR C. L. BERRY

SESSION
ORGANISER   MR P. H. ROSE

INVITED PAPERS   3B-1 to 3B-4

MECHANISMS OF CHEMICAL CARCINOGENESIS: APPLICATION TO SAFETY ASSESSMENT OF
PESTICIDES

G.M. Williams, L.K. Verna, J. Whysner

American Health Foundation, 1 Dana Road, Valhalla, New York 10595

ABSTRACT

Cancer risk assessment for any chemical, including pesticides,
requires an understanding of the mechanism of the chemically-
induced neoplastic process. The evolution of a neoplasm is a
complex multi-event and multi-stage process, which proceeds
through two sequences: the conversion of a normal cell to a
neoplastic cell and the development of neoplastic cells into
tumors. Pesticides can affect the carcinogenic process in a
variety of ways, both by altering the genome and by providing a
growth advantage for neoplastic cells. The risk assessment model
should reflect these differences in cancer mechanism. For
epigenetic carcinogens, the use of a model requiring a minimum
dose (threshold) for cellular responses, essential for neoplastic
development, greatly affects the assessment of risk at low
exposure levels in humans. For DNA-reactive carcinogens, the
current understanding of neoplastic processes warrants the use of
a linear-at-low-dose (non-threshold) model in most instances.

INTRODUCTION

The pathogenesis of chemically-induced cancer is highly complex,
consisting of a series of events. The process can be divided into two
distinct sequences, neoplastic conversion, involving changes in the genetic
apparatus of cells leading to generation of a neoplastic cell (often by way
of altered preneoplastic cells) followed by neoplastic development, in which
the neoplastic cell evolves into a tumor. In experimental models,
pesticides can influence both sequences, either by enhancement or inhibition
(Williams, 1990; Williams, 1984).

The tumorigenic effects of carcinogens can be exerted by several
mechanisms. Evidence of this is provided by observations that, although
many carcinogens give rise to chemically reactive species that damage DNA,
some animal carcinogens, notably certain pesticides, do not have these
properties. In recognition of this fundamental difference, a mechanistic
categorization of carcinogens into two main types, DNA-reactive and
epigenetic, has been developed (Weisburger & Williams, 1981) and applied to
a wide spectrum of chemical carcinogens (Williams & Weisburger, 1991). The
distinction between DNA-reactive or genotoxic carcinogens and the epigenetic
type has, in turn, provided a basis for the selection of the type of model
used for risk assessment by some regulatory agencies (Whysner and Williams,
1992).

THE NEOPLASTIC PROCESS

The neoplastic phenotype is transmitted to the progeny of neoplastic
cells as a consequence of a change in the structure or expression of genetic
information. DNA-reactive carcinogens are capable of effecting such an
alteration directly through a mutational event, either in gene structure or

arrangement. In contrast, epigenetic agents may act either by facilitating expression of a preexisting abnormal genome or by inducing an abnormal genome through: 1) spontaneous mutation during increased levels of induced cell proliferation; 2) induced mutation through impairment of the fidelity of DNA polymerases; 3) induction of a stable altered state of gene expression; or 4) generation of intracellular reactive species such as activated oxygen, which are in turn genotoxic. The sequence of events by which chemicals produce cancer from their action on normal cells is outlined in Figure 1.

Sequences of Neoplasia

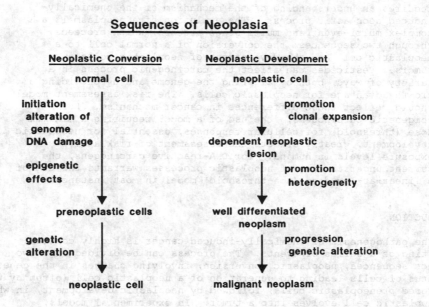

Neoplastic Conversion

normal cell

initiation
alteration of
genome
DNA damage

epigenetic
effects

preneoplastic cells

genetic
alteration

neoplastic cell

Neoplastic Development

neoplastic cell

promotion
clonal expansion

dependent neoplastic
lesion

promotion
heterogeneity

well differentiated
neoplasm

progression
genetic alteration

malignant neoplasm

Formation of DNA reactive species

Some DNA-reactive carcinogens have chemical reactivity inherent in their structures. Apart from these, most DNA-reactive carcinogens require biotransformation into reactive metabolites. Biotransformation results from the operation of enzyme systems usually involved in the metabolism of endogenous substrates, but which can also operate on xenobiotics. The principal enzymes that biotransform chemicals are part of the cytochrome P-450 dependent monooxygenase system associated with the endoplasmic reticulum. For all classes of genotoxic and epigenetic carcinogens, except nitrosamines, most metabolic steps generate detoxified, water-soluble metabolites, which can be excreted usually in the form of conjugates. Thus, the metabolism of carcinogens to activated forms is a minor byproduct of biotransformation.

A variety of chemicals modify biotransformation processes (Williams, 1984). Among these are a number of organochlorine pesticides, such as DDT, which induce liver enzyme activities. In general, such pesticides inhibit the carcinogenicity in experimental animals of activation-dependent carcinogens by inducing detoxification systems.

The ultimate reactive form of organic direct-acting carcinogens and activated metabolites of procarcinogens is an electrophilic reactant. For epigenetic carcinogens, it is also possible that reactive species could be generated from normal cellular constituents. For instance, a class of epigenetic carcinogens has the characteristic of inducing proliferation of the cytoplasmic organelles peroxisomes. Peroxisome proliferators appear to lead to generation of reactive oxygen species as a result of production of H_2O_2 during oxidation of lipids in peroxisomes (Rao & Reddy, 1987). A member of this class is the herbicide lactofen.

The ultimate electrophilic reactants of carcinogens can bind to all four bases of DNA as well as to the phosphodiester backbone. The base adducts are formed at several sites, with the most susceptible site appearing to be the purine nitrogen. Considerable evidence now indicates that binding to DNA is a critical reaction of carcinogens. The particular regions of DNA i.e., the specific genes whose modification is essential to initiation of the carcinogenic process are beginning to be identified. Several carcinogenic pesticides are known to be DNA-reactive, for example, ethylene dibromide. Most, however lack this activity (Blair et al., 1990).

If the damage to DNA by a DNA-reactive carcinogen is not repaired, or is repaired incorrectly, and the affected region is used as the template for synthesis of new DNA, a permanent mutation can be introduced through mispairing of bases. Because repair does not occur immediately, rapidly proliferating tissues and those stimulated to proliferate are highly susceptible to carcinogens. Several types of damage to DNA are now known to be promutagenic. For example, alkylation of the 0^6 position of guanine results in base pairing with thymine rather than cytosine.

Cells are endowed with a variety of elements that protect them against DNA-reactive chemicals. As mentioned, detoxification predominates over activation. Reactive species undergo reaction with abundant cellular nucleophiles such as protein, glutathione, etc., which limit reaction with DNA. The small amount of reactive agents that reach the nucleus may undergo random reaction with portions of the genome that, unlike oncogenes and tumor suppressor genes, do not lead to neoplasia. Damage to DNA arrests DNA replication, perhaps through induction of anti-proliferative factors, allowing for DNA repair. Finally, DNA repair is highly efficient, commencing almost instantly after DNA damage and proceeding rapidly with high fidelity. All of these elements, individually and in combination function to diminish the carcinogenicity of DNA-reactive agents. Depending upon the particular agent, the resultant effect at low doses may be negligible. In some cases, qualitative differences in effect at low doses may result in no carcinogenic effect. The presence of a threshold dose, even for a DNA-reactive substance, could occur where detoxification is complete at low doses. Such may be the case for the oxidation products caused by peroxisome proliferators in the presence of abundant amounts of antioxidant. The antioxidants neutralize (reduce) the oxidants before they become capable of causing DNA damage.

Neoplastic cells

Neoplastic cells have an altered genome, which may include DNA and chromosomal mutations. The essential biological abnormality in neoplastic cells is a loss of growth control. Certain lines of evidence suggest that the neoplastic state is a homozygous recessive condition, which may reflect inactivation of anti-oncogenes. Other studies point to the activation of dominant cellular oncogenes. Oncogenes code for factors involved in cellular growth, whereas tumor suppressor genes code for factors that restrain proliferation.

Neoplastic cells occur spontaneously or can be induced by chemical or other agents. They may persist in a dormant state for long periods in spite of genetic alterations, or, depending upon host conditions, grow to form a neoplasm. The elements that prevent expression of initiated cells as neoplasms are poorly understood, but may involve factors, such as chalones, which regulate growth and differentiation. Large molecules can be exchanged between cells through specialized membrane structures known as gap junctions. In this way, transmission of regulatory factors from normal to initiated cells may effect control of the initiated cells. The cells of fully developed neoplasms are deficient in gap junctions and possess other membrane abnormalities, indicating a limitation in their ability to receive regulatory signals.

Promotion

The classical definition of promotion is the enhancement of the carcinogenicity of an agent by a second agent, not carcinogenic by itself under the test conditions, acting after exposure to the first has ended. In experimental animals, promotion has been shown to occur in most organs, including skin, liver, stomach, colon, breast, and bladder. Promoters are capable of eliciting tumor formation, albeit in small yield, when administered alone under conditions of prolonged exposure at high levels. Under these conditions, promoters presumably act on initiated cells that "normally" occur. Therefore, promoters do not cause neoplasia but enhance the neoplastic process. This is probably the basis for the tumorigenicity in the liver of certain organochlorine pesticides shown in Table 1.

Table I. Liver Neoplasm Promotion by Organochlorine Pesticides

Pesticide	Species	Effect	Reference	
DDT	rat	+	Peraino et al.	(1975)
	mouse	+	Williams & Numoto	(1984)
	hamster	−	Tanaka et al.	(1987)
Chlordane	mouse	+	Williams & Numoto	(1984)
heptachlor	mouse	+	Williams & Numoto	(1984)
lindane	mouse	+	Schroter et al.	(1987)

Promoters could also give rise to tumors by inducing cell proliferation (hyperplasia), and, thereby, a variety of effects have been suggested to underlie the promoting action of chemicals (Williams, 1984). Since initiated cells can remain dormant in tissues for many months, it seems evident that these altered cells, in the absence of promotion, are being kept under some type of growth regulation. Non-covalent binding to components of cell membranes, including various receptors, may underlie the action of epigenetic carcinogens that operate as tumor promoters. For the organochlorine pesticides that act as tumor promoters, such effects on cell membranes may be critical.

As described above, cells exchange molecules through membrane gap junctions. If this kind of intercellular exchange is involved in the regulation of differentiation and growth, then interference with this process could release dormant tumor cells for growth into neoplasms. Thus, one mechanism for tumor promotion may involve interference with the growth control suppression of latent tumor cells. A large number of tumor promoters have now been demonstrated to have the ability to inhibit intercellular communication (Tong & Williams, 1987), and therefore, this effect assumes importance as one basis for tumor promotion.

The enhancement of cell proliferation is a characteristic of epigenetic carcinogens. Chemically induced cell proliferation may be a primary event affecting mitotic rate (mitogenesis), a secondary event following cell necrosis (toxicity), or a selective effect on initiated cells (promotion). The selectivity of the chemical may result from a differentially high stimulation of mitosis of initiated cells, a greater toxicity for normal cells, or another effect. It is not clear whether non-selective mitogens or toxins can affect promotion.

Regardless of the underlying cause, tumor promoters release the initiated cell from growth control, resulting in proliferation of the initiated cell line. The result is an increase in the number, or clonal expansion, of initiated cells. These mechanisms of tumor promotion all require high and sustained levels of the agent to elicit the effect. This is presumably due to the necessity for a cellular response which overcomes growth control mechanisms, resulting in cell division. Also, the agent must affect a large number of cells, and the effect must be of sufficient duration to allow neoplastic cells to achieve a state of clonal expansion that cannot be brought under homeostatic regulation in the absence of the chemical.

The biologic effects that are required for release of control mechanisms would not be predicted to occur from trivial amounts of chemicals. For example, if cell damage and death are required for a proliferative response, then toxic amounts of chemical are required for tumor promotion. Likewise, a large dose would be required to disrupt receptor-mediated mechanisms, such as those involving hormones, which are under homeostatic feedback control. An example of a pesticide affecting hormonal control is amitrole, which produces thyroid tumors in rodents.

MECHANISM-BASED APPROACHES FOR RISK ASSESSMENT OF PESTICIDES

Ethylene dibromide as an example of a genotoxic carcinogen

Ethylene dibromide (EDB or 1,2 dibromoethane) was used as a fumigant for stored crops from 1948 until 1983, when it was banned in the U.S. by the Environmental Protection Agency (EPA) after ostensibly hazardous levels were discovered in finished grain products. EDB has been found to be carcinogenic in rats and mice by different routes of exposure and in multiple target organs including forestomach, lung, liver, connective tissue, spleen, mammary gland, and nasal cavity (IARC, 1987). Genotoxicity testing has been mostly positive in bacterial and mammalian systems including DNA binding and unscheduled DNA synthesis.

Guengereich et al., (1987) found that EDB was activated to an electrophilic species by conjugation with glutathione and that this conjugate reacted with DNA through an episulfonium ion intermediate. They identified the major DNA adduct as S-[2-(N7-guanyl)ethyl]glutathione. Evidence that EDB is a DNA-reactive carcinogen raises the possibility that even low exposure doses could modify the genome, thereby resulting in neoplastic conversion. Such initiated cells have a finite probability of escaping homeostatic control and progressing to neoplasms under circumstances that provide a growth advantage. It is possible that adequate protective mechanisms, as discussed above, are operative in the case of EDB to prevent a tumorigenic effect at low exposure. However, until more is known about processes that could mitigate the carcinogenic potential of EDB, the use of a conservative linear-at-low-dose extrapolation is warranted. EPA has, thereby, calculated oral and inhalation cancer potency factors of 85 and 0.76 $(mg/kg/day)^{-1}$, respectively.

Lindane as an example of an epigenetic carcinogen

Lindane is a polychlorinated hydrocarbon pesticide that exemplifies an epigenetic carcinogen. It has been found to induce benign tumors of the liver only in certain strains of mice (IARC, 1987). Numerous studies of genotoxic effects have been negative in both bacterial and mammalian systems (IARC, 1987). Most importantly, tests for DNA binding and unscheduled DNA synthesis in mouse and rat liver have been negative, indicating that lindane is not a DNA-reactive carcinogen in the target organ. Lindane has been found to promote but not initiate tumors of the liver, and other studies such as the inhibition of cell-cell communication substantiate that tumor promotion is the mechanism of tumorigenicity. Consequently, lindane appears to enhance the incidence of spontaneous liver tumors in these mice due to the promotion of spontaneously transformed cells.

The finding that lindane acts by enhancement of tumorigenicity rather than by causing a neoplastic conversion should be the determining factor in the choice of a risk assessment model. Consequently, lindane does not "cause" cancer in rodents but acts by modifying an inherent neoplastic process. Tumor promotion is associated with a cellular response that is reversible and would be expected to have a threshold dose as in the cases of other toxic effects involving cell growth (mitogenesis), cell damage (necrosis), or programmed cell death (apoptosis). These cellular effects have been associated with the ability of a chemical to promote initiated cells into neoplasms. The risk assessment for such effects involves establishing a relevant no-observed-effect-level (NOEL) and dividing by an uncertainty factor. This results in determination of an acceptable daily intake (ADI). The magnitude of the uncertainty factor depends upon many considerations, but most commonly, uncertainty factors of 100 to 1,000 are used. This is the risk assessment model recommended for pesticide residues in food by the International Programme on Chemical Safety (IPCS, 1990).

One method of determining a NOEL for the tumorigenic effects of lindane is by transforming a large number of cells in the liver (initiation) using a proven carcinogen, and determining the dose-response for promotion of these transformed cells. Utilizing the data of Schroter et al. (1987) the NOEL for lindane was found to be 0.5 mg/kg/day for the development of altered foci in liver initiated with N-nitrosomorpholine. Altered foci are preneoplastic lesions of the liver, a small fraction of which progress to tumors (Williams, 1980). Consequently, the calculated ADI for lindane would be 5μg/kg/day utilizing an uncertainty factor of 100.

The NOEL calculation above for promotion of altered foci is much lower than the lowest dose of 160 mg/kg/day, which induced benign tumors in mice. Utilizing this NOEL for enhancement of preneoplastic lesions, the derived acceptable daily intake (ADI) will include an additional margin of safety compared to a neoplastic end-point. In contrast, in the past the U.S. EPA has used the no-threshold, linear-at-low-dose risk assessment model for lindane (EPA, 1991). The use of this model has developed a cancer potency factor of 1.8 $(mg/kg/day)^{-1}$. Therefore, the regulatory limit associated with a lifetime cancer risk of 10^{-6} would be 0.0005 μg/kg/day. (It should be noted that the EPA is currently re-evaluating its carcinogenic assessment of lindane and has in some instances used a safety factor approach).

CONCLUSIONS

Most chemicals that have caused cancer in humans are of the DNA-reactive type (Williams, 1987). Given sufficient exposure, it seems likely that any experimental carcinogen of this type would produce cancer in humans. Many animal carcinogens have not been proven to cause cancer in humans in spite of significant exposures (IARC, 1987), which may be due to the defense mechanisms (i.e. chemical detoxification and DNA repair processes) with which humans are endowed. Regardless, pesticides of this type such as EDB should be regarded as qualitative hazards (Williams, 1987). Alternatively, an approach such as that utilized by the U.S. EPA can be used which assumes no threshold and results in the development of a linear-at-low-dose cancer potency factor.

Few carcinogens of the epigenetic type have been associated with cancer in humans, and these are mainly hormones or immunosuppressants which are used therapeutically at tumorigenic doses (Williams & Weisburger, 1991). Humans have been exposed to many pesticides known to cause cancer in experimental animals, but none has been definitely linked to cancer in humans (IARC, 1990). The absence of effects in humans has been suggested to be due to the fact that exposures of humans are below the threshold for the biological effect, which includes cell proliferation response. In addition, some effects may be specific to the rodent test animal and not at all relevant to human. Lindane has been used as an example of an epigenetic pesticide, in which the dose-response information indicates that the NOEL for the development of neoplastic foci is 0.5 mg/kg/day. The use of an uncertainty factor of 100 for this preneoplastic end-point would indicate that exposure to 5 μg/kg/day would not pose a carcinogenic risk in humans. In contrast, an acceptable risk of 10^{-6} risk (one additional chance of cancer in a million over a lifetime) would be associated with a dose 10,000 times less using the linear-at-low-dose extrapolation.

The identification of carcinogenic mechanism for a pesticide in order to distinguish which risk assessment model should be used is recommended for regulatory procedures. A DNA-reactive pesticide such as EDB, which has been shown to produce tumors at multiple sites, in different species, and by different routes of administration, should be regulated more stringently than the epigenetic tumorigen lindane, which enhances benign tumors in mice. The linear-at-low-dose risk assessment method results in similar cancer potency factors for EDB and lindane, considering them similarly hazardous to humans. Likewise, the use of a safety factor approach for both pesticides, would have a similar result although the acceptable doses would be much higher.

Due to the current understanding of the role of cancer mechanism to predict human risks, DNA-reactive carcinogens should be treated as qualitative hazards and eliminated, or the risks should be determined by a non-threshold model in most cases. In contrast, the use of a safety factor approach for epigenetic carcinogens will adequately protect humans against potential hazards due to these pesticides.

REFERENCES

Blair, A.; Axelson, O.; Franklin, C.; Paynter, O.E.; Pearce, N.; Stevenson, D.; Trosko, J.E.; Vainio, H.; Williams, G.; Woods, J.; Zahm, S.H. (1990) Carcinogenic effects of pesticides. *The Effects of Pesticides on Human Health*, Princeton Scientific Publishing Company, Princeton, NJ, 201-260.

Environmental Protection Agency (EPA) (1991) Health Effects Assessment Summary Tables. *Health Effects Assessment Summary Tables,*, OERR 9200.6-303 (91-1), Washington, D.C., U.S. Environmental Protection Agency, .

Guengerich, F.P.; Paterson, L.A.; Cmarik, J.L.; Koga, N.; Inskeep, P.B. (1987) Activation of dihaloalkanes by glutathione conjugation and formation of DNA adducts. *Environmental Health Perspectives*, **76**, 15-18.

International Agency for Research on Cancer (IARC) (1987) IARC Monographs on the Evaluation of Carcinogenic Risks to Humans Overall Evaluations of Carcinogenicity. *IARC Monographs on the Evaluation of Carcinogenic Risks to Humans Overall Evaluations of Carcinogenicity,*, Supplement 7, Lyon, France IARC.

International Agency for Research on Cancer (IARC) (1991) Occupational Exposures in Spraying and Application of Insecticides. *IARC Monographs on the Evaluation of Carcinogenic Risks to Humans,*, Lyon, France, 45-92.

International Programme on Chemical Safety (IPCS) (1990) Principles for the toxicological assessment of pesticide residues in food. *World Health Organization, Environmental Health Criteria*, **104**, 1-114.

Peraino, C.; Fry, R.J.; Staffeldt, E.; Christopher, J.P. (1975) Comparative enhancing effects of phenobarbital, amobarbital, diphenylhydantion and dichlorodiphenyltrichloroethane on 2-acetylaminofluorene-induced hepatic tumorigenesis in the rat. *Cancer Research*, **35**, 2884-2890.

Rao, M.S.; Reddy, J.K. (1987) Peroxisome proliferation and hepatocarcinogenesis. *Carcinogenesis*, **8**, 631-636.

Schroter, C.; Parzefall, W.; Schroter, H.; Schulte-Hermann, R. (1987) Dose respone studies on the effects of α, β-and γ-hexachlorocyclohexane on putative preneoplastic foci, monooxygenases and growth in rat liver. *Cancer Research*, **47**, 80-88.

Tanaka, T.; Mori, H.; Williams, G.M. (1987) Enhancement of dimethylnitrosamine-initiated hepatocarcinogenesis in hamsters by subsequent administration of carbon tetrachloride but not phenobarbital or p,p'-dichlorodiphenyltrichloroethane. *Carcinogenesis*, **8**, 1171-1178.

Tong, C.C.; Williams, G.M. (1987) The effect of tumor promoters on cell-to-cell communication in liver epithelial cell systems. *Biochemical Mechanisms and Regulation of Intercellular Communication*, Princeton Scientific Publishing Company, Princeton, NJ, 251-263.

Weisburger, J.H.; Williams, G.M. (1981) Carcinogen testing: current problems and new approaches. *Science*, **214**, 401-407.

Whysner, J.; Williams, G.M. (1992) International cancer risk assessment: the impact of biologic mechanisms. *Regulatory Toxicology and Pharmacology*, **15**, 41-50.

Williams, G.M. (1980) The pathogenesis of rat liver cancer caused by chemical carcinogens. *Biochemica ET Biophysica Acta*, **605**, 167-189.

Williams, G.M. (1984) Modulation of chemical carcinogenesis by xenobiotics. *Fundamental & Applied Toxicology*, **4**, 325-344.

Williams, G.M. (1987) Nongenotoxic mechanisms in carcinogenesis. *Banbury Report*, **25**, 367-380.

Williams, G.M. (1990) Epigenetic mechanisms of liver tumor promotion. *Mouse Liver Carcinogenesis*, Alan R. Liss, Inc., New York, 131-145.

Williams, G.M.; Numoto, S. (1984) Promotion of mouse liver neoplasms by the organochlorine pesticides chlordane and heptachlor in comparison to dichlorodiphenyltrichloroethane. *Carcinogenesis*, **5**, 1689-1696.

Williams, G.M.; Weisburger, J.H. (1991) Chemical carcinogenesis. *Casarett and Doull's Toxicology The Basic Sciences of Poisons*, Pergamon Press, New York, 127-200.

PROGRESS IN THE INTERNATIONAL HARMONISATION OF METHODS TO INVESTIGATE THE
NEUROTOXICITY OF CHEMICALS.

R J FIELDER

HEF(M) Division, Department of Health, Hannibal House, Elephant & Castle,
London SE1 6TE

ABSTRACT

There are marked differences between the requirements of the UK
and the US Regulatory Authorities with regard to the assessment
of the neurotoxicity of chemicals. In the UK it is believed that
careful observation of animals in routine toxicity studies will
allow the identification of essentially all compounds with
neurotoxic potential. If warranted, effects can then be
characterised by studies designed to investigate specific
neurotoxic effects. The particular studies appropriate in a
given instance need to be identified on a case-by-case basis.
The EPA however have published comprehensive guidelines on the
testing of chemicals for neurotoxicity. These include a
neurotoxicity screening battery (based on a 'Functional
Observation Battery', motor activity studies and neuropathology)
together with guidelines to investigate specific aspects (eg
peripheral neuropathy, scheduled-controlled operant behaviour,
and developmental neurotoxicity). Attempts to harmonise these
approaches based on proposals for OECD test guidelines are
considered.

INTRODUCTION

There are significant differences in the requirement of Regulatory
Authorities in different countries for the testing of chemicals in order to
assess their potential for neurotoxicity. These are particularly marked as
regards the US Regulatory Authorities, principally the EPA, and the UK and
EC Member States in general. This paper will focus on the differences and
will cover attempts to harmonise the requirements through the OECD test
guidelines programme.

In this regard the OECD programme is particularly relevant. The OECD
comprises 24 member countries including USA and Canada, the EC and Nordic
countries, Japan and Australia. Under the mutual acceptance of data (MAD)
agreement member countries agree to accept toxicity data on chemicals
provided that they are generated to an OECD test guideline and in
compliance with the OECD principles of Good Laboratory Practice (OECD
1981). During the period 1981-6 the OECD agreed numerous guidelines
covering all the relatively routine methods in toxicology. Such
international harmonisation has been important in reducing the needless
duplication of studies, with minor variations, for different regulatory
authorities and has played a significant role in reducing the number of
animals used in toxicity testing.

There is however no agreement as to the total package of testing
required by different regulatory authorities, the MAD agreement only

covering methodology. It is here that there are at present major differences between the UK and the USA with regard to neurotoxicity testing requirements.

DEFINITION OF NEUROTOXICITY

It is pertinent to first consider what it meant by a neurotoxic substance. The simple definition is that it is a chemical that produces an adverse change in the structure or function of the nervous system. Adverse effects are treatment related changes which interfere with normal function and compromise adaption to the environment. However to be of value this definition needs to be refined by considering primary as opposed to secondary effects. Some of the classical signs of neurotoxicity (ataxia, convulsions, behavioural changes etc) will clearly be produced by all chemicals if given at sufficiently high enough dose levels and hence all chemicals could be regarded as being potentially neurotoxic. For practical purposes chemicals should be considered neurotoxic if this is a primary event, rather than being secondary to general systemic toxicity.

UK APPROACH TO TESTING CHEMICALS FOR NEUROTOXICITY

In the UK there are no regulatory requirements specifically for investigating neurotoxicity other than the investigation of delayed neurotoxicity of organophosphorus compounds (OPs) in the hen. This is very much a special case, the animal model (hen) used being specific for one type of end-point (delayed neurotoxicity) induced by a specific class of chemical (OPs) (OECD Guideline No. 418). The hen is given a single high dose of compound (together with atropine to protect against the acute cholinergic effect of the compound if appropriate) and observed clinically for behavioural abnormalities, ataxia and paralysis. At autopsy selected neural tissues are examined histologically. This model is a sensitive method for detecting delayed neurotoxicity produced by OPs but it is not sensitive to delayed neuropathy produced by other chemicals such as n-hexane, acrylamide and carbon disulphide.

The approach adopted in the UK to detect compounds with neurotoxic potential is based on a careful clinical examination of animals in routine acute and repeated dose toxicity studies. This should be carried out at least once a day and should include observations for signs of toxicity on skin, eyes, fur, mucous membranes, the respiratory, circulatory, autonomic and central nervous systems, somato-motor activity and behavioural pattern. Such observations provide a comprehensive basis for the initial assessment of effects on the nervous systems eg changes in arousal state (hyperactivity or lethargy) motor function (disturbances in gait, abnormal posture or muscle tone) or pharmacological effects (sedation). Effects on the autonomic nervous system can be assessed from observations on functions such as salivation, lachrymation, urination or defecation.

In this regard there is a need to consider both acute toxicity (single dose) data and repeated dose studies. Some chemicals produce marked neurotoxicity after a single dose (eg trimethyltins), whereas in other cases, for example acrylamide or carbon disulphide induced peripheral neuropathy, prolonged exposure is needed and 90 day studies are essential for detection of these effects.

In addition to the clinical (cage-side) observations, in the repeated dose studies full autopsies will be carried out with histopathological examination of representative tissues of the nervous system (brain, spinal cord, peripheral nerve etc) together with many other tissues/organs.

It is considered important that the neuropathological data are integrated with the clinical observations; an overall assessment using expert judgement is then made as to whether the compound has neurotoxic potential.

It is the UK view that such studies can identify those compounds with significant neurotoxic potential. If further in-depth testing is warranted to characterise these effects, and to provide more information on mode of action, the appropriate studies need to be identified on a case-by-case basis. Additional studies that may be warranted in a given instance include additional behavioural studies, detailed investigation of sensory function, electrophysiological studies, neuropathology (perfusion fixation of tissues in situ and possibly examination by electron microscopy) and neurochemical studies.

APPROACH ADOPTED BY EPA (USA)

The EPA adopt a somewhat different approach. Detailed guidelines for the testing of pesticides for neurotoxicity were first published in 1982. Their guidelines were comprehensively updated in 1991 and now cover both chemical submissions (under TOSCA) and pesticide submissions (under FIFRA) (EPA 1991).

The current guidelines are comprehensive and include a neurotoxicity screening battery of tests together with specific guidelines covering the following aspects:-

Delayed neurotoxicity of OPs (hen model).

Developmental neurotoxicity (to provide data on effects on the nervous system which might arise following exposure during pregnancy and lactation).

Tests to investigate peripheral nerve function (substances believed to produce peripheral neuropathy).

Scheduled-controlled operant behaviour (designed to evaluate effects on rate and pattern of response under schedules of re-enforcement and intended to be used for compound that have shown neurotoxic signs such as CNS depression or stimulation in other toxicity studies).

Hence the major difference between the US approach and the UK is the need for a specialised 'neurotoxic screening battery' (described in detail later) to identify compounds with neurotoxic potential, rather than the use of the repeated dose toxicity study for this purpose.

POSSIBILITIES OF HARMONISATION : OECD ACTIVITIES

The US presented proposals to the OECD for an OECD test guideline entitled 'Neurotoxicity Screening Battery' in 1988; these were co-sponsored by the Netherlands. They were based essentially on the EPA screening tests and comprised the inclusion of the following in both single and repeated dose studies:-

A functional observational battery (FOB). This is a set of non-invasive procedures designed to detect gross functional deficits in animals and to better quantify behavioural or neurological effects detected in other studies. In addition to a careful clinical examination of the animals outside the home cage the following additional studies were included. Forelimb/hindlimb grip strength - initially using a semi-quantitative measure but followed-up by quantitative methods when abnormalities were seen (Meyer OA et al 1979); this test is designed to detect compounds that induced peripheral neuropathy. Tests for sensory function to detect gross sensory deficits (sight, hearing) (Marshall JF and Teitelbaum 1974; Tupper DE and Wallace RB 1980; WHO/IPCS 1986).

Motor activity tests were also recommended using an automated device capable of detecting both decreases and increases in activity.

At autopsy enhanced examination of the nervous system was required, and specifically perfusion fixation in situ of tissues from at least 6 high dose animals and controls.

Although it was recommended that these tests were combined routinely with acute and repeated dose toxicity studies, this would not be possible without using considerably more animals than in the 'conventional' toxicity studies.

In addition the proposals raised concerns about the interpretation of the data generated particularly the motor activity studies. Such activity is not a simple function, but the combination of many different activities, walking, rearing, sniffing, grooming etc (Rice DC 1990). There are a large number of methods available, many automated (Reiter LW 1978, Evans HL et al 1986). In addition to the need to distinguish primary effects from secondary effects due to general toxicity, the results are markedly affected by complexity and novelty of the environment, nutritional and hormonal status, biological rhythm, age and social setting (Reiter LW 1978). Interpretation of any data generated is thus very difficult.

RECOMMENDATIONS OF AN OECD EXPERT WORKING GROUP

The US proposals were considered by an ad hoc OECD expert working group on neurotoxicity testing at a meeting hosted by the EPA in Washington in 1990.

The recommendations of this working group were that the FOB part of these proposals should be made as compatible as possible with the OECD systemic toxicity guidelines. It was known that the OECD had recognised that the existing guidelines for a 28 day repeated dose oral toxicity study (Guideline 407) and the corresponding 90 day study (Guideline 409) needed updating, and the UK were preparing proposals for consideration by the OECD. It was agreed that the recommendations from the Washington neurotoxicity meeting should be considered when preparing the proposals for updating the 28 day study. The concerns from the US for a greater emphasis on the need for careful clinical observation of the treated animals with some minimal testing for neuromuscular and sensory function, were recognised.

Regarding neuropathology, the expert working group recommended that perfusion fixation techniques should be regarded as a second-tier procedure, for investigation of a suspect or proven effect. It was recognised that this was not an appropriate 'primary surveillance' method and it should not be required in routine toxicity testing.

PROGRESS ON UPDATING OECD REPEATED DOSE (28 DAY) ORAL TOXICITY (GUIDELINE 407)

Proposals from the UK for updating this guideline which included greater emphasis on the need for careful clinical observation, and also studies of hindlimb grip strength, sensory function and with the option of measuring motor activity together with somewhat enhanced (conventional) histopathology have been circulated to OECD member countries for a first round of commenting. Comments received were considered by a small expert working group meeting in Paris in February 1992. It was agreed to recommend the following for the critical 'observations' section of the guideline.

> "Clinical observations should be made once daily and signs noted should include, but not be limited to, changes in skin, fur, eyes, mucous membranes, occurrence of secretions and excretions and autonomic activity (eg lachrymation, piloerection, pupil size, usual respiratory pattern). Changes in gait, posture and reactivity to handling as well as presence of clonic or tonic movements, stereotypes (eg excessive grooming, repetitive circling) or bizarre behaviour (eg self-mutilation, walking backwards) should also be recorded. Observations should be made outside the home cage in a standard arena. Observations should be detailed and carefully recorded preferably using explicitly defined scales. In the fourth exposure week sensory reactivity to stimuli of different modalities (eg auditory, visual and proprioceptive stimuli), assessment of grip strength and motor activity assessment should be conducted. Effort should be made to ensure that variations in the test conditions are minimal and that observations are preferably conducted by observers unaware of the treatment".

PROPOSALS FOR OECD NEUROTOXICITY GUIDELINE

The OECD are now in the process of preparing a Neurotoxicity Guideline as a second tier study which could be used when there is cause for concern based on the results of previous studies eg the updated Guideline 407. This is likely to incorporate parts of the EPA neurotoxicity guideline and will be a further aid to harmonisation.

CONCLUSIONS

If these proposals are accepted in the second commenting round, they will be adopted by the OECD in an updated Guideline 407. Similar changes are then likely to be agreed for the sub-chronic (90 day) Guideline (guideline 409). This should enable the US regulatory authorities to obtain sufficient information to identify compounds with neurotoxic potential from the routine repeated dose toxicity studies.

More detailed Tier II studies should then only be used to characterise the neurotoxic effects of compounds already identified as having neurotoxic potential.

Some degree of harmonisation of testing requirements may thus be achievable. This would have benefits for industry as the need for additional specific studies for certain regulatory authorities would be reduced.

_____

Note: The views expressed in this paper are those of the author and in no way commit the Department of Health.

REFERENCES

EPA (1991) Revised neurotoxicity guidelines for pesticides. Document PB 91-154617 NTIS US Dept Commerce, Springfield Virginia.

Evans HL; Bushnell PJ; Taylor JD; Monico A; Teal JJ; Pontecarva (1986). A system for assessing toxicity of chemicals by continuous monitoring of home cage behaviour. *Fund Appl Tox* 6 721-32.

Marshall JF; Teitelbaum P (1974) *J Comp Physiol Psychol* 86 375-95.

Meyer OA; Tilson HA; Byrol WC; Riley MT (1979). A method for the routine assessment of fore and hind limb grip strength in rats and mice. *Neurobeh Tox* 1 233-36.

OECD (1981). Decision of the OECD Council concerning the mutual acceptance of Data in the assessment of chemicals C-81-30 final OECD Paris.

Reiter LW (1978). Use of activity measurements in behavioural toxicology. *Env Hlth Persp* 26 9-20.

Rice DC (1990). Principles and procedures in behavioral toxicity testing In *Handbook of in vivo Toxicology Testing Procedures*. Arnold DL, Grice HC, Krewski DR (eds). Academic Press Inc. p.383.

Tupper DE; Wallace RB (1980). Utility of neurological examination of rats. *Acta Neurobiol Exp* 40 999-1003.

WHO (1986) Principles and methods for the assessment of neurotoxicity associated with exposure to chemicals 60.

HAZARD ESTIMATION FOR PESTICIDE APPLICATORS

N.G. CARMICHAEL

Rhône-Poulenc Secteur Agrochimie, Crop Protection Division, 14-20, rue Pierre Baizet 69009 Lyon, France

ABSTRACT

Worker exposure studies are used to measure the external contamination of pesticide applicators and toxicology studies to predict the consequences of an absorbed dose. There is, however, no rule of thumb which allows exposure on the skin to be converted to internal dose. This presentation is intended to show that several methods exist to calculate the extent of absorption from simple *in vitro* bridging from rodent to human skin to kinetic modelling and biomonitoring. A stepwise approach should be adopted according to the available data and levels of concern surrounding the toxicology.

INTRODUCTION

In recent years it has become clear that the assessment of hazard to pesticide applicators is at least as important as the significance of crop residues to consumers. It is indisputable that the applicator has greater risk of exposure by virtue of his contact with the concentrated product, whereas many pesticides leave very small or undetectable residues in food crops. This is not to say that the applicator is necessarily at significant risk of intoxication, as many other factors come into play such as :
a) the application method
b) the amount and concentration applied
c) formulation and packaging technology
d) skin penetration
e) the toxicity of the active ingredient.

A risk assessment compares toxicity with either a predicted or measured value for absorbed dose. Clearly there is a need to progress from estimation to measurement of unknowns where the toxicity gives greatest concern. Hence a tiered approach to exposure estimation would progress from modelling based on conservative assumptions, at the level of least concern, to field measurement of actual absorbed dose (biomonitoring) at the other extreme.

This presentation is intended to demonstrate some of the techniques which can be used in estimation of the absorbed dose and from this the margin of safety with respect to the toxicity of the compound.

This presentation is limited to a consideration of the dermal route of exposure as it is generally considered to be the most important. It should be noted, however, that oral ingestion and inhalation may be significant routes of exposure under certain circumstances.

The parameters of hazard estimation for pesticide applicators

The important parameters in hazard estimation for pesticide applicators are conventionally considered to have the following relationships.

$$MOS = \frac{NOAEL}{Da}$$

$$Da = Ed\ Ca$$

NOAEL = No Observed Adverse Effect Level
MOS = margin of safety
E_d = dermal exposure
C_a = coefficient of absorption
D_a = absorbed dose

The NOAEL originates from toxicology studies in animals or less often from human data. The margin of safety is arbitrary and while conventionally set at 100 may vary according to the perceived quality of the data or seriousness of the effect.

Dermal exposure is the value most readily obtained from field studies either by patch or whole suit methods. This type of data lends itself to generic treatment as it is usually a function of the applicaton method, rather than the properties of the active ingredient. Skin absorption, on the other hand, varies according to the product in question and cannot easily be treated generically. For modelling without actual data it is necessary to adopt some conventional and usually pessimistic, value for skin penetration.

Exposure models

Provided generic data bases are subject to quality control with respect to their contents and updated to reflect changes in technology it should be possible to extract a value for dermal exposure (E_d) for the equations shown.

There are now four models or more correctly generic data bases for the estimation of applicator exposure : these are from U.K. (Martin, 1990), Germany (Lundehn et al, 1992), The Netherlands (van Hemmen, 1992)) and North America (PHED, 1991). This means that for common application techniques there now exists sufficient data on exposure that it is probably not worthwhile to
further duplicate this data. Although it remains necessary to confirm that sufficient data exists and that it can meet criteria for quality before this conclusion is made final. However, it may be useful to do exposure studies to demonstrate the efficiency of technological advances (eg. engineering controls, formulation, technology, etc). As a simple illustration, fig. 1 demonstrates the protection from exposure when applying a maize herbicide in spring which is afforded by a cab, even an open cab.

This leaves dermal absorption as the principal unknown. Skin penetration should normally be expressed as a rate constant, which is the only true basis of comparison between compounds. However, such a constant is hard to use directly as the area of skin exposed is unknown and for various practical reasons is bound to stay unknown. The pragmatic approach normally taken is to express skin penetration as a percentage of the material available for absorption (i.e., on the skin) for the actual assessment.

FIGURE 1.   Herbicide application on corn
Actual contamination according to the type of tractor cabin.*

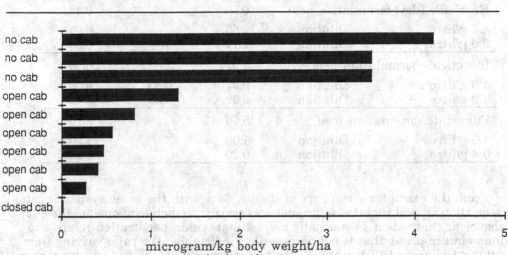

* Each bar represents an individual applicator

Measurement of skin penetration

Skin penetration can be measured in a number of ways each with advantages and disadvantages. The traditional approach is with radiolabelled compound applied to the skin of a rat or rabbit. Usually the area of skin exposed is proportionately greater than expected for most human exposures during normal agricultural operations. Furthermore as rodent skin is dissimilar to human skin in structure and physiology it may provide an unreliable model.

More recently techniques have been developed to measure penetration through epidermal membranes which can be prepared from rat, rabbit and human skin. Such *in vitro* systems are subject to the normal criticism of being artificial and in this case also of having no blood supply to the receptor surface. For this reason the choice of receptor medium may influence the permeation of the solute in a way which is not necessarily representative of the *in vivo* situation. However, such techniques are very useful as a basis of comparison between compounds and between species (table 1).

More recently techniques have been developed to measure penetration through epidermal membranes which can be prepared from rat, rabbit and human skin. Such *in vitro* systems are subject to the normal criticism of being artificial and in this case also of having no blood supply to the receptor surface. For this reason the choice of receptor medium may influence the permeation of the solute in a way which is not necessarily representative of the *in vivo* situation. However, such techniques are very useful as a basis of comparison between compounds and between species (table 1).

TABLE 1.   In vitro skin penetration (8 h) = mg/cm^2/h

		Rat	Rabbit	Human
Herbicide (dry) formulation neat		0.68		0.42
3.3 g/litre	Dilution	2.85		0.61
2.0 g/litre	Dilution	2.71		0.93
Insecticide formulation neat		1.92	1.68	0.18
4.0 g/litre	Dilution	0.07	0.33	0.003
0.2 g/litre	Dilution	0.02	0.35	0.02
Fungicide formulation neat		15.50		2.10
4.0 g/litre	Dilution	1.00		1.20
0.4 g/litre	Dilution	0.20		0.20

From the examples given here of studies done with the same system it can be seen that rat and rabbit skin are not necessarily predictive of one another. It is also clear that rodent skin usually overestimates skin penetration relative to humans but in a way that is not necessarily predictable ; the ratio varying from about 0.8:1 to around 18:1 in the illustration given.

The third approach which is clearly the method of choice from the scientific point of view is measurement of dermal absorption in human volunteers. This approach is however constrained by ethical considerations or even forbidden in some countries. Assuming that the ethical requirements can be met and that techniques exist to analyse the compound or metabolites with sufficient sensitivity to be useful, this approach can give very valuable information.

In an example given below with triclopyr (work done at Dow Chemical : Carmichael *et al*, 1989) data were obtained on oral and dermal pharmacokinetics of triclopyr which is excreted in urine, by animals and man, as the unchanged compound. Modelling was performed in the first instance by the oral route and confirmed by dermal application. This showed that triclopyr kinetics could be modelled with a two comportment model with a fast (alpha) elimination phase and a slower (beta) elimination phase (see table 2). Relative to elimination the speed of dermal penetration (half-life abs) was quite slow. The modelling gave a good correspondence between the predicted amount of triclopyr absorbed and that found in urine and demonstrated that approximately 1-2 % of applied dose was absorbed following 8 hours exposure.

TABLE 2.   Triclopyr pharmacokinetic parameters

Parameters	3.7 mg/kg dermal dose
Body weight (kg)	73.0
Half-life$_{abs}$ (h)	16.8
Half-life$_{elim}$ alpha (h)	1.3
Half-life$_{elim}$ beta (h)	5.0
Urine, % dose found (96 h)	1.37
Urine, % dose predicted (96 h)	1.58
Dermal absorption corrected for recovery %	1.65

Biomonitoring

The approach described above for measuring dermal absorption in humans is directly applicable to calculations of hazard based on actual or theoretical values for exposure. The only major assumption to be made is that the absorption study employed a skin surface 1 cm2/kg body weight similar to that which would be exposed in the field.

However, with much smaller assumptions this data could be applied to applicator biomonitoring studies where no exposure measurement is made. The only requirement would be complete collection of urine (e.g., 48 hours). Fig. 2 illustrates, for the triclopyr example, the relationship between time and urinary excretion of the parent compound before modelling. The pharmacokinetic model is able to predict from the duration of the collection interval what proportion of the absorbed dose is excreted ; therefore a direct estimation of the absorbed dose can be made.

FIGURE 2.   Herbicide X in urine - Dermal dose equivalent to 3.7 mg/kg

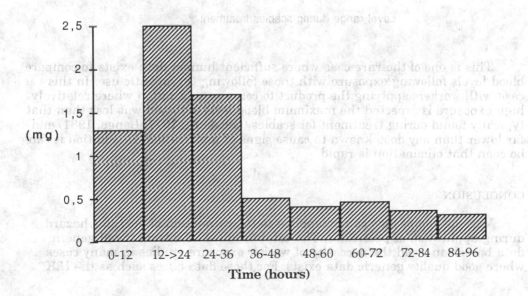

Effect biomonitoring

Another approach which can be used, if appropriate, is direct measurement of an indicator of exposure. In practice there are few indicators sufficiently sensitive for this approach. Blood cholinesterase depression is the best known example and can be measured with organophosphates, although it is not reliable with carbamates due to spontaneous reversion of the inhibition (Vandekar, 1980).

Occasionally a hybrid type of study can be envisaged as illustrated in fig. 3 with Lindane.

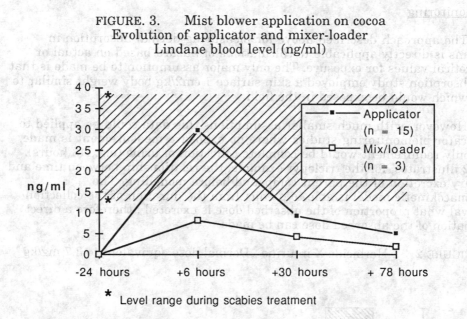

FIGURE. 3.   Mist blower application on cocoa
Evolution of applicator and mixer-loader
Lindane blood level (ng/ml)

* Level range during scabies treatment

This is one of the rare case where sufficient human data exists to compare blood levels following exposure with those following therapeutic use. In this case with workers applying the product to cocoa in a situation where relatively high exposure is expected the maximum blood level attained was less than that typically found during treatment for scabies (Ginsburg, 1977; Lange, 1981) and far lower than any dose known to cause signs of intoxication. In addition it can be seen that elimination is rapid.

CONCLUSION

Various approaches can be applied to the estimation of operator hazard during application of pesticides. The establishment of international generic data bases can avoid the necessity of worker exposure studies in many cases where good quality generic data exists. For those data bases such as the U.K.

where the actual data are not open to peer review there remain doubts as to the validity of the generic values. These concerns are being addressed and are elaborated upon in the next paper by W. Chen. A tiered approach is suggested to increase the precision of skin absorption estimation according to the gap between the apparent margin of safety based on calculation and the margin of safety required. Very often the rodent skin *in vivo* system will provide sufficient reassurance that a substance is not a fast skin penetrant. *In vitro* measurement allows further refinement and comparison between animal and human skin, but remains a model system. It is clear that the least assumptions are made with human volunteer studies, but for ethical or practical reasons these are not always feasible. They are also expensive and time consuming and such precision is not always necessary.

Assuming that exposure data of a representative nature is available a tiered approach to exposure estimation also appears reasonable. The first stage being simple paper calculation. Conventional exposure studies are therefore only useful to demonstrate technological improvements in formulation, mixing, loading or application or where generic values of sufficient quality do not exist. If measurement of skin absorption and reference exposure values leave the issue unresolved the final resort is a pharmacokinetic study followed by biomonitoring.

REFERENCES

Carmichael, N.G.; Nolan, R.J.; Perkins, J.M.; Davies, R.; Warrington, S.J. (1989) Oral and dermal Pharmacokinetics of Triclopyr in Human Volunteers *Human Toxicol..,* 8, 431-437

Ginsburg, C.M.; Lowry, W.; Reish, J.R. (1977) Absorption of Lindane (gamma benzene hexachloride) in infants and children. *Journal of pediatrics.* **91**(6), 913-917.

Lange, M.; Nitzsche, K.; Zesch, A. (1981) Percutaneous absoption of lindane in healthy volunteers and scabies patients. *Arch Dermato Res.,* 387-399.

Lundehn, J.R.; Westphal, D.; Kieczka, H.; Krebs, B.; Löcher-Bolz, S.; Maasfeld, W.; Pick, E.D. (1992) Einheitliche Grundsätze zur Sicherung des Gesundheitsschutzes für den Anwender von Pflanzenschutzmitteln (Einheitliche Grundsätze Anwenderschutz). *Mitteilungen aus der Biologishen Bundesanstalt für Land-und Forstwirtschaft, Berlin-Dahlem*

Martin, A.D. (1990) A predictive model for the assessment of dermal exposure to pesticides, in Prediction of Percutaneous Penetration. Methods, Measurements, Modelling (R.C.Scott, R.H.Guy and J.Hadgraft, eds) *IBC Technical Services Ltd.,* pp 273-278.

PHED, Pesticide Handler Exposure Database (1991) *Reference Manual, Versar Inc. Springfield, VA 22151, USA.*

van Hemmen, J.J. (1992) Assessment of occupational exposure to pesticies in agriculture. *SZW, Ministry of Social Affairs and Employment,* S 141-1, S 141-2, S 141-3.

Vandekar, M. (1980) Minimizing occupational exposure to pesticides : Cholinesterase determination and organophosphorus poisoning. *Residue Rev.* **75**,., 67-80.

THE HARMONISATION OF OPERATOR EXPOSURE RISK ASSESSMENT

W.L. CHEN

Department of Regulatory, Toxicology and Environmental
Affairs, DowElanco Europe, Letcombe Regis, Wantage,
Oxfordshire, OX12 9JT

ABSTRACT

In connection with the development of Uniform
Principles, an ad hoc working group on operator
exposure was formed, consisting of specialised
experts from European Community (EC) countries.
The aims of the working group are to establish
the scientific basis for: (1) A new and harmonised
EC protocol for the estimation of operator
exposure by modelling. (2) To build an European
operator exposure database. (3) To develop a new
EC protocol for the measurement of operator
exposure. (4) To define a tier risk assessment
process for field applicators.

INTRODUCTION

The European Communities (EC) Registration Directive
91/414/EEC provides a harmonisation regime for the
authorisation by Member States of plant protection products
in accordance with Community rules, namely the Uniform
Principles.

In connection with the development of Uniform
Principles, an ad hoc EC working group on operator exposure
was formed, consisting of specialised experts from France,
Germany, U.K., The Netherlands and Ireland. The objectives
of the working group are to establish the scientific basis
for: (1) A new and harmonised EC protocol for the estimation
of operator exposure by modelling. (2) To build an European
operator exposure database. (3) To develop a new EC
protocol for the measurement of operator exposure. (4) To
define a tier risk assessment process for field workers.

Starting with the existing U.K. and German models and
databases, the working group has developed the scientific
basis for new and harmonised protocols for the estimation
(modelling) and measurement of operator exposure. A tier
operator risk assessment scheme has been defined
incorporating these new protocols.

TOXICOLOGICAL ASSESSMENT

In assessing the risks to operators working with crop
protection products, it is important to recall the
fundamental principle of toxicology, namely "Dose Makes the

Poison". Risk is dependent on both toxicity and exposure. Therefore, in the operator risk (or safety) assessment, both toxicological assessment and exposure assessment must be taken into consideration.

The endpoint of the toxicological assessment of a crop protection product is the determination of an Acceptable Operator Exposure Level (AOEL), derived after a thorough evaluation of the toxicological profile of the product. This process involves:

(1)   Examination of all the relevant toxicological data ensuring both high quality and compliance with the data and protocol requirements set forth in Annexes II and III of the EC Registration Directive (European Communities, 1991) and the study report on Uniform Principles by Dr. Mark Lynch (Lynch, 1992).

(2)   Selection of the relevant No-observed-adverse-effect-level (NOAEL) which is based primarily on the subchronic toxicity and developmental toxicity studies [including reproductive effects on the parent (Fo) generation of a two-generation reproduction study]. These studies are selected because short-term repeated (subchronic) exposures are the ones experienced by field applicators using crop protection products.

(3)   Application of the appropriate safety factor which is dependent on the toxicological profile of the product. Traditionally, a 10-fold safety margin is used for setting occupational exposure limits in the manufacturing plant. In the German model (Lundehn, 1992) for field exposure, a 25-fold safety factor is applied to general toxicological effects. A 100-fold safety factor is conventionally used for more severe toxicological endpoints.

(4)   Finally, the AOEL is determined by applying the appropriate safety factor to the relevant NOAEL.

EXPOSURE ASSESSMENT

The Ad Hoc EC Operator Exposure Working Group has developed a tier scheme for the determination of operator exposure. This is summarised in the following.

Tier 1   Estimation of operator exposure

There is a general agreement among scientific experts that sufficient exposure data have been generated in recent years, which enables the development of a generic European operator exposure database. This database is built according to application methods categorised as follows:

    Boom Spray Applicators
    Mixer and Loader Exposure
    Air Blast Application
    Hand Held Application
    Bystander Exposure
    Harvester (Re-entry) Exposure
    Mediterranean Region Exposure
    Glasshouse/Greenhouse Exposure
    Seed Treatment Exposure
    Grain Storage Products
    Application of Solids, Granules and Dusts
    Aerial Applications

Starting with the existing U.K. (U.K. Report, 1986) and German (Lundehn, 1992) models and databases, the Ad Hoc EC Working Group has developed the scientific basis for a new and harmonised EC protocol (model) for a first tier estimation of operator exposure.

In this new protocol (model), the exposures to mixer/loader and applicators are estimated using an European operator exposure database. Dermal, inhalation and oral routes of exposure are taken into consideration. The European operator exposure database is categorised according to application techniques and a large number of variables are taken into account, e.g. concentration of the active ingredient, formulation type, application rate, work rate, container type and size, clothing and gloves, etc.

Tier 2   Specific measurements of model parameters

It is important to recognise that the first tier estimation using the generic database and modelling is usually an over-estimation of the actual operator exposure. A number of conservative assumptions are generally used in the model calculations. In the event that the first tier estimation shows that the margin-of-safety (MOS) to operators applying the product is inadequate, then a second tier approach is used, employing actual data on specific model parameters such as dermal absorption and protective clothing penetration.

Both In Vitro and In Vivo methods for the measurement of skin absorption have been developed and submitted to the Organisation for Economic Cooperation and Development (OECD) for their validation and adoption as OECD/EEC test protocols.

Tier 3   Determination of operator exposure

Finally, as a third tier, actual field operator exposure studies can be conducted to determine more precisely the level of exposure to applicators. A state-of-art protocol, including the measurement of external exposure (contaminations) by dermal, inhalation and oral routes, the performance of pharmacokinetics studies applicable to humans and the determination of internal dose by biomonitoring (urine, plasma, etc.), has been developed and discussed in the recent International Workshop on Risk Assessment for Worker Exposure to Agricultural Pesticides in Hague, The Netherlands (International Workshop, 1992). This test protocol will be submitted to OECD for their review and adoption as an OECD/EEC guideline.

A TIER PROCESS FOR ASSESSING OPERATOR SAFETY

A tier process for assessing operator safety has been developed by the Ad Hoc EC Operator Exposure Working Group (Figure 1). This tier process was presented at the recent International Workshop on Risk Assessment for Worker Exposure to Agricultural Pesticides in Hague, The Netherlands (International Workshop, 1992). This scheme was supported by scientific experts from Europe, United States and Canada attending the Workshop.

As a first tier of safety assessment, operator exposure can be estimated from the use of the EC operator exposure model and generic database. Certain assumptions for unknowns (e.g. dermal absorption to be 10%) would be used. If an acceptable margin-of-safety (MOS) to operators can be demonstrated, based on the estimated operator exposure level as compared with the AOEL (determined from the toxicological assessment), then the crop protection product can be approved without further investigation.

However, if the first tier estimation shows that the MOS is inadequate, then a second tier study would be performed, using actual data on specific model parameters e.g. skin absorption, protective clothing penetration, container size and design, etc. This would improve the risk assessment.

Finally, as the third tier, actual field operator exposure studies can be conducted to determine more precisely the operator exposure and safety assessment. Measurements of external exposure and the internal dose (by biomonitoring of urine, etc.) can be performed and the results used in the safety assessment.

CONCLUSION

The investigation and assessment of the toxicological profile of plant protection products will largely be completed for the inclusion of active substances in Annex I of the EC Registration Directive 91/414/EEC. Those assessments will include the selection of appropriate safety factors and the setting of Acceptable Operator Exposure Levels (AOEL) and Acceptable Daily Intake (ADI) levels for man. While AOEL is determined for the purpose of assessing operator safety, the ADI is established for consumer safety assessment.

Figure 1. TIERED REGULATION OF APPLICATOR HAZARD

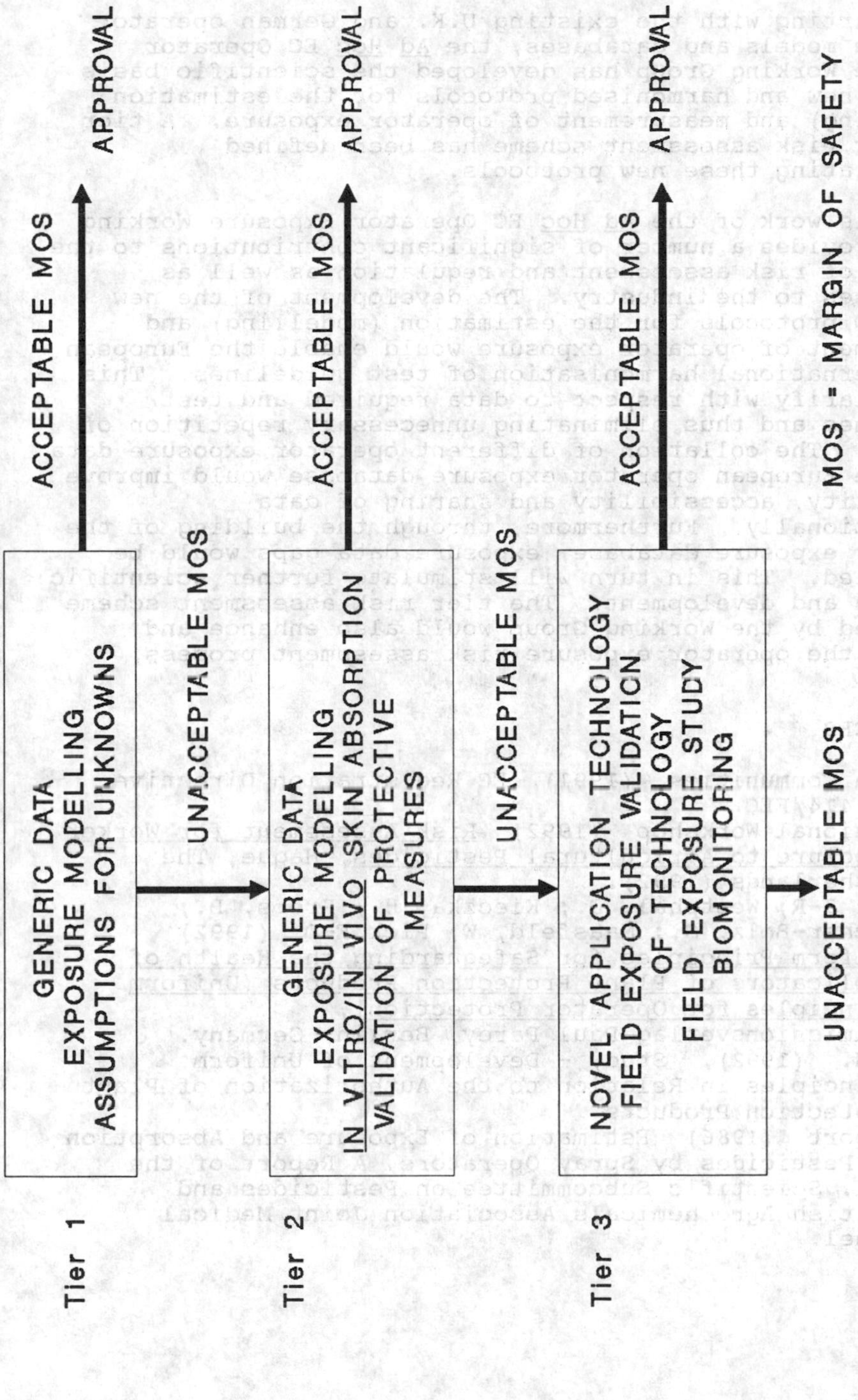

Starting with the existing U.K. and German operator exposure models and databases, the Ad Hoc EC Operator Exposure Working Group has developed the scientific basis for the new and harmonised protocols for the estimation (modelling) and measurement of operator exposure. A tier operator risk assessment scheme has been defined incorporating these new protocols.

This work of the Ad Hoc EC Operator Exposure Working Group provides a number of significant contributions to the science of risk assessment and regulation as well as advantages to the industry. The development of the new EEC/OECD protocols for the estimation (modelling) and measurement of operator exposure would enable the European and international harmonisation of test guidelines. This would clarify with respect to data required and test guidelines and thus eliminating unnecessary repetition of testing. The collation of different operator exposure data into the European operator exposure database would improve the quality, accessibility and sharing of data internationally. Furthermore, through the building of the operator exposure database, exposure data gaps would be identified. This in turn will stimulate further scientific research and development. The tier risk assessment scheme developed by the Working Group would also enhance and improve the operator exposure risk assessment process.

REFERENCES

European Communities (1991) EC Registration Directive 91/414/EEC.

International Workshop (1992) Risk Assessment for Worker Exposure to Agricultural Pesticides, Hague, The Netherlands (1992).

Lundehn, J-R; Westphal, D.; Kieczka, H.; Krebs, B.; Locher-Bolz, S.; Maasfeld, W; Pick E-D (1992) Uniform Principles for Safeguarding the Health of Applicators of Plant Protection Products (Uniform Principles for Operator Protection), Kommissionsverlag Paul Parey, Berlin, Germany.

Lynch, M. (1992), Study - Development of Uniform Principles in Relation to the Authorization of Plant Protection Products.

U.K. Report (1986) Estimation of Exposure and Absorption of Pesticides by Spray Operators, A Report of the U.K. Scientific Subcommittee on Pesticides and British Agrochemicals Association Joint Medical Panel.

SESSION 3C

PEST AND DISEASE RESISTANCE TO AGROCHEMICALS

SESSION
ORGANISER   DR D. R. JONES

POSTERS   3C-1 to 3C-17

FUNGICIDE SENSITIVITY IN YELLOW RUST OF WHEAT (*PUCCINIA STRIIFORMIS*)

R.A.BAYLES, E.G.BARNARD AND P.L.STIGWOOD

National Institute of Agricultural Botany, Huntingdon Road, Cambridge, CB3 0LE

ABSTRACT

Isolates of *Puccinia striiformis* collected between 1961 and 1990 were tested for sensitivity to triadimenol and fenpropimorph using seedlings sprayed with low doses of fungicide. Isolates varied in their sensitivity, but there was no evidence that sensitivity had declined over time. There were indications that variation in sensititvity was associated with the geographical origin and specific virulence of isolates. Isolates from the north of the U.K., and those possessing virulence for the wheat cultivar Hornet, tended to be more sensitive than isolates from the south and those lacking virulence for cv. Hornet. There was no relationship between the sensitivity of isolates and whether fungicide had been applied to the crop from which they came.The relative sensitivity of two isolates remained constant for a range of triazole fungicides.

INTRODUCTION

Puccinia striiformis, the causal agent of yellow rust, is a major pathogen of winter wheat in the U.K. Significant outbreaks of the disease occur once every three to four years and are most likely when susceptible varieties dominate the wheat acreage. The risk of disease is usually greatest in the east and north-east regions. Although fungicides of the triazole and morpholine groups have been widely used to control yellow rust, there have been no substantiated reports of loss of disease control in the field. No previous studies of fungicide sensitivity in *P.striiformis* are known, but Boyle *et al.*,(1988) reported variation in sensitivity to triazole fungicides in populations of *P.recondita* (brown rust of wheat) and *P.hordei* (brown rust of barley).

The aims of the investigation reported here were to examine the variation in fungicide sensitivity in *P.striiformis*, determine whether sensitivity has altered over the past twenty years and establish a base-line measure of sensitivity against which to gauge future changes.

Variation in *P.striiformis* for virulence for the genetic resistances of cultivars has been monitored since 1967 by the U.K. Cereal Pathogen Virulence Survey, which maintains an extensive collection of isolates, classified on the basis of virulence and origin. These isolates were the main source of material for fungicide sensitivity tests.

METHODS

Screening of isolates collected 1961-1990

Isolates were screened for sensitivity to triadimenol and fenpropimorph using a seedling test. Each test included a standard isolate for reference. Ten seedlings of the universally susceptible wheat cultivars Sappo or Vuka were grown in 2.5" pots. Seedlings were sprayed with fungicide when the first leaf had expanded (7-8 days after sowing). The dose rates used changed during the testing period, but the following rates were common to all tests:

Triadimenol	15.63 mg AI/l	1/40 field rate
Fenpropimorph	187.50 mg AI/l	1/20 field rate
Nil control		

A field application simulator sprayer, delivering 200 l.ha^{-1} at a pressure of 2 bars was used.

24 hrs after spraying, seedlings were inoculated in a rotary spore inoculator, using fresh uredospores of *P.striiformis* mixed with talc. After incubation for 48 hrs at 7°C and high relative humidity, seedlings were transferred to a controlled environment growth room with 16 hrs light at 18°C and 8 hrs dark at 11°C.

Four to five days after the appearance of yellow rust pustules on untreated seedlings (14-15 days after inoculation), the percentage leaf area covered with pustules was assessed on first leaves. For each isolate, the mean infection on treated seedlings was expressed as a percentage of that on the nil control. The value for the standard isolate was then subracted from that for the test isolate to give an index of infection 'I'. Positive values of 'I' indicated higher infection than the standard isolate i.e lower sensitivity, whilst negative values of 'I' indicated lower infection than the standard i.e greater sensitivity.

Isolates were classified according to:
1. Year of collection
2. Whether or not from a fungicide-treated crop (F+ or F-)
3. Geographical location, north or south of River Tyne (N or S)
4. Virulence or avirulence for cv. Hornet (V or A)

Using these criteria, mean 'I' values for groups of similar isolates were compared using a t-test, to indicate associations between sensitivity to fungicides and other characteristics.

Tests of two isolates with contrasting sensitivity to triadimenol for sensitivity to other triazoles

Two isolates, 90/20 (with low sensitivity to triadimenol) and 83/62 (with near average sensitivity to triadimenol) were tested for sensitivity to five triazoles, at dose rates ranging from 1/40 to 1/5 field rate.

RESULTS

Screening of isolates collected 1961-1990

Results were obtained for 291 isolates tested for sensitivity to triadimenol and 268 isolates tested for sensitivity to fenpropimorph. For triadimenol, 'I' ranged from -40 to +71, (approximately 10%-90% of the infection level on the nil control). For fenpropimorph, 'I' ranged from -54 to +41, (approximately 1%-65% of the infection level on the nil control). There was no significant correlation between sensitivity to triadimenol and sensitivity to fenpropimorph.

Mean infection indices for different groups of isolates, and the significance of the differences between them, are given in Tables 1 to 5.

TABLE 1. Mean infection indices for isolates classified according to year.

Fungicide	Year	No. isolates	mean 'I'	comparison	significance
Triadimenol	pre-1989	102	-3.25	pre '89 v '89	P=0.05
	1989	115	0.082	'89 v '90	P=0.01
	1990	74	-4.51	pre '89 v '90	NS
Fenpropimorph	pre-1989	95	-7.33	pre '89 v '89	NS
	1989	111	-7.89	'89 v '90	NS
	1990	62	-9.45	pre '89 v '90	NS

TABLE 2. Mean infection indices for isolates classified according to fungicide application.

Fungicide	Fungicide application	No. isolates	mean 'I'	significance of difference
Triadimenol	+F	73	-2.70	NS
	-F	215	-2.17	
Fenpropimorph	+F	69	-7.54	NS
	-F	196	-8.33	

TABLE 3. Mean infection indices for isolates classified according to geographical location.

Fungicide	Location	No. isolates	mean 'I'	significance of difference
Triadimenol	N	71	-5.07	P=0.05
	S	205	-1.31	
Fenpropimorph	N	66	-16.25	P=0.001
	S	188	-5.17	

TABLE 4. Mean infection indices for isolates classified according to virulence for cv. Hornet.

Fungicide	Virulence for cv. Hornet	No. isolates	mean 'I'	significance of difference
Triadimenol	V	114	-3.82	P=0.05
	A	167	-0.90	
Fenpropimorph	V	102	-12.05	P=0.01
	A	157	-5.11	

TABLE 5. Mean infection indices for isolates classified according to location and virulence.

Fungicide	Location	Virulence for cv. Hornet	No. isolates	mean 'I'	comparison	significance
Triadimenol	N	V	53	-5.42	N,V v S,V	NS
		A	18*			
	S	V	61	-2.42	S,V v S,A	NS
		A	141	-0.75		
Fenpropimorph	N	V	49	-14.97	N,V v S,V	P=0.05
		A	4*			
	S	V	53	-9.35	S,V v S,A	P=0.001
		A	132	-3.31		

* number of isolates too small for valid comparisons

Tests of two isolates with contrasting sensitivity to triadimenol for sensitivity to other triazoles

Results are given in Table 6.

TABLE 6. Percentage leaf area infected with yellow rust (relative to untreated control) for wheat seedlings treated with five triazole fungicides and inoculated with two isolates of *P.striiformis*

Fungicide	Field rate (mg AI/l)	Dose* rate	Isolate	
			90/20	83/62
Triadimenol	625	1/40	78	54
		1/20	63	44
		1/10	54	23
		1/5	30	8
Cyproconazole	400	1/40	49	7
		1/20	15	2
		1/10	3	0
		1/5	0	0
Flusilazole	1000	1/40	99	99
		1/20	99	88
		1/10	76	49
		1/5	37	22
Propiconazole	625	1/40	73	10
		1/20	37	2
		1/10	13	0
		1/5	1	0
Tebuconazole	1250	1/40	13	4
		1/20	3	0
		1/10	0	0
		1/5	0	0

* fraction of full field rate

Infection levels varied between fungicides, but isolate 90/20 produced consistently more disease than isolate 83/62.

DISCUSSION

Isolates of *Puccinia striiformis* collected between 1961 and 1990 varied widely in their sensitivity to low doses of fungicides, equivalent to 1/40 field rate triadimenol and 1/20 field rate fenpropimorph. As might be expected from the different modes of action of triazole and morpholine fungicides, sensitivity to the two was unrelated. There was no evidence of any consistent trend in sensitivity over this period. The only significant differences were between isolates from the 1989 season and those from both earlier and later years. The 1989 isolates appeared to be less sensitive to triadimenol than isolates collected either before 1989 or during 1990. This may have been associated with unusually high levels of fungicide use during the severe epidemic of yellow rust in 1989.

There was no indication that fungicide application to a crop had influenced the sensitivity of isolates collected from it. However, the analysis of fungicide effects was limited by the lack of detailed information on products and timing of applications. It is also possible that ingress of inoculum from outside the sprayed crop may have masked the effects of selection taking place within the crop.

The most consistent differences in sensitivity were between isolates of different geographical origin and virulence. The possibility of an association between these two characters was recognised, since virulence for cv. Hornet was first detected in the north in 1988 and became common in this region before establishing further south (Bayles et al.,1989, Bayles and Stigwood, 1991)

Isolates from the south tended to be less sensitive to both chemicals than isolates from the north. This observation may be partly accounted for by the more intensive use of fungicides on wheat in the south, but may also be related to geographical differences in pathogen virulence. When comparisons between north and south were restricted to isolates of similar virulence (i.e those virulent on cv. Hornet), the geographical contrast was less pronounced.

Isolates virulent on cv.Hornet were more sensitive than avirulent isolates. When the geographical influence was removed by confining comparisons of virulent and avirulent isolates to those from the south, the differential was maintained for fenpropimorph, but not for triadimenol. The fact that virulent isolates were first selected from northern populations, which were themselves relatively sensitive, may be a partial explanation for their greater sensitivity.

There was evidence that sensitivity to different chemicals in the triazole family is related, implying that insensitivity to the older triazoles would confer insensitivity to newer products.

ACKNOWLEDGEMENTS

This work was funded by a research grant from the Home-Grown Cereals Authority.

REFERENCES

Bayles, R.A.; Stigwood, P.L. (1991). Yellow rust of wheat. 90, 15-20. *United Kingdom Cereal Pathogen Virulence Survey Annual Report for 1990*, 15-20.

Bayles, R.A.; Channell, M.H.; Stigwood, P.L. (1989). Yellow rust of wheat. *United Kingdom Cereal Pathogen Virulence Survey Annual Report for 1988*, 11-15.

Boyle, F.; Gilmour, J.; Lennard, J.H.; Clifford, B.C.; Jones, E.R.L. (1988). Sensitivity of cereal brown rust fungi to triadimefon and propiconazole. *Proceedings of the 1988 Brighton Crop Protection Conference - Pests and Diseases*, 1, 379-384.

LONG TERM MONITORING RESULTS OF WHEAT POWDERY MILDEW SENSITIVITY TOWARDS FENPROPIMORPH AND STRATEGIES TO AVOID THE DEVELOPMENT OF RESISTANCE

G. LORENZ, R. SAUR, K. SCHELBERGER

BASF Aktiengesellschaft, Crop Protection Division, Research and Development, D-6703 Limburgerhof, Federal Republic of Germany

B. FORSTER, R. KÜNG, P. ZOBRIST

CIBA-Geigy Ltd., Plant Protection Divison, CH-8157 Dielsdorf, Switzerland

ABSTRACT

Both triazole and morpholine fungicides are classified as compounds with a low risk of resistance development. On the other hand, wheat powdery mildew clearly belongs to the group of high risk fungi as far as the development of fungicide resistance is concerned.

Therefore, in order to closely follow the sensitivity development of wheat powdery mildew towards fenpropimorph from the very beginning, long term monitoring programmes were initiated, independently from each other, in Switzerland in 1982 by Maag/CIBA-Geigy and in Germany in 1984 by BASF, which coincided with the official launching of this fungicide in the respective countries. A long term field trial with different spray regimes (i.e. combinations and alternations) of fenpropimorph and triadimenol was started in Germany in 1986 in order to obtain data for possible resistance strategies.

The first signs of a slight reduction in the sensitivity of wheat powdery mildew populations to fenpropimorph became apparent in 1989 in both Switzerland and Germany. As far as counter measures are concerned, data from the long term field trial indicate that triazole/morpholine combinations and alternations are equally well suited to avoid a shift in fenpropimorph sensitivity. For practical reasons the use of combinations, either as tank or ready mixtures, is the preferred and widely recommended anti-resistance strategy.

INTRODUCTION

Both triazole and morpholine fungicides, currently the most important groups of fungicides for the control of cereal powdery mildews in Europe, are classified as compounds with a low risk of resistance development. The current situation generally supports this classification, although in the case of triazoles a shift in the sensitivity of cereal powdery mildew populations was recorded in the early 1980s (Fletcher & Wolfe, 1981; Butters et al., 1984) which resulted in the necessity for counter measures by the mid-1980s (Heaney et al., 1988).

Therefore, monitoring programmes for fenpropimorph were initiated with the official launching of this product in Switzerland in 1982 and in Germany in 1984 (Lorenz & Pommer, 1984). Since both programmes have been run independently from each other, the methods and aims are slightly different.

In addition to this, in Germany a specially designed long-term field trial was initiated in 1986, in which in each year and in the same plots the influence of fenpropimorph, alone and in combination or alternation with triazoles, on the sensitivity of powdery mildew populations has been studied. This trial was established in order to obtain data upon which resistance strategies could be based.

171

MATERIALS and METHODS

Maag/CIBA-Geigy - Switzerland

To follow the development of the sensitivity situation of wheat powdery mildew in Switzerland, bulk samples of powdery mildew were collected at the end of June every other year in the areas of Zürich, Schaffhausen and Solothurn from commercially fenpropimorph-treated fields. These were transferred on the same day to 7-day old wheat plants (cv. Probus) by rubbing the mildew colonies against the leaves of the seedlings in a sterile bench. To avoid cross contamination, the isolates were kept apart by isolating the pots of plants with PVC-tubing. To test sensitivity, plants were sprayed to run-off with a range of fenpropimorph concentrations: 0.3, 1.3, 10, 30, 60 and 100 mg/l AI. After the plants had dried, they were inoculated by passing infected leaves through the seedlings. The inoculated plants were again covered with PVC-tubes and transferred to a glasshouse for about seven days.

A reference isolate was included in each test to check the variability of the results. Assessments were made by estimating the percentage of powdery mildew coverage on the primary leaves per pot and MIC (minimal inhibitory concentration) -values of each isolate were recorded.

BASF-Germany

Bulk samples of powdery mildew were also collected each year at growth stage (GS) 26-30 (Zadoks *et al.*, 1974) from 10 different locations within Germany. At the time of collection, the plants had not been treated. The powdery mildew was immediately transferred onto primary leaf segments of untreated wheat seedlings (cv. Kanzler) inserted into an agar medium, which contained 10 ppm benzimidazole, in Petri dishes.

To test sensitivity, segments of primary leaf of wheat seedlings were used which had been treated to run-off with a concentration range of fenpropimorph: 0.1, 0.5, 1, 5, 10, 50, 100, 250 mg/l AI. The leaf segments, inserted in benzimidazole agar, were inoculated using dry spores and a settling tower. The Petri dishes were then placed in a climate chamber at 18° C and 8000 lux for 14 h/day.

Results were recorded after 8-10 days by counting the number of powdery mildew pustules on the leaf segments. LD98-values were calculated by probit analysis from dose-response curves.

In a long-term field trial with the wheat variety Disponent, which was started in 1986 at a site near the BASF Agricultural Research Station Limburgerhof, the following treatments were included:

I   = untreated
II   = triadimenol at 125 g/ha
III = fenpropimorph at 750 g/ha in alternation with triadimenol at 125 g/ha
IV   = fenpropimorph at 375 g/ha in combination with triadimenol at 125 g/ha
V   = fenpropimorph at 750 g/ha

The same plots were used for the same treatments each year. The plot size was 5000 m². All plots were sprayed with the onset of powdery mildew attack using standard field-spraying equipment. Applications were repeated in the different plots whenever new powdery mildew infections were recorded. Bulk samples of powdery mildew were collected before the first fungicide application (GS 26-30) and after the last application (GS 68-69). Visual assessments of the infected leaves were recorded as percentage leaf area affected for the entire plot. The trials were harvested using a small plot combine harvester and yields were corrected to 86% dry matter.

RESULTS

The data listed in Table 1 are those obtained from the first sampling at the beginning of the growing season in each year from 10 different regions in Germany. The 1984 values practically represent the base-line data of the powdery mildew populations, since to this date there had not been any large volume/acreage treatment with fenpropimorph. Notable is the relatively wide variation in the reaction of the powdery mildew populations from the different sites. This obviously represents the natural variation within the populations, a factor which was largely maintained until 1988.

TABLE 1. Monitoring data (LD98-values in ppm AI) of wheat powdery mildew and fenpropimorph from different regions in Germany for the years 1984-1988

Location	1984 LD98	1985 LD98	1986 LD98	1987 LD98	1988 LD98
Kiel	-	8	8	2	7
Oldenburg	15	-	-	-	14
Münster	11	-	10	12	4
Hannover	13	15	14	12	3
Köln	8	5	7	4	-
Giessen	-	8	6	3	3
Böhl	8	7	7	5	-
Erlangen	3	5	-	-	2
Stuttgart	-	4	4	-	-
München	7	7	-	2	-

In Table 2, values from all samples from one season in Germany and Switzerland have been combined and arranged into sensitivity classes. There is a remarkable comparability of the sensitivity distributions in both countries, especially when considering the fact that for Germany LD98- and for Switzerland MIC-values are recorded.

TABLE 2. Sensitivity distribution of wheat powdery mildew in Germany and Switzerland (numbers represent percentage of isolates in the respective sensitivity classes)

Year	Germany LD98 (mg/l AI) fenpropimorph						Switzerland MIC (mg/l AI) fenpropimorph					
	No. of isolates	< 1	> 1-3	> 3-10	> 10-30	> 30-60	> 60-100 No. of isolates	< 1	> 1-3	> 3-10	> 10-30	> 30-60	> 60-100
1982	-	-	-	-	-	-	- 84	*	0	30	70	0	0
1983	-	-	-	-	-	-		*	-	-	-	-	-
1984	14	*	22	57	21	0	0 94	*	1	42	57	0	0
1985	34	*	6	55	39	0	0 -	*	-	-	-	-	-
1986	28	11	82	7	0	0	0 -	*	-	-	-	-	-
1987	35	0	77	17	6	0	0 58	*	0	38	62	0	0
1988	74	3	54	30	14	0	0 -	*	-	-	-	-	-
1989	67	0	21	24	52	3	0 146	*	0	41	46	14	0
1990	137	0	15	32	45	8	0 60	*	0	30	58	11	0
1991	112	0	21	46	30	4	0 73	*	7	44	36	14	0
1992	-						-						

* not tested

TABLE 3. Influence of different spray regimes with morpholines and triazoles on sensitivity and control of wheat powdery and on wheat yield

Treatment	Sampling date: GS 26-30 LD98 (mg/l AI)		GS of treatments	Sampling date: GS 68-69 LD98 (mg/l AI)		% infected leaf area	yield (t/ha)
	fenpropi-morph	triadi-menol		fenpropi-morph	triadi-menol		
1986							
I	3	14	-	1	15	32	4,7
II	-	-	47;61	3	30	10	5,9
III	-	-	47;61	3	14	6	6,4
IV	-	-	47;61	3	8	2	6,6
V	-	-	47;61	2	7	2	6,6
1987							
I	8	8	-	2	28	19	5,5
II	2	26	32;47;59	2	45	4	5,4
III	2	3	32;59	2	20	2	5,9
IV	1	3	32;59	2	30	1	5,9
V	2	2	32;59	6	26	1	6,0
1988							
I	4	5	-	6	16	25	4,5
II	8	7	31;37;51;61	4	45	12	6,3
III	2	8	31;51;61	1	52	3	7,8
IV	1	3	31;51;61	3	26	0	7,8
V	1	1	31;51;61	1	4	0	7,9
1989							
I	15	26	-	4	10	15	5,8
II	8	8	30;33;37;65	2	30	11	7,3
III	2	21	30;37;65	2	29	5	8,4
IV	1	7	30;37;65	2	15	0	8,5
V	4	7	30;37;65	12	6	4	8,1
1990							
I	30	39	-	5	27	18	6,4
II	29	58	32;39;59	2	61	5	7,0
III	7	7	32;39;59	6	16	2	7,6
IV	9	31	32;39;59	4	52	2	7,8
V	2	8	32;39;59	18	29	2	7,7
1991							
I	9	93	-	3	15	14	5,7
II	4	28	32;55;65	6	135	5	6,3
III	8	8	36;65	8	30	0	6,8
IV	2	15	32;65	4	29	0	7,0
V	8	31	32;65	33	37	0	6,9

Treatments:

I   = untreated
II = triadimenol   at 125 g/ha
III = fenpropimorph at 750 g/ha in alternation with triadimenol at 125 g/ha
IV = fenpropimorph at 375 g/ha in combination with triadimenol at 125 g/ha
V   = fenpropimorph at 750 g/ha

From 1982 up to 1988 some variability in sensitivity can be seen which is reflected in the numbers of isolates present in the respective classes. It was not until 1989 that a slight but nevertheless real shift towards a decreased sensitivity to fenpropimorph became apparent. This occurred in both countries and was marked by the establishment of a new sensitivity class (30 - 60 ppm) which has remained up to 1991 without any further increase. Thus, apart from this initial shift in 1989 the situation has re-stabilized itself.

Table 3 includes all the assessment data collected from the long-term wheat trial with the variety Disponent over the period 1986-1991. At the beginning of this trial period in spring 1986, a slightly reduced triadimenol sensitivity of the powdery mildew population was recorded at this site. Consequently, there was a distinct reduction in sensitivity in the triadimenol treated plot at the end of the season; this was also reflected in the degree of powdery mildew attack and correlated with the yield.

This effect continued to develop in the following years. From 1987 it became necessary to apply an additional treatment to the triadimenol plot. However, despite the pronounced variation of sensitivity values from year to year, a clear reduction in sensitivity was not observed until 1991.

The sensitivity of the wheat powdery mildew towards fenpropimorph was very high at the beginning of the trial in 1986. The first signs of a slight change in this level of sensitivity were seen in 1987 and in 1989, when this change had become more apparent. This tendency has continued in the following years. A comparison of the yearly values obtained so far in this trial suggests that a not very pronounced, but still clearly distinct shift in the powdery mildew population in its sensitivity towards fenpropimorph has occured, although this is still well within the range of the overall sensitivity distribution, as shown in Table 2. As can be seen from the data relating to % attack and yield, the performance of fenpropimorph remained totally unaffected by this shift.

In contrast to these observations are those recorded from the other two treatments - the alternating spray regime (treatment III) and the combination of fenpropimorph with triadimenol (treatment IV) - where, as yet, there is no indication of a shifting in sensitivity towards fenpropimorph. Both treatments would appear to be equally well suited to avoid this. The same applies with respect to powdery mildew control and triazole sensitivity in these two treatments, although values differ slightly from one year to the other.

DISCUSSION

Whereas in the period from 1982 to 1988 in Germany and in Switzerland there were only insignificant, if any, changes in the sensitivity of wheat powdery mildew populations towards fenpropimorph, the first signs of a sensitivity shift became apparent in 1989. Although this development has re-stabilized itself and the field performance of fenpropimorph, when applied according to label recommendations, has remained unaffected. Nevertheless increased attention must be paid to employ resistance strategies, such as alternating spray regimes or the use of product combinations. This is especially important in view of the fact that the selection pressure exerted by morpholine or triazole treatments alone could be clearly shown in a long-term field trial especially designed to deal with these questions. The trial results obtained so far indicate that both strategies, if handled properly, produce the desired effect. For practical reasons the use of triazole/morpholine combinations, either as tank or ready mixtures, is the preferred and widely recommended anti-resistance strategy.

REFERENCES

Butters, J.; Clark, J.; Hollomon, D.W. (1984) Resistance to inhibitors of sterol biosynthesis in barley powdery mildew. *Mededelingen van de Faculteit Landbouwwetenschappen Rijksuniversiteit Gent,* **49**, 143-151.

Fletcher, J.T.; Wolfe, M.S. (1981) Insensitivity to triadimefon, triadimenol and other fungicides. *Proceeding British Crop Protection Conference, Pests and Diseases,* 633-640.

Heaney, S.P.; Martin, T.J., Smith, J.M. (1988) Practical approaches to managing anti-resistance strategies with DMI fungicides. *Proceedings Brighton Crop Protection Conference, Pests and Diseases,* 1988, **3**, 1097-1106.

Köller, W.; Scheinpflug, H. (1987) Fungal resistance to sterol biosynthesis inhibitors: A new challenge. *Plant Disease,* **71**, 1066-1074.

Lorenz, G.; Pommer, E.H. (1984) Investigations into the sensitivity of wheat powdery mildew population towards fenpropimorph (monitoring programme). *Proceedings British Crop Protection Conference, Pests and Diseases,* **2**, 489-493.

Zadoks, I.E.; Chang, T.T.; Konzak, C.F. (1974) A decimal code for the growth stages of cereals. *Weed Research,* **14**, 415-421.

PRACTICAL ASPECTS OF RESISTANCE TO DMI FUNGICIDES IN BARLEY POWDERY MILDEW *ERYSIPHE GRAMINIS*

W.S.CLARK

ADAS Cropping and Horticulture Development Centre, Brooklands Avenue, Cambridge, CB2 2BL

ABSTRACT

From 1976 until 1988, ADAS conducted field experiments to develop strategies for disease control in spring barley. Part of the work included comparison of fungicides from different chemical groups. The work was carried out partly to detect any practical changes in the level of disease control achieved as a result of changes in the sensitivity of mildew populations. The series of experiments clearly demonstrates the decline in activity of the DMI fungicides over a 12-year period. In the mid 1970s the DMI fungicides gave good control of mildew but by the mid-1980s the activity of the DMI's had declined to a level whereby disease control failure was commonly encountered. In direct contrast to the DMI's, the activity of the morpholine fungicide tridemorph was maintained throughout the period of the experiments.

INTRODUCTION

Changes in the sensitivity of fungal plant pathogens to fungicides are commonly recorded following the widespread use of a product. Where the product belongs to a fungicide group which has members which are already widely used, cross resistance is also often claimed. The degree to which populations of fungal pathogens develop insensitivity determines whether or not field resistance has developed. The demonstration of a shift in sensitivity in laboratory tests does not in itself indicate that resistance has developed in practice.

In the mid 1970s ADAS began a series of field experiments to develop strategies for disease control in spring barley. The experiments involved aspects of fungicide timing in response to disease thresholds and fungicide comparison. The comparison of fungicides from different chemical groups enabled the detection of any practical changes in the level of disease control achieved as a result of changes in the sensitivity of mildew populations. Such changes in sensitivity have been investigated by a number of workers (Fletcher and Wolfe, 1981 ; Heaney et al., 1986 ; Wolfe and Minchin, 1976). The results of such experiments were usually expressed as a range of FD_{50} values (i.e. the fungicide concentration which would give a 50% reduction in the level of disease compared with an untreated control).

Although a wide range of FD_{50} values was detected in these experiments, no change in the field performance of the fungicides had been reported. The work of Fletcher and Wolfe demonstrated a wide range of sensitivities of *E. graminis* populations collected throughout the UK. The major conclusion of the work was that "Although there has not been any obvious loss in effectiveness of these (sterol inhibiting) fungicides due to insensitivity, the trends observed give rise to concern".

Fletcher continued his work in 1982 and in his conclusions he stated that "...the survey provides no clear evidence that the insensitivity of mildew populations to sterol inhibiting fungicides is affecting their field performance". Very shortly after this work, failures to control mildew effectively in ADAS field experiments were commonly detected and within 3 years there was a range of DMI fungicides which were no longer giving acceptable levels of mildew control.

METHODS

The main disease problem on spring barley in the UK is powdery mildew and there is frequently a high correlation between disease levels and yield. The relationship between yield and the level of mildew infection in these experiments frequently gives very high correlation coefficients, often in the region of (-)0.95. This relationship allows the disease control performance of a fungicide to be judged by the yield responses achieved. The relative performance of the DMI fungicides throughout this experiment series was measured against that of tridemorph, a morpholine fungicide used commonly in the UK. Although resistance to morpholine fungicides in mildew populations has been discussed by some workers (Walmsley-Woodward *et al.*, 1979; Brown *et al.*, 1991), the changes in sensitivity which were detected were very small and it is still generally agreed that the level of disease control achieved in field situations remains high.

The experiments were conducted in commercial crops of spring barley. A randomised block design with four replicates was used at all sites in all years. Plots were approximately 0.01 ha in size. Fungicides were applied at label recommended rates using knapsack sprayers. Diseases were assessed on 10 tillers per plot and individual leaves were assessed for disease as % leaf area affected using keys from the MAFF Manual of Plant Growth Stage and Disease Assessment Keys. Leaf 1 was taken as the youngest fully expanded leaf (the flag leaf in the mature plant). Plots were combine harvested and yields corrected to 85% dry matter. All data were subjected to analysis of variance and treatment means separated using Duncan's Multiple Range Test.

RESULTS

    The performance of triadimefon and triadimenol in controlling barley powdery mildew over the 13-year period of the experiment is represented in Fig.1. This shows the range of yield responses achieved by these products when used to control mildew in crops of spring barley. The yield response is shown as a comparison with that achieved by application of tridemorph in the same experiment at each site. The four experiments in 1976 show clearly that treatment with triadimefon consistently gave higher yield responses than treatment with tridemorph. In most years at most sites, the main disease present was powdery mildew and the yield response at any one site can be largely attributed to the control of mildew.

    In 1977, at 10 sites out of 11, application of triadimefon gave yield responses equal to or greater than those achieved by the application of tridemorph. This trend of good performance of triadimefon compared with tridemorph continued until the early 1980's when an increasing number of sites was found where triadimefon gave yield responses below those of tridemorph. By 1984, there had been a total reversal of the relative activities of the products. At all 11 sites, the application of tridemorph gave a larger yield response than where triadimefon had been applied. Over a period of 8 years, the relative activities of the two fungicides against barley powdery mildew had been reversed.

Figure 1. Relative yield response of spring barley to treatment with triadimefon or triadimenol (1976-1988)

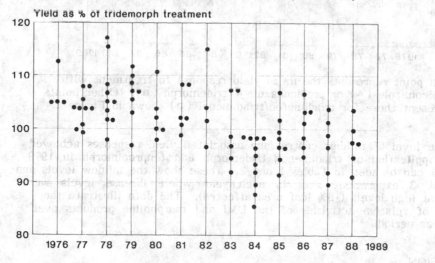

Each point on the chart (●) represents the mean yield response to treatment with triadimefon or triadimenol from a fully replicated experiment. (Triadimefon used 1977-83, triadimenol used 1984-88).

Propiconazole, another DMI fungicide with similar activity to triadimefon, was introduced into the experiment series in 1980 and it can be seen from Figure 2 that it follows the trend set by triadimefon in terms of declining activity. Figure 2 shows that although there is an apparent decline in the activity of propiconazole following its introduction into the experiment series its activity was generally better than that of triadimefon. This appears as a lag in the decline of activity when compared with triadimefon. The use of products containing two fungicides with different modes of action did improve the activity against mildew as can be seen in Figure 2 with the introduction of Tilt Turbo (propiconazole + tridemorph) into the experiment series in 1985.

Figure 2. Relative yield response of spring barley to treatment with propiconazole and propiconazole + tridemorph.

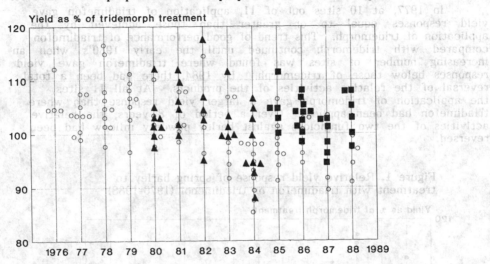

Each point represents the mean yield response to treatment with propiconazole (▲) or propiconazole + tridemorph (■). Other points represent those for triadimefon/triadimenol (○) shown in Figure 1.

The level of mildew control and associated yield responses achieved by the application of triadimenol, tridemorph and fenpropimorph in 1979 and 1987 can be seen in Tables 1 and 2. These show the mildew levels and yields at 3 experiment sites in each year where disease levels were present at high levels (>9% leaf area affected). The data illustrate the reversal of relative activities of the DMI and morpholine products over the 8-year period.

DISCUSSION

The series of experiments carried out by ADAS and described here clearly demonstrates the decline in activity of the DMI fungicides (also referred to in earlier papers variously as triazoles and EBI fungicides but belonging to the sterol biosynthesis inhibitor group of fungicides which act at the point of C_{14} demethylation). The experiments also support the view that there has been no comparable shift in the sensitivity of populations of *E. graminis* to the morpholine fungicide tridemorph over the same period.

The introduction of the 'newer' DMI fungicides such as propiconazole in the early 1980s came at a time when fungicide resistance in spring barley mildew populations had reached a level where failure to control mildew with DMI fungicides was commonplace. The slight improvement in activity following their introduction was therefore shortlived.

Recently published work (Brown *et al.*, 1991) claimed to clearly identify isolates of *E. graminis* collected from Scotland which were 'resistant' to fenpropimorph and fenpropidin. However, the level of resistance was low in relation to field application rates and there was no suggestion of failure of disease control. The same report stated that there was comparatively little variation in the sensitivity of isolates to tridemorph. This work confirmed the value of using tridemorph as a standard in this experiment series against which other fungicide performance could be measured.

The morpholine fungicides, like the DMI's, act by inhibiting sterol biosynthesis but do not act at the C_{14} demethylation point. Members of the morpholine group do not all act in the same way and there is good evidence that tridemorph acts differently from fenpropimorph and fenpropidin, its main activity being the inhibition of sterol $\Delta^8 \rightarrow \Delta^7$ isomerase (Brown *et al.*, 1991). Although the point of inhibition in the pathway is different from that of the DMI's, this alone cannot explain why their activity has remained relatively unaffected in the last decade. Mildew control in cereals now relies almost totally on the morpholine fungicides. We must guard their activity with rational fungicide policies which minimise pressure on the pathogen population and prevent the decline in activity which followed the widespread use of their cousins the DMI's.

TABLE 1. Mildew levels and yield at each of 3 sites showing the effect of fungicide treatment (1979).

Treatment	Site 1		Site 2		Site 3	
	% Mildew*	Yield+	% Mildew*	Yield+	%Mildew*	Yield+
Untreated	10.0 c	4.66 a	28.3 e	4.25 a	9.7 c	6.04 a
triadimefon	0.1 a	5.23 bc	1.1 ab	5.49 d	0.0 a	6.34 a
tridemorph	4.1 ab	4.96 b	13.4 d	5.02 c	0.8 ab	5.97 a
fenpropimorph	0.3 a	5.04 b	5.7 abc	4.69 b	-	-

*   % Mildew on Leaf 3, GS 75
+   Yield in t/ha at 85% DM

(Site 1 : South Milford;   Site 2 : Headley Hall;   Site 3 : Womersley)

TABLE 2. Mildew levels and yield at each of 3 sites showing the effect of fungicide treatment (1987).

Treatment	Site 1		Site 2		Site 3	
	% Mildew*	Yield+	% Mildew*	Yield+	% Mildew*	Yield+
Untreated	11.9 b	3.08 a	12.4 c	5.17 a	23.1 c	5.64 a
triadimenol	9.0 ab	3.58 b	9.5 c	5.24 ab	20.5 c	5.76 ab
tridemorph	6.6 a	3.86 bc	9.4 c	5.32 abc	14.7 b	6.30 c
fenpropimorph	6.4 a	3.81 bc	8.6 c	5.37 bc	9.8 a	6.34 c

* % Mildew on Leaf 3, GS 75
+ Yield in t/ha at 85% DM

(Site 1 : East Rigton; Site 2 : High Mowthorpe; Site 3 : Wark)

ACKNOWLEDGEMENTS

Thanks are due to the Ministry of Agriculture, Fisheries and Food for funding the experiments described here. The author also thanks J.E.E.Jenkins for his guidance and efforts in initiating this work.

REFERENCES

Brown, J.K.M.; Slater, S.E.; See, K.A. (1991) Sensitivity of *Erysiphe graminis f.sp. hordei* to morpholine and piperidine fungicides. *Crop Protection*, **10**, 445-454.

Fletcher, J.T.; Wolfe, M.S. (1981) Insensitivity of *Erysiphe graminis f.sp. hordei* to triadimefon, triadimenol and other fungicides. *Proceedings British Crop Protection Conference - Pests and Diseases* 1981, *2*, 633-640.

Heaney, S.P.; Hutt, R.T.; Miles, V.G. (1986) Sensitivity to fungicides of barley powdery mildew populations in England and Scotland : Status and implications for fungicide use. *Proceedings British Crop Protection Conference - Pests and Diseases* 1986, 2, 793-800.

Walmsley-Woodward, D.J.; Laws, F.A.; Whittington, W.J. (1979) The characteristics of isolates of *Erysiphe graminis f. sp. hordei* varying in response to tridemorph and ethirimol. *Annals of Applied Biology*, 92, 211-219.

Wolfe, M.S.; Minchin, P.N. (1976) Quantitative assessment of variation in the field populations of *Erysiphe graminis f.sp.* hordei using mobile nurseries. *Transactions of the British Mycological Society*, **66**, 332-334.

EFFECTS OF CROP HISTORY ON SENSITIVITY TO PROCHLORAZ OF PSEUDOCERCOSPORELLA HERPOTRICHOIDES ISOLATES FROM CEREALS IN WESTERN EUROPE

R J BIRCHMORE, P I ASHMAN, S STANLEY, P E RUSSELL

Schering Agrochemicals Limited, Chesterford Park Research Station, Saffron Walden, England.

H BUSCHHAUS

Schering AG., Postfach 65 03 31, D-1000 Berlin 65, Deutschland.

ABSTRACT

In vitro dose-response testing of the sensitivity to prochloraz of populations of Pseudocercosporella herpotrichoides from France, Germany, Denmark and the UK showed no major changes in any of the countries between 1985 and 1991. Isolates from UK and Danish trial plots treated with prochloraz during the 1991 season showed no evidence of selection for lower sensitivity when their in vitro responses to 0.5 mg/l prochloraz were compared with those of isolates from untreated plots. The effects of applications made between 1988 and 1990 on the sensitivity of isolates obtained in 1991 were inconsistent. Although the mean growth of isolates from sites treated 3, 4 and 5 times with prochloraz were higher than some of those from untreated plots this was not always the case, as some of the means from untreated plots were equally high. Further investigation is required before conclusions can be drawn on effects of treatment on sensitivity.

INTRODUCTION

Prochloraz is widely used throughout Europe to control the eyespot disease of cereals, caused by Pseudocercosporella herpotrichoides. Since resistance has developed to carbendazim in most European countries, prochloraz is now the only fungicide which will give commercially acceptable control of all strains within the eyespot population. Prochloraz has been used in cereals for approximately 10 years and, as yet, there is no evidence that field activity has been threatened by development of resistance. However, French workers have recently reported the discovery in Northern France of P. herpotrichoides isolates which they claim to possess laboratory resistance, although there is no proof that these have caused a reduction in the level of control given by prochloraz applications (Leroux and Marchegay, 1991).

Since 1984 the Schering eyespot monitoring programme has examined the sensitivity to prochloraz of isolates of the pathogen from field trials and farmers crops in the UK, France, Germany and Denmark. General monitoring results have been reported previously (Gallimore et al., 1987, Birchmore et al., 1990) and the situation in France has been examined in detail in recent publications (Birchmore et al., 1992 a and b). This current paper reviews the overall levels of sensitivity to prochloraz in the 4 countries, from 1985 to 1991, and also examines in detail the effects of selection pressure from prochloraz applications on the sensitivity of isolates from France, the UK and Denmark.

MATERIALS AND METHODS

Approximately 20 infected stems were removed from each plot within a trial, or 50 stems from a farmers field. These were despatched by air-freight to Chesterford Park Research Station, in Essex, England. P. herpotrichoides cultures were then isolated from eyespot lesions by the method reported by Birchmore (1991).

A two-step, in vitro, testing procedure was used to evaluate the sensitivity of isolates to prochloraz. This consisted of a preliminary step in which the response of each of the isolates to 0.5 mg/l prochloraz incorporated into agar was evaluated, followed by a dose-response test which more accurately defined the responses of randomly selected isolates to prochloraz. The concentrations used were 2.0, 1.0, 0.5, 0.25, 0.10, 0.075, 0.05, 0.0025, 0.01, 0.0075 and 0.005 mg/l prochloraz. Both tests were incubated at 20°C for 14 days and assessed by measurement of colony diameter. The results of both were expressed by growth on treated agar as a percentage of growth on untreated agar. In the case of the dose-response test, these percentages were transformed into logarithmic values and subsequently used in a linear regression analysis to determine the fungicide concentration which inhibited growth by 50% (IG_{50} values).

The results of the dose response test were used for the distributions in Figure 1. However, these results are based on relatively small numbers of isolates, so for the detailed comparisons in Figure 2 and Tables 1, 2 and 3, the initial 0.5 mg/l prochloraz data were used as these are based on larger sample sizes.

RESULTS AND DISCUSSION

Sensitivity distributions

The distribution of prochloraz IG_{50} values obtained from the dose-response testing of cultures from the UK, France, Germany and Denmark are shown in Fig 1. The 1985 and 1991 distributions are shown to illustrate the similarity of the responses, despite the seven-year interval between them. The 1985 Danish distribution showed a higher level of sensitivity than the others, probably due to the small number of isolates tested. The 1991 Danish distribution was very similar to the 1985 distributions from the other countries.

Influence of fungicide applications

A number of fungicide applications may be made to a cereal crop during the growing season, from seed-treatment to flag-leaf spray. Many of these, while not giving commercially acceptable control of eyespot, may have an effect on the pathogen population. However, a major selection pressure must come from applications of prochloraz, which are intended to control the pathogen. Results of an examination of the effects of prochloraz applications on French eyespot isolates have been published (Birchmore et al., 1992 a and b).

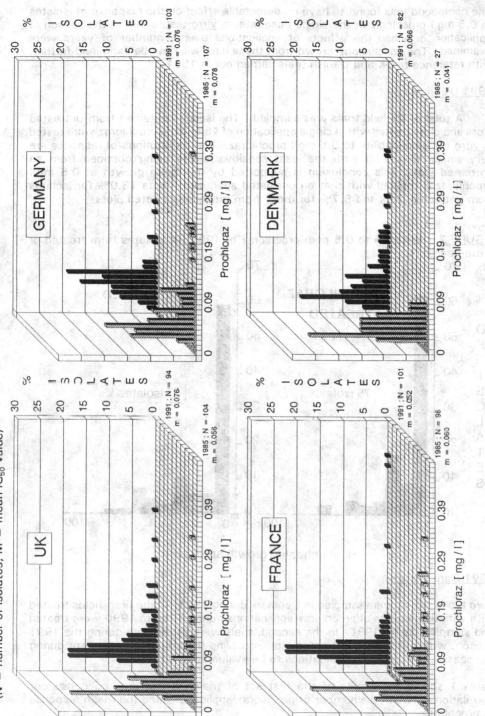

<u>FIGURE 1.</u> Distributions of prochloraz IG_{50} values of isolates from the UK, France, Germany and Denmark; 1985-1991
(N = number of isolates, M = mean IG_{50} value)

The compound was found to have no detectable effect on the response of isolates to 0.5 mg/l prochloraz in the single dose-rate, in vitro test, either in the season of application or when the effects of applications over a number of years were examined. The conclusions drawn from these data will now be examined further, with reference to UK and Danish trials carried out in 1991.

1991 UK trials

A total of 27 field trials was sampled. The isolates obtained from untreated plots and plots treated with a single application of 450g ai/ha prochloraz were tested in vitro for susceptibility to 0.5 mg/l prochloraz. The distributions of response are very similar (Figure 2) with the least sensitive isolate being obtained from an untreated plot. This conclusion is supported by the mean growth at 0.5 mg/l prochloraz compared with that on untreated agar, which was 13.0% for isolates from untreated plots and 8.7% for those from prochloraz treated plots.

FIGURE 2. Response to 0.5 ppm prochloraz of 1991 UK isolates from treated or untreated plots.

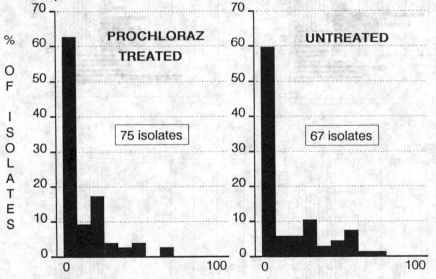

% of untreated growth at 0.5 ppm

1991 Danish trials

Two types of site were sampled in Denmark during 1991. In the first, fields treated with various numbers of prochloraz applications during 1988 to 1990 were treated and sampled during 1991. In the second, trials were established during the 1991 season, with treated and untreated plots, enabling the effects of treatment during the season and split-rate applications to be evaluated.

Table 1 shows the results of the first set of trials. There was no consistent correlation between the number of prochloraz applications and the mean response to prochloraz.

TABLE 1. Effects of prochloraz applications made between 1988 and 1990 to 10 Danish sites on sensitivity to prochloraz of isolates obtained in 1991.

Site	Number of prochloraz applications in 1988-90 seasons	Number of isolates recovered	Mean colony diameter (mm) at 0.5 mg/l prochloraz as a % of growth on untreated agar
1	0	3	3.0
2	0	8	4.8
3	0	9	38.0
4	0	2	17.8
5	1	2	0
6	1	6	8.7
7	2	5	8.4
8	3	8	42.4
9	4	6	35.9
10	5	3	40.8

The mean colony diameter on sites which had received no prochloraz applications varied from 3.0 to 38.0% of untreated, while those for 3, 4 and 5 applications were 42.4, 35.9 and 40.8% respectively. While this could indicate a trend towards lower sensitivity, or a loss of the most sensitive isolates from the population, the evidence is by no means conclusive as the numbers of isolates recovered were small, the mean values from sites receiving 1 and 2 applications were as low, or lower than those from untreated sites, and there was an overlap between the highest mean from an untreated site and the lowest from a treated site. This lack of correlation agrees with data published previously on French sites (Birchmore et al., 1992).

Tables 2 and 3 show the effects of prochloraz applications during the 1991 season on isolate sensitivity. There was no correlation between the amount of prochloraz applied to plots and the in vitro sensitivity of the isolates obtained.

TABLE 2. Effects of prochloraz applications in 1991 season on sensitivity of P. herpotrichoides isolates taken from 3 Danish trials, each containing 8 treatments.

Treatment	No. of applications made in 1991 season	Total quantity of prochloraz (g AI/ha) applied in season	Mean colony diameter (mm) on 0.5 mg/l prochloraz as % of growth on untreated agar
1	0	0	14.3
2	5	337.5	9.64
3	5	225.0	23.13
4	5	337.5	12.07
5	5	112.5	16.13
6	2	450.0	10.43
7	5	300.0	30.49
8	2	225.0	21.54

TABLE 3. Effects of prochloraz applications in 1991 season on sensitivity of
P. herpotrichoides isolates taken from 6 Danish trials, each containing 10 treatments

Treatment	No. of applications made in 1991 season	Total quantity of prochloraz applied in season (g Al/ha)	Mean colony diameter on 0.5 mg/l prochloraz as % of growth on untreated agar
1	0	0	14.70
2	0	0	19.03
3	2	373.5	19.00
4	2	450.0	22.95
5	2	450.0	14.98
6	2	225.0	24.04
7	2	225.0	21.71
8	2	450.0	25.42
9	1	450.0	18.85
10	1	497.0	19.32

In conclusion, the evidence from our monitoring results indicates that the mean reaction to prochloraz of European populations of P. herpotrichoides has remained stable over the years 1985 to 1991. Applications of prochloraz to fields over a number of years may reduce the number of very sensitive isolates in a population, although this effect has not been seen in all locations. However, these applications do not lead to the emergence of a new, resistant strain. Applications of prochloraz during the season of sampling did not have any detectable effect on the eyespot population.

REFERENCES

Birchmore, R.J. (1991), Monitoring populations of Pseudocercosporella herpotrichoides for sensitivity to prochloraz. OEPP Bulletin, 21, 313-315.
Birchmore, R.J.; Russell, P.E.; Buschhaus, H. (1990). Long-term monitoring of Pseudocercosporella herpotrichoides populations for sensitivity to prochloraz and carbendazim. Proceedings of the 1990 Brighton Crop Protection Conference - Pests and Diseases, 1153-1158.
Birchmore, R.J.; Russell, P.E.; de Saint-Blanquat, A.; Salembier, E.; Tromas.J. (1992a). Le prochloraze, résultats des travaux sur Piétin-Verse (1985-91). Phytoma 437, 33-36.
Birchmore, R.J.; Russell, P.E.; Ashman, P.I.; Stanley, S.; Buschhaus, H. (1992b). 44th International Symposium on Crop Protection, Gent (in press).
Gallimore, K.; Knights, I.K.; Barnes, G. (1987) Sensitivity of Pseudocercosporella herpotrichoides to the fungicide prochloraz. Plant Pathology 36, 290-296.
Leroux, P.; Marchegay, P. (1991). Caractérisation des souches de Pseudocercosporella herpotrichoides, agent de piétin-verse des céréales, résistantes au prochloraze, isolées en France sur blé tendre d'hiver. Agronomie 11, 767-776.

RESISTANCE OF THE EYESPOT FUNGUS, *PSEUDOCERCOPORELLA HERPOTRICHOIDES*, TO DMI FUNGICIDES

N. CAVELIER, F. LORÉE, M. PRUNIER

I.N.R.A., S.R.I.V., Domaine de la Motte, B.P. 29, 35650 Le Rheu – France

ABSTRACT

Populations of *Pseudocercosporella herpotrichoides* were monitored for sensitivity to triazoles and to the imidazole prochloraz in 1990 and 1991. The pathogen was isolated from cereal stems obtained in fields in different regions in France. A stable proportion of fast growing strains was resistant to triazoles. Few isolates were resistant to prochloraz in both the fast and the slow growing type. In greenhouse experiments, plants were inoculated with strains resistant to triazoles and prochloraz and then treated with hepoxiconazole, cyproconazole and prochloraz. For the triazoles, the efficacy declined markedly, and the activity of prochloraz was poorer against prochloraz resistant strains. The isolates remain resistant after inoculation on plants. In practice, if the frequency of resistance is increasing, chemical control of eyespot may become unreliable.

INTRODUCTION

Since MBC generating fungicides have become ineffective for eyespot control because of the development of resistance in the pathogen *Pseudocercosporella herpotrichoides*, prochloraz and flusilazole are the most commonly used fungicides for controlling this pathogen.

The pathogen population can be divided according to the growth speed into two types : the fast growing (N) and the slow growing (L) strains. An important variability is observed between the two types : pathogenicity, cultural and conidial characteristics, fungicide sensitivity. L strains are less susceptible than N type to triazoles, (Leroux & Gredt, 1985 ; Cavelier, 1988). However even if most of the N isolates are susceptible to triazoles (so–called Na isolates) some of them (so–called Nb) are resistant to this fungicide group (Leroux & Gredt, 1988 ; Cavelier et al., 1990). Prochloraz has been found to be equally effective against both types, L and N (Leroux & Gredt, 1985 ; Cavelier et al., 1987). However several prochloraz resistant strains were isolated for the first time in France during the year 1990 on winter wheat (Leroux & Marchegay, 1991).

This paper presents the results of characterizing eyespot strains according to the sensitivity of the fungus to triazoles and prochloraz in 1990 and 1991 and describes glasshouse experiments which compare the sensitivity of Na, Nb, L isolates to triazoles and prochloraz.

MATERIALS AND METHODS

1 – Characterization of *P. herpotrichoides* populations

Population of *P. herpotrichoides* were characterized from about 200 treated or untreated plot per year in different regions in France. 50 stems with eyespot lesions were collected per plot. *P. herpotrichoides* isolated from eyespot lesions was identified as L type or N type by colony diameter and colony morphology on potato dextrose agar (PDA Bio–Mérieux) after 14 days growth at 20° C : L type grew at about half the rate of N type isolates and producted colonies with feathery margins. To test the sensitivity of isolates to fungicides, three replicate colonies of each isolate were transferred to three different Petri dishes amended with triadimenol at 30 μg/ml or prochloraz at 0.5 μg/ml or 2 μg/ml. Formulated compounds were used. The cultures were incubated at 20° C for 2 weeks and colony diameters were measured.

2 – Greenhouse experiments

The strains selected for this study were isolated from winter wheat in 1988, 1989, 1990, 1991 in different regions in France. Five isolates were triazole–sensitive N type (Na), five were triazole–resistant N type (Nb), five were prochloraz–sensitive L types (Ls) and five were prochloraz–resistant L type (Lp) isolated by Leroux in the North of France (Leroux & Marchegay, 1992).

Experiments were in a glasshouse heated only to give frost protection. Pots were arranged in a randomised design with five blocks and five plants per pot. Plants, cv. Camp–Rémy, were inoculated at the three leaf growth stage by a suspension of finely chopped mycelium. Treatments were applied four weeks after inoculation. The fungicides tested were two triazoles : cyproconazole at the rate of 100 g AI/ha, hepoxiconazole at the rate of 180 g AI/ha and one imidazole : prochloraz at the rate of 600 g AI/ha.

The severity of eyespot was assessed at GS 60 (Zadoks *et al.*, 1974) by the method of Cavelier and Le Page (1985). Plants were distributed on a 0–2 scale : 0–healthy plants, 1–sheaths with lesions, 2–stems with stroma, a mean score was calculated. On stem, when eyespot lesions were present, the mean proportion of stem cross–section infected was calculated.

RESULTS

1 – Distribution and frequency of Nb strains in France

The Nb type was isolated in all regions of France, with the exception of the North because in this region L type is prevalent. These results were similar to those obtained in 1988–1989 (Cavelier *et al.*, 1990).

The proportion of the Nb type in the N–population seemed to be stable, suggesting the possibility of a rather slow selection for less sensitive strains to triazoles. However, variable results were observed according to the season, (from 0 to 38 %) and to the region (from 0 to 100 %). In some plots where N type was prevalent, more than half N strains were Nb strains (Table 1).

TABLE 1. Frequency (%) of Nb strains in 1990 and 1991

	Departments	Nb strains %		Nb strains % / N strains isolated	
		1990	1991	1990	1991
02	Aisne	22	–	–	–
03	Allier	0	–	–	–
08	Ardennes	100	–	–	–
10	Aube	15	0	–	–
14	Calvados	–	6	–	17
17	Charentes maritime	68	32	64	25
21	Côte d'Or	0	38	–	72
22	Côtes d'Armor	0	6	–	67
28	Eure et Loir	8	20	27	39
29	Finistère	0	–	–	–
31	Garonne (haute)	0	12	–	24
35	Ille et Vilaine	5	0	36	–
37	Indre et Loire	34	16	–	37
41	Loir et Cher	0	–	–	–
45	Loiret	0	32	–	50
49	Maine et Loire	0	–	–	–
51	Marne	63	25	68	39
53	Mayenne	–	21	–	29
56	Morbihan	14	–	–	–
60	Oise	2	–	–	–
62	Pas de Calais	0	0	–	–
76	Seine maritime	0	0	–	–
77	Seine et Marne	–	16	–	45
78	Yvelines	19	17	19	39
80	Somme	–	0	–	–
86	Vienne	10	–	–	–
91	Essonne	0	–	–	–

2 – Frequency of isolates resistant to prochloraz

In 1990 a very low percentage of isolates were found which grew on agar amended with 0.5 or 2 μg/ml of prochloraz.

In 1991, the percentage of isolates growing on prochloraz was consistently higher, especially on 0.5 μg/ml and with both types N and L (table 2). These results differ from the observations of Leroux and Marchegay (1991) ; the test used was not the same but, the number of isolates tested was higher and came from different regions in France, not only from the North.

TABLE 2. Percentage of isolates growing on 0.5 μg/ml or 2 μg/ml of prochloraz

Strain type		1990	1991
L	0.5	0	4.8
	2	0.1	1.5
N	0.5	2.4	7.1
	2	0	2.2
Number of plots tested		109	182

3 – Effects of DMI fungicides on different types of *P. herpotrichoides* in glasshouse experiments (Table 3)

TABLE 3. Effects of fungicides on different types of *P. herpotrichoides*

Strain type		Mean disease score		mean proportion of stem cross–section infected	
Na	untreated	1.98	a*	53.5	a*
	Hepoxiconazole	0.94	b	23.7	b
	cyproconazole	0.90	b	16.7	b
	Prochloraz	0.32	c	5.9	c
Nb	untreated	1.80	a	55.2	a
	Hepoxiconazole	1.56	b	44.6	b
	cyproconazole	1.51	b	39.4	b
	Prochloraz	0.39	c	8.2	c
Ls	untreated	1.45	a	18.1	a
	Hepoxiconazole	1.39	a	15.5	a
	cyproconazole	1.38	a	23	a
	Prochloraz	0.23	b	2.1	b
Lp	untreated	1.70	a	34.3	a
	Hepoxiconazole	1.55	a	27.1	a
	cyproconazole	1.10	b	17.5	b
	Prochloraz	1.08	b	12.6	b

* significant (p = 0.05)

Hepoxiconazole and cyproconazole decreased eyespot incidence in both samples Na and Nb but eyespot severity remained high in Nb plots (Table 3). Prochloraz was the most effective in both cases.

Triazoles failed to control eyespot in plots inoculated with L type, prochloraz was effective against sensitive L type but was less effective in plots inoculated with resistant L type.

No significant difference was observed between hepoxiconazole and cyproconazole.

The mean IG 50 value of L isolates resistant to prochloraz was about 0.3 μg/ml on PDA (0.04 μg/ml for the sensitive strains) ; with a resistance level of 7.5 the efficacy of prochloraz decreased from 84 % to 36 % (calculated on disease score).

The pathogenicity of resistant isolates was at least the same as that of sensitive isolates (Table 4)

TABLE 4. Pathogenicity of DMI – sensitive or resistant isolates of *P. herpotrichoides*

Isolate type	Mean disease score		Mean proportion of stem cross-section infected	
Na	1.98	a *	53.5	a *
Nb	1.80	ab	55.2	a
Lp	1.70	b	34.4	b
Ls	1.38	c	23.0	c

*Significant ($p = 0.05$)

DISCUSSION

The mean frequency of Nb strains seemed to be stable, but the variability was high between the seasons and between the regions. After artificial inoculation, the efficacy of cyproconazole and hepoxiconazole fell severely. These results confirms the results of previous experiments (Cavelier *et al.*, 1990) in wich fluzilazole was used instead of hepoxiconazole and the sensitivity of Nb and L isolates was nearly the same. This suggests that for a single isolate the resistance is stable and that with a high proportion of Nb strains in a field the efficacy of triazoles is not sufficient to control eyespot. The frequency of isolates resistant to prochloraz was rather low, but also in this case, after artificial inoculation the resistance of resistant isolates persisted, the efficacy of prochloraz fell. Even if the level of resistant isolates is not very high and even if a fluctuation in the distribution of IG 50 values was previously observed (Birchmore *et al.*, 1990), the risk of development of resistant strains to prochloraz in the eyespot population exists. However, in the plots tested the percentage of resistant isolates was too low to explain a possible decrease of the efficacy of prochloraz.

It is now well known that eyespot population is not stable. We do not know the mechanism of selection of fast growing strains resistant to triazoles (Nb type) and a crucial threshold is perhaps reached with the use of prochloraz. If the frequency of resistance is increasing, chemical control of eyespot may become unreliable.

ACKNOWLEDGEMENTS

The authors thank Schering S.A. for financial assistance.

REFERENCES

Birchmore, R.J. ; Russell, P.E. ; Buschhaus, H. (1990) Long-term monitoring of *Pseudocercosporella herpotrichoides* populations for sensitivity to prochloraz and carbendazim. 1990 British Crop Protection Conference - Pests and Diseases, **3**, 1153–1158.

Cavelier, N. (1988) Variability of the sensitivity of different isolates of *Pseudocercosporella herpotrichoides* to sterol biosynthesis inhibitors fungicides. Conference of the Cereal Section of EUCARPIA, Wageningen, 1988.02.24–26 in : Cereal breeding related to integrated cereal production, Pudoc Wageningen, 140–144.

Cavelier, N. ; Le Page, D. (1985) Caractéristiques de souches de *Pseudocercosporella herpotrichoides* (Fron) Deighton (agent du piétin-verse des céréales) résistances aux fongicides benzimidazoles et thiophanates : pouvoir pathogène, capacité de développement. ANPP, 1ères journées d'études sur les maladies des plantes, **1**, 49–56.

Cavelier, N. ; Lucas, E. ; Prunier, M. (1990) Sensibilité de différents isolats de *Pseudocercosporella herpotrichoides* à des fongicides inhibiteurs de la biosynthèse de l'ergostérol. Mededelingen van de Faculteit Landbouwwetenschappen Rijksuniversiteit Gent, **55**, 989–995.

Cavelier, N. ; Rousseau, M. ; Le Page, D. (1987) Variabilité de *Pseudocercosporella herpotrichoides*, agent du piétin-verse des céréales : comportement *in vivo* de deux types d'isolats et d'une population en mélange. Zeitschrift für Pflanzenkrankheten und Pflanzenschutz, **94**, 590–599.

Leroux, P. ; Gredt, M. (1985) Caractéristiques des souches de *Pseudocercosporella herpotrichoides*, agent du piétin-verse des céréales, résistantes à des inhibiteurs de la biosynthèse des stérols. Comptes-rendus de l'Académie des Sciences - Paris, **301**, 785–788.

Leroux, P. ; Gredt, M. (1988) Caractérisation des souches de *Pseudocercosporella herpotrichoides*, agent du piétin-verse des céréales résistantes à des inhibiteurs antimitotiques et à des inhibiteurs de la biosynthèse des stérols. Agronomie, **8**, 719–729.

Leroux, P. ; Marchegay, P (1991) Caractérisation des souches de *Pseudocercosporella herpotrichoides*, agent du piétin-verse des céréales au prochloraze, isolées en France sur blé tendre d'hiver. Agronomie, **11**, 767–776.

Leroux, P. ; Marchegay, P. (1992) Variabilité chez l'agent du piétin-verse des céréales : implications pratiques. Phytoma - La Défense des Végétaux, **437**, 25–28.

Zadoks, J.C. ; Chang, T.T. ; Konzak, C.F. (1974) A decimal code for the growth stages of cereals. Weed research, **14** 415–421.

SENSITIVITY OF APPLE POWDERY MILDEW (*PODOSPHAERA LEUCOTRICHA*) TO TRIADIMEFON

U. SCHULZ

BAYER AG, PF/E-F, Pflanzenschutzzentrum Monheim, D-509 Leverkusen

ABSTRACT

Sensitivity tests with triadimefon against apple powdery mildew
Podosphaera leucotricha have been conducted throughout the years 1991
and 1992 on isolates from England, Belgium, The Netherlands and
Germany. The data demonstrate that failures in disease control in practice
are not due to field resistance of the pathogen to the fungicide.
The performance of triadimefon in a long-lasting trial in South Tyrol (1973
to 1991) was continuously good despite intensive applications.

INTRODUCTION

Poor spray scheduling or wrong fungicide dosages often have been the cause for
reports of decreasing performance of azole fungicides in apple powdery mildew.
Nevertheless, it has been suspected that the selection of resistant mildew strains has
negatively influenced azole performance. This has been investigated throughout the years
1991 and 1992. Isolates from England, Belgium, The Netherlands and Germany were tested
for sensitivity to triadimefon.

METHODS

Twig-tips or leaves infected with powdery mildew were taken from commercial
orchards. These samples were either examined directly in a whole plant test or first
transferred to plants for propagation of the inoculum and then tested after one step of
subculture where possible.

Young apple seedlings, variety 'Morgenduft' were used. Two weeks after
transplantation the little plants had four well developed leaves and were suitable for the test.

The test plants were sprayed with two discriminating dosages of triadimefon (as
(R)Bayleton 25 WP) : 100 and 10 mg/l, and sometimes in addition with 50 or 30 mg/l
respectively. Control plants were sprayed with water+blank formulation. The plants were
inoculated after the spray deposit had dried, using a spore-suspension of each mildew
sample prepared in water. In each test a standard-isolate was included. This isolate had been
taken from an orchard near Monheim and is sensitive to azole fungicides.

The inoculated plants were covered with cellophane bags which were not opened
during the whole test run. The plants were incubated in a greenhouse or growth chamber at
22°C.

The evaluations were carried out about 10 to 14 days after inoculation. The efficacy
was assessed either on whole plants or younger and older leaves separately.

RESULTS

In Tables 1 to 3 representative results are presented which were obtained with samples from The Netherlands and England. In 1990 the fungicidal performance was not satisfactory in the English orchard 'Gore Farm' but was satisfactory in the neighbouring 'Bridge Orchard'.

First of all it is noticeable that many mildew samples grew badly if at all. This is particularly marked for the samples from the English orchards (Tables 2,3). The mildew inoculum of twig-tips taken from 'Bridge Orchard' did not produce any infections in the test. This indicates that although the mildew could be seen macroscopically it had largely been killed by the fungicide treatments in the orchard.

The fungicide concentrations in the test have been chosen in such a way that the standard mildew isolate is controlled completely at 100, 50 and 30 mg triaidmefon/l and the efficacy decreases at 10 mg/l under the standard test conditions. Comparing the Abbott values at 10 mg triadimefon/l, within a certain variation the control of the isolates from the orchards was very good to quite satisfactory independent of the method of assessment. The range of efficacies was greater with English isolates than with the Dutch ones. 100 % control was achieved at 50 mg/l (Table 1) and very good efficacy at 30 mg/l.
A certain variation in sensitivity of the different mildew isolates is normal. Therefore the results do not indicate any resistance in practice and give no cause for concern.

The long-lasting efficacy of different triadimefon formulations compared to sulphur is shown in Table 4. This trial has been running for over twenty years now and a large number of triadimefon sprays have been applied annually. The efficacy of the azole is still excellent. In this orchard no mildew isolates have accumulated which are resistant to azoles despite this high selection pressure.

DISCUSSION

Whenever a problem comes up in practice that cannot be explained for the moment, the question is asked whether a pathogen has become resistant to azole fungicides. Under certain conditions azoles are able to select resistant pathogen strains, as has been experienced with powdery mildew in cereals. In trying to recognize problems early enough and to avoid them, it makes sense to follow up the 'resistance question' for apple powdery mildew as well.

In this paper some results of the resistance research are presented as an example. Further tests with isolates from Belgium and Germany confirm the conclusions.
The available data demonstrate that the reasons for bad perfomance in some orchards are not due to field resistance of the pathogen to triadimefon.

It is necessary that growers reconsider critically any changes in application of plant protection compounds, especially reduced rates of fungicides, reduced water quantities, and the use of ULV sprays.

TABLE 1. Apple Powdery Mildew - The Netherlands

Trial in Beesd 1991
Variety: Elstar
sampling 27.6.91, twig-tips, isolates tested directly

test on whole plants, variety 'Morgenduft' with triadimefon

treatment isolate	older leaves			younger leaves		
	% attack control	mg triadimefon/l 100	% efficacy 10	% attack control	mg triadimefon/l 100	% efficacy 10
Standard	21	100	82	66	100	90
untreated						
a	67	100	94	81	100	69
b	75	100	92	91	100	55
c	71	100	93	79	100	55
d	82	100	95	92	100	60
Bayleton						
a	55	100	93	65	100	72
b	62	100	84	70	100	78
c	73	100	79	78	100	57
nargin	66	100	80	72	1C0	81

treatments in the orchard: 7x triadimefon (as Bayleton 5WG, 0,05%)
1C.4./19.4./2.5./13.5./23.5./5.6./17.6.91(Pyrifenox before bloom)

Plot	number of secondary infect. 125 leaves/repetition				assessments in the orchard: 3.7.91
	a	b	c	d	sum
untreated	64	35	64	39	202
Bayleton	0	2	3	2	7

Trial in Varik 1992
Variety: Elstar
Sampling 20.5.92, twig-tips
isolates tested directly

test on whole plants, variety 'Morgenduft'
with triadimefon

Treatment isolate	Sensitivity test assessment on whole plant % efficacy		
	% attack control	mg triadimefon/l 100	50	10
Standard	52	100	88
untreated *			
a	52	100 100	90
b	77	100 100	90
c	70	100 100	85
d	55	100 100	95
Bayfidan *			
a	27	100 100	90
b	15	100 100	95
c	67	100 100	96
d	12	100 100	78

treatments in the orchard:
3x triadimenol (as Bayfidan 50 EW, 0,03%)
29.4./6.5./14.5.92
* = + Captan against scab

27.5.92: assessment of secondary infections
in the orchard:97,5% efficacy of triadimenol

197

TABLE 2. Apple Powdery Mildew 1991 - England

Gore Farm and Bridge Orchard, Kent

Variety: Cox Orange (both farms)
Sampling: 24.4.91, blossom trusses
        mildew isolates subcultured once before tests

2 tests on plants, variety 'Morgenduft' with triadimefon

Farm Treatment Isolate	Sensitivity test % attack control	% efficacy (Abbott) mg triadimefon/l 100	10	treatments:
Standard	53	100	74	Gore Farm 1991: 2 winter sprays penconazole, sulphur 2 spring sprays myclobutanil (ULV-sprays, reduced application rates)
Gore Farm untreated				
1	24	99	38	
2	13	100	54	
3	29	100	52	history:
4	18	97	56	triadimefon
5	20	100	20	penconazole
6	13	100	50	
7	<10	--	--	
8	22	100	59	Bridge Orchard:
9	12	99	77	history:
10	15	99	30	triadimefon
treated				penconazole
1	<10	--	--	
2	<10	--	--	
3	<10	--	--	
4	15	100	62	
5	14	99	69	
6	19	100	52	
7	10	100	74	
8	10	99	95	
9	<10	--	--	
10	15	97	68	
Bridge Orch.				
1	27	100	62	
2	<10	--	--	
3	18	100	23	
4	10	99	57	
5	18	100	32	

TABLE 3. Apple Powdery Mildew 1992 – England

Gore Farm and Bridge Orchard, Kent
Varieties: Gore Farm 'Cox Orange' and 'Golden Delicious'
         Bridge Orchard 'Cox Orange'

Sampling: 8.6.92, tips of young shoots from treated trees
                    mildew isolates tested directly without subculture

2 tests on plants, variety 'Morgenduft' with triadimefon

Farm Variety Isolate	% attack control	Sensitivity test % efficacy (Abbott) mg triadimefon/l 100	30	10	treatments:
Standard	52	100	96	90	Gore Farm 1992: 7x penconazole + nitrothal-isopropyl & metiram (ULV-sprays with 55 l/ha)
Gore Farm					
Golden					
1	--	no mildew infections			
2	<10	--	--	--	
3	<10	--	--	--	
4	--	no mildew infections			
5	<10	--	--	--	
6	<10	--	--	--	Bridge Orchard 1992:
7	14	98	98	83	5x penconazole & dithianon
8	<10	--	--	--	1x benomyl
Cox					1x nitrothal-isopropyl
1	42	99	87	33	& metiram
2	47	100	95	44	1x myclobutanil
3	77	100	89	48	(ULV-sprays with 56 l/ha)
4	65	100	90	43	
5	57	99	83	7	
6	27	99	91	69	
7	<10	--	--	--	
8	<10	--	--	--	
9	47	100	86	51	
10	17	100	77	71	
11	17	100	71	70	
12	13	100	100	38	
Bridge Orch.					
1	<10	--	--	--	
2	--	no mildew infections			
3	--	"			
4	--	"			
5	--	"			
6	--	"			
7	--	"			
8	--	"			
9	--	"			
10	--	"			
11	--	"			

TABLE 4. Long-term trial with triadimefon

Podosphaera leucotricha - leaf symptoms

Variety: Jonathan
Site   : South Tyrol / Leifers

Year	Number of applications	Efficacy (% Abbott) triadimefon * % a.i.			sulphur	Control % attack
		0,0025	0,0031	0,0062	0,18%a.i	
1973	14		65	61	59	64
1974	12		83	92	70	64
1975	11		91	95	41	73
1976	10	75	74	88	69	65
1977	12	94	97	97	85	74
1978	12	96	97	98	92	76
1979	15	93	98	98	91	61
1980	15	97	100	100	97	64
1981	12	96	99	100	92	34
1982	11	99	99	100	92	75
1983	11	97	98	100	78	69
1984	10	98	99	100	89	75
1985	12	96	99	99	91	61
1986	9	65	78	92	53	55
1987	12	96	98	99	75	75
1988	11	79	91	95	42	57
1989	12	93	96	98	83	88
1990	12	85	92	96	75	83
1991	12	92	97	98	82	87

* = different formulations
    partly in mixture with captan

PHENYLAMIDE RESISTANCE IN *PHYTOPHTHORA INFESTANS* IN NORTHERN IRELAND - A CHANGING SITUATION

L.R. COOKE, R.E. PENNEY

Plant Pathology Research Division, Department of Agriculture for Northern Ireland, Newforge Lane, Belfast, Northern Ireland, BT9 5PX.

ABSTRACT

Since 1981, the incidence of phenylamide-resistant *Phytophthora infestans* has been surveyed annually using isolates derived from samples of potato blight collected from seed crops throughout the potato-growing areas of Northern Ireland. The percentage of isolates containing resistant strains was below 50% up to 1987 when it increased to over 80%. However, for the last three successive seasons, the proportion has declined from a peak of 90% in 1988 to 42% in 1991. This trend appears to be related to a decline in the usage of phenylamide fungicides and also to weather in July-August not particularly favourable to blight during 1989-1991. The distribution of phenylamide-resistant strains within crops was investigated in 1990 using single lesion isolates. Each of the six crops sampled was found to contain both resistant and sensitive strains, but only one yielded less than 50% resistant isolates.

INTRODUCTION

In Northern Ireland, where a formulation containing the phenylamide fungicide metalaxyl plus mancozeb, introduced in 1978, was widely used against potato blight (caused by *Phytophthora infestans*), phenylamide-resistant strains were first detected in tubers from the 1980 crop (Cooke, 1981). In the years 1981-86, despite continued use of phenylamide plus protectant fungicide products, there was no consistent trend in the incidence of phenylamide-resistant strains and the proportion of isolates containing resistance was under 30% in every year except 1984 (Cooke, 1986). The situation changed in 1987; over 80% of isolates tested contained resistant strains. This high incidence of resistant strains was maintained in 1988 and 1989 and it was suggested that one of the major factors which led to selection for resistance was a succession of summers from 1985 to 1988 with weather very conducive to blight (Cooke, 1991). This paper reports the results of surveys of the occurrence of phenylamide-resistant *P. infestans* in Northern Ireland up to 1991 and of an investigation into the incidence of phenylamide-resistant strains within crops in 1990.

MATERIALS & METHODS

Sampling of potato crops for blight

Samples of infected potato foliage were collected by members of the Department of Agriculture's Potato Inspection Service, during the course of seed potato crop inspections. The 18 inspectors, each responsible for a specific geographical area, were asked to supply samples from at least three crops, preferably from cultivars typical of their regions. Foliage was collected from up to five sites within each crop and bulked together. Data on sample location, potato cultivar, fungicide usage and disease incidence were obtained for each sample and stored on a DATATRIEVE database.

In 1990, six crops with a foliage blight incidence of between 1 and 5% were selected for sampling in detail. Twenty single lesion samples (either one leaf or one stem) were collected from within each crop. Isolates from these were maintained and tested separately.

At the end of each season, Inspectors supplied details of fungicide usage for all seed potato crops in their areas.

Maintenance of isolates

Samples were maintained on detached leaves of glasshouse-grown potato plants cv. King Edward and sporangial/zoospore suspensions prepared as previously described (Cooke, 1986).

Tests for phenylamide resistance

Isolates were tested using the floating leaf disc technique (Cooke, 1986). Isolates were designated resistant if they sporulated on 100 mg metalaxyl/litre-treated discs and sensitive if they sporulated on untreated discs but not any metalaxyl-treated disc. Isolates which failed to grow on at least four out of six untreated discs were re-tested.

RESULTS

Incidence of phenylamide resistance

The overall proportion of isolates containing phenylamide-resistant strains of *P. infestans* for each of the years 1981-1991 is shown in Figure 1. In 1988, a peak of 90% of isolates containing resistance was reached, but since 1989 the proportion has declined to 42% in 1991.

When product usage on sampled crops was examined, it was found that those which had received phenylamide applications tended to have a greater proportion of isolates containing resistant strains, but that even crops where only protectant fungicides were used or where no fungicide had been applied often yielded resistant strains (Table 1). However, the decline in the proportion of isolates containing resistance was faster on non-phenylamide-treated crops.

FIGURE 1. The proportion of Northern Ireland isolates of *Phytophthora infestans* containing phenylamide-resistant strains, 1981-1991.

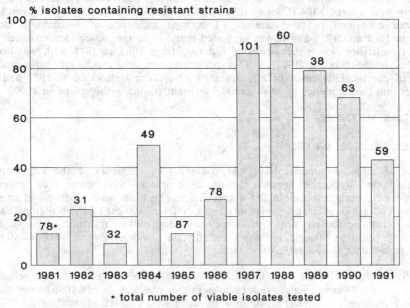

* total number of viable isolates tested

TABLE 1. Fungicide usage on potato crops sampled for *P. infestans* phenylamide resistance survey, 1988-91

Product type	% crops yielding isolates containing resistant strains[*]			
	1988	1989	1990	1991
none	100 (3)	67 (3)	60 (5)	100 (1)
unknown [**]	93 (15)	100 (3)	60 (10)	0 (0)
mancozeb	85 (26)	75 (28)	67 (42)	29 (38)
phenylamide	94 (16)	100 (4)	100 (6)	65 (20)
total	90 (60)	79 (38)	68 (63)	42 (59)

[*]   total numbers of isolates tested are shown in brackets
[**]   no usage of phenylamide-containing products

Investigation of the incidence of phenylamide-resistant *P. infestans* within crops, 1990

Of the six crops selected for detailed sampling in 1990, one was untreated at the time of sampling, three had received mancozeb only, and two had been treated with phenylamides (Table 2). Of these, Crop 5 had been sprayed once with metalaxyl plus mancozeb, whilst Crop 6 had received several applications of phenylamides (metalaxyl and oxadixyl).

TABLE 2. Incidence of phenylamide-resistant *P. infestans* within crops, 1990

Crop number	County	Potato cultivar	Fungicide treatment	No. of isolates tested	% isolates resistant
1	Down	Home Guard	none	20	10
2	Antrim	Home Guard	mancozeb	15	53
3	L'derry	Kerr's Pink	mancozeb	18	56
4	Antrim	Dunbar Standard	mancozeb	20	80
5	L'derry	King Edward	phenylamide	20	60
6	Antrim	Dundrod	phenylamide	19	95

Of the 20 single lesion samples collected from each crop, it proved possible to isolate from at least 15 and sometimes all 20 in each case. All the crops sampled proved to contain both resistant and sensitive strains, the lowest proportion of resistance being found in the unsprayed crop and the greatest in the crop which had received several phenylamide applications (Table 2). However, even one of the crops which had been treated with mancozeb alone yielded 80% resistant strains. After the lesions had been tested separately, those from each crop were bulked together and re-tested. All six bulk isolates gave a resistant result in the disc test; this was as expected since only 1% resistant sporangia are needed to give a resistant result in the disc test (Sozzi & Staub, 1987).

Usage of phenylamide-containing products

Potato Inspectors' estimates of usage of products containing phenylamides on seed potato crops are shown in Figure 2. Data for 1981 and 1982 are not available since in these years the agrochemical companies and the Department of Agriculture advised Northern Ireland

FIGURE. 2. Estimated seed potato crop area treated with phenylamides, 1983-1991.

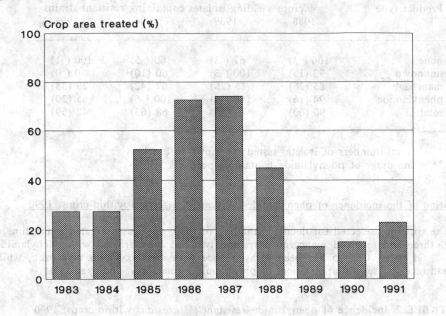

FIGURE 3. Total monthly rainfall for July-August, 1981-1991, Co. Londonderry.

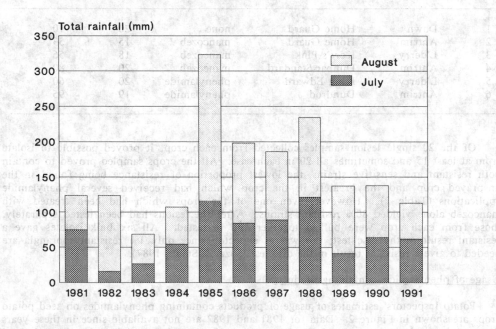

growers not to use products containing phenylamides. Whereas in 1986-87 over 70% of the crop area was treated with phenylamides, after 1987 usage declined. In 1991, there was an increase in the reported area treated, although the proportion of growers using phenylamide-containing products for most of the season was slightly lower than in 1990 (10% compared with 15%). This may be due to a greater number of growers using one or two applications of phenylamides, rather than using them for most of the spray programme.

Meteorological data

In Northern Ireland, the first outbreaks of potato blight each year generally occur sporadically in mid-late June (once the night minimum temperature reaches c. 10°C) and infection builds up in July and August. Generally, rainfall and humidity in July and August have the greatest influence on foliage and tuber blight incidence, since at this time of the year night temperatures are not usually limiting. Rainfall data for July–August for the years 1981-91 are shown in Figure 3. The four seasons 1985-88 had unusually high rainfalls in July and August and in each of these years blight was widespread on crops in Northern Ireland. In contrast, the summers of 1989-91 had much lower rainfall and blight was generally well controlled.

DISCUSSION

The floating leaf disc test for phenylamide resistance is non-quantitative and detects resistant strains when they are present in an isolate at proportions greater than 1% (Sozzi & Staub, 1987). This may lead to an overestimation of resistance present in the field, if resistant strains are widespread, but at a low level. Using a semi-quantitative technique developed by Ciba-Geigy, only one of 10 Northern Ireland *P. infestans* isolates designated as resistant was confirmed to contain a mixture of resistant and sensitive sporangia, but, due to experimental variability, an isolate could not be identified as mixed unless it contained at least 30% sensitive sporangia (Walker, 1990). The investigation of the incidence of phenylamide-resistant *P. infestans* within crops reported here was based on the assumption that single lesion isolates should be clonal in origin and consist of all resistant or all sensitive strains. The results indicate that although both resistant and sensitive strains were found to occur together within crops, the resistant strains were in the majority in most cases and that taken together the mean proportion of resistant strains found in the single isolate tests (59%) was not far different from the overall result of the bulk isolate tests for that year (68%). There was no evidence to suggest that the overall results of the annual surveys were being severely distorted by a widespread but very sparse distribution of resistant strains.

After a dramatic increase in the proportion of isolates of *P. infestans* containing phenylamide-resistant strains in 1987-88 in Northern Ireland, the proportion has declined for three successive seasons (1989-1991). A similar trend has been observed in surveys in the Republic of Ireland (Dowley, L.J., personal communication). Two major factors *viz*. phenylamide usage and incidence of *P. infestans*, have interacted during this period to reduce the selection pressure in favour of resistance.

Usage of phenylamides on seed crops in Northern Ireland declined after 1987. Blight was widespread in phenylamide-treated crops in that season and growers were probably influenced by their perception of product performance. The Department of Agriculture also advised that the benefits of using phenylamides might not justify the additional cost in years when resistant strains were present in the great majority of *P. infestans* isolates tested (Cooke, 1990). Data for fungicide usage on ware crops are not available for most years. However, a Department of Agriculture survey of pesticide usage in 1990 indicated that 30% of the maincrop ware potato area was treated with phenylamides, a rather greater proportion than was estimated for seed crops in that year (15-20%), but that the great majority of crops received only one or two applications (Jess *et al.*, 1992).

In each of the years 1989-91, blight incidence in Northern Ireland was relatively low. The proportion of seed crops with more than 5% foliage infection at haulm destruction was been between 1 and 6%, in contrast to 1985 when it was >50%. Consequently, in each of these years only a minority of crops was treated with phenylamides and these were only exposed to a relatively small *P. infestans* population. Thus the selection pressure in favour of resistance was much reduced in contrast to the overwhelming pressure of the years 1985-88.

However, reduced pressure in favour of resistance alone will not bring about a decline in the proportion of resistant strains. If resistant and sensitive strains were identical in all respects save their response to phenylamides, the resistant proportion of the population might be expected to remain constant or decline very slowly as the resistant character was lost by random mutation. That a quite marked decline has occurred within three years suggests that the resistant strains may not be as fit as their sensitive counterparts. This may be due to a poorer capacity to survive the winter and produce primary infections the following season (Walker & Cooke, 1988, 1990). Nonetheless, it is clear that in years when foliage blight infection spreads rapidly, resistant strains will build up very quickly if application of phenylamides is widespread. The present moderate level of phenylamide usage is more likely to ensure that these fungicides continue to make some contribution to controlling potato blight than if they were once again to be applied to the majority of crops for most of the season.

ACKNOWLEDGEMENTS

The authors are very grateful to members of the Department of Agriculture's Potato Inspection Service for supplying samples of potato blight and crop information. Mr. D.G. Wilson and Mr. R.S. Miller are thanked for technical assistance.

REFERENCES

Cooke, L.R. (1981) Resistance to metalaxyl in *Phytophthora infestans* in Northern Ireland. *1981 British Crop Protection Conference - Pests and Diseases*, 2, 641-649.
Cooke, L.R. (1986) Acylalanine resistance in *Phytophthora infestans* in Northern Ireland. *1986 British Crop Protection Conference - Pests and Diseases*, 2, 507-514.
Cooke, L.R. (1990) Potato blight control - the current position. *Agriculture in Northern Ireland*, 4 (8), 16-17.
Cooke, L.R. (1991) Current problems in potato blight control: the Northern Ireland experience. In: *Phytophthora*, J.A. Lucas, R.C. Shattock, D.S. Shaw and L.R. Cooke (Eds), Cambridge: Cambridge University Press, pp. 337-48.
Jess, S.; McCallion, T.; Kidd, S.B.L. (1992) *Pesticide usage in Northern Ireland - Survey Report 105 - Arable Crops 1990*, Department of Agriculture for Northern Ireland, in press.
Sozzi, D.; Staub, T. (1987) Accuracy of methods to monitor sensitivity of *Phytophthora infestans* to phenylamide fungicides. *Plant Disease*, 71, 422-425.
Walker, A.S.L. (1990) *Comparison of the fitness of phenylamide-sensitive and phenylamide-resistant strains of* Phytophthora infestans. Ph.D. Thesis, The Queen's Univeristy of Belfast, pp. 50-53.
Walker, A.S.L.; Cooke, L.R. (1988) The survival of phenylamide-resistant strains of *Phytophthora infestans* in potato tubers. *Brighton Crop Protection Conference - Pests and Diseases 1988*, 1, 353-358.
Walker, A.S.L.; Cooke, L.R. (1990) The survival of *Phytophthora infestans* in potato tubers - the role of phenylamide resistance. *Brighton Crop Protection Conference - Pests and Diseases 1990*, 3, 1109-1114.

USE OF POLYMERASE CHAIN REACTION FOR THE DIAGNOSIS OF MBC
RESISTANCE IN *BOTRYTIS CINEREA*

L.A. MARTIN, R.T.V. FOX

University of Reading, Dept. of Horticulture, School of Plant Sciences, P.O Box 239, Earley
Gate, Reading, Berks. RG6 2AU.

B.C. BALDWIN

ICI Agrochemicals, Jealott's Hill Research Station, Bracknell, Berks. RG12 6EY.

I.F. CONNERTON

A.F.R.C. Institute of Food Research, Reading Laboratory, Earley Gate, Reading, Berks.
RG6 2 EF.

ABSTRACT

In recent years resistance to methylbenzimidazole carbamate (MBC) in fungal
pathogens has been attributed to single amino acid changes in the β-tubulin subunit.
The majority of these changes are located between amino acids 100 and 300. Using
conserved oligonucleotide primers encompassing this region we have been able to
amplify, clone and sequence part of the β-tubulin gene from two *Botrytis cinerea*
isolates with MBC resistant and sensitive phenotypes. A point mutation at amino
acid 198, causing a change from glutamic acid to alanine, confered MBC resistance.
We synthesised two oligonucleotide primers incorporating the point mutation for
resistance and sensitivity. These allele specific oligonucleotides (ASO) were used
in a nested primer PCR to determine the phenotype of several *B. cinerea* isolates
of known sensitivity or resistance to MBC. The resistant and sensitive strands were
successfully diagnosed by PCR amplification and Southern blot hybridisation.

INTRODUCTION

Resistance to benzimidazole fungicides was reported soon after these fungicides were
released (Bollen & Scholten, 1971; Delp, 1980). Extensive studies concerning the mode of
action of methyl benzimidazole carbamate (MBC) have been closely paralleled by those on the
mechanism of resistance. MBC has been shown to bind preferentially to β-tubulin (Davidse,
1973; Davidse & Flach, 1977) and small changes in the β-tubulin protein result in reduced
affinity for the fungicide (Sheir-Neiss *et al* ., 1978).

The study of fungal resistance has been greatly enhanced by the isolation of laboratory
mutants resistant to these mitotic inhibitors (van Tuyl, 1975; Orbach *et al* ., 1986). Cloning and
sequencing of β-tubulin genes from these isolates has enabled the cause of MBC resistance in
many fungal strains to be located as point mutations in the β-tubulin gene and which result in
single amino acid changes (Thomas *et al* ., 1985; Orbach *et al* ., 1986; Jung *et al* ., 1987) and
which influence the electrophoretic properties of the protein subunit (Shier-Neiss *et al* ., 1976
& 1978; May *et al* ., 1985 & 1987).

In this paper we discuss the discovery of the point mutation responsible for MBC
resistance in *B. cinerea* isolates and its diagnosis by use of the polymerase chain reaction
(PCR) adopting allele-specific oligonucleotide primers (ASO).

MATERIALS AND METHODS

Strains and plasmids

B.cinerea isolates used in this study are listed in Table 1. The EC$_{50}$ and phenotypes were predetermined by growth on DYP agar (Groves *et al.*, 1988) in the presence of MBC. Isolate K1145, resistant to MBC (MBCR), and PC9385S, sensitive to MBC (MBCS) were used as a source of genomic DNA for cloning and sequencing of the β-tubulin gene. Genomic DNA was extracted from 3 day old mycelial cultures according to Stevens *et al* . (1982).

The bacterial strain *Escherichia coli* DH5α (BRL, Life Technologies, Gaithersberg, Md.) cultured on or in Luria-Bertani medium (Maniatis *et al.*, 1982) was used for transformation and isolation of plasmids.

Amplification of β-tubulin target sequence by PCR

The β-tubulin gene segment from *B. cinerea* genomic DNA (1μg) was amplified using primers β–101 and β-293 (see below) in 100μl reaction volumes containing 200μM of each deoxynucleotide triphosphate (dNTPs),400pM of each primer , 2.5units of *Ampli* Taq® polymerase (Perkin-Elmer Cetus, Norwalk, Conn.), 50mM KCl, 10mM Tris-HCl (pH 8.3), 1.5mM MgCl$_2$, and 0.01% gelatine.The procedure was as follows: denaturation at 95°C for 2 min; annealing at 55°C for 2min; extension at 72°C for 3 min for 30 cycles with a final extension at 72°C for 7 min. Reaction mixture (8μl) was loaded on to 1.5% (w/v) agarose gels containing ethidium bromide and run at 50V. The amplified DNA was visualised by u.v. light and the position of bands compared to a standard λ ladder .

Diagnosis of resistance using ASO in a nested primer system

Reaction mixtures (50μl) were prepared in duplicate containing approximately 100ng of amplified β-tubulin (1μl of PCR product), primer β-293 and tailed primer R or tailed primer S. The samples were amplified using the following conditions: denaturation at 95°C for 1.5 min, annealing at 62°C for 1.5 min, extension at 72°C for 3 min - for 2 cycles followed by the same process with an annealing temperature of 67°C for 28 cycles. The products were run on 1.5% agarose gels as previously described.

Cloning and sequencing

The recessed ends of the amplified β-tubulin gene segment were filled using the Klenow fragment of *E. coli* DNA polymerase I, followed by the addition of phosphates using polynucleotide kinase. The amplified gene fragment was ligated to dephosphorylated (calf intestinal phosphatase) pBluescript SK+ (Stratagene, La Jolla, Ca) in the presence of T4 ligase (BRL) and blunt end ligation buffer . The mixture was used to transform *E. coli* DH5α. Transformants, identified by blue/white selection, were recultured and plasmid DNA isolated and screened for the presence of the β-tubulin insert by restriction digest using BamH1 and Hind III. All methods described above are according to Maniatis *et al* . (1982) and Sambrook *et al* . (1989).

Plasmid DNA was isolated from selected clones and nucleotide sequence analysis performed using the dideoxy chain termination method (Sanger *et al* .,1977) with the Sequenase® kit (U.S. Biochemicals, Cleveland, Ohio).

RESULTS AND DISCUSSION

Amplification of part of the β-tubulin gene from *B. cinerea* and its subsequent cloning and sequencing.

The majority of mutations causing MBC resistance have been located between amino acid residue 100 and 300 of the β-subunit (reviewed by Leroux, 1991). Primers β-101 and β-293 were designed in highly conserved regions of the β-tubulin gene flanking this area of interest based upon the β-tubulin amino acid sequence comparisons outlined by Orbach *et al..* (1986). Primer oligonucleotide sequences are shown in Figure 1.

Primers and Probe

Amplification of β-tubulin gene

Primers: β-101:   TGG GCT AAA GGT CAC TAC AC
      β-293:   CAT TTG TTG TGT TGT TAA TTC TGG

Diagnosis of MBC resistance using ASO primers

Primer S: G AGA ACT CTG ACG A
Primer R: G AGA ACT CTG ACG C

Tailed Primer S: GCT GGC CAA CTG AGA ACT CTG ACG A
Tailed Primer R: GCT GGC CAA CTG AGA ACT CTG ACG C

Southern blotting R- probe:

                    TCT GAC GCG ACC TTC TGT

FIGURE 1. Nucleotide sequences for primers and probe.

Amplification by PCR of genomic DNA from *B. cinerea* K1145 (MBCR) and PC9385S (MBCs) resulted in a fragment 579bp in size as predicted for these chosen primer positions. These fragments were cloned into pBluescript and 30 positive DH5α transformants which grew as white colonies were selected. Restriction digest with Hind III and Bam HI revealed 8 clones with plasmids containing the β-tubulin insert. Three transformants containing plasmids with inserts from K1145 (MBCR) and one from PC9385S (MBCs) were chosen. From these the plasmids were purified on a caesium chloride gradient (Maniatis *et al* ., 1982) and sequenced. The nucleotide sequence for *B. cinerea* K1145 is shown in Figure 2.

To verify that the PCR fragment was indeed part of the *B. cinerea* β-tubulin gene, we compared the predicted protein sequence with published data for several other fungal β-tubulin genes (within the region amino acid 100 - 300). The amino acid sequence for the *B. cinerea* β-tubulin is highly homologous to *Neurospora crassa* (FGSC 3460) 98% (Orbach *et al* ., 1986), *Schizosaccharomyces pombe* 83% (Hirako *et al* ., 1984), *Aspergillus nidulans* 97% (May *et al* ., 1987) and *Saccharomyces cerevisiae* 84% (Neff *et al* ., 1983) (Figure 3).

Mapping of the point mutation responsible for MBC resistance in *B. cinerea.*

Sequence comparisons of the target DNA from *B. cinerea* K1145 (MBCR) and PC9385S (MBCs) revealed a single transversion from A to C at nucleotide 295 of the K1145

```
                                      *30
TGG GCG AAG GGT CAT TAC ACT GAG GGT GCT GAG CTT GTC GAC CAA GTT CTT GAT
Trp Ala Lys Gly His Tyr Thr Glu Gly Ala Glu Leu Val Asp Gln Val Leu Asp
101                                     110

      *60                                           *90
GTT GTC CGT CGT GAA GCT GAA GGC TGT GAC TGC CTT CAA GGA TTC CAA ATT ACC
Val Val Arg Arg Glu Ala Glu Gly Cys Asp Cys Leu Gln Gly Phe Gln Ile Thr
      120                                     130

          *120                                          *150
CAC TCT CTC GGT GGT GGA ACT GGT GCC GGT ATG GGT ACG CTT TTG ATC TCC AAG
His Ser Leu Gly Gly Gly Thr Gly Ala Gly Met Gly Thr Leu Leu Ile Ser Lys
          140                               150

ATC CGC GAG GAG TTC CCA GAT CGT ATG ATG GCT ACC TTC TCC GTC GTC CCA TCG
Ile Arg Glu Glu Phe Pro Asp Arg Met Met Ala Thr Phe Ser Val Val Pro Ser
                        *180                                    *210
                        160                                     170

                              *240                                  *270
CCA AAG GTT TCC GAT ACC GTT GTC GAG CCA TAT AAC GCA ACT CTC TCT GTC CAT
Pro Lys Val Ser Asp Thr Val Val Glu Pro Tyr Asn Ala Thr Leu Ser Val His
                              180                                    190

                                    *300
CAA TTG GTT GAG AAC TCT GAC GCG ACC TTC TGT ATC GAT AAC GAG GCT CTT TAC
Gln Leu Val Glu Asn Ser Asp Ala Thr Phe Cys Ile Asp Asn Glu Ala Leu Tyr
                                    200

      *330                                          *360
GAT ATT TGC ATG AGA ACC TTG AAG CTC AGC AAC CCA TCT TAC GGA GAT CTT AAC
Asp Ile Cys Met Arg Thr Leu Lys Leu Ser Asn Pro Ser Tyr Gly Asp Leu Asn
      210                                     220

          *390                                          *420
CAC TTG GTT TCC GCC GTC ATG TCC GGT GTT ACC ACC TGT CTC CGT TTC CCT GGT
His Leu Val Ser Ala Val Met Ser Gly Val Thr Thr Cys Leu Arg Phe Pro Gly
          230                                     240

              *450                                          *480
CAA CTT AAC TCA GAT CTC CGA AAG TTG GCT GTT AAC ATG GTT CCA TTC CCC CGT
Gln Leu Asn Ser Asp Leu Arg Lys Leu Ala Val Asn Met Val Pro Phe Pro Arg
              250                                     260

                  *510                                          *540
CTC CAT TTC TTC ATG GTT GGA TTT GCT CCT TTG ACC AGT CGT GGC GCA CAC TCT
Leu His Phe Phe Met Val Gly Phe Ala Pro Leu Thr Ser Arg Gly Ala His Ser
                  270                                     280

                      *570
TTC CGT GCT GTC ACC GTT CCC GAA CTG ACA CAA CAG ATG
Phe Arg Ala Val Thr Val Pro Glu Leu Thr Gln Gln Met
                      290
```

FIGURE 2. DNA sequence for part of the β-tubulin gene from *B. cinerea* K1145 (MBCR). The nucleotide sequence is numbered above and relates to the cloned β–tubulin gene fragment. The amino acids are numbered below the sequence and relate to the position of the residue in relation to the whole β-tubulin sequence.

```
            *101       *111       *121       *131       *141
B.cK        WAKGHYTEGA ELVDQVLDVV RREAEGCDCL QGFQITHSLG GGTGAGMGTL
B.cP
N.crassa 3460
A.nidulans             N V
S.cerevisiae           S M I             S                       S
S.pombe                AVA L           A A         L             S


            *151       *161       *171       *181       *191
B.cK        LISKIREEFP DRMMATFSVV PSPKVSDTVV EPYNATLSVH QLVENSDATF
B.cP                                                             E
N.c                                                             E
A.n                                                        H    E
S.c         F   K L            L       T                   H  E
S.p           L   Y          A A S                 M            E


            *201       *211       *221       *231       *241
B.cK        CIDNEALYDI CMRTLKLSNP SYGDLNHLVS AVMSGVTTCL RFPGQLNSDL
B.cP
N.c                                          VS
A.n
S.c              Q      NQ          N        S    Y
S.p            SS IAN  IKS       D         A    S    E


            *251       *261       *271       *281       *291
B.cK        RKLAVNMVPF PRLHFFMVGF APLTSRGAHS FRAVTVPELT QQM
B.cP
N.c                                          H    S
A.n         W                                Y    S
S.c              L              Y     AI SQ     SL
S.p                              AAI SS    Q    S
```

FIGURE 3. Comparison of the amino acid sequence for β-tubulin from residue 101 to 193 of *B. cinerea* (K1145 and Pc9385S) with those of other fungal β-tubulin genes. Only residues varying from *B. cinerea* are shown. Numbers at the top of the sequence denote the position of the amino acid residue in relation to the whole β-tubulin sequence.

β-tubulin sequence. This resulted in a glutamic acid to alanine change at position 198 (numbered in relation to the whole β-tubulin subunit).

As stated earlier the majority of mutations resulting in MBC resistance have been mapped between amino acids 100 and 300 of the β-tubulin subunit. Orbach *et al* . (1986) localised resistance as a phenylalanine to tyrosine change at amino acid 167 for *N. crassa*. In *S. cerevisiae* a change from arginine to histidine at amino acid 241 was responsible for benomyl resistance (Jung *et al* ., 1985). More recently MBC resistance has been attributed to point mutations at amino acid 198. For *Venturia inaequalis* a change from glutamate to alanine (Leroux, 1991) and for *N. crassa* F914 glutamic acid to glycine substitution resulted in MBC resistance (Fujimura *et al* ., 1992). We concluded that the mutation at position 198 for *B. cinerea* K1145 is responsible for its MBC resistance.

Development of a PCR diagnostic test.

We proceeded on the basis that allele-specific oligonucleotide primers (ASO) (incorporating the base change for either MBC resistance or sensitivity) could be used in conjunction with primer β-293 as a diagnostic assay, able to discriminate between the genotypes of *B. cinerea* isolates.The assay would involve selective amplification of β-tubulin with corresponding MBC sensitive or resistant nucleotide sequences.

Originally the primers R and S outlined above were synthesised (see Figure 1). It was assumed a PCR product of approximately 300bp would be amplified. This was achieved and a PCR fragment of 300bp obtained, but without selectivity. The major cause was thought to be the non-specific priming ability of *Ampli* Taq® polymerase. To overcome the problem, primers were designed with a tail region which was unrelated to the tubulin sequence within the area of the mutation (see Figure 1.) . The use of tailed primers has been outlined by Jefferies *et al* . (1991). However in the authors' technique a third primer was added after the initial PCR cycles. In the technique described below the same increase in specificity was achieved by altering the annealing temperature after the first two cycles.

The assay was extremely successful when using a nested primer system. A PCR fragment of 310bp (as predicted) was amplified with both tailed primers-S and R. The results (Table 1) indicated amplification of the β-tubulin sequence by the S-primer, (but not the R-primer) for *B. cinerea* B4, A19 and PC9385S. These isolates had been previously characterised as MBC sensitive. Isolates Pc9385R, K1145, and 1805R were amplified using the R-primer, (but not by the S-primer). It was concluded that they were MBC resistant. Poison plate analysis confirmed these cultures were indeed resistant. Amplification of β-tubulin from an intermediate isolate GB111/74 occurs with both tailed primer S and tailed primer R. In this case an alternative point mutation or another mechanism of resistance may be in operation. Koenraadt *et al* . (1991) claimed that a mutation at amino acid 198 from glutamate to glycine caused intermediate resistance in an *V. inaequalis* isolate.

TABLE 1. Screening of *B. cinerea* isolates for MBC resistance.

Isolate	EC50 µg.ml-1	Phenotype	Presence of resistant sequence PCR primer S	R	Southern blot R-probe
PC9385R	775	Resistant	-	+	+
K1145	733	Resistant	-	+	+
1805R(b)	425	Resistant	-	+	+
GB 111/74	17.8	Intermediate	+	+	not tested
PC9385S	0.066	Sensitive	+	-	-
A19	0.055	Sensitive	+	-	not tested
B4	0.075	Sensitive	+	-	-

EC50 reduction in colony diameter by 50%
+ indicates strong amplification by PCR and /or hybridisation by Southern blotting
- indicates no visible amplification by PCR and/or hybridisation by Southern blotting

To confirm the results above, Southern blots (Southern, 1975) of the amplified β-tubulin target sequences from five of the *B. cinerea* isolates were hybridised with an 18-mer oligonucleotide probe (sequence corresponding to MBC resistance (Figure 1) with the mutation placed centrally to aid hybridisation. The probe was labelled with [γ32P] ATP (Maniatis *et al* ., 1982). Autoradiographs showed that the probe bound specifically to the corresponding resistant sequences (Table 1). It was concluded that the diagnostic PCR was able to discriminate between the point mutations for resistance and sensitivity.

Possible use of PCR as a rapid diagnostic test

We found that it was possible to assess MBC resistance or sensitivity within 48-72 hours. The test is far more rapid than standard poison plate assays which can take up to three weeks and rely on clean cultures. The ASO-PCR is remarkably sensitive, with the potential to amplify as little as 1ng of target DNA. We believe that less fungal material will be required for this method than for those based on monoclonal antibodies (Martin *et al.*, 1992). PCR will detect genotypic rather than phenotypic resistance, which is potentially more useful when diagnosing resistance in a heterokaryotic fungus such as *B. cinerea*.

Thus our attempts amplify specifically R and S β-tubulin sequences from genomic DNA from *B. cinerea* have proven as yet unsuccessful, whereas we have succeeded using a nested primer system, whereby the 579bp fragment is amplified non-specifically, followed by a specific detection step for the 310bp fragment. Similar results have been reported for other diagnostic tests using PCR. Amplification of target sites is influenced by the cleanness of genomic DNA preparations (A. Daly, unpublished). It may be concluded that specificity of the assay will rely on the continued use of a nested primer system. This has potential for development into a sensitive diagnostic test, and future work will attempt to increase the ease and throughput of the assay.

ACKNOWLEDGEMENTS

We would like to extend our thanks to Dr. P.G. Thomas and Dr. J.D. Windass for providing many of the reagents used. Miss R.E.Duncan and Mr. F. Sgard for useful discussions. Special thanks to Miss M.-M.Suner and Mr A Daly for advice concerning sequencing and use of PCR as a diagnostic tool.

This work was supported by an SERC CASE award with ICI Agrochemicals.

REFERENCES

Bollen, G.J.; Scholten, G.(1971) Acquired resistance to benomyl and some other systemic fungicides in a strain of *Botrytis cinerea* in cyclamen. *Netherlands Journal of Plant Pathology* , **77**, 83-90

Davidse, L.C. (1973) Antimitotic activity of methyl benzimidazole carbamate (MBC) in *Aspergillus nidulans*. *Pesticide Biochemistry and Physiology*, **3**, 317-325

Davidse, L.C.; Flach, W. (1977) Differential binding of methyl benzimidazol-2-yl carbamate to fungal tubulin as a mechanism of resistance to this anti-mitotic agent in mutant strains of *Aspergillus nidulans*. *Journal of Cell Biology* , **72**, 174-193.

Delp, C.J. (1980) Coping with resistance to plant disease control agents. *Plant Disease*, **64**, 652-657.

Fujimura, M.; Oeda, K.; Inoue, H.; Kato, T. (1992) The single amino acid substitution in the beta tubulin gene of *Neurospora crassa* confers both carbendazim resistance and diethofencarb sensitivity. *Current Genetics* , **21**, 399-404

Groves, J.D.; Fox, R.T.V.; Baldwin, B.C. (1988) Modes of action of carbendazim and ethyl *N* -(3,5-dichlorophenyl) carbamate on field isolates of *Botrytis cinerea*.. *Brighton Crop Protection Conference- Pest and Diseases 1988*, **1**, 397-402

Hiraoka, Y.; Toda, T. ; Yanagida, M. (1984) The NDA3 gene of fission yeast encodes β-tubulin: a cold-sensitive nda3 mutation reversibly blocks spindle formation and chromosome movement in mitosis. *Cell* , **39** , 349-358

Koenraadt, H.; Somerville, S.C.; Jones, A.L.(1991) Molecular characterisation of the β-tubulin gene from benomyl sensitive and benomyl resistant field strains of *Venturia inaequalis*. *Abstracts of the American Chemical Society , April 1991*, AGRO 87

Jeffreys, A.J.; MacLeod, A.; Tamaki, K.; Neil, D.L.; Monckton D.G. (1991) Minisatellite repeat coding as a digital approach to DNA typing. *Nature*, **354**, 204-209

Jung, M.K.; Dunne, P.W.; Suen, I.-H. ; Oakley, B.R. (1987) Sequence alterations in β-tubulin mutations of *Aspergillus nidulans. Journal of Cell Biology*, **105**, Abstracts, 277a.

Leroux, P. (1991) Résistance des Champignons phytopathogénes aux fongicides.*Phytoma - La Défenses des végétaux*, **434**, 20-26

Maniatis, T.; Fritsch, E.F. ; Sambrook.J. (1982) *Molecular cloning: a laboratory manual.* Cold Spring Harbour Laboratory, Cold Spring Harbour, N.Y.

Martin, L.-A.; Fox, R.T.V.; Baldwin, B.C. (1992) Rapid methods for detection of MBC resistance in fungi: I. Immunological approach. *Proceedings of 10th International Reinhardsbrunn Symposium.* (in press)

May, G.S.; Gambino, J.; Weatherbee, J.A.; Morris, N.R. (1985) Identification and functional analysis of beta-tubulin genes by site specific integrative transformation in *Aspergillus nidulans. Journal of Cell Biology*, **101**,712-719

May, G.S.; Tsang, M.L.S.; Smith, H.; Fidel, S.; Morris, N.R. (1987) *Aspergillus nidulans* β-tubulin genes are unusually divergent. *Gene*, **55**, 231-243

Neff, N.F.; Thomas, J.H.; Grisafi, P.; Botstein, D. (1983) Isolation of the β-tubulin gene from yeast and a demonstration of its essential function *in vivo. Cell*, **33**, 211-219

Orbach, M.J.; Porro, E.B.; Yanofsky, C. (1986) Cloning and characterization of the gene for β-tubulin from a benomyl-resistant mutant of *Neurospora crassa*, and its use as a dominant selectable marker. *Molecular and Cellular Biology*, **6**, 2452-2461.

Sambrook, J.; Fritsch, E.F.; Maniatis, T. (1989) Molecular cloning: a laboratory manual. Cold Spring Harbour Laboratory, Cold Spring Harbour, N.Y.

Sanger, F.; Nicklen S.; Coulson, A.R. (1977) DNA sequencing with chain-terminating inhibitors. *Proceedings of the National Academy of Science. USA* ,**74**, 5463-5467

Sheir-Neiss, G.; Nardi, R.V.; Gealt, M.A.; Morris, N.R. (1976) Tubulin like protein from *Aspergillus nidulans. Biochemical and Biophysical Research Communications* , **69**, 285-290

Sheir-Neiss, G.; Lai, M.; Morris, N.R. (1978) Identification of a gene for β-tubulin in *Aspergillus nidulans. Cell* , **15**, 639-647

Southern, E.M. (1975) Detection of specific sequences among DNA fragments seperated by gel electrophoresis. *Journal of Molecular Biology*, **98**, 503-517

Stevens, J.N.; Metzenberg, R.L. (1982) An easy method for preparing *Neurospora* DNA. *Neurospora News Letters*, **29**, 27-28

Thomas, J.H.; Neff, N.; Botstein, D. (1985) Isolation and characterization of mutations in the β-tubulin gene of *Saccharomyces cerevisiae. Genetics* , **112**, 715-734

van Tuyl, J.M. (1975) Genetic aspects of acquired resistance to benomyl and thiabendazole in a number of fungi. *Mededelingen van de Faculteit Landbouwwetenschappen Rijksuniversiteit Gent*, **40**, 691-697

EFFECT OF MORPHOLINE-LIKE FUNGICIDES ON GROWTH AND STEROL COMPOSITION OF A WILD-TYPE STRAIN AND A STEROL MUTANT OF *USTILAGO MAYDIS* DEFECTIVE IN STEROL $\Delta^8 \rightarrow \Delta^7$ ISOMERASE ACTIVITY

C.S. JAMES, J.A. HARGREAVES, R.S.T. LOEFFLER, R.S. BURDEN

Department of Agricultural Sciences, University of Bristol, AFRC Institute of Arable Crops Research, Long Ashton Research Station, Bristol, BS18 9AF.

ABSTRACT

The effect of tridemorph, fenpropimorph and fenpropidin on the growth and sterol content of a *Ustilago maydis* wild-type strain and a sterol mutant, defective in sterol $\Delta^8 \rightarrow \Delta^7$ isomerization, has been examined. The results, which are in agreement with previous findings, indicated that tridemorph primarily affects sterol $\Delta^8 \rightarrow \Delta^7$ isomerization, whereas fenpropidin was more active against sterol Δ^{14} reduction. In contrast, fenpropimorph appeared to be inhibitory against both these enzyme activities. Inhibition of growth by fenpropimorph and fenpropidin, in both the wild-type and the mutant, coincided with the accumulation of the Δ^{14} sterol, ignosterol. Although tridemorph inhibited growth of the mutant by 45%, its sterol composition was unaffected. These results suggests that the fungicidal effectiveness of fenpropidin and fenpropimorph is associated with the accumulation of ignosterol, while inhibition of growth by tridemorph appears to result, in part, from additional effects on processes unrelated to sterol biosynthesis. Exposure of the wild-type and the sterol mutant to tridemorph or fenpropimorph also led to an increase in the degree of unsaturation of fatty acids.

INTRODUCTION

The outstanding success of sterol biosynthesis inhibitors (SBIs) as fungicides has been qualified in recent years by the appearance of resistant fungal strains in the field (Koller & Scheinpflug, 1987). This problem is particularly evident with inhibitors of sterol C-14 demethylase (DMIs). In contrast, the morpholine-type fungicides, while having a narrower spectrum of fungicidal activity, seem to be less beset by resistance problems (Brent, 1988). Unlike DMIs, which act at a single site, morpholines are generally considered to have a dual mode of action and inhibit both sterol $\Delta^8 \rightarrow \Delta^7$ isomerization and sterol Δ^{14} reduction to different degrees, depending on the structure of the inhibitor and the species of fungus under investigation (Mercer, 1991).

Fungal strains deficient in sterol biosynthesis are,

paradoxically, viable and able to accumulate abnormal sterols which are not normally found in the wild-type. In a recent study we isolated a number of polyene-resistant mutants of *Ustilago maydis*, defective in ergosterol biosynthesis (James *et al*,. 1992). Among these mutants was a pimaricin-resistant isolate which contained no ergosterol but instead accumulated Δ^8 sterols. This isolate, which is presumed to be defective in sterol $\Delta^8 \rightarrow \Delta^7$ isomerase activity, has been used to study the mode of action of morpholine fungicides and to identify potential sources of resistance to these inhibitors. We reasoned that fungicides that primarily affect sterol $\Delta^8 \rightarrow \Delta^7$ isomerization should be ineffective against this mutant, while those that inhibit sterol Δ^{14} reduction or both enzymatic steps should retain their activity because $\Delta^8 \rightarrow \Delta^7$ isomerization follows Δ^{14} reduction in ergosterol biosynthesis. However, care is needed in interpreting the effects of these inhibitors on fungal growth because any biochemical compensation which permits growth and allows Δ^8 sterols to substitute for ergosterol might also allow other sterols, including Δ^{14} sterols, to functionally replace ergosterol.

STEROL CONTENT AND GROWTH OF *U. MAYDIS* PIMARICIN-RESISTANT MUTANT

Characterization of the pimaricin-resistant mutant, P51, has been described previously (James *et al.*, 1992). Unlike the wild-type, IMI103761, this mutant contained no detectable ergosterol, but instead accumulated the Δ^8 sterols, ergost-8-enol, ergosta-8,22-dienol, ergosta-5,8,22-trienol and fecosterol (ergosta-8,24(28)-dienol). The growth of the mutant was reduced as compared to the wild-type. Sporidia produced by this mutant were morphologically abnormal and often grew as multicellular clumps of cells. However, subculturing the mutant during the early stages of log growth enabled growth rates of between 38-58 % of the wild-type to be attained. Cultures of the mutant grown in this way contained many single cells along with the characteristic cell clumps. However, no changes in the type of sterols formed by the mutant was observed after continuous subculture and cultures grown in this way were used in the experiments described below.

SENSITIVITY OF *U.MAYDIS* WILD-TYPE AND STEROL MUTANT TO MORPHOLINE-LIKE FUNGICIDES

Tridemorph, fenpropimorph and fenpropidin were potent inhibitors of growth of the *U. maydis* wild-type (Figures 1A,1C,1E). In agreement with a recent study (Girling 1991), fenpropidin was significantly less active than the other two inhibitors. As compared to the wild-type, the mutant was appreciably less sensitive to tridemorph (Figure 1B) but comparable in growth after exposure to inhibitory concentrations of fenpropimorph (Figure 1D). Surprisingly, the sterol mutant was more sensitive to fenpropidin than the wild-type (Figure 1F).

STEROL COMPOSITION OF *U. MAYDIS* WILD-TYPE AND STEROL MUTANT
FOLLOWING TREATMENT WITH MORPHOLINE-LIKE FUNGICIDES

Ergosterol was the predominant sterol in the wild-type.
Exposure to all three inhibitors depleted ergosterol and this was
closely associated with a reduction in growth (Figures 1A,1C,1E).
Increasing the concentration of tridemorph led to a progressive
increase in ergost-8-enol and ergosta-8,22-dienol in the wild-
type, whereas within the same concentration range, tridemorph did
not alter the sterol composition of the mutant, even though
growth was reduced by up to 45 percent (Figure 1B). In contrast,
ergost-8-enol and ergosta-8,22-dienol in the wild-type initially
increased with increasing concentrations of fenpropimorph and
then declined at higher concentrations. This decline in Δ^8
sterols was associated with an increase in the Δ^{14} sterol,
ignosterol. Δ^8 sterols did not accumulate in the wild-type
following exposure to fenpropidin. In this case, depletion in
ergosterol was associated with an accumulation of ignosterol
(Figure 1E). Inhibition of growth of the mutant by either
fenpropimorph or fenpropidin was correlated with a reduction in
ergost-8-enol and ergosta-8,22-dienol and an increase in
ignosterol (Figure 1D,1F).

EFFECT OF INHIBITORS ON FATTY ACID COMPOSITION OF POLAR LIPIDS
FROM *U.MAYDIS* WILD-TYPE AND STEROL MUTANT

The effect of tridemorph and fenpropimorph, at selected
concentrations, on fatty acids derived from polar lipids of the
wild-type and the mutant is shown in Table 1. Both strains
exhibited a pronounced increase in the degree of fatty acid
unsaturation following treatment with the fungicides.

DISCUSSION

The results presented here demonstrate the potential value
of sterol biosynthesis mutants for unravelling the mode of action
of SBIs. Considering the potency of SBIs, it is surprising that
mutants defective in sterol biosynthesis are viable and able to
grow, albeit, at reduced rates. The sterol mutant used in this

FIGURE 1. Effect of tridemorph (A,B), fenpropimorph (C,D) and
fenpropidin (E,F) on growth (———) and sterol composition of the
U. maydis wild-type (A,C,E) or the C-8 sterol isomerase deficient
mutant (B,D,F). ergosterol (-----), ergost-8-enol and ergosta-
8,22-dienol (·········); ignosterol and fecosterol (- — -). The
amounts of ergosterol, ergost-8-enol and ergosta-8,22-dienol were
calculated as described previously (James *et al.*, 1992). Due to
difficulties in separating ignosterol from fecosterol by
capillary GC, UV absorbtion of the crude sterol extracts at 250
nm was used to detect the presence of ignosterol (molar
extinction coefficient, 18000) (Baloch *et al.*, 1984). The
fungicide treatments at which UV absorption due to ignosterol was
first detected are marked with an asterisk.

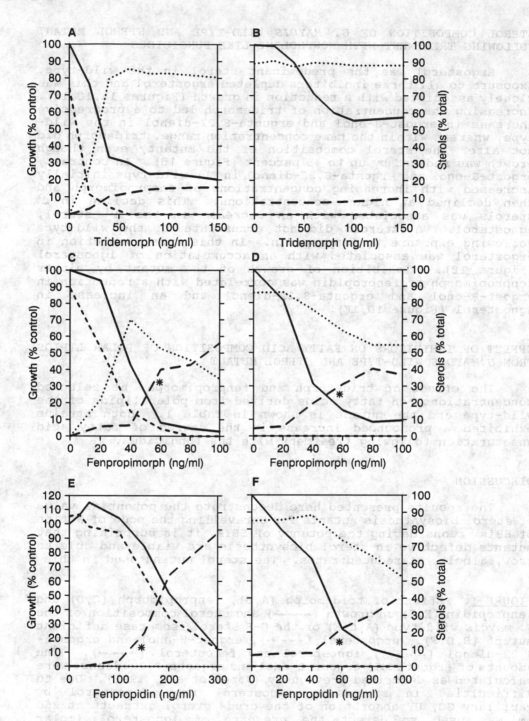

TABLE 1. Fatty acid composition of *U. maydis* wild-type
and sterol mutant following treatment with tridemorph or
fenpropimorph. Analysis of polar lipids was as described
by Carter *et al.*, (1989).

U. maydis strain	Treatment (% inhibition)	Fatty acid composition				
		16.0	18.0	18.1	18:2	18:2/ 18.3
IMI103761	Untreated (0%)	18.1	2.0	52.0	21.5	0.41
IMI103761	Tridemorph, 100 ng/ml(75%)	20.5	1.4	7.2	62.3	8.65
IMI103761	Fenpropimorph, 40 ng/ml(60%)	26.1	2.4	12.7	53.3	4.19
P51	Untreated (0%)	21.6	2.4	29.6	40.7	1.37
P51	Tridemorph, 100 ng/ml(45%)	23.2	1.0	6.1	62.4	10.23
P51	Fenpropimorph, 40 ng/ml(70%)	21.8	1.0	6.9	61.6	8.93

study, as with other fungal sterol mutants (Garber *et al.*, 1989),
is defective in membrane function.   Such a membrane impairment,
caused by ergosterol deficiency, could prevent biotrophic fungi
from acquiring essential nutrients and metabolites from the host
plant during infection and this may contribute to the
effectiveness of these inhibitors as fungicides.

These data support the view that although inhibition of
sterol $\Delta^8 \to \Delta^7$ isomerase contributes to the action of morpholine
fungicides, inhibition of sterol Δ^{14} reductase may be more
effective in preventing fungal growth.   Indeed, it is possible
that ignosterol is toxic to fungi. However, this seems unlikely
since a *Neurospora crassa* sterol mutant which accumulates Δ^{14}
sterols, including ignosterol, can grow and is viable (Ellis *et
al.*, 1991).

The increase in unsaturated fatty acids following treatment
with either tridemorph or fenpropimorph, is similar to those
reported in *U. maydis* exposed to the DMI, triarimol (Ragsdale
1975).   This change in fatty acid composition of treated cells
may compensate for the altered sterol content of cell membranes.
However, this pattern of fatty acid saturation is likely to
result from impaired growth rather than from a reduction in
ergosterol content (Weete *et al.*, 1991).

Finally these results confirm a dual site of action for the
morpholine fungicides in sterol biosynthesis and suggests that,
at least in the case of tridemorph, another site of action
unconnected with sterol biosynthesis exists. The multiple action
of this type of inhibitor may, thus, explain the observed lack
of resistance to morpholines observed in the field.

REFERENCES

Baloch, R.I.; Mercer, E.I.; Wiggins, T.E.; Baldwin, B.C. (1984) Inhibition of ergosterol biosynthesis in *Saccharomyces cerevisiae* and *Ustilago maydis* by tridemorph, fenpropimorph and fenpropidin. *Phytochemistry*, **23**, 2219-2226.

Brent, K.J. (1988) Resistance experiences in Europe. In *Fungicide Resistance in North America*, C.J. Delph (Ed), St Paul, APS Press, pp 19-27.

Carter, G.A.; Kendall, S.J.; Burden, R.S.; James, C.S.; Clarke, T. (1989) The lipid compositions of two isolates of *Cladosporium cucumerinum* do not explain their differences in sensitivity to fungicides which inhibit sterol biosynthesis. *Pesticide Science*, **26**, 181-192.

Ellis, S.W.; Rose, M.E.; Grindle, M. (1991) Identification of a sterol mutant of *Neurospora crassa* deficient in $\Delta^{14,15}$ reductase activity. *Journal of General Microbiology*, **137**, 2627-2630.

Garber, R.F.; Copple, D.M.; Kennedy, B.K.; Vidal, M.; Bard, M. (1989) The yeast gene *ERG6* is required for normal membrane function but is not essential for biosynthesis of the cell-cycle-sparking function. *Molecular and Cellular Biology*, **9**, 3447-3456.

Girling, I.J. (1991) The mode of action of morpholine fungicides and their mechanism of selectivity between fungal species. *PhD Thesis,* University of Bristol.

James, C.S.; Burden, R.S.; Loeffler, R.S.T.; Hargreaves, J.A. (1992) Isolation and characterization of polyene-resistant mutants from the maize smut pathogen, *Ustilago maydis*, defective in ergosterol biosynthesis. *Journal of General Microbiology*, **138**, 1437-1443.

Koller, W; Scheinpflug, H. (1987) Fungal resistance to sterol biosynthesis inhibitors: A new challenge. *Plant Disease*, **71**, 1066-1074.

Mercer, E.I. (1991) Sterol biosynthesis inhibitors: Their current status and modes of action. *Lipids*, **26**, 584-597.

Ragsdale, N.N. (1975) Specific effects of triarimol on sterol biosynthesis in *Ustilago maydis*. *Biochemica et Biophysica Acta*, **380**, 81-96.

Weete, J.D.; Sancholle, M.; Patterson, K.A.; Millar, K.S.; Huang, M.Q.; Campbell, F.; Van den Reek, M. (1991) Fatty acid metabolism in *Taphrina deformans* treated with sterol biosynthesis inhibitors. *Lipids*, **26**, 669-674.

MOLECULAR GENETIC ANALYSIS OF CARBOXIN RESISTANCE IN *USTILAGO MAYDIS*

J.P.R. KEON, P.L.E. BROOMFIELD, J.A. HARGREAVES

Department of Agricultural Sciences, University of Bristol, AFRC Institute of Arable Crops Research, Long Ashton Research Station, Long Ashton, Bristol, BS18 9AF.

G.A. WHITE

Agriculture Canada, Research Centre, 1400 Western Road, London, Ontario, N6G 2V4, Canada

ABSTRACT

A gene which conferred resistance to the systemic fungicide carboxin was isolated from the maize smut pathogen, *Ustilago maydis,* using gene transfer techniques. The sequence of this gene showed a high degree of homology to succinate dehydrogenase iron-sulphur protein (Ip) subunit genes from a number of other organisms. Comparison of this sequence with that of an allele encoding the Ip subunit from a carboxin-sensitive *U. maydis* strain identified a two-base difference between the sequences. This divergence in the nucleotide sequences led to a single amino-acid change within the third cysteine-rich cluster of the Ip subunits, with a leucine residue being substituted for a histidine residue in the carboxin-resistant form. Site-directed mutagenesis and expression of the mutated gene in a carboxin-sensitive *U. maydis* strain showed that replacement of the histidine residue with leucine restored resistance to carboxin.

INTRODUCTION

Carboxin (5,6-dihydro-2-methyl-1,4-oxathiin-3-carboxanilide) is a systemic fungicide which is active against Basidiomycetes and is particularly effective in controlling bunt and smut diseases. Fungitoxic concentrations of carboxin inhibit respiration in *Ustilago maydis* by preventing the oxidation of succinate by succinate dehydrogenase (Mathre, 1971). This enzyme is composed of two subunits, a flavoprotein (Fp) and an iron-sulphur protein (Ip), which along with two other ubiquinone-binding proteins (CII-3 and CII-4) make up Complex II (succinate-ubiquinone reductase) of the respiratory electron transport chain in mitochondria (Figure 1). Although its precise mechanism of action is unclear, carboxin appears to prevent the transfer of electrons from succinate to ubiquinone by inhibiting reoxidation of the iron-redox centres of the Ip subunit (Ackrell *et al.*, 1977).

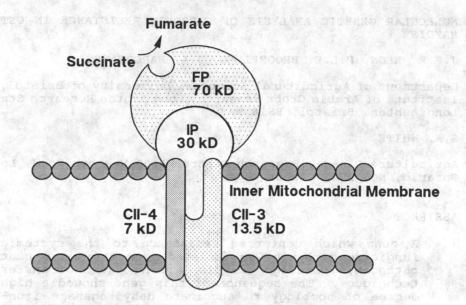

FIGURE 1. Schematic representation of the distribution of Complex II subunits.

Mutations at two nuclear loci lead to carboxin resistance in *U. maydis* (Georgopoulos *et al.*, 1972, 1975). The *oxr-1*B mutation, which confers a relatively high degree of resistance, has been shown to reduce the sensitivity of Complex II to carboxin (Georgopoulos *et al.*, 1972). This suggests that resistance in strains carrying this mutation is due to a conformational change at the site of action of carboxin.

Recent advances in the molecular genetics of *U. maydis* make it possible to routinely move DNA into and out of cells, and to gain expression of genes transferred into the cells (Tsukuda *et al.*, 1988; Wang *et al.*, 1988). Here we describe the application of modern fungal molecular genetic techniques to study the mode of action of, and the basis of resistance to, carboxin.

ISOLATION OF CARBOXIN RESISTANCE GENE

A genomic library from an *U. maydis* strain carrying the *oxr-1*B mutation was constructed by partially digesting genomic DNA with the restriction endonuclease *Sau*3A, to generated near-random DNA fragments (5-9 kb), and by ligating these into a unique *Bam*H1 site in plasmid pCM54 (Figure 2). This plasmid carries the *U. maydis hsp*70 promoter in transcriptional fusion with a gene conferring resistance to hygromycin B, an antibiotic which can be used as a selectable marker for gene transformation in *U. maydis* (Wang *et al.*, 1988; Tsukuda *et al.*, 1988).

The plasmid gene library was transferred into a carboxin-sensitive *U. maydis* strain using standard PEG-mediated transformation procedures (Hargreaves & Turner, 1992). Transformants (*c.* 10,000) were recovered by selection on media containing hygromycin B (200 μg/ml) and then tested for their ability to grow on media containing concentrations of carboxin (2 μg/ml) that inhibited the growth of the sensitive strain. Five different carboxin-resistant transformants were recovered. Plasmids rescued from these transformants carried *U. maydis* DNA inserts which overlapped and transformed the *U. maydis* carboxin-sensitive strain to carboxin resistance at high frequency (*c.* 5,000 transformants/μg DNA). This indicated that the plasmids harboured identical DNA fragments containing the gene responsible for carboxin resistance.

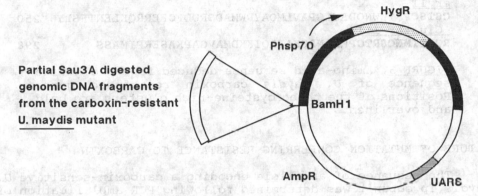

Partial Sau3A digested genomic DNA fragments from the carboxin-resistant *U. maydis* mutant

FIGURE 2. Construction of plasmid gene library from a carboxin-resistant mutant strain of *U. maydis* in *U. maydis* transformation plasmid, pCM54. Phsp70 - *U. maydis* hsp70 promoter, HygR - hygromycin B resistance gene, UARS - a *U. maydis* autonomously replicating sequence, AmpR - ampicillin resistance gene.

CHARACTERIZATION OF CARBOXIN RESISTANCE GENE

The gene was localised on the cloned DNA fragments by sub-cloning and deletion analysis and then sequenced (Keon *et al.*, 1991). A continuous open reading frame of 886 bases was detected which encoded a protein of *c.* 33,000 *k*D. Comparison of the deduced amino-acid sequence from this nucleotide sequence with EMBL and Genbank database accessions revealed extensive homology between the *U. maydis* carboxin resistance gene and the succinate dehydrogenase Ip subunit genes from humans, *E. coli* and yeast (66.3%, 58.1%, 64.3% identity respectively). The three cysteine-rich clusters at positions Ser105-Cys126 (Cluster 1), Glu198-Pro210 (Cluster 2) and Arg255-Pro267 (Cluster 3) were particularly well conserved (Figure 3).

The N-terminal amino-acid sequence of the *U. maydis* Ip subunit up to residue 50 was rich in basic (arginine) and hydroxylated (serine and threonine) amino-acids and part of this sequence formed a amphipathic helical structure. These features are characteristic of cleavable N-terminal presequences necessary for the import of mitochondrial proteins encoded by nuclear DNA (Hartl *et al.*, 1989).

```
MSLFNVSNGLRTALRPSVASSSRVAAFSTTAAARLATPTSDNVGSSGKPQ   50

HLKQFKIYRWNPDKPSEKPRLQSYTLDLNQTGPMVLDALIKIKNEIDPTL  100
           Cluster I
TFRRSCREGICGSCAMNIDGVNTLACLCRIDKQNDTKIYPLPHMYIVKDL  150
                                            Clust
VPDLTQFYKQYRSIEPFLKSNNTPSEGEHLQSPEERRRLDGLYECILCAC  200
er II
CSTSCPSYWWNQDEYLGPAVLMQAYRWMADSRDDFGEERRQKLENTFSLY  250
 Cluster III
RCLTIMNCSRTCPKNLNPGKAIAQIKKDMAVGAPKASERPIMASS       298
```

FIGURE 3. Amino-acid sequence deduced from nucleotide sequence of *U. maydis* carboxin resistance gene. Positions of the three cysteine-rich clusters are bold and overlined.

NATURE OF MUTATION CONFERRING RESISTANCE TO CARBOXIN

The sequence of an allele encoding a carboxin-sensitive *U. maydis* Ip subunit was determined following PCR amplification of genomic DNA from a carboxin-sensitive *U. maydis* strain. Comparison of this sequence with that of the carboxin resistance gene revealed a two base difference between the sequences at nucleotide positions 758 and 759 (Broomfield & Hargreaves, 1992). This nucleotide divergence led to the substitution of a leucine residue for a histidine residue within the third cysteine-rich cluster of the carboxin-resistant Ip subunit (Figure 4). Confirmation that these nucleotide substitutions were responsible for carboxin resistance was obtained following site-directed mutagenesis of the sensitive Ip subunit gene so that it encoded a peptide identical to the resistant form. This *in vitro* mutated gene was transferred into a carboxin-sensitive strain of *U. maydis* and shown to restore resistance to carboxin.

DISCUSSION

Identification of the gene product responsible for conferring carboxin resistance in *U. maydis* as the succinate dehydrogenase Ip subunit, and the determination of the precise nature and location of the mutation leading to carboxin resistance within the resistant allele, allows a further assessment of the mechanism of action of carboxin to be made.

Carboxin-sensitive allele

```
750   CGA TGC CAC ACC ATC ATG AAC TGC 774
      Arg Cys His Thr Ile Met Asn Cys
```

Carboxin-resistant allele

```
750   CGA TGC CTT ACC ATC ATG AAC TGC 774
      Arg Cys Leu Thr Ile Met Asn Cys
```

FIGURE 4. Comparison of nucleotide sequences and deduced amino-acid sequences of *U. maydis* carboxin-sensitive and carboxin-resistant Ip subunits within the third cysteine-rich cluster. Codon CAC (position 757-760) in the carboxin-sensitive allele encodes for histidine, whereas codon (CTT) at this position in the carboxin-resistant form encodes for leucine.

Previous work had established that carboxin exerts its inhibitory effect by preventing electron transfer from the Ip subunit of succinate dehydrogenase to ubiquinone (Ackrell *et al.*, 1977). The third cysteine-rich cluster of the Ip subunit, in which the carboxin resistance mutation occurred, is associated with the S3 [3Fe-4S] high energy iron-redox centre. This centre is believed to be involved in the transfer of electrons to ubiquinone (Salerno, 1991) and carboxin is thought to act by preventing its reoxidation (Ackrell *et al.*, 1977). The results obtained in this study support the conclusion that carboxin interferes with the function of the S3 iron-redox centre of the Ip subunit. However, this interference with electron transfer to ubiquinone cannot be simply explained by carboxin binding to the Ip subunit. This is because the soluble form of succinate dehydrogenase (the flavoprotein subunit and the Ip subunit) is not affected by carboxin (Ulrich & Mathre, 1972) and photoaffinity labelling studies indicate that azidocarboxin does not selectively bind to the Ip subunit (Ramsay *et al.*, 1981). In simplest terms, carboxin could, therefore, be considered to exert its inhibitory effect by being lodged between the S3 centre of the Ip subunit and the ubiquinone binding site, in such a way as to hinder electron transfer to ubiquinone. Resistance to carboxin may, thus, be a result of a conformational change to the S3 iron-redox centre which allows electron transfer to proceed in the presence of carboxin.

REFERENCES

Ackrell, B.A.C., Kearney, E.B., Coles, C.J., Singer, T.P., Beinert, H., Yieh-Ping, W., Folkers, K. (1977) Kinetics of the reoxidation of succinate dehydrogenase. *Archives of Biochemistry and Biophysics*, **182,** 107-117.

Broomfield, P.L.E., Hargreaves, J.A. (1992) A single amino-acid change in the iron-sulphur protein subunit of succinate dehydrogenase confers resistance to carboxin in *Ustilago maydis*. *Current Genetics*, **21,** in press.

Georgopoulos, S.G., Alexandri, E., Chrysayi, M. (1972) Genetic evidence for the action of oxathiin and thiazole derivatives on the succinate dehydrogenase system of *Ustilago maydis* mitochondria. *Journal of Bacteriology*, **110**, 809-817.

Georgopoloulos, S.G., Chrysayi, M., White, G.A. (1975) Carboxin resistance in the haploid, the heterozygous diploid and the plant-parasitic dicaryotic phase of *Ustilago maydis*. *Pesticide Biochemistry and Physiology*, **5**, 543-551.

Hargreaves, J.A., Turner, G. (1992) Gene transformation in plant pathogenic fungi. In: *Molecular Plant Pathology: A Practical Approach, Vol. 1*, S.J. Gurr, M.J. McPherson and D.J. Bowles (Eds), Oxford, New York, Tokyo: IRL Press, pp. 79-97.

Hartl, F-U, Pfanner, N., Nicholson, D.W., Neupert, W. (1989) Mitochondrial protein import. *Biochemica et Biophysica Acta*, **988**, 1-45.

Keon, J.P.R., White, G.A., Hargreaves, J.A. (1991) Isolation, characterization and sequence of a gene conferring resistance to the systemic fungicide carboxin from the maize smut pathogen, *Ustilago maydis*. *Current Genetics*, **19**, 475-481.

Mathre, D.E. (1971) Mode of action of oxathiin systemic fungicides. III. Effect on mitochondrial activities. *Pesticide Biochemistry and Physiology*, **1**, 216-224.

Ramsay, R.R., Ackrell, B.A., Coles, C.J., Singer, T.P., White, G.A., Thorn, G.D. (1981) Reaction site of carboxanilides and of thenoyltrifluoroacetone in complex II. *Proceeding of the National Academy of Sciences, USA*, **78**, 825-828.

Salerno, J.C. (1991) Electron transfer in succinate:ubiquinone reductase and quinol:fumarate reductase. *Biochemical Society Transactions*, **19**, 599-605.

Tsukuda, T., Carleton, S., Fotheringham, S., Holloman, W.K. (1988) Isolation and characterization of an autonomously replicating sequence from *Ustilago maydis*. *Molecular and Cellular Biology*, **8**, 3703-3709.

Ulrich, J.T., Mathre, D.E. (1972) Mode of action of oyxathiin systemic fungicides. V. Effect on electron transport system of *Ustilago maydis* and *Saccharomyces cerevisiae*. *Journal of Bacteriology*, **10**, 628-632.

Wang, J., Holden, D.W., Leong, S.A. (1988) Gene transfer system for the phytopathogenic fungus *Ustilago maydis*. *Proceedings of the National Academy of Sciences, USA*, **85**, 865-869.

IDENTIFICATION OF MECHANISMS OF RESISTANCE IN LARVAE OF THE TOBACCO BUDWORM *HELIOTHIS VIRESCENS* FROM COTTON FIELD POPULATIONS

A.R. McCAFFERY, J.W. HOLLOWAY

Insect Physiology and Toxicology Research Unit, Department of Pure and Applied Zoology, School of Animal and Microbial Sciences, University of Reading, Whiteknights, Reading RG6 2AJ,

ABSTRACT

Eggs and young larvae of *Heliothis virescens* were taken directly from cotton fields in various locations in the southern USA and examined for the presence of common mechanisms of resistance to cypermethrin. Nerve insensitivity was common in all the strains especially in the Saint Joseph, Louisiana strain in which over 50% of individuals were highly nerve insensitive. Delayed penetration of cypermethrin was found in all strains except that from Hondo, Texas. Metabolic resistance appeared rare. Some individuals of the Saint Joseph and Hondo strains were notable for high levels of metabolite production. Synergist studies gave little evidence for metabolic resistance although the use of discriminating doses with pbo suggested that metabolically resistant individuals were present in most strains.

INTRODUCTION

Resistance to the synthetic pyrethroids is common in the tobacco budworm *Heliothis virescens* throughout the cotton growing regions of the USA and in parts of central and south America. Continuous monitoring of resistance is conducted in the USA to provide data for effective management of the pest (Plapp *et al.*, 1990) although this information gives no indication of the mechanisms that are responsible for the resistance of these insects.

We have previously examined resistance mechanisms in strains of the related species *H. armigera* from Thailand (Ahmad & McCaffery, 1991) and India (West and McCaffery, 1992) and in a laboratory strain of *H. virescens* from the USA (Little *et al.*, 1989) and Colombia (Holloway and McCaffery, unpublished). Whilst metabolic mechanisms of resistance such as those conferred by enhanced monooxygenases or esterases are common in the former species they have been considered as rare or absent in field strains of *H. virescens* especially in the cotton-growing, southern states of the USA. Nevertheless, as indicated by a comprehensive program of adult vial assays, there has been a gradual increase in tolerance of the insects throughout the region over a number of seasons. Previous evidence suggests that the major mechanism of resistance to the synthetic pyrethroids in larvae of this species in the USA has been due to a form of nerve insensitivity (Plapp *et al.*, 1990) although the extent to which this has spread and the proportions of the populations that have acquired the mechanism have only been briefly examined (McCaffery *et al.*, 1991). There remains the possibility that the metabolic mechanism of resistance is being acquired by heavily selected strains of the insects and that this trend is occurring unnoticed. The work described here attempts to discover whether there is any basis to this by examining strains of insects from cotton fields in the USA in 1991 for the known major mechanisms of resistance.

MATERIALS AND METHODS

Insects

Samples of eggs or larvae of *Heliothis virescens* were collected from cotton plants in various locations in the US Cotton belt (Table 1) and shipped to Reading as eggs and young larvae. The insects were reared in a similar manner to that described previously (McCaffery *et al.* 1991). No insecticide selection was applied at any stage to any of these strains. All the experiments were

TABLE 1. Field strains of *Heliothis virescens* examined for presence of major resistance mechanisms

Strain name	Collection site	Date collected	Host plant
Tillar	Tillar, Arkansas	12 June 1991	Cotton
Hondo	Hondo, Texas	31 July 1991	Cotton
College Station	College Station, Texas	08 Aug. 1991	Cotton
Saint Joseph	Saint Joseph. Louisiana	25 Aug. 1991	Cotton
Leland	Leland, Mississippi	29 Sept.1991	Cotton

carried out using the field collected generation of the insects except for some synergist studies where the first laboratory generation was used.

Insecticides

Technical *cis*-cypermethrin (98.4%) and ^{14}C-*cis*-cypermethrin (2.0GBq.mMol^{-1}) was supplied by Shell Research Limited Sittingbourne, UK and ICI Agrochemicals, Jealott's Hill, UK. Piperonyl butoxide (2-(2-butoxyether)-ethyl-6-propyl piperonyl ether) (pbo) was supplied as technical (98%) material by Wellcome Environmental Health, Berkhamsted, UK.

Insecticide and Synergist Bioassays

Dose mortality studies on all the strains with serial dilutions of technical grade *cis*-cypermethrin in acetone were carried out (full data not shown). A discriminating dose of 0.1µg of *cis*-cypermethrin (LD$_{99}$ of susceptible BRC strain) was used to distinguish between resistant and susceptible phenotypes. One µl drops of *cis*-cypermethrin in acetone were applied to the mesothorax of test insects (19 and 24 mg). Control insects were treated with acetone. Further larvae were treated on the mesothorax with a 1µl drop (20µg) of piperonyl butoxide in acetone. After 30 min these were treated with 0.1µg of *cis*-cypermethrin as described above. For each control and treatment group at least four replicates, each of ten insects were used. The insects were fed and mortality of both the synergised and unsynergised insects was assessed after 72 h as previously (McCaffery *et al.*, 1991). Synergist ratios were obtained using dose mortality assays (full data not shown).

Neurophysiological Assay

The effects of *cis*-cypermethrin on the spontaneous multiunit activity of nerves from larvae of each of the strains were measured at 25 ± 0.5°C using a modified 'cumulative dose response' assay (Gladwell *et al.*, 1990). *Cis*-cypermethrin in acetone was diluted directly into lepidopteran saline to give a final range of concentrations of 1.0 to 100nM (10^{-9} to 10^{-7}M). Third instar larvae were decapitated, opened dorso-medially and pinned out on a layer of Sylgard (Dow Corning). A peripheral nerve was picked up with an insulated stainless steel, suction electrode connected to a high gain, low noise amplifier and conditioning system (Neurolog, Digitimer Ltd.). Neural activity was monitored on an oscilloscope and recorded on magnetic tape. Nerve action potentials were identified by amplitude discrimination and a microcomputer used to record their frequency. The number of action potentials in each successive 15s period over a 5min control period in cypermethrin-free saline was recorded. The saline was then replaced with saline containing 1.0nM *cis*-cypermethrin, washed once and the recording continued. At 5min intervals the preparation was washed and immersed in fresh saline containing increasing concentrations of the insecticide. The end point of the assay was defined as the lowest concentration at which the frequency of action potentials was over five times greater than the mean value during the pre-treatment control period.

Assay of Penetration, Metabolism and Excretion

Individual fifth instar larvae, with a mean weight of 280±57mg (SEM±SD), in 50mm glass, carbowax-coated, petri dishes were topically dosed on the mesothorax with 1µl drops containing

0.05μg and 500Bq of ^{14}C-*cis*-cypermethrin. Insects were provided with small blocks of the standard artificial diet and left for 24h at 25°C. After 24h the the quantity of unpenetrated radioactivity, faecal radioactivity and the radioactive metabolite components of the faeces were determined all as described previously (Little *et al.*, 1989; Clarke *et al.*, 1990).

RESULTS

Toxicology and Synergism

A comparison of the resistance factors (full dose mortality data not shown) presented in Table 2 shows that, irrespective of location, resistance to cypermethrin increased markedly throughout the 1991 season. Values for the Tillar strain were very similar to those obtained with the susceptible BRC reference strain. The most resistant insects were found at St. Joseph and Leland whilst the Hondo and College Station strains were intermediate between these two extremes (Table 2). The mortality values obtained using the discriminating dose of 0.1μg very effectively ranked the the field strain insects in a similar manner with larvae of the Tillar strain being the most susceptible and larvae of the Saint Joseph and Leland strains being the most resistant (Table 2). Susceptible insects were present in all the field collections confirming their heterogeneous nature.

TABLE 2. Percentage mortality of third instar larvae of various strains of *Heliothis virescens* treated with *cis*-cypermethrin and the effects of pre-treatment with piperonyl butoxide.

Strain	Resistance Factor[a] at LD$_{50}$	Percentage mortality		Synergist Ratio[b] at LD$_{50}$
		0.1μg *cis*-cypermethrin	20μg pbo + 0.1ug *cis*-cyper.	
BRC	-	100	100	
Tillar	2.6	05	98	1.2
Hondo	14	45	70	2.6
College Station	30	45	75	1.8
Saint Joseph	103	28	40	2.2
Leland	97	30	55	4.1

[a] RF = Resistance Factor = LD$_{50}$ Resistant Field Strain/LD$_{50}$ of Susceptible BRC strain
[b] SR = Synergist Ratio = LD$_{50}$ Insecticide alone/LD$_{50}$ Insecticide + Synergist

Topical pre-treatment with PBO gave slight but non-significant synergism with cypermethrin in larvae of the field strains as indicated by the synergist ratios obtained in dose mortality bioassays (Table 2). In all the strains treatment with pbo and a discriminating dose of 0.1μg of *cis*-cypermethrin gave increased levels of mortality compared to that seen with cypermethrin alone (Table 2). The highly resistant Saint Joseph strain had the lowest mortality in the discriminating dose assay and pbo only marginally raised this mortality suggesting that enhanced monooxgenase activity was unlikely to be the major mechanism of resistance in this strain.

Neurophysiology

A range of phenotypes with respect to nerve insensitivity was seen in larvae of all the strains examined (Table 3). Every class of response was represented in the profile for each strain. However, there were clear indications of a substantial proportion of highly nerve insensitive larvae present in the St. Joseph and Leland strains. In the former strain the largest class of individuals in the profile was of the very highly resistant non-responding group. In both strains there was a trend towards a bi-modal distribution in responses with a minimum around 50nM cypermethrin. In contrast, the Tillar, Hondo and College Station strains had profiles in which the majority of larvae

TABLE 3. Phenotypic distribution of individual third instar larvae of susceptible strain (BRC) and field strains of *Heliothis virescens* showing responses in the cumulative dose response nerve assay.

cis-cypermethrin concentration (nM)	Number of individuals responding in each strain					
	BRC	Tillar	Hondo	College Station	Saint Joseph	Leland
1	23	13	9	10	4	11
5	7	5	8	6	6	3
10	0	2	8	3	4	5
50	0	3	3	4	1	1
100	0	2	3	5	3	2
>100	0	5	4	2	12	8
Total number of larvae tested	30	30	35	30	30	30

were susceptible although a few resistant individuals were identified. With the BRC susceptible strain the responses were confined to the two lowest concentrations (Table 3).

Penetration, Metabolism and Elimination

There were large differences between some of the strains in the degree of penetration of the applied dose are shown in Table 4. The Hondo strain was characterised by a large proportion of individuals with a very clearly defined high level of penetration of the applied dose of radiolabeled cypermethrin and this strain appeared very susceptible. The Leland strain was ranked as the next most susceptible in this respect whilst a large proportion of the Tillar, College Station and Saint Joseph larvae showed considerably lower levels of penetration (Table 4).

TABLE 4. Penetration of ^{14}C-*cis*-cypermethrin into fifth instar individuals of field strains of *Heliothis virescens*. The data are expressed as number of larvae from a sample of thirty showing various levels of penetration of the applied dose in 24h

Percentage penetration of applied dose	Number of larvae in each strain				
	Tillar	Hondo	College Station	Saint Joseph	Leland
81 - 100 %	3	18	1	3	3
61 - 80 %	6	10	9	11	15
41 - 60 %	13	1	13	10	10
21 - 40 %	8	1	6	6	2
0 - 20 %	0	0	1	0	0
Total number of larvae tested	30	30	30	30	30

The elimination profiles in Table 5 show a range of distributions of individuals with respect to their ability to void radiolabel from the body so that all the strains contained individuals in each class with respect to this parameter. The Tillar, Hondo and Saint Joseph strains all contained a high proportion of individuals able to eliminate a high proportion of the penetrated dose in 24h whereas somewhat fewer individual larvae of the College Station and Leland strains appeared to be able to do this. In general, there was little evidence for a marked ability to rapidly eliminate the penetrated toxicant but some larvae of the College Station and Hondo strains were particularly competent.

TABLE 5. Elimination of ^{14}C-*cis*-cypermethrin from fifth instar individuals of field strains of *Heliothis virescens*. The data are expressed as number of larvae from a sample of thirty showing various levels of elimination of the penetrated dose in 24h

Percentage elimination of penetrated dose	Number of larvae in each strain				
	Tillar	Hondo	College Station	Saint Joseph	Leland
0 - 20 %	6	7	6	3	2
21 - 40 %	5	4	7	7	7
41 - 60 %	8	5	9	6	13
61 - 80 %	9	11	4	8	6
81 - 100 %	2	3	4	6	2
Total number of larvae tested	30	30	30	30	30

The radiolabelled components of the faecal samples were analysed and the percentages of excreted material appearing as polar conjugates, primary metabolites and parent compound were calculated. Excretion of conjugates of primary metabolites was generally common but with all the strains examined there was little evidence of differences between strains. Nevertheless, there was a rather increased level of conjugate excretion from larvae of the St. Joseph strain compared with all the other strains. Slightly raised levels of acid production in the Tillar and Leland strains are unlikely to be significant. Evidence for significant monooxygenase action was not seen. There was little difference in the profiles of hydroxylated metabolite excretion between the strains although a few individuals of most of the strains, especially the Hondo strain, appeared to have a high activity in this regard and may represent individual resistant insects present at a lower frequency.

DISCUSSION

Heliothis species may possess physiological, biochemical and behavioural mechanisms of resistance (Nicholson and Miller, 1985). In this study we have attempted to define, using relatively rapid methodologies as far as possible, which of the mechanisms of delayed penetration, nerve insensitivity and enhanced monooxygenase activity, were present in strains taken directly from USA cotton fields.

Previous work (Gladwell *et al.*, 1990; McCaffery *et al.*, 1991) has shown the feasibility of distinguishing resistant and susceptible larvae on the basis of their response in a cumulative dose response assay performed on semi-isolated larval nervous systems. The assay gives a reliable indication of the frequency of appearance in a strain of individuals with particular levels of nerve insensitivity and is considered to give an efficient discrimination between phenotypes with respect to nerve insensitivity. The technique has been used to screen a large number of individuals to obtain a frequency profile for each strain. Such large scale testing with a quantitative electrophysiological technique has never been attempted before and we believe this gives a valuable insight into the occurrence of this mechanism. In the absence of a DNA probe diagnostic it is considered that this neurophysiological technique has very considerable utility. The St. Joseph strain contained a high proportion of highly nerve insensitive, resistant individuals. Other strains had lesser proportions of these resistant insects although they were present throughout all the strains and this confirms our view and that of other authors that this is the major mechanism or resistance to synthetic pyrethroids in *Heliothis virescens* in USA cotton.

From dose mortality assays there is no evidence of significant widespread synergism of cypermethrin with pbo in third instar larvae of any of the strains examined. Mild synergism of cypermethrin with pbo in larvae of the Leland strain suggests a possible minor role for monooxygenases in these insects although the method cannot detect rare, strongly resistant individual insects. Using pbo with a discriminating dose of cypermethrin there was a small increase in larval mortality in all strains except Tillar suggesting that a small proportion of individuals of the Hondo, College Station, Saint Joseph and Leland strains were resistant to cypermethrin due to the presence of a pbo-suppressible monooxygenase. The mechanism, if present, occurs at a relatively low frequency.

In assessing the role of metabolism several factors were considered. First the quantity of penetrated radioactivity eliminated via the faeces was determined. This may include primary metabolites, conjugates of these as well as unchanged parent compound and it gives an overall indication of the ability of the insect to eliminate the toxicant. The Tillar Hondo and Saint Joseph strains contained rather more larvae capable of eliminating large quantities of the material than the College Station and Leland strains although the differences are marginal. The proportion of the excreted radioactivity represented by the various classes of metabolite was determined and whilst, in general, there were few differences between larvae of the different strains some strains contained individuals with better than average levels of elimination of radiolabeled metabolites. Conjugate production by some individuals of the Saint Joseph strain and monohydroxylated metabolite production by some individuals of the Hondo strain larvae were notable.

Whilst nerve insensitivity appears widespread the evidence for metabolic resistance is less convincing. There are clearly some individuals in the populations which are likely to be metabolically resistant and this is probably due to the presence of monooxygenases. Although the numbers appear small it needs to be borne in mind that for each strain we examined 30 individuals in detail. The finding that even a few of these individuals may have metabolic resistance is significant since these represent a large number in the field. Under increased selection pressure we would expect metabolic resistance to become significant in USA cotton.

ACKNOWLEDGEMENTS

We are grateful to the Insecticide Resistance Action Committee for funding for this work, to to Dan Clower for collection of the insects, to Ben Rogers and Gay Simms of ICI Americas Inc. for coordination of strains and to John Mortimer and Melanie Wainwright for technical assistance.

REFERENCES

Ahmad, M.; McCaffery, A.R. (1991) Elucidation of detoxication mechanisms involved in resistance to insecticides in the third instar larvae of a field-selected strain of *Helicoverpa armigera* with the use of synergists. *Pesticide Biochemistry and Physiology* **41**, 41-52.

Clarke, S.E.; Walker, C.H.; McCaffery, A.R. (1990) A comparison of the *in vitro* metabolism of *cis*-cyp ermethrin in a resistant and a susceptible strain of *Heliothis virescens*. *Proceedings 1990 Brighton Crop Protection Conference - Pests and Diseases*, 1201-1206.

Gladwell, R.T.; McCaffery, A.R.; Walker, C.H.(1990) Nerve insensitivity to cypermethrin in field and laboratory strains of *Heliothis virescens*. *Proceedings 1990 Beltwide Cotton Production Conferences*, 173-177.

Little, E.J.; McCaffery, A.R.; Walker, C.H.; Parker, T. (1989) Evidence for an enhanced metabolism of cypermethrin by a monooxygenase in a pyrethroid-resistant strain of the tobacco budworm (*Heliothis virescens* F.). *Pesticide Biochemistry and Physiology* **34**, 58-68.

McCaffery, A.R.; Gladwell, R.T.; El-Nayir, H.; Walker, C.H.; Perry, J.N.; Miles, M.M. (1991) Mechanisms of resistance to pyrethroids in laboratory and field strains of *Heliothis virescens*. *Southwestern Entomologist Suppl.* **15**, 143-158.

Nicholson, R.A.; Miller, T.A. (1985) Multifactorial resistance to transpermethrin in field collected strains of the tobacco budworm *Heliothis virescens* F. *Pesticide Science*, **16**, 561-570.

Plapp, F.W.Jr.; Campanhola, C.; Bagwell, R.D.; McCutchen, B.F. (1990) Management of pyrethroid resistant tobacco budworms on cotton in the United States. In: *Pesticide Resistance in Arthropods*, R.T. Roush and B.E. Tabashnik (Eds), New York: Chapman and Hall, pp. 237-260.

West, A.J.; McCaffery, A.R. (1992) Evidence of nerve insensitivity to cypermethrin from Indian strains of *Helicoverpa armigera*. *Proceedings 1992 Brighton Crop Protection Conference - Pests and Diseases*, In press.

EVIDENCE OF NERVE INSENSITIVITY TO CYPERMETHRIN FROM INDIAN STRAINS OF HELICOVERPA ARMIGERA

A.J. WEST, A.R. McCAFFERY

Insect Physiology and Toxicology Research Unit, Department of Pure and Applied Zoology, School of Animal and Microbial Sciences, University of Reading, Whiteknights, Reading RG6 2AJ,

ABSTRACT

Pupae of *Helicoverpa armigera* were collected from various cotton growing regions of India and transported to the Reading laboratory for rearing. Using a robust, tested and reliable electrophysiological assay and a wide range of concentrations of *cis*-cypermethrin large numbers of larvae of the first laboratory generation were tested for the presence of nerve insensitivity. The results showed that each strain had a unique response profile and for all the strains this differed from that of the susceptible strain. Some of the strains possessed individuals who demonstrated nerve insensitivity to a high degree.

INTRODUCTION

The cotton bollworm, *Helicoverpa armigera* (Hubner) is a polyphagous noctuid pest damaging a wide range of crops in many parts of the world including Asia, Africa and Australia. The synthetic pyrethroids are highly effective larvicides for this pest, being efficacious at low doses and maintaining favourable residual profiles on leaves. Combined with ready availability, generally low non-target toxicity and being relatively inexpensive they have been very widely used. However, the intensive use of these compounds has led to the development of resistance. The failure of synthetic pyrethroids to control *H. armigera* has been reported in Australia (Gunning *et al.*, 1984), Indonesia (McCaffery *et al.*, 1989), Thailand (Ahmad *et al.*, 1989; Ahmad & McCaffery, 1988) and India (McCaffery *et al.*, 1989; Dhingra *et al.*, 1988; Armes *et al*, 1992).

Physiological and biochemical mechanisms of resistance to pyrethroids can be categorised into three types; delayed penetration, enhanced metabolism and nerve insensitivity. Of these nerve insensitivity has been considered to be the more important mechanism (Sawicki, 1985). It is generally agreed that it is the voltage-gated sodium channels that are the primary neuronal target sites for the pyrethroid insecticides (Nicholson & Miller, 1985) and that the compounds exert their effect by causing the open state of the gates of the sodium channel to persist. The observed neurophysiological effect of this is to induce repetitive firing in the peripheral and central nervous systems.

Evidence of a mechanism conferring resistance to both DDT and pyrethroids due to target site insensitivity has been known for some time. This nerve insensitivity to pyrethroids has been observed in lepidopteran species around the world and in *Heliothis virescens* (Gladwell *et al.*, 1990), and *H. armigera* (Gunning *et al.*,1984; Gunning *et al.*, 1991).

In this paper we report on investigations into the presence and degree of nerve insensitivity in field populations of *H.armigera* from India.

MATERIALS AND METHODS

Insects

Field collections of pupae were made in various locations in India between April and October 1992 and sent to the Reading laboratory via the Natural Resources Institute. Since no susceptible Indian strain was available we used the Sim Sim strain, derived from a susceptible Sudanese field strain and kept in the laboratory for several generations. All strains were bred and reared as described previously

(Ahmad & McCaffery, 1988) and all experiments were carried out at a constant temperature of 25±1°C.

Insecticide

Technical grade *cis*-cypermethrin (99%) was obtained from Shell Research Limited, Sittingbourne, UK and used to make up a 1mM stock solution in analytical grade acetone. The stock was then diluted with modified Weevers lepidopteran saline (Weevers, 1966) into thoroughly cleaned, Carbowaxed glassware to gave a range of concentrations from 0.0001nM to 100nM.

Neurophysiological assay

For each strain tested, third instar larvae weighing between 30 and 40mg were decapitated and a longitudinal dorso-median incision made, whereupon the insect was pinned onto a layer of Sylgard resin (Dow Corning) in a 50mm petri-dish. The intestinal tract, fat body and any loose tissue were removed and the preparation rinsed with several washes of saline, before being bathed in fresh saline. A peripheral nerve was picked up by means of a suction electrode constructed from 29 gauge stainless steel hypodermic tubing, the outer surface of which was coated with Epoxy resin. The preparation was grounded through a stainless steel entomological pin.

The recording electrode was connected to a high gain, low noise signal conditioning system, Neurolog (Digitimer Ltd., Herts, UK). The signal was displayed on an oscilloscope (Kenwood CS-8010) and an amplitude discriminator was used to distinguish the action potentials from the background noise. The nerve impulses were counted in epochs of 15s by a microcomputer.

The spontaneous multiunit activity (MUA) was recorded from the preparation whilst bathed in pesticide free saline. The saline was then aspirated and replaced with fresh saline containing 0.0001nM *cis*-cypermethrin, and the recording continued. After successive 5min periods the saline was aspirated off to be replaced by saline containing increasing concentrations of pesticide. The end point was determined by the lowest concentration of pesticide that caused a 5-fold increase in the MUA compared with the mean MUA of the saline control period.

Providing that the saline was replenished every five minutes the MUA remained relatively stable and the preparation would continue to be viable for over an hour. In order to confirm the stability of the preparation the MUA from several susceptible larvae was recorded for a period of 35 minutes before the saline was replaced with a 10 nM solution of *cis*-cypermethrin. In all cases application of the insecticide caused an increase in the MUA within five minutes showing that the preparations were capable of showing a response after forty minutes and that five minutes was a sufficient period of time for any response to manifest itself (Figure 1).

Around thirty larvae were used from each strain and to simplify comparisons between the strains the results from each strain are expressed in the form of a percentage of individuals responding at each of the concentrations.

RESULTS

Baseline MUA varied between preparations but did not bear any correlation with the degree of resistance of the larvae. Such variance is likely to be related to the variable number of nerves that are picked up by the suction electrode.

All the individual preparations from the Sim Sim susceptible strain clearly showed a distinct nerve intolerance to the pesticide demonstrated by a large increase in the MUA frequency, typically ten times the control value, upon application of the lowest or occasionally the second lowest concentration (Figure 2).

The responses from the field strain preparations (Figures 2-7) all differed from that of the known susceptible, although the majority of individuals again responded at either the first or second concentration. What we consider to be of more significance is the number of individuals responding at

234

the higher concentrations as this gives each of the strains a unique and characteristic profile (Figures 2-7).

Two of the strains Dhopibet and Pulladigunta, included a number of individuals in which the preparation did not respond even at the highest concentration, 100nM (maximum solubility of *cis*-cypermethrin in saline). These individuals were thus considered to have very highly insensitive nervous systems.

These two strains also showed a decrease in the proportion of individuals which responded at the first concentration, small in the case of the Dhopibet strain but clearly marked in the Pulladigunta strain and this leads to a well defined shift in the profile towards nerve insensitivity.

DISCUSSION

Most of the investigations concerned with pyrethroid pesticide resistance in Indian *H. armigera* have inclined to concentrate on the mechanism of enhanced metabolism (Phokela *et al*, 1989; Phokela & Mehrotra 1989; McCaffery *et al.*, 1989). Work carried out in this laboratory also concludes that enhanced metabolism, by mixed function oxidases, is a major mechanism of resistance in Indian strains of this insect. Such a conclusion is not unexpected when one considers the prominent polyphagous nature of the species and the mechanism is common in *H.armigera* for other areas of the world.

The results presented here clearly indicate that all of the field strains of *H. armigera* sampled from India included individuals with varying degrees of nerve insensitivity compared to the susceptible, and a number of insects exhibited this mechanism to a high degree.

Wilkinson (1991) postulated that even highly resistant larvae of *Heliothis virescens* that exhibit an elevated enhanced enzymic resistance mechanism may also possess a nervous system that has some tolerance to pyrethroids in order to provide sufficient time for metabolism to reduce the quantity of pyrethroid in the body of the insect to a non-lethal threshold. The initial concentrations used in the course of this study are extremely dilute (0.0001nM), but they are of the same order as was found to be present in the excised CNS of *H. virescens* following topical dosing with *cis*-cypermethrin (Wilkinson, 1991). Moreover, the fraction of sodium channels that need to be modified to cause repetitive discharging has been calculated, using tetramethrin on squid axons, (Lund & Narahashi, 1982) to be less than 0.1% or less, so that low concentrations of this order are legitimate.

Thus by utilising very low concentrations of pyrethroids and an extensive range of concentrations it is possible to distinguish, to a fine degree, the incidence and level of nerve tolerance in individuals of each strain. It is also feasible to chart the progress of an specific population with respect to nerve insensitivity over a series of seasons.

The results presented here suggest that there is presently a trend towards an increased incidence of highly nerve insensitive insects in various locations in India. Such populations currently exist in Australia (Gunning *et al.*, 1991), and in Thailand (Ahmad *et al.*, 1989). Since this resistance mechanism is more difficult to counteract from a management point of view, careful monitoring and sound pesticide management practices should be employed in order to prevent nerve insensitivity from becoming established in populations of the insect in India.

ACKNOWLEDGEMENTS

The authors are grateful to the Natural Resources Institute for funding of this work, to Dr A.B.S. King and Dr N. Armes of NRI for supply of the insects and useful discussions and to Dr. Richard Gladwell for helpful advice.

REFERENCES

Ahmad, M.; Gladwell, R.T.; McCaffery A.R. (1989) Decreased nerve sensitivity is a mechanism of resistance in a pyrethroid resistant strain of Heliothis armigera from Thailand. Pesticide Biochemistry and Physiology, 35, 165-171.

Ahmad, M; McCaffery A.R. (1988) Resistance to insecticides in a Thailand strain of Heliothis armigera (Hubner) (Lepidoptera: Noctuidae). Journal of Economic Entomology, 81, 45-48

Armes, N.J.; Jadhav, D.R.; Bond, G.S.; King, A.B.S. (1992) Insecticide resistance in Helicoverpa armigera in South India. Pesticide Science, 34, 355-364.

Dhingra, S.; Phokela, A.; Mehrotra, K.N. (1988) Cypermethrin resistance in the population of Heliothis armigera Hubner. National Academy Science Letters, 11, 123-125.

Gammon, D.W. (1980) Pyrethroid resistance in a strain of Spodoptera littoralis is correlated with decreased sensitivity of the CNS in vitro. Pesticide Biochemistry and Physiology, 13, 53-62.

Gladwell, R.T.; McCaffery A.R.; Walker, C. H. (1990) Nerve insensitivity to cypermethrin in field and laboratory strains of Heliothis virescens. Proceedings 1990 Beltwide Cotton Production Conference, 173-175.

Gunning, R.V.; Easton, C.S.; Balfe, M.E.; Ferris, I.G. (1991) Pyrethroid resistance mechanisms in Australian Heliothis armigera. Pesticide Science, 33, 472-490.

Gunning, R.V.; Easton, C.S.; Greenup, L.R.; Edge, V.E. (1984) Pyrethroid resistance in Heliothis armigera (Hubner) (Lepidoptera: Noctuidae) in Australia. Journal of Economic Entomology, 77, 1283-1287.

Lund, A.E.; Narahashi, T. (1982) Dose-dependent interaction of the pyrethroid isomers with sodium channels of squid axon membranes. Neurotoxicology 31, 11-24.

McCaffery, A.R.; Ahmad, M. (1991) Elucidation of detoxication mechanisms involved in resistance to insecticides in the third instar larvae of a field selected strain of helicoverpa armigera with the use of synergists. Pesticide Biochemistry and Physiology, 41, 41-52.

McCaffery, A.R.; King A.B.S.; Walker, A.J.; El-Nayir, H. (1989) Resistance to Synthetic Pyrethroids in the Bollworm, Heliothis armigera from Andhra Pradesh, India. Pesticide Science, 27, 65-76.

McCaffery, A.R.; Walker, A.J.: Topper, C.J. (1991) Insecticide resistance in the bollworm, Helicoverpa armigera from Indonesia. Pesticide Science, 32, 85-90.

Narahashi, T. (1985) Nerve membrane ionic channels as the primary target of pyrethroids. Neurotoxicology 6, 3-22.

Nicholson, R.A.; Miller, T.A. (1985) Multifactorial resistance to transpermethrin in field collected strains of the tobacco budworm Heliothis virescens F. Pesticide Science, 16, 561-570.

Phokela, A.; Dhingra, S.; Mehrotra, K.N. (1989) Pyrethroid resistance in Heliothis armigera Hubner I. Response to cypermethrin. Proceedings of the National Academy of Science, India 59b, 373-381.

Phokela, A.; Mehrotra, K.N. (1989) Pyrethroid resistance in Heliothis armigera Hubner II. Permeability and Metabolism of Cypermethrin. Proceedings of the National Academy of Science, India 55b, 235-238.

Sawicki, R. M. (1985) Resistance to pyrethroid insecticides in arthropods. In: Insecticides, D.H. Hutson and D.R. Roberts, (Eds), New York, Wiley, pp. 143-191.

Weevers, R.de G. (1966) A Lepidopteran saline: Effects of inorganic cation concentration on sensory,

Wilkinson, I.J. (1991) A pharmacokinetic investigation of the expression of pyrethroid resistance in third instar *Heliothis virescens* (Lepidoptera; Noctuidae) larvae. Ph.D Thesis, University of Reading.

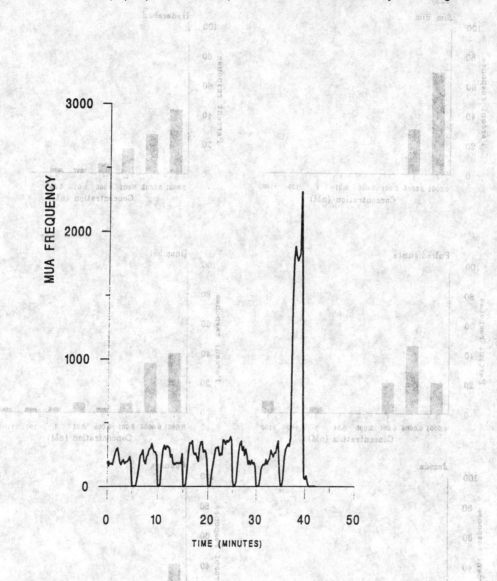

Figure 1. Graph showing impulse frequency from a third instar susceptible larva under pesticide free and pesticide containing saline.

Figures 2-7 Percentage of third instar larvae of various field strains of *Helicoverpa armigera* showing responses to various concentrations of *cis*-cypermethrin in the cumulative dose response neurophysiological assay.

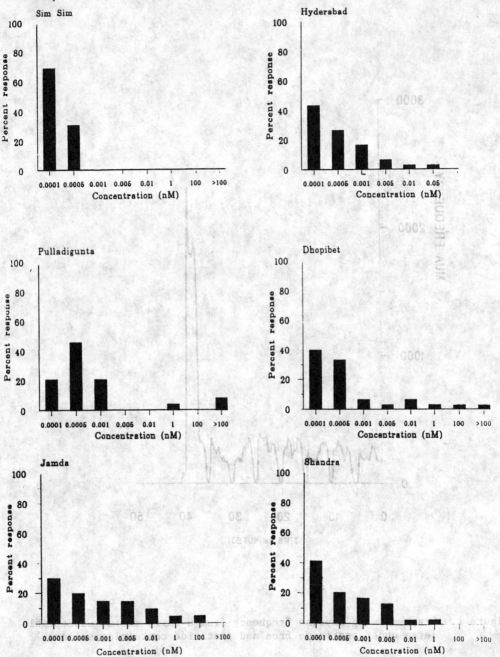

PYRETHROID RESISTANCE IN THE POD BORER, *HELICOVERPA ARMIGERA*, IN SOUTHERN INDIA.

N.J.Armes

Natural Resources Institute (NRI), Chatham, Kent ME4 4TB

D.R. Jadhav

International Crops Research Institute for the Semi Arid Tropics (ICRISAT), Patancheru, Andhra Pradesh 502324, India

A.B.S.King

Natural Resources Institute (NRI), Chatham, Kent ME4 4TB

ABSTRACT

Changes in the LD_{50} of *Helicoverpa armigera* to cypermethrin at the International Crops Research Institute for the Semi-Arid Tropics (ICRISAT) and in the coastal cotton-growing region of Andhra Pradesh State during the period 1986-92 are summarised and discussed. A provisional discriminating dose of 1ug cypermethrin was evaluated at ICRISAT and changes in resistance to cypermethrin monitored throughout 1991/92. Resistance was related to seasonal changes in insecticide use; it was lowest in August and increased with progression of the season. Prospects for insecticide resistance management of *H. armigera* in Andhra Pradesh are briefly discussed.

INTRODUCTION

Synthetic pyrethroids were first used on cotton in S India in 1982 mainly against *Spodoptera litura* (F.) and *Earias* spp.; and were increasingly used against *Helicoverpa armigera* as it replaced these species. Pyrethroid resistance in *H armigera* was heralded in 1987 by widespread field control failures over much of the coastal cotton-growing belt of Andhra Pradesh (Dhingra *et al*, 1988; McCaffery *et al* 1989), and with a decline in average lint yields from over 430 to under 170 kg/ha (Anon, 1989 b and c). NRI, in collaboration with ICRISAT and Reading University, has been monitoring resistance in *H.armigera* since 1986. This paper summarises the techniques used, compares the data obtained in Andhra Pradesh, with particular reference to the 1991-92 season, and discusses future prospects for resistance management of *H.armigera* in southern India.

METHOD AND MATERIALS

Dose/response monitoring

From 1986 to 1991 bioassays were performed on the F1 of larvae field-collected from sorghum, pigeonpea, chickpea and cotton at ICRISAT and farms in Andhra Pradesh. Cypermethrin (cis:trans, 1:1) (ICI Agrochemicals Ltd) was applied topically to larvae in the weight range 30-50 mg, as described by Armes *et al* (1992).

Discriminating dose monitoring

Two strains were used to calibrate a cypermethrin discriminating dose for *H.armigera* larvae weighing 30-50 mg. The NRI strain, originally from Sudan, was wholly susceptible; the other, from the Indian Agricultural Research Institute (IARI), Delhi, was slightly tolerant (Figure 1). A provisional discriminating dose of 1ug/larva, which killed 95% of the Delhi strain larvae, was derived (Figure 1).

FIGURE 1. Response to cypermethrin of the 'NRI laboratory' and 'Delhi' strains of *H.armigera*.

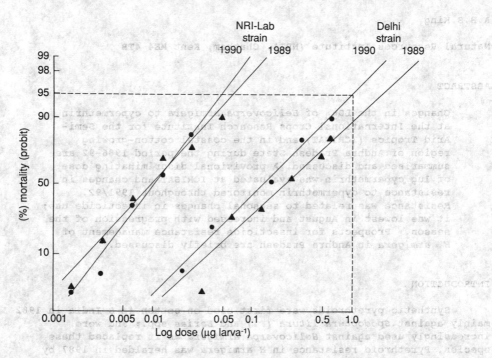

From June 1991 to April 1992, samples of 150-400 eggs and/or small larvae were taken from infested host plants every 1-2 weeks at ICRISAT, reared on diet to the 30-50 mg range and treated with the discriminating dose. Control larvae were treated with acetone alone. Larvae were held at $26\pm1°C$ and mortality assessed after 72 hours.

RESULTS AND DISCUSSION

Dose/response monitoring

Between 1986 and 1992 pyrethroid resistance varied considerably between and within years and locations (Figure 2) In July 1986, there was no evidence of tolerance to cypermethrin at ICRISAT, but by October 1987, field failures were reported from cotton in eastern A.P. and control problems were experienced at ICRISAT (Figure 2). In general, resistance levels over the 5 seasons increased as each season progressed. This was particularly evident for the 1991/92 season for which there was continuous data.

FIGURE 2. Seasonal changes in cypermethrin resistance in *H.marmigera* from ICRISAT (unshaded) and Andhra Pradesh coastal cotton districts (shaded). Based on average monthly LD50 values; from McCaffery *et al.* (1989) and Armes *et al.* (1992).

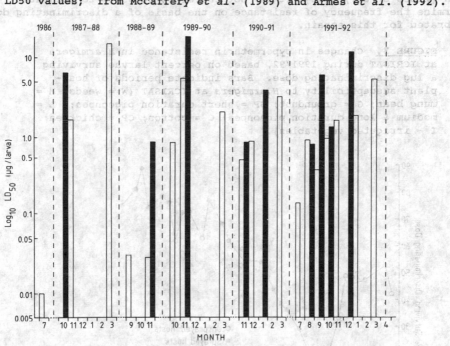

In the cotton areas, increases in resistance could be attributed to local selection of resistant genotypes in response to applications of pyrethroids. However at ICRISAT, where pyrethroids were not extensively used, little local selection for resistance would have taken place. Seasonal increases in pyrethroid resistance at ICRISAT tended to reflect those recorded in the cotton areas in Eastern A.P., and may therefore have resulted from immigration of resistant moths into the Hyderabad area on the prevailing NE to E winds between October and December (Pedgley *et al.*, 1987; McCaffery *et al.*, 1989).

Discriminating dose monitoring

Ideally, monitoring should be able to detect resistant individuals at a phenotypic frequency close to 1%, a level not attainable with dosage/response assays (Roush and Miller, 1986). Moreover, the large numbers of insects required, inevitable time lag, and dubious accuracy of assays performed on the F1, are not compatible with a reactive IRM strategy.

Although a discriminating dose of 1ul was effective, the Delhi strain, on which it was based, was significantly more tolerant, and had a lower log-dose-probit (ldp) slope, than the NRI (Sudan) susceptible strain.

It has not been possible to isolate a homogenous, pyrethroid susceptible field strain in India, and, as a discriminating dose based on the NRI strain would overestimate pyrethroid resistance in Indian *H.armigera*, the Delhi strain was used as the standard. However, because of its low slope with cypermethrin, the ldp line of the Delhi strain significantly overlapped those of resistant field populations from southern India (Armes *et al.*, 1992). It was not therefore possible to accurately determine the frequency of resistance on the basis of a discriminating dose calibrated for this strain.

FIGURE 3. Changes in cypermethrin resistance in *H.armigera* at ICRISAT during 1991/92, based on percent larvae surviving a lug discriminating dose. Bars indicate periods of host-plant susceptibility to *H.armigera* at ICRISAT (W = weeds; M = mung bean; G = groundnut; SP = short duration pigeonpea; L = medium & long duration pigeonpea; C = cotton; CP = chickpea; I - irrigated vegetables).

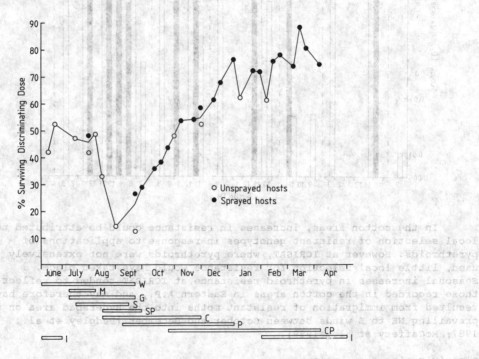

At ICRISAT, resistance in the first *H.armigera* generation of the kharif (rainy) season in late June-late July 1991 was high, probably as a result of insecticide use during the March-May summer period on irrigated vegetables (Figure 3). Its subsequent decline could have resulted from early-season build up on unsprayed crops and weed hosts, and dilution by susceptible populations. However, by late October resistance had re-attained the early kharif level of about 45%. This increase was closely synchronised with the appearance of the first generation of moths from early planted cotton, which would have received 2-3 applications of insecticides. Resistance continued to increase until February, as an overlapping succession of host crops were available (sorghum, pigeonpea, chickpea, groundnut), with the legumes receiving 1-6 sprays against *H.armigera*. Resistance remained high up to the end of the cropping season in early April (Figure 3).

Prospects for Insecticide Resistance Management in Andhra Pradesh

For a resistance management strategy to be successful it must be conducted on an area-wide basis, particularly for highly mobile pests like *H. armigera*. In Australia, a strategy where pyrethroid use is restricted to defined periods during the growing season, has been in operation since 1983 (Forrester and Cahill, 1987), and has effectively prevented field failures, despite steadily increasing resistance. Despite adherence to the strategy, pyrethroid resistance has continued to increase annually and field control has only been maintained with pyrethroid products because of tightly controlled rates and times of application. Factors contributing to the success of the Australian strategy, such as area-wide management, are consistent with farming conditions in developed countries.

In Andhra Pradesh area-wide management is likely to be extremely difficult in view of the large number of farmers involved and wide range of host crops grown at different times. Farmers are generally ill-informed as to the most appropriate management practices, application is often poor, tank mixes of different chemicals are frequent and the purity of some locally purchased chemicals has been questioned (Anon, 1990). Commonly, farmers do not scout their fields for eggs and only perceive *H.armigera* as a problem when larvae, or their damage, have become conspicuous. Control action is then less effective and selection for resistance more intense. It is hardly surprising therefore that resistance should appear under these conditions in a State which accounts for over 40% of pesticide sales in India (Anon, 1990) and where pyrethroids comprised 50-70% of all applications to cotton (Jayaswal, 1989).

In southern India, summer season (March-June) survival presents a potential weak link in the pest's life cycle. However, the increasing trend to grow host crops such as okra, eggplant and tomato under irrigation is almost certainly increasing survival over this period, as well as maintaining resistance when these crops are sprayed. Summer vegetables could well be an important contributory factor to the emergence of *H.armigera* as a major pest in cotton over the past ten years.

Clearly there is a need for IPM rationale, with room for major improvements in the efficiency of insecticide use. These would include need-based application, using thresholds for eggs and small larvae. A legislative, or incentive, system to restrict the use of pyrethroids on cotton, legumes and summer vegetabls during critical periods would also need to be implemented. In cotton, the potential and economics of varietal and agronomic changes to cotton crop management need also to be explored thoroughly.

ACKNOWLEDGEMENT

Dr K N Mehrotra and A. Phokela (Indian Agricultural Research Institute, New Delhi) for providing the Delhi strain of *H.armigera*.

REFERENCES

Anon, 1989b. *Agricultural situation in India* XLIII, p801.

Anon, 1989c. *Agricultural situation in India* XLIV, p535.

Anon, 1990. Guidelines for the implementation of quality control of insecticides in Andhra Pradesh. *Pesticides Annual* 1989-90 II, 5-9.

Armes, N.J., Jadhav, D.R., Bond, G.S. and King, A.B.S. 1992. Insecticide resistance in *Helicoverpa armigera* in South India. *Pesticide Science* 34, 355-364.

Dhingra, S., Phokela, A. and Mehrotra, K.N. 1988. Cypermethrin resistance in the populations of *Heliothis armigera* Hubner. *National Academy of Sciences Letters* 11 (4), 123-125.

Forrester, N.W. and Cahill, M. 1987. Management of insecticide resistance in *Heliothis armigera* (Hubner) in Australia. In: *Combating Resistance to Xenobiotics; Biological and Ecological Approaches,* M.B. Ford, D.W. Holloman, B.P.S. Khambay, and R.M. Sawicki, (Eds.), Ellis Horwood, UK, pp 127-137.

Jayaswal, A.P. 1989. Management of American bollworm on cotton in Andhra Pradesh. *Indian Farming;* July 1989, pp 6,7 & 17.

McCaffery, A.R., King, A.B.S., Walker, A.J. and El-Nayir, H. 1989. Resistance to synthetic pyrethroids in the bollworm, *Heliothis armigera* from Andhra Pradesh, India. *Pesticide Science* 27, 65-76.

Pedgley, D.E., Tucker, M.R. and Pawar, C.S. 1987. Windborne migration of *Heliothis armigera* (Hubner) (Lepidoptera: Noctuidae) in India. *Insect Science and its Application* 8, 599-604.

Roush, R.T. and Miller, G.L. 1986. Considerations for design of insecticide resistance monitoring programs. *Journal of Economic Entomology* 79, 293-298.

PROBLEMS WITH ESTIMATING THE TOXICITY OF AMITRAZ TO SUSCEPTIBLE AND
RESISTANT SPIDER MITES

T. J. DENNEHY

Cornell University, New York State Agricultural Experiment Station,
Department of Entomology, Geneva, New York, 14456

A. W. FARNHAM AND I. DENHOLM

AFRC Institute of Arable Crops Research, Department of Insecticides and
Fungicides, Rothamsted Experimental Station, Harpenden, Herts, AL5 2JQ

ABSTRACT

Acaricides, such as amitraz, that elicit behavioral effects pose
special challenges to evaluating their toxicity because mites are
inclined to abandon treated surfaces by moving onto untreated areas
of bioassay apparatus. Thus, bioassay methodology may greatly
influence the pest-pesticide interface for such compounds, altering
both observed toxicity and expression of resistance. The influence of
bioassay choice on estimates of toxicity of amitraz against
susceptible *Tetranychus urticae* was investigated by comparing
mortality observed in leaf disk, residual cell, and microimmersion
bioassays. All three bioassay methods produced comparable and low
estimates of the toxicity of amitraz to susceptible populations.
Resistance to amitraz, readily isolated by selection with amitraz of
a New York population of *T. urticae*, was manifest in residual cell
and microimmersion (topical) bioassays as 15.5-fold and 6.4-fold
increases in LC_{50}s, respectively. Selection reduced susceptibility
to both amitraz and dicofol, indicating the presence of cross-
resistance in this strain. We conclude that cross-resistance between
dicofol and amitraz should be ascertained in programmes for managing
mite pest populations but the bioassay method employed for assessing
resistance must provide realistic estimates of responses to amitraz.

INTRODUCTION

Management of resistance in spider mites is of great concern to
agriculturalists throughout the developed world. Success of resistance
management hinges on using appropriate bioassays to detect differences in
susceptibility of pests that are diagnostic of genetic changes, and on the
identification of countermeasures, such as rotations of insecticides,
predicated on known occurrences of cross-resistance. Indeed,
recommendations formulated by the Insecticide Resistance Action Committee
(IRAC), Fruit Crops Working Group (Leonard 1992) are based on
classification of insecticides and acaricides into cross-resistance
groups, to avoid repeated use of compounds that select common resistance
mechanisms. Acaricides that elicit behavioral effects, such as feeding
deterrence, increased locomotory activity, and repellency, pose particular
challenges in this respect since mites are inclined to abandon treated
leaf surfaces or, when enclosed on treated surfaces in cell bioassays,
move to untreated areas of the enclosure (e.g., see Kolmes et al. 1991).
With behaviorally-active acaricides, interactions between behavioral
responses, innate toxicity of the chemicals, and bioassay-specific
factors, such as the availability of untreated areas and mode of exposure
of subjects to the chemicals, can influence greatly the outcome of
toxicity estimates, as well as the expression of resistances.

Recent discrepancies in the literature regarding toxicity of amitraz to *Tetranychus urticae* Koch and cross-resistance between amitraz and dicofol exemplify well the difficulties experienced in bioassaying acaricides that strongly influence behavior. Fergusson-Kolmes et al. (1991) described the response to amitraz of near-isogenic dicofol-susceptible and -resistant strains of *T. urticae* and reported that the resistant one exhibited a pronounced cross-resistance to amitraz. Aveyard et al. (1992) challenged this report of cross-resistance, having failed to find reduced sensitivity to amitraz in 3 laboratory strains of *T. urticae* resistant to dicofol. Inspection of concentration-response data in these papers revealed very large differences in the toxicity of amitraz to susceptible mites, Aveyard et al. (1992) reporting comparable mortality from amitraz at concentrations 10-50 fold lower than that reported by Fergusson-Kolmes et al. (1991). Given the importance of eliminating this discrepancy, we examined the toxicity of amitraz using multiple bioassay methods, and we measured the responses of populations selected with amitraz or dicofol.

INFLUENCE OF BIOASSAY CHOICE ON ESTIMATES OF THE TOXICITY OF AMITRAZ

Methods

Studies were conducted at the Rothamsted Experimental Station, Harpenden, Herts, against the GSS strain, a susceptible laboratory population, obtained from Schering AG, Agrochemical Div., Berlin. The residual cell and microimmersion bioassays are described and contrasted in Farnham et al. (this volume) and Dennehy et al. (in press). The residual cell method confines groups of 20-25 young, adult, female mites within plastic (perspex) cells positioned over acaricide-treated leaves. Mites are placed within the cell after a leaf has been dipped in acaricide and allowed to dry; subjects are exposed to acaricide only by contact with the treated leaf. The microimmersion method is a newly-developed bioassay in which groups of 25 young, adult female mites are immersed in acaricide for 30 seconds, allowed to dry, and then treated subjects are confined on untreated leaves. The third method evaluated was a leaf disk bioassay described by Aveyard et al. (1992). With this residual contact method 10-15 young, adult, female mites were placed on 15 mm leaf disks that had been previously dipped in amitraz and allowed to dry. An important difference between the leaf disk method and the other two methods is that spider mites could walk off of the leaf disks onto the moistened, untreated substrate. 'Mitac 20', 200 g/l EC (Schering AG), and 0.01% Triton X-100 diluted in distilled water was used for acaricide solutions. Controls consisted of water and 0.01% Triton X-100. All assays were held 72 h post-treatment, under ambient light in a room maintained at 21 ± 2°C. Mites exhibiting repetitive (non-reflex) movement of more than one locomotory appendage after this period were recorded as alive. Concentration-response data were computed as mean mortality (±SEM), corrected for control mortality. Differences between bioassay methods were investigated using one-factor ANOVA (StatView, Brain Power Inc., Calabasis, California) of proportional mortality data transformed with the arcsin transformation.

Results and Discussion

Significant differences were found between mortality observed with amitraz in leaf disk, residual cell, and micrommersion bioassays ($p < .001$), but all methods yielded relatively low mortality of the susceptible strain (Figure 1). The three bioassay methods produced susceptibility estimates that were much closer to those reported by Fergusson-Kolmes et al. (1991) than to those reported by Aveyard et al. (1992). The leaf disk method produced the lowest mortality with amitraz. However, using this method, we observed that up to 66 percent of test subjects abandoned the disks, this effect being most pronounced at the higher concentrations. We cannot explain fully the discrepancy between our results with this method and those of Aveyard et al. (1992), though we postulate that they scored as dead mites that had abandoned the leaf disks. Ignoring or scoring as dead individuals that move off treated surfaces of bioassays could exaggerate mortality estimates. However, this factor alone cannot account totally for the high mortality reported by Aveyard et al. (1992) at 100 ppm because we observed low repellency (only 12%) in bioassays of this concentration.

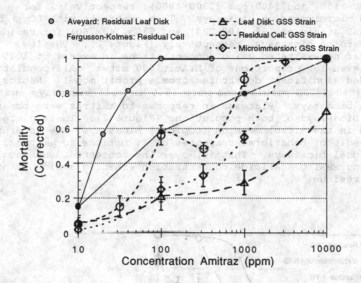

FIGURE 1. Influence of bioassay choice on estimates of the toxicity of amitraz to adult female *Tetranychus urticae*. Results of leaf disk, residual cell, and microimmersion bioassays are compared with toxicity estimates published in Aveyard et al. (1992) and Fergusson-Kolmes et al. (1991).

INFLUENCE OF BIOASSAY ON THE EXPRESSION OF RESISTANCE TO AMITRAZ IN ADULT *TETRANYCHUS URTICAE*.

Methods

Two populations were contrasted, the GSS strain, described above (non-selected), and the NYAmit1000 strain, an amitraz-selected strain of *T. urticae* from Cornell University. The NYAmit1000 strain originated from a highly characterized susceptible laboratory colony, Orchard-12, maintained since 1985 at Cornell University, Geneva, New York. Beginning in July, 1991, this strain was selected with increasingly higher concentrations of amitraz. Mites from the Orchard-12 strain were put into an isolated cage on plants that had been treated to run off with 10 ppm amitraz for the first four weeks, with 100 ppm for the next four weeks, and thereafter with 1000 ppm amitraz. By September, 1991, the population was growing well on plants sprayed with 1000 ppm amitraz and selection was sustained at this level throughout the period when bioassays were conducted. Mite responses to amitraz were plotted as mean (±SEM) mortality, corrected for control mortality, and analyses were conducted using the POLO probit analysis program (LeOra Software, Berkeley, California). Ninety-five percent fiducial limits for LC_{50} are presented. Owing to significant departures from the probit model, differences between populations were analyzed using one-factor ANOVA as detailed above.

Results and Discussion

Resistance to amitraz was readily isolated from the New York population of *T. urticae* (Figure 2):significant differences were found between the GSS and the NYAmit1000 populations with both residual cell ($P<.001$) and microimmersion bioassays ($P<.001$). The LC_{50} of the NYAmit1000 population was 2300 ppm (1600-3100) and 3400 ppm (2300-4800), respectively, for residual cell and microimmersion bioassays. This contrasts with LC_{50}s for the susceptible GSS strain of 150 (100-220) and 530 (340-760) for residual cell and microimmersion bioassays, respectively (Figure 2). The low toxicity of amitraz necessitated using concentrations in excess of 1000 ppm in order to kill even low proportions of NYAmit1000 mites. All populations and methods yielded significant departures from a probit model. Ratios of LC_{50}s of the NYAmit1000/GSS populations were 15.5 in cell bioassays and 6.4 in microimmersion bioassays. Plateaus in response to amitraz were observed in residual cell bioassays of both populations (Figure 2). These plateaus were not observed in the microimmersion (topical) bioassays. We interpret this to be the result of behavioral responses of *T. urticae* to amitraz, expressed in residual bioassays. That is, over the concentrations involved in the plateau, increasing acaricide concentration enhanced avoidance of contact with the residue.

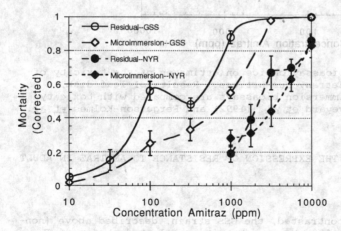

FIGURE 2. Influence of bioassay on the expression of resistance to amitraz in adult female *Tetranychus urticae*. A non-selected, susceptible population (GSS) and an amitraz-selected population (NYAmit1000) were tested in residual cell and microimmersion (topical) bioassays.

CROSS-RESISTANCE BETWEEN AMITRAZ AND DICOFOL IN A NEW YORK POPULATION OF *TETRANYCHUS URTICAE*.

Methods

Studies were conducted in 1991-2 at Cornell University, Geneva, New York. The Orchard-12 (susceptible) strain was split into two isolated populations, one maintained without selection and one selected with amitraz (NYAmit1000). In addition, the dicofol-selected strain, near-isogenic to

Orchard-12 (Fergusson-Kolmes et al. 1991), was maintained as a standard on
caged plants that had been treated to run-off with 1000 ppm dicofol. After
a total of 5 months of selection with amitraz, NYAmit1000 was bioassayed
with 6-10 replications of residual cell bioassays of amitraz concentrations
of 0, 10, 100, 1000, and 10,000 ppm. Similar assays were done of the
Orchard-12 population and the dicofol-resistant strain. Results were
computed for each population as mean ± SEM mortality observed for each
concentration tested, corrected for control mortality. Differences between
non-selected, amitraz-selected, and dicofol-selected populations were
evaluated using one-factor ANOVA as noted above.

Results and Discussion

Five months of selection of the susceptible Orchard-12 population with
amitraz resulted in significant reductions in susceptibility to both
amitraz ($\underline{P}$<.001) and dicofol ($\underline{P}$<.001) (Figure 3), indicating the presence
of cross-resistance between these acaricides in the population originating
from New York. However, selection with amitraz reduced susceptibility to
dicofol less than did selection with dicofol. This supports the conclusion
of multiple factors, a single major gene plus modifiers, conferring dicofol
resistance (Rizzieri et al. 1988) and indicates that cross-resistance
between dicofol and amitraz involves a subset the factors. We hypothesize
that the cross-resistance described herein involves the minor resistance
factors described by Rizzieri et al. (1988), since the reduction in
susceptibility to dicofol caused by selection with amitraz was not nearly
as great as the reduction caused by selection with dicofol.

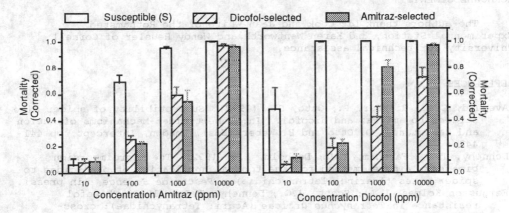

FIGURE 3. Cross-resistance between amitraz and dicofol is demonstrated by
selection of a susceptible New York population of Tetranychus urticae with
amitraz and testing susceptibility to amitraz and dicofol in residual
bioassays. The dicofol-selected population, near-isogenic to the
susceptible population, was used as a standard.

The toxicity of amitraz to susceptible forms of T. urticae, illustrated
herein, is sufficiently low that relatively minor resistance mechanisms,
such as those responsible for the above-mentioned 6- to 15-fold reduction
in susceptibility to amitraz, rendered mites capable of surviving bioassays
of very high concentrations, ones well in excess of common field rates.
Our findings support the previous conclusion of Fergusson-Kolmes et al.
(1991) regarding positive cross-resistance between dicofol and amitraz in
mites from New York. Comparable reductions in susceptibility to amitraz
were elicited by selection with dicofol or amitraz (Figure 3). We are

concerned about the ramifications that this cross resistance could have for selecting a mechanism of dicofol resistance. Resistance to dicofol is being successfully managed in some key systems (e.g., California cotton, Florida citrus, Brazilian citrus) by using rotations of materials that do not exhibit cross resistance. If this cross-resistance between dicofol and amitraz is expressed similarly in other pests populations, it could hamper efforts to sustain efficacy of both acaricides.

BIOASSAYING BEHAVIORALLY-ACTIVE ACARICIDES

We are unable to account fully for the the large discrepancy highlighted herein between previous reports of the toxicity of amitraz. However, we hypothesize that the problem centers around the effects of amitraz on spider mite behavior, effects that can result in mites abandoning treated surfaces in bioassays. Especially with behaviorally-active compounds, care must be taken when conducting bioassays to account for all subjects, and especially those that leave the pesticide treated area. Despite its low intrinsic toxicity to *T. urticae*, we are concerned not to undervalue the potential of amitraz as a mite control agent. Our results merely highlight the extreme difficulty of using laboratory bioassays to predict the likely field performance of behaviorally-active chemicals. Indeed, compounds that disrupt normal activity without imposing selective mortality offer tremendous scope for combating or avoiding resistance, and techniques for anticipating and documenting such effects under realistic conditions should be developed as a matter of priority.

ACKNOWLEDGEMENTS

The authors thank Liz Cook and Jean White of the Rothamsted Experimental Station, and Karen Wentworth and Wendy Heusler of Cornell University for technical assistance.

REFERENCES

Aveyard, C.S.; Richter, P.; Otto, D. (1992) Susceptibility of spider mite strains to amitraz and dicofol. In: Insecticides-Mechanisms of Action and Resistance, D. Otto and B. Weber (Eds), London, Intercept, pp 441-447.

Dennehy, T.J.; Farnham, A.W.; Denholm, I. (1992) The microimmersion bioassay: a novel method for the topical application of pesticides to spider mites (Acarina: Tetranychidae). *Pesticide Science*, (in press).

Fergusson-Kolmes, L.A.; Scott, J.G.; Dennehy, T.J. (1991) Dicofol resistance in *Tetranychus urticae* (Acari: Tetranychidae): cross-resistance and pharmacokinetics. *Journal of Economic Entomology*, 84,41-48.

Kolmes, S.A.; Dennehy, T.J.; Broadwater, E.B. (1991) Effects of residence time and webbing upon dicofol-avoidance behavior in two-spotted spider mites (Acari:Tetranychidae). *Experimental & Applied Acarology*, 12, 181-193.

Leonard, P.K. 1992. IRAC Fruit Crops Working Group: Spider mites. *In*, Resistance 91, Achievements and Developments in Combating Pesticide Resistance, I. Denholm, A.L. Devonshire and D. W. Hollomon (eds), Barking, UK, Elsevier. pp 41-47.

Rizzieri, D.A.; Dennehy, T.J.; Glover, T.J. (1988) Genetic analysis of dicofol resistance in two populations of twospotted spider mite (Acari: Tetranychidae) from New York apple orchards. *Journal of Economic Entomology*, 81, 1271-1276.

INSECTICIDAL ACTIVITY AND EXPRESSION OF PYRETHROID RESISTANCE IN ADULT
BEMISIA TABACI USING A GLASS VIAL BIOASSAY.

M.R. CAHILL and B. HACKETT

AFRC Institute of Arable Crops Research, Department of Insecticides and
Fungicides, Rothamsted Experimental Station, Harpenden, Herts, AL5 2JQ

ABSTRACT

The reasons and methods for bioassaying *B. tabaci* are discussed
and the published data reviewed. Large variations in baseline
LC50's suggest that not all strains are truly susceptible.
Screening small amounts of experimental material imposes
constraints that preclude the use of the established leaf dip
technique. An adult vial bioassay is presented that satisfies the
requirements. Resistance to pyrethroids in the leaf dip bioassay
is compared to that expressed in the vial test. The established
method provides the greater discrimination.

INTRODUCTION

Within the last decade tobacco whitefly (*Bemisia tabaci*) has become a
major pest of many crops in many countries. It is a pest because it causes
direct feeding damage, exudes copious honeydew which is a substrate for
fungi and creates harvesting difficulties (in cotton especially), and also
transmits a large number of plant viruses. It is well established in
glasshouse horticulture in continental Europe where it has severely
disrupted the biological control programmes directed against *Trialeurodes
vaporarorium* (Wilson & Anema, 1988). *B. tabaci* poses a constant threat to
agriculture in the United Kingdom despite the efforts at quarantine.

Its elevation in status from an incidental to a primary pest has been
attributed to many factors including increased use of insecticides and
changes in cropping patterns (e.g. Dittrich *et al.*, 1986) as well as events
that have lead to the dissemination of a biotype of *B. tabaci* that is
highly fecund, has a wider host range, causes previously unreported
physiological symptoms in host plants and in all examples tested to date is
resistant to the major groups of insecticides (Costa & Brown, 1991; Cohen
et al., 1992).

These factors have increased the interest and urgency in conserving
the existing xenobiotics for whitefly control and also stimulated the
search for novel molecules to provide chemical control of this pest. It is
therefore appropriate to review and assess the methods used to evaluate the
laboratory efficacy of existing insecticides and to present a new
technique.

THE ROLE OF BIOASSAYS

Bioassays fulfil a number of roles in arthropod toxicology. They may
be used to screen for activity in the search for new chemistry, to test the
laboratory efficacy of established and new insecticides, to provide
information on the resistance and cross resistance patterns of a population
and, by using synergists to assist in resistance mechanism studies. All of
these roles may not be satisfied by a single technique.

The most widely reported bioassay method for *B. tabaci* is the adult leaf dip test. There are minor variations on this test but the principle is to expose adults of either one or both sexes to a leaf which has been dipped in formulated product. The leaf may be attached to a growing plant, in which case the adults are confined by a clip cage, or the leaf may be excised and kept moist and turgid on a bed of agar or moist filter paper in a small plastic cylinder.

TABLE 1. Log Dose Probit Mortality adult bioassay parameters reported for susceptible *Bemisia tabaci*. Test methods are 1= whole plant with leaf clip cage 2= leaf disc on agar gel 3= leaf with petiole in water 4= leaf dipped but not kept moist. F= females only tested, all others are mixed. RES signifies new Rothamsted leaf dip data.

REFERENCE	COMPOUND	LC50 (mg/l)	SLOPE	TEST METHOD	END PT (h)
Ahmed *et al.*, 1987	Endosulfan	1.1	1.18	3	24
Dittrich *et al.*, 1983	Endosulfan	1.6	3.40	2	24
Yassin *et al.*, 1989	Endosulfan	9.6	1.76	4	6
Prabhaker *et al.*, 1985	DDT	10.0	1.15	1	24
Dittrich *et al.*, 1983	DDT	11.5	2.40	2	24
Abdeldaffie *et al.*, 1987	Chlorfenvinphos	6.0	1.73	3	24
RES	Chlorpyriphos	2.8	4.70	2 F	48
Yassin *et al.*, 1989	Chlorpyriphos	17.4	1.56	4	6
Prabhaker *et al.*, 1985	Chlorpyriphos	190.0	2.14	1	24
Dittrich *et al.*, 1983	Dicrotophos	12.8	2.90	2	24
Ahmed *et al.*, 1987	Dimethoate	2.2	0.89	3	24
Dittrich *et al.*, 1983	Dimethoate	12.2	2.90	2	24
Prabhaker *et al.*, 1985	Fenthion	670.0	1.75	1	24
Prabhaker *et al.*, 1989	Malathion	127.0	4.00	1	24
Prabhaker *et al.*, 1985	Malathion	1440.0	1.69	1	24
Dittrich *et al.*, 1983	Monocrotophos	6.5	3.40	2	24
RES	Monocrotophos	24.8	4.90	2 F	48
Prabhaker *et al.*, 1989	Monocrotophos	80.0	3.80	1	24
Prabhaker *et al.*, 1985	Monocrotophos	820.0	3.17	1	24
Prabhaker *et al.*, 1985	Parathion	340.0	2.27	1	24
Prabhaker *et al.*, 1989	Parathion-methyl	67.0	4.50	1	24
Prabhaker *et al.*, 1985	Parathion-methyl	110.0	1.32	1	24
Horowitz *et al.*, 1988	Parathion-methyl	1900.0	2.43	2 F	24
Rowland *et al.*, 1991	Profenofos	0.7	2.00	2	48
RES	Profenofos	2.2	2.60	2 F	48
Dittrich *et al.*, 1983	Profenofos	4.9	4.40	2	24
Prabhaker *et al.*, 1989	Sulprophos	47.0	7.60	1	24
Prabhaker *et al.*, 1985	Sulprophos	80.0	1.70	1	24
Horowitz *et al.*, 1988	Sulprophos	300.0	1.90	2 F	24
RES	Bifenthrin	0.3	2.40	2 F	48
Rowland *et al.*, 1991	Cypermethrin	0.2	1.80	2	48
Dittrich *et al.*, 1983	Cypermethrin	2.9	1.70	2	24
RES	Cypermethrin	4.6	0.80	2 F	48
Horowitz *et al.*, 1988	Cypermethrin	75.0	1.22	2 F	24
Abdeldaffie *et al.*, 1987	Deltamethrin	0.1	0.77	3	24
Prabhaker *et al.*, 1985	Fenvalerate	20.0	1.23	1	24
Horowitz *et al.*, 1988	Permethrin	19.0	0.73	2 F	24
Prabhaker *et al.*, 1989	Permethrin	26.0	3.20	1	24
Prabhaker *et al.*, 1985	Permethrin	100.0	1.14	1	24

The LC50 values produced by the well established leaf dip method on ostensibly susceptible *B. tabaci* vary considerably between laboratories (Table 1). Cypermethrin LC50's differ by up to 375-fold while chlorpyriphos LC50's vary 68-fold. These differences may be the result of slightly different rearing, testing, holding and assessment methods, but the susceptibility of some of the strains must be questioned. The GH strain used as the susceptible reference by Prabhaker *et al.* (1985) was tested some time later (Prabhaker *et al.*, 1989) and in each retest produced lower LC50's and higher slopes. The susceptible strain used by Horowitz *et al.* (1988) was derived from the colony used by Prabhaker *et al.* (1985)

Resistance ratios are by definition dependent on the response of a susceptible strain. Although the delineation between susceptibility, tolerance and low level resistance to an insecticide is not always entirely clear, consistency of response over time is important. Homogeneity of a strain may be assumed by a high LDPM slope or verified by the use of biochemical/electrophoretic markers. Whatever the bioassay method the importance of a susceptible strain and associated baseline data can not be overestimated.

The leaf dip test is not a suitable bioassay method to screen experimental compounds. In our laboratories small amounts (<5ml) of dilute (<2%) technical material in acetone are provided by the chemists to the toxicologists. These compounds are expensive and time-consuming to produce and may be required to challenge a number of arthropod species.

To overcome these constraints a novel glass vial technique has been developed to test the contact activity of small amounts of technical compounds on adult *B. tabaci*. Preliminary tests with this technique to bioassay the parasitoids of *B. tabaci* (e.g. *Eretomocerus mundus* and *Encarsia lutea*) are also encouraging. A molecule toxic to *B. tabaci* and non-toxic to its natural enemies would provide a valuable tool for the management of this pest.

The impact of bioassay method on resistance expression has been widely reported (e.g. Dennehy *et al.*, 1983) and the development of a new bioassay method for testing adult whitefly provided the opportunity to investigate the expression of pyrethroid resistance in both the established leaf dip test and the new vial technique. An adult vial test has been used extensively in the USA for monitoring pyrethroid resistance in *Heliothis virescens* (Campanhola & Plapp, 1987) and a similar exercise is planned in the USA for *B. tabaci*.

DEVELOPMENT OF THE ADULT VIAL TEST

The optimum volume of liquid to give even coverage on the inside of the 10ml glass vial was determined using a red dye in acetone and 100μl found to be the most appropriate. New vials are used for all tests. The vials are soaked for 12h in Decon 75® to remove the shiny glass finish which causes the acetone to 'bead' and consequently leave untreated areas. The 100μl aliquot is dispensed into each vial which is then rolled on a purpose built roller for approximately 10min by which time the acetone evaporates. Adults are anaesthetised with CO_2 and 30 females are transferred to the vial where they are contained by a gauze lid held in place with a rubber band. Controls are handled in the same manner using vials coated with acetone. After exposure to the insecticide the adults are transferred to a small (38mm diam. x 15mm high) plastic cylinder with an untreated leaf disc on a bed of agar gel. Mortality is scored at 24h and 48h with the latter considered the most appropriate end point. Control mortality of >15000 adults in 174 tests has averaged 7.5%.

The optimum exposure period was determined by exposing pyrethroid susceptible (SUD-S) female whiteflies to 0.1mg/l, 1mg/l 10mg/l or 100mg/l of technical cypermethrin in acetone for either 20min, 40min, 60min, or 120min and assessing at 48h (Figure 1).

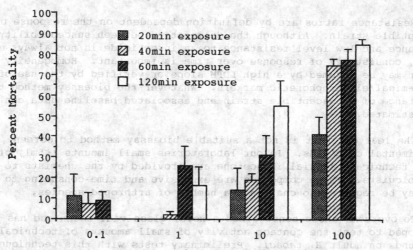

FIGURE 1. Mortality at 48h of pyrethroid susceptible *Bemisia tabaci* females exposed to cypermethrin in the glass vial test for 20, 40, 60, or 120min. All figures are corrected for control mortality. Bars indicate standard errors.

The 20min and 40min exposures gave the least consistent responses over the full dose range tested and the control mortality in the 120min exposure was higher (18%) than the 60min exposure (15%). For these reasons the 60min exposure was chosen for all subsequent tests.

COMPARISON BETWEEN THE ADULT VIAL TEST AND THE LEAF DIP TEST

A series of pyrethroids was tested on females of the SUD-S strain and a pyrethroid resistant strain (BELZ) using the vial test with 100μl of solution, 60min exposure and 48h end point (Table 2). Two of the pyrethroids were also tested with the leaf dip bioassay as reported in Rowland *et al.* (1991) using formulated product (Table 3).

The Log Dose - Probit Mortality (LDPM) determinations for bifenthrin and cypermethrin on susceptible *B. tabaci* with the vial test compare favourably with published data and with leaf dip data produced on the same strain at Rothamsted. However the resistance ratios derived for the BELZ strain differ considerably between the two test methods (Figure 2). The resistance ratios produced by the leaf dip bioassay are 3 to 4-fold higher than with the adult vial test (Tables 2,3)

TABLE 2. LC50's (mg/l), slopes and resistance ratios for females of two *Bemisia tabaci* strains tested using the adult vial technique.

Pyrethroid	SUDS		BELZ		RESIS.
	LC50 (limits)	Slope (se)	LC50 (limits)	Slope (se)	RATIO
Bifenthrin	0.3 (.26-.37)	2.8 (.25)	4.6 (3.2-7.8)	1.4 (.14)	15
Cypermethrin	9.5 (7.1-13)	1.6 (.13)	166 (105-265)	1.3 (.17)	17
Fenpropathrin	4.9 (2.-7)	2.6 (.50)	47.1 (32-67)	1.5 (.12)	10
Tefluthrin	1.0 (.7-1.2)	4.9 (1.1)	39.2 (23-56)	1.7 (.20)	39

TABLE 3. LC50's (mg/l), slopes and resistance ratios for females of two *Bemisia tabaci* strains tested using the leaf dip technique.

Pyrethroid	SUDS		BELZ		RESIS.
	LC50 (limits)	Slope (se)	LC50 (limits)	Slope (se)	RATIO
Bifenthrin	0.3 (.27-.44)	2.4 (.30)	21 (8.7-300)	0.9 (.12)	70
Cypermethrin	4.6 (1.9-40)	0.8 (.12)	248 (190-320)	2.0 (.18)	54

DISCUSSION

The influence of bioassay method on resistance ratios has been reported (Dennehy et *al.*, 1983). Roush & Miller (1986) suggested that bioassay techniques that are 'ecologically realistic' may improve resistance detection or at least indicate the extent of the field resistance problem. Recent experience with *B. tabaci* however does not confirm this. Rowland et *al.*(1991) reported that *B. tabaci* adults did not express resistance to cypermethrin in a set of field simulator experiments in spite of an 83-fold resistance ratio in the leaf dip bioassay.

The most appropriate method for detecting resistance is that method which provides greatest discrimination. The greatest discrimination between the pyrethroid susceptible and resistance strains of *B. tabaci* was produced using the leaf dip bioassay.

If the extreme LC50 values from Table 1 are disregarded on the basis of suspected resistance then the remaining values for each compound are similar enough to suggest that the leaf dip method is stable and robust. Resistance ratios should however be based on true susceptible strains tested in-house.

Sanderson & Roush (1992) found their glass vial bioassay technique inappropriate for testing *Trialeurodes vaporariorum* because the adults stuck to the residue inside the vial. We encountered this difficulty when high (>1000mg/l) concentrations were used which would preclude full LDPM line construction on highly resistant populations.

The glass vial technique described in this paper was designed with a specific objective i.e. to test the contact activity of small amounts of technical compounds on adult *B. tabaci* and whitefly parasitoids. The technique is now in routine use at Rothamsted and is providing valuable information on the activity of established and novel molecules.

ACKNOWLEDGEMENTS

The authors thank Dr Ian Denholm for discussions and suggestions on the manuscript and Kevin Gorman for technical assistance.

REFERENCES

Abdeldaffie, E.Y.A.; Elhag, E.A.; Bashir, N.H.H. (1987) Resistance in the cotton whitefly, *Bemisia tabaci* (Genn.), to insecticide recently introduced into Sudan Gezira. *Tropical Pest Management*, **33**, 283-286.

Ahmed, A.H.M.; Elhag, E.A.; Bashir, N.H.H. (1987) Insecticide resistance in the cotton whitefly (*Bemisia tabaci* Genn.) in the Sudan Gezira. *Tropical Pest Management*, **33**, 67-72.

Campanhola, C.; Plapp, F.W. Jr. (1989) Pyrethroid resistance in the tobacco budworm (Lepidoptera: Noctuidae): insecticide bioassays and field monitoring. *Journal of Economic Entomology*, **82**, 22-28.

Cohen, S.; Duffus, J.E.; Liu, H.Y. (1992) A new *Bemisia tabaci* biotype in the southwestern United States and its role in silverleaf of squash and transmission of lettuce infectious yellows virus. *Phytopathology*, **82**, 86-90.

Costa, H.S.; Brown, J.K.; (1991) Variation in biological characteristics and esterase patterns among populations of *Bemisia tabaci*, and the association of one population with silverleaf symptom induction. *Entomologia experimentalis et applicata*, **61**, 211-219.

Dennehy, T.J.; Granett, J.; Leigh, T.F.; (1983) Relevance of Slide-Dip and Residual Bioassay Comparisons to Detection of Resistance in Spider Mites. *Journal of Economic Entomology*. **76**, 1225-1230.

Dittrich, V.; Ernst, G.H. (1983) The resistance pattern in whiteflies of Sudanese cotton. *Mitteilungen der Deutschen Gesellschaft fur Allgemeine und Angewandte Entomologie*, **4**, 96-97.

Dittrich, V.; Hassan, S.O.; Ernst, G.H. (1986) Development of a new primary pest of cotton in the Sudan: *Bemisia tabaci*, the whitefly. *Agriculture Ecosystems and Environment*, **17**, 137-142.

Horowitz, A.R.; Toscano, N.C.; Youngman, R.R.; Georghiou, G.P. (1988) Synergism of insecticides with DEF in sweetpotato whitefly (Homoptera: Aleyrodidae). *Journal of Economic Entomology*, **81**, 110-114.

Prabhaker, N.; Coudriet, D.L.; Meyerdirk, D.E. (1985) Insecticide resistance in the sweetpotato whitefly, *Bemisia tabaci* (Homoptera: Aleyrodidae). *Journal of Economic Entomology*, **78**, 748-752.

Prabhaker, N.; Toscano, N.C.; Coudriet, D.L. (1989) Susceptibility of the immature and adult stages of the sweetpotato whitefly (Homoptera: Aleyrodidae) to selected insecticides. *Journal of Economic Entomology*, **82**, 983-988.

Roush, R.T; Miller, G.L. (1986) Considerations for Design of Insecticide Resistance Monitoring Programs. *Journal of Economic Entomology*, **79**, 293-298.

Rowland, M.; Hackett, B.; Stribley, M. (1991) Evaluation of insecticides in field-control simulators and standard laboratory bioassays against resistant and susceptible *Bemisia tabaci* (Homoptera: Aleyrodidae) from Sudan. *Bulletin of Entomological Research*, **81**, 189-199.

Sanderson, J.P.; Roush, R.T.; (1992) Monitoring Insecticide resistance in Greenhouse Whitefly (Homoptera: Aleyrodidae) with Yellow Sticky Cards. *Journal of Economic Entomology*, 85, 634-631.

Wilson, D.; Anema, B.P. (1988) Development of Buprofezin for control of *Trialeurodes vaporariorum* and *Bemisia tabaci* on glasshouse crops in the Netherlands and the UK. *Brighton Crop Protection Conference - Pests and Diseases 1988*, **1**, 175-180.

Yassin, K.M.; Bashir, N.H.H.; Gadalla, B.H. (1990) Effects of endosulfan, chlorpyrifos and their mixtures on *Bemisia tabaci* of Sudan Gezira. *Tropical Pest Management*, **36**, 230-233.

THE MICROIMMERSION BIOASSAY: A NOVEL METHOD FOR MEASURING ACARICIDAL ACTIVITY
AND FOR CHARACTERISING PESTICIDE RESISTANCE IN SPIDER MITES

A.W. FARNHAM, T.J. DENNEHY[1], I. DENHOLM, J.C. WHITE

AFRC Institute of Arable Crops Research, Department of Insecticides and
Fungicides, Rothamsted Experimental Station, Harpenden, Herts. AL5 2JQ, UK, and
[1]Cornell University, Department of Entomology, New York State Agricultural
Experiment Station, Geneva, New York 14456, USA

ABSTRACT

A novel and versatile method is described for measuring the contact
activity of acaricides against spider mites, and for detecting and
characterising acaricide resistance. The microimmersion (MI)
bioassay involves drawing batches of 25 mites into small pipette
tips under vacuum pressure, immersing them for 30 s in 35ul of a
test solution, and then confining the treated subjects on clean
foliage in holding cells. Evaluations of amitraz, bifenthrin,
chlorpyrifos and dicofol against susceptible strains of *Tetranychus
urticae* showed the MI bioassay to be equally applicable to
formulated and technical acaricides, and to give LC_{50} values that
corresponded well with those from a conventional residue bioassay.
The method also clearly diagnosed previously unreported resistance
to bifenthrin in *T. urticae*, and a novel mechanism conferring
strong, and apparently specific resistance to chlorpyrifos.

INTRODUCTION

Only two topical exposure bioassays have been published for spider mites
(Helle and Overmeer, 1985): the slide-dip or slide-spray method (Voss, 1961),
and a technique for topical application to individual mites (Harrison, 1961).
The latter is considered too cumbersome for testing large numbers of
subjects. Slide-based methods are well-established but encounter two major
limitations. Firstly, they are only applicable for acaricides that act within
the period (ca. 2 days) that mites can survive without feeding. Secondly, the
inability to recover survivors is a major constraint on its use in acaricide
resistance studies.

We describe here a novel topical-type bioassay that overcomes these
limitations. This microimmersion (MI) bioassay is relatively fast and simple,
allows recovery of treated subjects, and requires only small amounts of
either formulated or technical acaricide solution. Using *Tetranychus urticae*
as the test organism, we have evaluated this method for measuring the
activity of four acaricides against a susceptible strain, and for diagnosing
resistance to two of these chemicals.

DESCRIPTION OF THE MI BIOASSAY

The apparatus used to collect and treat mites requires four sections of
plastic pipette tip as shown in Figure 1. 25 adult mites are collected under
suction pressure into the small pipette tip, which fits over a filter paper
disc on the end of Large Tip A. The latter (with the small tip still

attached) is then detached from the base piece and affixed to the first of two Gilson P100 pipettes. This pipette is held vertically and 35 ul of solution is drawn up slowly to fill the small tip and run a short distance into Large Tip A.

FIGURE 1. Configuration and dimensions of pipette tips used for MI bioassays.

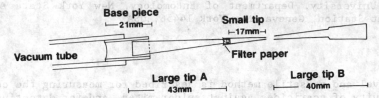

FIGURE 2. Construction of holding cell for confining mites.

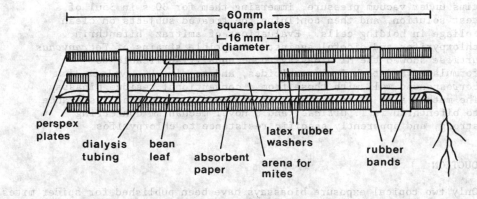

Timing of the 30 s immersion period begins as soon as the fluid contacts the filter paper plug. After 20 s, the small tip containing immersed mites is detached from Large Tip A, inverted, and attached to Large Tip B (Figure 1) already in place on a second Gilson P100 pipette. At the end of the immersion period, the paper plug is removed with fine forceps and mites exhausted onto a filter paper disc. Great care is needed at this stage to avoid damaging the treated subjects (Dennehy *et al.*, in press).

After 10-20 s of drying on the filter paper, treated mites are transferred to holding cells (Figure 2) and enclosed within an arena formed on the upper leaf surface of an intact bean (*Phaseolus vulgaris*) seedling. Fully assembled cells are stored on racks for a prescribed period, and then disassembled to enable live and dead mites to be removed from the arena and counted. If required, survivors can be recovered and cultured on clean plant material.

EVALUATION OF THE MI BIOASSAY

Spider Mite Cultures

Two susceptible cultures, UKS and GSS, were obtained from Shell Research Limited, Sittingbourne, England, and Schering AG, Berlin, respectively. These gave very similar responses to the acaricides tested, and are referred to collectively as the susceptible strain. NYR is a composite resistant population originating from intensively-sprayed apple orchards in New York State. Sub-cultures that had been maintained under strong selection pressure with bifenthrin or amitraz at Cornell University were bulked as a single strain. Susceptible and resistant strains were reared in separate rooms on 10-20 day old *P. vulgaris* seedlings at 23+3 °C with a 16 h photoperiod.

Acaricides and acaricide solutions

Diluted formulations of amitraz ('Mitac 20', 200 gl^{-1} EC, Schering AG), bifenthrin ('Talstar', 100 gl^{-1} EC, DowElanco Ltd), chlorpyrifos ('Dursban', 480 gl^{-1} EC, DowElanco Ltd) and dicofol ('Kelthane', 180 gl^{-1} EC, Rohm and Haas Ltd) were prepared as parts per million (ppm) of active ingredient on a weight-to-weight basis in distilled water containing 0.01% Triton X-100 as a surfactant.

Technical samples of amitraz (Schering Agrochemicals, Chesterford Park, England), bifenthrin (FMC Corporation, Princeton, New Jersey, USA) and chlorpyrifos (Promochem Ltd, St. Albans, England) were of 99.6%, >95% and 99.9% purity respectively. Solutions of technical products were initially prepared in acetone (AR grade) on a weight-to-volume basis. Immediately before immersion, these were diluted further with distilled water containing 0.0125% Triton X-100 to achieve final concentrations of 20% acetone, 0.01% surfactant, and the desired amount of acaricide. To compensate for the poor solubility of amitraz, vials containing serial dilutions of this chemical were held in an ultrasonic bath up to the period of immersion.

Design and scoring of bioassays

Tests involving 6-12 different concentrations of each chemical were replicated a minimum of 4 times and a maximum of 23 times to yield adequate data for statistical analysis. All bioassays were held for 72 h post-treatment, under ambient light in a room maintained at 21+2 °C. Mites exhibiting repetitive (non-reflex) movement of more than one locomotory appendage after this period were recorded as alive.

MI BIOASSAYS AGAINST SUSCEPTIBLE MITES

Responses to formulated bifenthrin, chlorpyrifos and dicofol were very homogeneous, and gave close fits to the probit model. LC_{50} values for bifenthrin and dicofol did not differ significantly, but both these compounds were more toxic at LC_{50} than amitraz, and less toxic than chlorpyrifos (Table 1). Hence, the ranking of toxicity in MI bioassays was chlorpyrifos > bifenthrin/dicofol > amitraz, with LC_{50} values ranging from 10 ppm for chlorpyrifos to 530 ppm for amitraz. Slopes of the probit lines also fell into three groups; those for chlorpyrifos (4.9) and dicofol (4.4) did not differ significantly, but were significantly different from that for bifenthrin (2.9). The slope for amitraz (1.5) was significantly lower than the other three.

Toxicities of the three technical acaricides evaluated with the MI bioassay followed the same pattern as that for the formulated products, with LC_{50} values ranked in the order chlorpyrifos > bifenthrin > amitraz (Table 1). The much larger standard error on the LC_{50} estimate for amitraz reflected a greater intrinsic heterogeneity in response, and problems with the solubility of this chemical at the concentrations required. As a result, the slope of the probit line was again much lower for amitraz than for bifenthrin and chlorpyrifos. Difficulties with measuring the toxicity of amitraz in both bioassays are covered by Dennehy *et al.* elsewhere in these Proceedings.

At the LC_{50} level, technical bifenthrin and chlorpyrifos were 2.3-fold and 17-fold more toxic than the corresponding formulated products. There was no significant difference in this respect for amitraz. It is noteworthy, however, that the much lower slope obtained for technical (2.3) compared to formulated chlorpyrifos (4.9) resulted in very similar LC_{90} values (18 ppm and 21 ppm respectively) in the two bioassays. In contrast, slopes for technical and formulated bifenthrin did not differ significantly (Table 1).

COMPARISON OF MI AND RESIDUAL BIOASSAYS

Comparative data for formulated acaricides were obtained with a residual method employing holding cells identical to those used in the MI bioassay. In this case, leaves were dipped for 5 s in the required concentration of acaricide, and left to dry before being enclosed in the cells. 25 mites were then loaded into each cell, and mortality was again assessed after 72 h.

TABLE 1. LC_{50} values (ppm a.i.) and slopes of probit lines obtained with MI and residual bioassays

Chemical	Susceptible strain			Resistant Strain		
	$LC_{50}{}^{1}$(x/÷ s.e.)	Slope[1]	LC_{50} (x/÷ s.e.)	Slope	R.F.[2]
(a) MI bioassays with formulated acaricides						
Amitraz	530[a] (1.20)	1.5[a]			
Bifenthrin	86[b] (1.08)	2.9[b]	36,000 (1.10)	3.4	420
Chlorpyrifos	10[c] (1.06)	4.9[c]	3,500 (1.11)	2.6	350
Dicofol	61[b] (1.06)	4.4[c]			
(b) MI bioassays with technical acaricides						
Amitraz	480[a] (1.41)	1.1[a]			
Bifenthrin	37[b] (1.09)	3.3[b]	7,200 (1.04)	3.4	190
Chlorpyrifos	5.8[c](1.13)	2.3[c]	2,100 (1.03)	11.0	360
(c) Residual bioassays with formulated acaricides						
Amitraz	150[a] (1.21)	1.2[a]			
Bifenthrin	71[b] (1.15)	2.1[b]	8,200 (1.20)	1.7	120
Chlorpyrifos	1.4[c](1.16)	2.3[b]	760 (1.13)	2.1	540
Dicofol	75[ab] (1.07)	3.3[c]			

[1]For each type of bioassay, superscripts identify LC_{50} values and slopes that do not differ significantly at the 95% probability level.
[2]Resistance factor at LC_{50} relative to the susceptible strain.

The relative toxicity of the four compounds was very similar in residual and MI tests (Table 1). LC_{50} values were ranked in an identical manner, and differed less than 10-fold between bioassay methods for all four chemicals. At LC_{50}, amitraz and chlorpyrifos were 3.5-fold and 7.1-fold more toxic respectively in the residual bioassay, whereas differences for bifenthrin and dicofol were small and not significant. The most notable difference between bioassay methods was that probit lines were consistently and steeper under the more uniform exposure conditions of the MI bioassay.

FIGURE 1. Probit lines for the susceptible (S) and NYR (R) strains tested with commercial formulations of (a) bifenthrin and (b) chlorpyrifos. MI = microimmersion bioassay; Res = Residual bioassay.

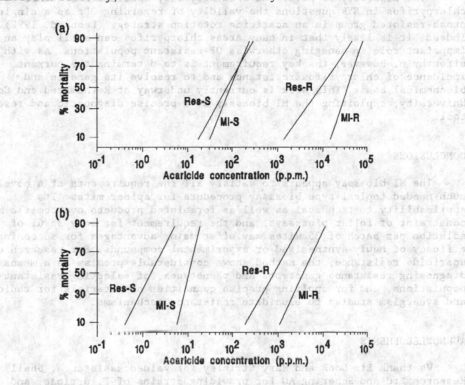

DIAGNOSIS OF RESISTANCE TO BIFENTHRIN AND CHLORPYRIFOS

The MI bioassay also proved extremely effective in diagnosing two very potent and previously unreported types of resistance present at high frequencies in the NYR strain. In the case of bifenthrin (Figure 3a), with which the strain had been intensively selected in the laboratory prior to testing, the resistance factor was 3.5-fold higher than with the residual bioassay, even though the two methods gave very similar results for the susceptible strain. In addition, the MI probit line for NYR was twice as steep as that obtained with the residual bioassay (Table 1). Resistance factors for chlorpyrifos were more consistent between bioassays, since the difference in toxicity recorded for susceptible mites was also apparent in bioassays against the NYR strain (Figure 3b). Since even the susceptible strain used for this work was highly tolerant of related chemicals such as parathion and azinphosmethyl, this resistance appears distinct to that conferred by older and more widely-distributed organophosphate (OP) resistance mechanisms. Cross-resistance between bifenthrin and chlorpyrifos is unlikely, as we have recorded equally high resistance to chlorpyrifos in a strain of _Panonychus ulmi_ retaining full susceptibility to bifenthrin.

Bifenthrin is becoming widely-used as an acaricide in several cropping systems, and there have, to our knowledge, been no prior reports of resistance in Tetranychid mites. Despite its history of laboratory selection with bifenthrin, results for the NYR strain highlight a potential for strong resistance in field populations of *T. urticae*, and the need to establish its occurrence and cross-resistance characteristics.

The discovery of novel and seemingly very specific resistance to chlorpyrifos in NYR questions the validity of regarding OPs as a single cross-resisted group in an acaricide rotation strategy (Leonard, 1992). Indeed, it is likely that in many areas chlorpyrifos can still play an important role in managing otherwise OP-resistant populations. As with bifenthrin, however, the key requirement is to determine the current incidence of chlorpyrifos resistance and to resolve its genetic and biochemical basis. This work is currently underway at Rothamsted and Cornell University, exploiting the MI bioassay as a precise diagnostic and research tool.

CONCLUSIONS

The MI bioassay appears to satisfy all the requirements of a novel and much-needed topical-type bioassay procedure for spider mites. Its applicability to technical as well as formulated products overcomes a major constraint of foliar bioassays, and the requirement for only 35 ul of solution per batch of 25 mites may offer major advantages for screening the efficacy of newly-synthesised or experimental compounds. For research on acaricide resistance, the method shows considerable promise as a means of diagnosing resistance genotypes and phenotypes, of selecting resistant populations, and for applying precise quantities of materials for radiolabel and synergism studies to elucidate resistance mechanisms.

ACKNOWLEDGEMENTS

We thank Liz Cook and Mary Stribley for valued assistance, Shell Research Ltd and Schering AG for providing strains of *T. urticae*, and Schering AG, DowElanco Ltd, Rohm and Haas Ltd and FMC Corporation for providing technical and formulated acaricides. Financial support by the British Technology Group and the Underwood Foundation for T.J.D's sabbatical studies at Rothamsted is gratefully acknowledged.

REFERENCES

Dennehy, T.J.; Farnham, A.W.; Denholm, I. The microimmersion bioassay: a novel method for the topical application of pesticides to spider mites. *Pesticide Science* (in press).
Harrison, R.A. (1961) Topical application of insecticide solutions to mites and small insects. *New Zealand Journal of Science*, 4, 534-539.
Helle, W.; Overmeer, W.P.J. (1985) Toxicological test methods. In: *Spider Mites: Their Biology, Natural Enemies and Control*, W. Helle and M.W. Sabelis (Eds), Amsterdam: Elsevier, pp. 391-395.
Leonard, P.K. (1992) IRAC Fuit Crops Working Group spider mite resistance management strategy. In: *Resistance 91: Achievements and Developments in Combating Pesticide Resistance*, I. Denholm, A.L. Devonshire and D.W. Hollomon (Eds), Barking, UK: Elsevier, pp. 41-47.
Voss, G. (1961) Ein neues Akarizid-Austestvarfahren fur Spinnmilben. *Anz. Schaedlingskd.* 34, 76-77.

TESTING INSECTICIDE USE STRATEGIES: A MODEL GRAIN STORE SYSTEM FOR THE SAW-TOOTHED GRAIN BEETLE, *ORYZAEPHILUS SURINAMENSIS*

P.L. MASON

Central Science Laboratory, Ministry of Agriculture, Fisheries and Food, London Road, Slough, Berkshire SL3 7HJ.

ABSTRACT

An experimental grain store model is described for the study of the ecology and population genetics of insecticide resistance in the saw-toothed grain beetle, *Oryzaephilus surinamensis*. Efficacy of control is shown to be related to the extent of insecticide treatment. The model demonstrates the ability of refuges to act as foci of infestation, and examines their role as a source of susceptible beetles that may retard the evolution of resistance.

INTRODUCTION

Insecticides remain indispensable in many integrated management strategies for the control of insect pests. There is an increasing requirement for improvements in the use of insecticides so that while control of target species is maintained, collateral impact on the environment is reduced, and the evolution of resistance is discouraged. Effective strategies must take account of the ecology, life-history and population genetics of pest species. Many analytical and simulation models have demonstrated the potential of these and other operational factors to affect the population dynamics and spread of resistance in local pest populations. Of primary importance are the relative fitnesses of genotypes, the strength of insecticide dose, the presence of refuges (wherein individuals escape selection by insecticide), and migration (Georghiou & Taylor, 1977; Caprio & Tabashnik, 1992).

A small number of laboratory studies have confirmed the importance of migration and the degree of dominance of the resistance allele (Taylor *et al.*, 1983). Indirect evidence of the influence of selection and migration on local, regional and worldwide patterns of resistance exists for several insect pest species (Unruh, 1990; Raymond *et al.*, 1991).

There is a lack of experimental studies that directly test the different insecticide use strategies derived from theoretical studies (but see Curtis & Rawlings, 1980). Some theoretical models have argued that refuges are an inevitable and fortuitous feature of pest population structure and insecticide treatment methods, and they are often regarded as a source of susceptible individuals that may retard the spread of resistance. Yet, no studies have demonstrated the influence of refuges in pest populations.

The comparatively simple post-harvest ecosystem of the grain store is prone to infestation by a range of pest species. Control is achieved through the practices of general hygiene, cooling and drying of grain, and the mainly prophylactic application of insecticides. Insecticide treatments are employed in 53.4% of farm and 85.4% of commercial grains stores in England and Wales. Pirimiphos-methyl, the most widely used of the 4 grain protectant compounds available in the UK, is used in 39.6% of farm and 69.4% of commercial grain stores (Prickett *et al.*, 1990).

One of the most widespread insect pest of stored grain in the UK, and the model species for this study, is the saw-toothed grain beetle, *Oryzaephilus surinamensis*. It has been detected in 4.8% of farm and 14% of commercial grain stores in England and Wales. Respectively, 27% and 82% of strains from these sites were found to be resistant in the laboratory to a discriminating dose of pirimiphos-methyl (Prickett *et al.*, 1990).

This paper describes an experimental model system that mimics the conditions in a grain store containing refuges. A compromise is struck between the conflicting requirements of reproducing the biological and operational conditions of the pest in the grain store, and restricting the number of variables to permit a meaningful interpretation of results. It is used to study the population genetics and ecology of *O. surinamensis* under putative chemical control strategies. Results of partial fabric treatments are compared and the role of refuges in maintaining insect pest populations is considered.

MATERIALS AND METHODS

Blockboard bins, measuring 2 x 2 x 1.25 m, were set up indoors on plywood bases. The interior was lined with renewable kraft paper, taking care to seal any gaps and overlapping edges to prevent insects escaping. A 10 cm-wide aluminium foil strip was glued around the interior at a height of 1 m and coated with Fluon (ICI Advanced Materials, UK), an aqueous suspension of polytetrafluoroethylene. This limited vertical movement and prevented escape.

Refuges of thin card were glued to the bin walls to form a pocket 20 cm long and 8 cm high. Each bin contained a total of 16 refuges, 4 to a wall, arranged in 2 rows (at heights of 0.315 and 0.685 m). Refuges were positioned at 0.225 m and 0.123 m (upper row) and at 0.775 m and 0.177 m (lower row) along from the far left of each wall. A standard volume of kibbled, pesticide-free, winter wheat cv. Avalon (weighing approximately 120 g) was placed in each refuge.

Actellic-40 wettable powder (40% wt/wt pirimiphos-methyl; ICI Plant Protection Division, UK) in water was applied to run off from a hand-held sprayer operated from within the bin, and allowed to dry overnight. An average dose of 20 mg/m^2 pirimiphos-methyl was applied to either 1, 2 adjacent, 3 or 4 walls of 4 bins. A control bin was left unsprayed. To assess the concentration delivered and the persistence of the residue over time, 8 x 8 cm squares of kraft paper were pinned to the walls before spraying. These were removed and quantitatively analysed for pirimiphos-methyl residues at bi-monthly intervals throughout the experiment (Chamberlain, 1990).

The laboratory strain 7022/1 of *O. surinamensis* was used because it comprised approximately 4% of pirimiphos-methyl-resistant phenotypes, as determined by a standard discriminating dose bioassay of 156 mg/m^2 of the insecticide (Prickett *et al.*, 1990) (96.0% knockdown, n = 571). It was a relatively new culture to the laboratory (c. 3 years), collected from a UK commercial grain store, and so was assumed to possess more of its original genetic variability than longer established strains. An initial population of 2000 beetles, drawn from different aged laboratory cultures, was divided so that 125 beetles were counted into each of 16 glass tubes containing 20 g kibbled wheat. The day after the bins had been treated, single tubes and their contents were slid into the kibbled wheat in each refuge in an attempt to reduce the initial agitation dispersal. The bins were covered with plywood sheets to ensure the near-dark conditions typical of grain stores. Throughout the experiment temperature varied between 18 and 27 °C, and relative humidity varied with the ambient conditions. Both were recorded on a thermohygrograph.

Pesticide-free Avalon wheat was fumigated overnight with methyl bromide to ensure that it did not contain live insects. The wheat was allowed to stand for 3 days so that any remaining methyl bromide vapour would diffuse out. On the 10th day 65 kg were placed in the centre of the floor of each bin.

The duration of the experiment was determined by the rate at which changes in population size and phenotypic proportions would have become apparent. Three pitfall-type PC traps (Cogan et al., 1990), containing a small amount of laboratory culture food to sustain trapped beetles until their retrieval, were placed beneath the surface of the grain at week 11. They were removed at week 13, after which time sufficient live beetles were present in even the most extensively treated bins to conduct resistance phenotype determination tests. Live and dead beetles were counted, and the resistance phenotypes of survivors were determined with discriminating dose bioassays. The experiment was completed after 16 weeks (≤ 2 generations), when the differences in trap totals between bins indicated the relative success of each treatment. The refuges were emptied and the live and dead insects counted. Resistance phenotypes were determined where possible.

RESULTS

Numbers of beetles recovered are presented in Table 1. Live beetles were recovered from all bins. More live beetles than in the initial populations were recovered from the control and single treated wall bins. It is not possible to infer whether there was an overall increase in numbers in the other bins as estimates of trap efficiency were not available. Fabric treatments reduced populations by at least an order of magnitude, even in the single treated wall bin. They produced a 16-fold or greater decrease in live beetles trapped in the grain compared with the control bin, although there was no clear relationship between the number of live beetles recovered after 16 weeks (l) and the number of treated walls (t) in the treated bins (regression: $l = 481 - 83.4 t$, $P = 0.356$; $r^2 = 0.12$). Numbers of beetles found dead in the traps varied inversely with the number of walls treated ($l = 64.5 - 17.1 t$, $P = 0.057$, $r^2 = 0.833$).

Increasing the number of treated walls reduced the mean number of live beetles recovered over a range of 4 orders of magnitude in refuges on treated walls. There was a weak inverse relationship between the number of treated walls and the number of live beetles recovered from refuges on treated walls ($l = 53.0 - 12.2 t$, $r^2 = 0.15$, $P = 0.008$). By comparison, there was a 1 order of magnitude reduction in the mean number of live insects in refuges on untreated walls. There was a strong inverse relationship between the treatment and live beetles recovered ($l = 256.4 - 77.9 t$; $r^2 = 0.53$, $P \approx 0.000$). Refuges on untreated walls harboured more beetles than those on treated walls in the same bin (two independent sample t-test: bin with 1 treated wall, $t_{13 d.f.} = 2.52$, $P = 0.026$; 2 treated walls, $t_{10 d.f.} = 5.01$, $P = 0.0005$; 3 treated walls, $t_{3 d.f.} = 4.90$, $P = 0.016$).

Discriminating dose tests detected no selection for resistance in any of the bins when compared with phenotypic proportions in the original cultures (Table 2). Only beetles from refuges in the single treated wall bin exhibited a significant change (contingency test, $\chi^2_{1 d.f.} = 23.80$, $P < 0.001$), and this was towards an increase in the proportion of susceptibles. Comparisons of

TABLE 1. Numbers of 7022/1 *O.surinamensis* recovered from grain trap samples (after 13 weeks) and refuges on pirimiphos-methyl-treated (initially 20.4 mg/m²) and untreated walls (after 16 weeks).

Number of walls treated	Grain		Refuges on treated walls		Refuges on untreated walls	
	Alive	Dead	Alive	Dead	Alive	Dead
0	>7800	700	-	-	247.9[a] (19.9)	19.8 (1.8)
1	277	50	130.3 (10.0)	441.8 (98.7)	201.7 (26.6)	15.8 (3.8)
2	485	32	15.3 (5.9)	191.7 (19.6)	82.7 (12.1)	17.6 (7.8)
3	251	2	2.6 (0.7)	68.3 (8.4)	23.8 (4.3)	38.3 (23.8)
4	77	3	0.3 (0.1)	82.3 (9.1)	-	-

[a] Mean values with standard errors in brackets

TABLE 2. Percentage knockdown (kd) of 7022/1 *O. surinamensis* with 156 mg/m² discriminating dose of pirimiphos-methyl.

Number of walls treated	Grain (11-13 weeks)			Refuges (16 weeks)		
	kd	n	χ^2	kd	n	χ^2
0	94.1	271	1.46 n.s. [a]	-	-	-
1	97.8	223	1.50 n.s.	99.0	1886	23.80 ***
2	94.7	360	0.80 n.s.	97.8	617	3.04 n.s.
3	94.7	228	0.59 n.s.	94.7	111	0.43 n.s.
4	100.0	63	2.63 n.s.	-	0	-

[a] Contingency $\chi^2_{1\,d.f.}$ values derived from comparison of totals of 23 live and 548 dead beetles (96.0% kd) in tests on original cultures.

knockdown of beetles from grain in the treated bins with that from the control bin indicated no selection for resistance. Beetles from the single treated wall bin were significantly more susceptible ($\chi^2_{1\,d.f.}$ = 4.03, $P < 0.05$). There was a small increase in the proportion of resistant phenotypes in the refuges as the extent of the treatment increased, consistent with weak selection for resistance. The differences in proportions were significant overall ($\chi^2_{2\,d.f.}$ = 17.12, $P < 0.005$), with only that of the pair-wise comparison between the bins with 2 and 3 treated walls barely failing to achieve significance ($\chi^2_{1\,d.f.}$ = 3.464, $P > 0.05$). Beetles from refuges in the bin with

2 treated walls had a higher knockdown than those from the grain ($\chi^2_{1\,\text{d.f.}}$ = 6.31, P < 0.05). There was no significant difference in the bins with 1 treated wall ($\chi^2_{1\,\text{d.f.}}$ = 2.70, P > 0.05) and with 3 treated walls ($\chi^2_{1\,\text{d.f.}}$ = 0.003, P > 0.99).

Insecticide residues decayed from a mean concentration at application of 20.4 mg/m², through 7.25 mg/m² after 8 weeks, to 2.89 mg/m² at the end of the experiment (16 weeks).

DISCUSSION

The concentration of insecticide applied was considerably lower than a recommended field dose (equivalent to 400 mg/m², Muggleton *et al.*, 1986), and decayed by an order of magnitude during the experiment. Nevertheless, it was sufficient to cause heavy mortality. Yet the discriminating dose tests revealed no increase in the proportion of resistant phenotypes in beetles sampled from the grain and only a small increase in those from the refuges from treated bins. It is likely that resistance alleles are present at negligible frequencies in this strain (subsequent dose-response tests indicate a resistance factor of 1.78 at the LD50 in the 7022/1 strain relative to the Laboratory Susceptible strain), so almost all individuals possessing them will be heterozygous at any resistance locus. The relationship between the response to long-term exposure to waning experimental doses and the brief exposure to a laboratory discriminating dose is not known. However, the lack of strong selection might be explained if the treatment had been sufficient to kill any heterozygotes as well as susceptible homozygotes. Mortality would be independent of the resistance genotype, and so survival would depend upon escaping a fatal dose of insecticide in the bin.

In this model of a fabric treatment with insecticide, a beetle is either in a refuge or in transit to another. The untreated grain itself may be considered as a very large refuge. Only while it is in transit may a beetle encounter a fatal dose of insecticide. Infestation of the grain will depend on the effectiveness of the fabric treatment as a *cordon sanitaire*, killing beetles moving from their original refuge into the grain. Beetles can disperse freely in the grain bins, so we would expect the efficacy of the control strategy to be related to the fraction of the surface that has been treated. This expectation is borne out by the size of refuge populations, and to a lesser extent by the grain populations.

Refuges were able to sustain beetles even in the most extensively treated bins. They acted as foci of infestation, enabling a strain containing a high proportion of susceptible individuals to colonise a central bulk of grain. If refuges can act as foci of reinfestation in grain stores then the frequency of resistance alleles in refuge populations will be crucial to the rate at which resistance evolves and control failure occurs when beetles migrate into a new grain bulk. This frequency will depend on the relative fitness of each genotype over the range of insecticide doses encountered, and the absolute rate of migration between refuges and grain.

The application of a dose sufficient to kill heterozygotes, while allowing the maximum acceptable number of individuals (which will be mainly homozygous susceptibles, initially) to escape exposure has been suggested as a strategy for delaying the spread of resistance, while maintaining control of pest numbers. In this study, the frequency of resistant beetles in the refuges appeared to increase as the treatment became more extensive, as would be expected under such a strategy. However, this strategy does not account for the apparent increase in the proportion of susceptible beetles in refuge populations compared with those of the original cultures and of the beetles from the grain in the control bin.

The grain bins function well as a model system for studying the response of *O. surinamensis* to insecticide use strategies under controlled, yet realistic, conditions. Their continued use will provide a much needed bridge between our understanding of this beetle as a laboratory organism and as a pest in the grain store by the study of dispersal behaviour, productivity and mortality in the refuges and grain.

ACKNOWLEDGEMENTS

I thank I. Taylor and A. Lord for technical assistance, and the Pesticide Safety Division of the Ministry of Agriculture, Fisheries and Food, UK, who funded the work.

REFERENCES

Caprio, M.A.; Tabashnik, B.E. (1992) Gene flow accelerates local adaptation among finite populations: simulating the evolution of insecticide resistance. *Journal of Economic Entomology*, **85**, 611-620.

Chamberlain, S.J. (1990) Determination of multi-pesticide residues in cereals, cereal products and animal feed using gel-permeation chromatography. *Analyst*, **115**, 1161-1165.

Cogan, P.M.; Wakefield, M.E.; Pinniger, D.B. (1990) PC, a novel and inexpensive trap for the detection of beetle pests at low densities in bulk grain. *Proceedings of the 5th International Working Conference on Stored-Product Protection*, 1321-1328.

Curtis, C.F.; Rawlings, P. (1980) A preliminary study of dispersal and survival of *Anopheles culicifacies* in relation to the possibility of inhibiting the spread of insecticide resistance. *Ecological Entomology*, **5**, 11-17.

Georghiou, G.P.; Taylor, C.E. (1977) Genetic and biological influences in the evolution of insecticide resistance. *Journal of Economic Entomology*, **70**, 319-323.

Muggleton, J; Pinniger, D.B.; Webb, D.P.; Woodward, M.A. (1986) Treatment of a farm grain store with pirimiphos-methyl and the consequences for resistance in saw-toothed grain beetles (*Oryzaephilus surinamensis*). *Brighton Crop Protection Conference - Pests and Diseases 1986*, **2**, 599-606.

Prickett, A.J; Muggleton, J.; Llewellin, J.A. (1990) Insecticide resistance in populations of *Oryzaephilus surinamensis* and *Cryptolestes ferrugineus* from grain stores in England and Wales. *Brighton Crop Protection Conference - Pests and Diseases 1990*, **3**, 1189-1194.

Raymond, M.; Callaghan, A.; Fort, P.; Pasteur, N. (1991) Worldwide migration of amplified resistance genes in mosquitoes. *Nature*, **350**, 151-153.

Taylor, C.E.; Quaglia, F.; Georghiou G.P. (1983) Evolution of resistance to insecticides: a cage study on the influence of migration and insecticide decay rates. *Journal of Economic Entomology*, **76**, 704-707.

Unruh, T.R. (1990) Genetic structure among 18 west coast pear psylla populations: implications for the evolution of resistance. *American Entomologist*, **36**, 37-43.

SESSION 4A

POST-HARVEST LOSSES FROM PESTS AND DISEASES

CHAIRMAN   DR A. R. HARDY

SESSION
ORGANISER   MR D. B. PINNEGER

INVITED PAPERS   4A-1 to 4A-2

RESEARCH REPORTS   4A-3, 4A-4

RECENT SURVEYS OF POST-HARVEST PEST PROBLEMS IN FARM AND COMMERCIAL GRAIN STORES IN THE UK.

A.J. PRICKETT

Central Science Laboratory, MAFF, London Road, Slough, Berkshire SL3 7HJ

ABSTRACT

The results of recent surveys of storage practice and pest presence in UK farm grain stores and in off-farm commercial or central stores are presented. Much of the cereal market demands pest-free grain and the extent to which the grain industry meets this stringent requirement is discussed. The implications of the MAFF Code of Practice for the Control of Salmonellae are considered. This Code was not published at the time of the surveys and stipulates the exclusion of birds and rodents from stores containing grain intended for incorporation in animal feedingstuffs. In general, the majority of stores are successful in controlling those insects regarded as primary pests but less successful in avoiding secondary insect pests and excluding rodents and birds.

INTRODUCTION

The expansion of the UK cereal industry during the decade 1975-1985 resulted in a doubling of production from 13.8M to 26.5M tonnes and an exportable surplus of 6-10M tonnes (Wilkin & Hurlock, 1986). This level of production has been maintained with an average of 22.4M tonnes for 1985-89, comprising 57% wheat, 41% barley and 2% oats (Anon., 1991). These proportions differ between the constituent countries of the UK, with more wheat than barley grown in England whereas barley is the predominant crop in Scotland, Wales and Northern Ireland.

At harvest time approximately 90% of the crop is put into farm grain stores (Taylor & Sly, 1986). By the end of September 80% of wheat and 60% of barley remains on-farm and then, between October and June, there is a fairly constant decline in stocks such that most stores are empty by July, ready for the next harvest (*Source*: MAFF Cereal Stocks Survey). In off-farm commercial stores grain may be stored for much longer, especially that sold into Intervention. The total throughput of these stores varies but was estimated to be 6M tonnes for England and Wales in 1977/78 (Taylor, 1978) and a survey by Garthwaite *et al* (1987) identified 7.4M tonnes in England in 1985/86 but the latter were uncertain what proportion of the total this represented. In the 1985/86 survey, 33% of the grain was identified as coming from harvests prior to 1985.

The historical need to prevent damage or loss of grain by protecting it against attack by mould, mite, insect, rodent or bird pests has, to a large extent, been superceeded by more stringent requirements. For example, the UK flour milling industry uses 30% of wheat production and has a general requirement of freedom from pests (*Source*: NABIM). Almost half the grain exported goes to countries that require a phytosanitary inspection to check for the presence of pests (Wilkin & Hurlock, 1986). Animal feed accounts for 40% of UK cereal production (*Source*: MAFF) and the *Code of Practice for the Control of Salmonellae* during the storage, handling and transport of raw materials intended for incorporation into animal feedingstuffs, published by MAFF in 1989, requires the exclusion of birds, rodents and insects from stores. These factors have imposed the need not only to prevent damage by pests but to provide pest-free grain. At the same time it is MAFF policy to minimise the use of pesticides.

Surveys of storage practice and pest presence in farm and commercial grain stores were carried out between 1987 and 1989. This paper presents a summary of the main results of these surveys and discusses their implications.

METHODS

Farm grain stores

A random sample of 742 farm grain stores were surveyed between April and August 1987, stratified such that there were approximately 50 farms in each of three size groups in each of five regions covering the whole of England. Size (small, medium and large) was based on area of cereal grown and defined as 5-29.9, 30-74.9 and 75ha or more, respectively. Further details of stratification are given in Prickett (1988). The sample was 1.7% of the estimated total number of farms in England that stored grain. National estimates derived from the survey data were weighted by the total number of farms in each stratum identified by the annual MAFF census.

Commercial grain stores

Commercial or central grain stores were surveyed between September 1988 and March 1989. The aim was to survey all sites in England and Wales that had a storage capacity of more than 1,000 tonnes and to inspect up to four individual stores at each site for the presence of pests. The total number of such sites that existed at the time of the survey was believed to be 179, determined from information from several sources. The actual number of sites surveyed was 171 and at 157 of these a total of 283 individual stores were inspected. External bins or silos were excluded from inspection on grounds of safety. Further details are given in Prickett & Muggleton (1991).

Pest detection

The detection methods used for insects and mites were visual observation, sieving of residues, and placement of bait-bags (Pinniger, 1975), probe traps (Burkholder, 1984) and pitfall traps (Cogan & Wakefield, 1987). Rodents and birds were assessed on the basis of animal sighted or recent physical signs, such as droppings. Pests were recorded as present or absent and no attempt was made to assess the size of populations.

RESULTS

Grain storage

National estimates of total cereal storage capacity and the types of storage facilities are given in Table 1. The majority (86%) of farms that grew grain had their own grain store and the raised total quantity of wheat, barley and oats taken into these stores from the 1986 harvest was 18.5M tonnes, 88% of the 21.0M tonnes harvested. The weighted average tonnage stored was 90t, 288t and 1,058t on small, medium and large farms respectively. The total on-farm storage capacity was estimated to be 21.2M tonnes, with 66% of this being floor-stores, 23% internal bins and 11% external bins or silos. A small proportion of farms (15%) intended to use all their stored grain on the farm, nearly all of whom were small farms; most farms (85%) intended to sell all or part of their grain. At 23% of farms there had been a carry-over of grain from the previous harvest and 16% of farms had taken grain in from elsewhere for drying or storage. Three-quarters (77%) of the farms were mixed rather than purely arable and this was reflected in the fact that 68% bought-in animal feed.

The estimated total storage capacity in commercial grain stores was 4.5M tonnes, 83% of this being floor-stores, 4% internal bins and 13% external bins or silos. At the time of the survey 2.4M tonnes was in store and throughput during the previous 12 months was 4.9M tonnes, giving a total content and throughput of 7.3M tonnes, with an average of 41,000 tonnes per site. Home-grown grain was received direct from farms at 98% of sites and from other stores at 33%; imported grain was stored at 5.5% of sites but only 0.6% stored exclusively imported grain; and Intervention grain was present at 30% of sites. Infestable commodities other than cereal grain were stored at nearly two-thirds (62%) of sites and consisted mostly of rapeseed and pulses. When asked about the intended market for the grain in store, most site managers identified several markets. Those most frequently specified were export (67% of sites), feed mill (65%), flour mill (41%) and malting (37%).

TABLE 1. Raised estimates of storage capacity on farms in England and in commercial grain stores in England & Wales.

| | Farm stores | | | All | Central |
	Small	Medium	Large	farms	sites
Total number	17,394	12,887	12,509	42,790	179
Capacity (tonnes)	1.9M	4.3M	14.9M	21.2M	4.5M
Floor stores (%)	46.1	57.1	70.6	65.6	83.2
Internal bins (%)	32.9	28.2	20.5	23.2	3.6
External bins (%)	19.9	14.0	8.9	11.0	13.3
Other (%)	1.1	0.7	0.1	0.3	0.0
Throughput (tonnes)	1.6M	3.7M	13.2M	18.5M	7.3M

Physical control methods

The extent to which physical methods, such as controlling the temperature and moisture content of the grain, and pesticides are used to protect the grain is shown in Table 2. Almost all farmers (97%) said that the grain store had been cleaned to remove residues before the harvest was taken in. Grain cleaning and drying to prevent the development of mould and mites occurred on 59% and 81% of large farms respectively, but the frequency dropped to 15% and 19% for small farms. Similarly, grain cooling to prevent insects from breeding was more common on large farms (72%) than on small ones (50%), but most common at central sites (91%)

Insecticides

Insecticide use followed the same pattern as that for physical methods, being more frequent on large farms than on small ones. Overall, insecticide treatment of the fabric or structure of the store was carried out on 52% of farms, whereas only 10% of farms applied insecticide to the grain itself. Almost all grain treatments were in stores where the fabric was also treated. A much greater percentage of central sites (72%) applied insecticide to the grain than did large farms (20%). Allowing for whether the whole of a bulk was admixed, or just the surface was treated, an estimated 9% of farm-stored grain and 23% of centrally-stored grain was treated with insecticide. In both farm and commercial stores, approximately 95% of fabric treatments and 80% of grain treatments were said to be prophylactic rather than to control an existing infestation.

TABLE 2. Physical and chemical methods used to maintain the quality of stored grain (percent of premises).

| | Farm stores | | | All farms | Central sites |
	Small	Medium	Large		
Store cleaned pre-harvest	92.8	99.1	99.5	96.6	-
Grain cleaner used	14.8	28.2	59.0	31.8	59.2
Grain dryer used	18.7	49.9	81.4	46.4	65.7
Grain cooled/aerated	48.8	64.0	72.2	60.2	90.6
Insecticide treatment*:					
Fabric of store	27.9	59.2	78.3	52.1	85.8
Grain (all or some)	2.1	9.6	20.2	9.7	71.6
Total, fabric or grain	28.2	60.3	81.6	53.4	94.1
Rodenticide treatment	67.5	83.3	85.5	77.5	97.7

* Pirimiphos-methyl was the most common insecticide, used in about 75% of treatments. For further details of insecticide use, see Prickett (1988) and Prickett & Muggleton (1991).

Pests

The percentage of farms where the different types of pest were detected are shown in Table 3. Beetles have been grouped as primary pests (those that may cause serious and damaging infestation) and secondary pests (those that are usually associated with poor hygiene or mouldy grain, but nevertheless may lead to rejection of grain offered for sale). The genera included in each grouping are given in the foot-note to the Table. One or more of the primary beetle pest genera occurred in 9.7% of farm stores and an estimated 7.8% of farm-stored grain from the 1986 harvest was put into these stores, amounting to 1.4M tonnes. Secondary beetle pests and moths were found two to three times more frequently than the primary pests and more often in small farms than large ones. Psocids, which may become a nuisance when present in large numbers, were detected in about half the stores. Mites were widespread, present in 72% of stores and there was little evidence of a difference in frequency between the farm sizes. Rodent presence was detected in 70% of stores, comprising 53% with rats and 59% with mice, whilst bird presence was noted in 62% of stores - 31% with pigeons and 53% with sparrows.

The three primary insect pest genera, *Oryzaephilus*, *Cryptolestes*, and *Sitophilus*, occurred with similar frequencies (Table 4) and, in each case, they were more common on mixed farms (those growing cereal and keeping livestock) than on purely arable farms. One or more of these pests were found on 70 out of 584 mixed farms and on 5 out of 158 arable farms, giving significantly different ($p<0.05$) weighted percentage occurrences of 11.9% and 2.4% respectively.

TABLE 3. The frequency with which pests were detected in farm grain stores (percent of farms).

Pest	Farm stores			All farms
	Small	Medium	Large	
Primary beetles (a)	11.4	9.3	7.7	9.7
Secondary beetles (b)	29.7	20.4	12.8	21.9
Moths (c)	36.7	23.6	21.4	28.3
Psocids	50.8	59.1	46.2	51.9
Mites (d)	73.5	71.5	69.2	71.6
Rodents	69.4	68.8	73.6	70.4
Birds (e)	58.4	63.5	64.4	61.7

(a) *Oryzaephilus*, *Cryptolestes*, *Sitophilus*; (b) *Ahasverus*, *Typhaea*; (c) *Endrosis*, *Ephestia*; (d) *Acarus*, *Glycyphagus*, *Tyrophagus*; (e) Pigeons, sparrows.

TABLE 4. The occurrence of primary insect pests on arable and mixed farms (percent of farms).

Pest	Arable	Mixed	All farms
Oryzaephilus	1.0	6.0	4.8
Cryptolestes	1.3	5.7	4.6
Sitophilus	0.8	5.3	4.2
Any of the above	2.4	11.9	9.7

See text for number of arable and mixed farms

Pest data for commercial or central stores are given in Table 5, on both a site and individual store basis. The pest groupings are similar to those for farm stores except that spider beetles (Ptinidae) have been included because they were found frequently. The percentages for pests found in stores are lower than those for sites, reflecting that pests found at a site were not necessarily present in all stores at that site. Primary beetle pests were detected in twice as many stores (27%) as were secondary beetle pests (12%). Ptinidae were found in 36% of stores and moths in 17%, whilst psocids and mites occurred in 55% and 81% respectively. Rodents, noted in 71% of stores, comprised rats in 33% and mice in 61% whilst birds, recorded in 46% of stores, comprised pigeons in 34% and sparrows in 24%.

In Table 6, insect occurrences have been partitioned by whether they were found only in the grain; in the grain and on the structure; or only on the structure. Occurrences in the grain are those detected by the use of probe traps or pitfall traps placed in the grain or by bait-bags placed on the grain. Occurrences classed as on the structure are those detected by bait-bags placed on the structure, by visual observation, or by the sieving of residues. The three beetle groups and psocids were detected more often in the grain than on the structure. The proportion of detections that were in the grain, rather than on the structure only, was approximately 85% for each of these four groups. Moths showed a different pattern and were found in the grain in 39% of the stores where they occurred.

TABLE 5. The frequency with which pests were detected in commercial grain stores (percent of sites and percent of individual stores).

Pest	Sites (N = 157)	Stores (N = 283)
Primary beetles (a)	39.5	26.5
Secondary beetles (b)	17.8	11.7
Spider beetles (*Ptinidae*)	49.0	35.7
Moths (c)	25.5	16.6
Psocids	65.0	54.8
Mites (d)	87.3	81.3
Rodents	79.0	71.4
Birds (e)	59.2	46.3

(a) *Oryzaephilus, Cryptolestes, Sitophilus*; (b) *Ahasverus, Typhaea*; (c) *Endrosis, Ephestia, Hofmannophila*; (d) *Acarus, Glycyphagus, Tyrophagus*; (e) Pigeons, sparrows.

TABLE 6. The occurrence of insects in the grain and on the structure of commercial grain stores (percent of stores).

Pest	Grain only	Grain & structure	Structure only	Location uncertain
Primary beetles	17.0	5.3	3.5	0.7
Secondary beetles	8.1	1.1	1.8	0.7
Spider beetles	23.0	6.4	4.9	1.4
Moths	3.2	2.8	9.2	1.4
Psocids	24.7	18.0	9.2	2.8

In response to questions on insect detection at commercial sites, managers at 94% of sites said that grain was checked for pests upon intake. Grain had been rejected upon intake because of infestation at 59% of sites - 80% of these had rejected grain from farms and 23% from other stores. Insect traps were used in 26% of stores to monitor the grain for pests and 80% used spear or vacuum sampling, giving an overall 92% of stores monitoring the grain. An insect and/or mite infestation was said to have occurred at 51% of sites during the previous 12 months, 23% having had an insect infestation and 40% a mite infestation.

DISCUSSION

The results show that the majority of stored grain was protected by physical control methods, such as store cleaning or manipulating the temperature and moisture content of the grain, and by treating the structure of the store with insecticide. Only 9% of farm-stored grain and 23% of grain in commercial stores was treated with insecticide. One measure of the success of this approach is that in 90% of farm stores and 73% of commercial stores no primary beetle pests were found, indicating that the majority of the industry is able to satisfy market demands for pest-free grain. However, there are still some problems that need to be addressed, including the development of insecticide resistance, the effective application of insecticides, the presence of secondary pests and the exclusion of rodents and birds from stores.

The percentage of farm grain stores with primary beetle pests (9.7%) is very similar to that found in previous surveys. In 1977 a survey of 368 farms in 12 English counties detected one or more of the primary pest species in 13.0% of stores (Anon., 1981). A more limited survey in 1980 of 129 farms in eastern England found these species in 8.5% of stores (Wilson, 1983). During this period, 1977 - 1987, the proportion of farms using insecticide in the grain store increased appreciably. In 1976/77 the percentages of small, medium and large farms using insecticide were 11%, 41% and 61% respectively (Taylor & Lloyd, 1978) and in 1986/87 (the current survey) these percentages had risen to 28%, 60% and 82%. Thus, despite increased insecticide use, there is very little evidence of any decrease in the frequency of pests.

The extent to which this may be due to the presence of insecticide resistance is unclear. Primary pests collected during the surveys were tested for resistance using discriminating doses of insecticide that were just sufficient to kill all individuals of normal susceptibility, following the general procedures set out in FAO Method No. 15 (Anon., 1974). The results of these tests showed that in *Oryzaephilus surinamensis* resistance to organophosphorus insecticides is widespread and more common in commercial stores than in farm stores, but that in *Cryptolestes ferrugineus* resistance to these insecticides is rare (Prickett *et al*, 1990). The resistances detected by the discriminating dose tests may not necessarily enable the insects to survive properly applied field treatments at the recommended dose but their presence greatly reduces both the safety margin between control success and failure and the effective life of a residual treatment.

In the 1980 farm survey, primary pests were found in 7% of stores that had used insecticide and in 9% that had not used insecticide (Wilson, 1983). Subjecting that data to Fisher's Exact Test shows that these rates are not significantly different (p=0.96). Wilson commented that those farms which both used insecticide and were infested gave support to the view that pesticides may not always be used in the most effective manner. The occurrence of primary pests in commercial grain stores has been examined in the light of this comment. To minimize differences other than insecticide use, stores were selected where: a) all grain had been cooled, b) all three methods of detecting insects in grain (pitfalls, probe traps and baitbags on the grain) had been used during the inspection, c) either all the grain in store had been admixed or none had been treated and d) if the grain had been treated it was a prophylactic treatment and not because of known infestation. These criteria were satisfied by 112 stores - 39

with treated grain and 73 with untreated grain.   The treatments were with
either chlorpyrifos-methyl, etrimphos, methacrifos or pirimiphos-methyl.
O. surinamensis was detected in the grain in 8% of the treated and 7% of
the untreated stores; C. ferrugineus in 3% and 14%; and Sitophilus spp in
3% and 10% respectively. One or more of these three pests occurred in the
grain in 10% of treated stores and 22% of untreated stores.   Statistical
comparisons showed no significant difference between rates for treated and
untreated grain (p>0.05 in all cases).   These results are of concern not
only because insects appear to have survived insecticide treatment, but
also because the presence of primary insects in the grain, whether it was
untreated or treated prophylactically, suggests that the stores were
insufficiently monitored to detect the presence of these pests.

    Since insects can hide in cracks and crevices in walls and floors and
develop in the residues that accumulate there, an important part of pest
control is the elimination of these harbourages and the removal of
residues.   Most of the farm stores were empty at the time of the survey
and therefore the occurrence of primary pests in 9.7% of stores reflects
the extent to which they were present on the structure or in residues.
These pests were detected in the structure of 8.8% of commercial stores -
33% of the detections. Further examination of the farm survey data showed
that primary pests occurred in 5.3% of stores that were cleaned by vacuum,
in 11.9% cleaned manually and in 10.9% of those that were not cleaned.
The figure for vacuum cleaned stores is significantly lower (p<0.05) than
that for the two other groups, which do not differ from each other.
This indicates that manual cleaning is not very effective and greater
attention to store cleaning and eliminating harbourages would reduce the
threat of infestation.

    The five-fold greater occurrence of primary beetle pests on mixed
farms than on arable farms requires further investigation. Barker & Smith
(1990) found that in Manitoba, Canada, C. ferrugineus occurred more often
than expected on farms where there were livestock.   They suggested that
bought-in animal feed can sometimes contain stored-product insects and
thereby introduce pests to the farm.   Wilkin & Hurlock (1986) reported
that, during 1981-85, a substantial proportion of certain food commodities
imported into the UK were infested and that grain pests were regularly
imported.   They commented that some of the infested commodities were used
in the manufacture of animal feed.   Thus it seems likely that the higher
frequency of pests on mixed farms may be attributable, at least in part,
to infested animal feed.

    Secondary beetle pests, Ahasvera advena and Typhaea stercorea, were
found in farm stores more commonly than were primary pests, but the
reverse was true for commercial stores.   These species are regarded as
quarantine pests by some countries that import grain and are sometimes
confused with primary pests.   It is therefore disturbing that in
commercial stores the majority of occurrences were detected in the grain.
It is equally disturbing to note that, comparing occurrences in treated
and untreated grain as was done above for primary pests, there was no
significant difference (p>0.05).

    Mites were shown by Griffiths et al (1976) to be a common feature of
stored grain during a survey of farms in 1973/74, but they did not specify
the frequency with which one or more of the genera Acarus, Glycyphagus or
Tyrophagus occurred.   The data from that survey have been re-examined
recently and the overall frequency for these three genera was 227 out of

236 farms or 96% (Muggleton, pers.comm.) whereas the figure for the 1987 survey was 72%. Whether this demonstrates a decrease is uncertain because the farms visited in 1973/74 were not a random sample and included farmers that had requested visits from MAFF staff. Mites collected during the recent surveys were tested for resistance by exposing them to 8mg/kg of pirimiphos-methyl applied to wheat (Stables & Wilkin, 1981). This is equivalent to twice the recommended field dose. Resistance was detected in 16% of the populations collected from farm stores and in 64% of the populations collected from commercial stores (Starzewski, 1991). The higher frequency in commercial stores probably reflects the greater use of insecticide in those stores and the concentration of grain from many different sources. Since pirimiphos-methyl is the most commonly used insecticide in grain stores (Prickett *et al*, 1990), these findings have serious implications for the successful control of mites.

The difficulty of excluding rodents is exemplified by their presence being noted in nearly three-quarters of grain stores despite the use of rodenticide in the majority of stores. The surveys did not investigate whether rodenticides were used in the most effective manner, whether rodents were resistant or whether stores were proofed against rodents but each of these aspects may have contributed to the level of rodent presence noted. Certainly the presence of birds in over half the stores suggests that buildings will need to be better proofed against vertebrate pests to meet the new requirements in the Code of Practice for the Control of Salmonellae.

In conclusion, the surveys have demonstrated a considerable investment in pest control by the grain industry with the result that the majority of stores are free from primary insect pests. However, the existence of laboratory-detected resistance in these pests may signal problems for the future. The frequency with which other insects, mites, rodents and birds were detected suggests that there is scope for a heightened awareness amongst store managers of the need for adequate control of these pests.

ACKNOWLEDGEMENTS

The author gratefully acknowledges the Pesticide Safety Division of the Ministry of Agriculture, Fisheries and Food for funding these investigations and the Home-Grown Cereals Authority for part-funding the commercial grain store survey. The author also acknowleges the members of the Central Science Laboratory and ADAS who participated in the surveys. Thanks also to those who allowed their farms or stores to be inspected and provided much information on their storage practice.

REFERENCES

Anon. (1974) Recommended methods for the detection and measurement of resistance of agricultural pests to pesticides. Tentative method for adults of some major beetle pests of stored cereals with malathion or lindane. FAO Method No. 15. *Plant Protection Bulletin, FAO*, **22**, 127-137.
Anon. (1981) Survey of farm grain stores 1977. *Pest Infestation Control Laboratory Report 1977-1979*, 19-20.

Anon. (1991) *Agricultural Statistics, United Kingdom, 1989.* London: HMSO, xv+96pp.

Barker, P.S.; Smith, L.B. (1990) Influence of granary type and farm practices on the relative abundance of insects in granary residues. *The Canadian Entomologist*, 122, 393-400.

Burkholder, W.E. (1984) Stored-product insect behaviour and pheromone studies: Keys to successful monitoring and trapping. *Proceedings of the 3rd International Working Conference of Stored Product Entomology, Manhatten, Kansas, USA*, pp 20-33.

Cogan, P.M.; Wakefield, M.E. (1987) Further developments in traps used to detect low level infestations of beetle pests in stored grain. *British Crop Protection Council Monograph* 37, 161-168.

Garthwaite, D.G.; Chapman, P.J.; Cole, D.B. (1987) *Pesticide usage survey report 63, Commercial grain stores 1985/86.* Alnwick: MAFF, 23pp.

Griffiths, D.A.; Wilkin, D.R.; Southgate, B.J.; Lynch, S.M. (1976) A survey of mites in bulk grain stored on farms in England and Wales. *Annals of Applied Biology*, 82, 180-185.

Pinniger, D.B. (1975) The use of bait traps for assessment of stored product insect populations. *U.S.D.A. Cooperative Economic Report* 25, 907-909.

Prickett, A.J. (1988) English farm grain stores 1987, Part 1, Storage practice and pest incidence. *ADAS Central Science Laboratory Report No. 23*, 122pp.

Prickett, A.J.; Muggleton, J. (1991) Commercial grain stores 1988/89, England and Wales, Pest incidence and storage practice. *HGCA Project Report No. 29*, 99pp+119pp.

Prickett, A.J.; Muggleton, J.; Llewellin, J.A. (1990) Insecticide resistance in populations of *Oryzaephilus surinamensis* and *Cryptolestes ferrugineus* from grain stores in England and Wales. *Brighton Crop Protection Conference - Pests and Diseases 1990*, 3, 1189-1194.

Stables, L.M.; Wilkin, D.R. (1981) Resistance to pirimiphos-methyl in cheese mites. *1981 British Crop Protection Conference - Pests and Diseases*, 2, 617-624.

Starzewski, J.C. (1991) The incidence of resistance to pirimiphos-methyl in stored product mites collected from commercial grain stores in the United Kingdom. *In:* Prickett & Muggleton (1991), *ibid.*

Taylor, J.K. (1978) *Pesticide usage survey report (Food storage). Commercial grain stores 1977-78.* London: MAFF.

Taylor, J.K.; Lloyd, G.M. (1978) *Pesticide usage survey report 17. Pesticide usage in food storage practice 1964-1977.* London: MAFF 47pp

Taylor, J.K.; Sly, J.M.A. (1986) *Pesticide usage survey report 50. farm grain stores 1983/84.* London: MAFF, 14pp.

Wilkin, D.R.; Hurlock, E.T. (1986) Stored grain pests and their management. In: *Spoilage and Mycotoxins of Cereals and other Stored Products*, B. Flannigan (Ed), *International Biodeterioration*, 22, (Supplement), 1-6.

Wilson, P. (1983) Insect infestation and pesticide usage in East Anglian farm grain stores. *International Pest Control*, 75, 116-118.

CURRENT TRENDS IN THE PROTECTION OF STORED CEREALS IN THE
TROPICS BY INSECTICIDES AND FUMIGANTS

R.W. TAYLOR, P. GOLOB AND R.J. HODGES

Natural Resources Institute, Chatham Maritime, Chatham Kent,
ME4 4TB.

ABSTRACT

Economic change and environmental concern both
have major roles to play in determining how and
with what chemicals stored cereals will be
protected. In tropical, developing countries both
these factors affect the future of pest control
in farm and central storage.

In central storage, increasing development of
resistance to phosphine and contact insecticides,
the uncertain future of the fumigant methyl bromide
due to its role in the depletion of atmospheric
ozone and cost constraints should lead to
a more careful and cost conscious application of
pest control measures.

On small farms, particularly in Africa, storage is
increasing as a result of market liberalisation.
This will result in the need for increased usage
of dilute dust insecticides. Furthermore,
improvement of small scale storage structures may
allow the use of phosphine formulations to
proliferate, with a concomitant increase in
problems due to resistance and safety.

INTRODUCTION

In developing countries huge quantities of cereals,
particularly maize, rice, sorghum and millet are stored on
farms and in large scale storage facilities. Nearly all
developing countries are in the tropics and in climates that
encourage the rapid growth of insect populations. Thus
effective pest control is crucial and is a burden borne across
a variety of income groups, including resource poor farmers,
commercial operations and national marketing boards. In
central storage, the principal means of pest control is by
fumigation, with ancillary use of contact insecticides for
protection against reinfestation. This contrasts with farm
storage where fumigation of grain has not been a widely
available option and when chemicals are used for grain
protection they are usually low-strength dust formulations of
contact insecticide.

PEST CONTROL IN CENTRAL STORAGE

Bag storage in hessian, jute or polypropylene bags is the most common storage technique in developing countries. With the exception of animal feed, which in any case tends not to be treated with pesticide, produce is rarely stored in bulk. In the few instances where bulk storage is practised, products may be fumigated or treated directly with contact insecticide dust or spray at the time of loading.

Fumigation

Fumigation remains the only means of disinfesting bag stacks of grain *in situ*, and is therefore of world-wide importance. In developing countries the commonest method of fumigation is the treatment of bag stacks under gas-tight sheets. Phosphine and methyl bromide are the only gases which continue to be used to any extent. Grain marketing organizations that originally used methyl bromide, later changed to phosphine, because it was easier to use, requiring less equipment for application and safety purposes. In many countries, methyl bromide application is restricted to specific purposes, to satisfy contract requirements, in circumstances where phosphine is not appropriate or where there is an advantage in completing the fumigation within 24 hours.

In many developing countries there is now easy access to phosphine preparations. This has led to their use by those with little understanding of the fact that insect eradication can only be achieved within reasonably gas-tight enclosures (Halliday *et al.* 1983). The great increase in the use of phosphine in the 1970s and 1980s, often under conditions of inadequate sealing, resulted in repeated exposure of insects to sub-lethal fumigant concentrations. This led to survival of insects and the development of fumigant resistance which is now widespread (Taylor, 1989). In most countries, the magnitude of resistance is still not sufficient to cause insect survival in field treatments, provided the recommended fumigant application rate and exposure period are used under gas-tight conditions. Currently, a minimum exposure period of five days at adequate concentration is necessary to avert or delay the development of phosphine resistance.

Fumigating whole stores, rather than covering individual bag stacks with gas-tight sheets, is practised in South Asia. Since most stores do not retain gas sufficiently well for effective fumigation, this technique has been instrumental in the development of phosphine resistance (Tyler *et al.*, 1983). In Pakistan, where whole-store fumigation has been practised for many years, phosphine resistance has increased so that fumigation exposure periods have to be extended in order to obtain control; some samples of *Tribolium castaneum* required exposure for 12 days at a standard dosage of 0.33 mg/litre (Mahmood *et al.*, 1992). Although there have been attempts in West Africa to design and build stores that are sufficiently gas-tight for effective fumigation, there is little evidence that they are being regularly used for this purpose.

Winks (1987) considered that it was necessary to prepare for the 'phosphine resistance era'. This theme has been taken further in recent recommendations made by the Association of South East Asian States (ASEAN) Food Handling Bureau, for fumigations involving phosphine (Annis & van Graver, in press). These authors recommend that phosphine should be used only under strictly gas-tight conditions, that have been pressure-tested, and where a total fumigation time of 10 days is available, including preparation and terminal airing. To ensure effective fumigation of bag stacks a plastic groundsheet beneath the stack is secured with adhesive to the stack covering sheet, which is tailored to the shape and size of the stack. At least one country in South East Asia has indicated its intention to adopt this sealed sheeted-stack technique of fumigation for national grain stocks. Implementation of the method will be more costly than the traditional sheeted-stack techniques and it may be some years before it is widely used.

For many years, methyl bromide has been a valuable alternative fumigant to phosphine, particularly where short exposure periods are essential. For example, Thailand which exports about four million tonnes of cereal grain each year uses methyl bromide to treat all of this produce immediately before shipment. Very recently however, methyl bromide has been identified for its capability to cause depletion of stratospheric ozone, raising doubts regarding its continued availability as a fumigant (Andersen & Lee-Bapty 1992). Decisions to limit the use of methyl bromide, under the Montreal Protocol Agreement are expected in November 1992. Irrespective of these decisions, it is likely that increasing pressure will come from environmental organizations to reduce atmospheric emissions from all uses of methyl bromide, including use for commodity fumigation.

Many developing countries rely on agricultural exports for a major proportion of their foreign exchange, and any factor affecting these exports, such as a ban on quarantine fumigation with methyl bromide, would have very serious consequences. No new fumigants which could be substituted for methyl bromide have been registered for many years, and research on controlled atmospheres, with carbon dioxide and nitrogen, has shown that neither of these can be used cost-effectively for the short-period treatments in which methyl bromide is widely employed.

The use of controlled atmosphere storage in developing countries is not widespread. Traditional hermetic storage in pits is practised on a small scale but more modern techniques have generally not been introduced since nearly all these are appropriate to bulk storage, which is rarely practiced in developing countries. One exception is the use of sealed bag-stack storage in South East Asia, pioneered by the Australian Centre for International Agricultural Research (ACIAR). In this case bag stacks are sealed into plastic envelopes, placed under a partial vacuum, to test for leaks, and then gassed with phosphine or, more commonly, carbon dioxide (Annis *et al.*, 1984). Only in Indonesia is this system used on a fully operational basis. Very good results have been achieved for the storage of milled rice stocks for periods of up to two years (Nataradja & Hodges, 1989).

Contact Insecticides

Insecticides are applied with the intention of reducing the frequency of fumigation when grain is stored in the medium or long-term or of obviating fumigation in short-term storage. The actual extent of pesticide usage is not known; manufacturers' sales figures are unlikely to be a reliable guide since few pesticides are sold exclusively for use in storage.

Only a limited number of pesticides are available for use in central storage. While individual countries differ in terms of which pesticides and which formulations are registered, those available are organophosphorous compounds (e.g. fenitrothion, pirimiphos-methyl, dichlorvos, chlorpyrifos-methyl), synthetic pyrethroids (e.g. permethrin, bioresmethrin) or carbamates (e.g. carbaryl, bendiocarb). The use of mixtures to broaden the spectrum of pests controlled is rare, although a combination of pyrethroid/organophosphorous insecticides, applied at ultra low volume, has been used in Senegalese stores. In Mali this treatment failed to show any residual efficacy.

In developing countries it appears that emulsifiable concentrates are the most commonly used pesticide formulations employed in stores, primarily because they are widely available for crop protection. Flowable concentrates and wettable powders are generally not available. Under many conditions the choice of formulation may make little difference to pest control efficiency since on absorbent surfaces such as whitewash, plaster, concrete, brick, jute or hessian, they are lost rapidly so that there is minimal residual action (Holborn, 1963; Chadwick, 1984; Webley & Kilminster 1980; Hodges & Dales, 1991). Webley (1985a) has stated that there is probably no truly residual spray on concrete. Adverse temperature and humidity conditions may also contribute to the reduced efficacy of pesticides in the tropics.

The development of resistance to contact insecticides is well known in strains of many species of storage insects; resistance to malathion is now so widespread (Champ & Dyte, 1976) that this pesticide is now little used. Current methods of application, in which a high dose of pesticide is applied and allowed to decline in concentration over a long period, would appear to encourage the development of resistance. In Indonesia, the National Logistics Agency (BULOG) is aware of the need to limit this effect and it avoids over-use of one compound by changing its operational pesticide fairly frequently.

The most widely used method for applying insecticides in bag stores is to spray store and stack surfaces with a dilute residual insecticide using knapsack sprayers or, more commonly, power sprayers. The normal procedure is to a) treat empty stores to destroy any residual infestation present in cracks and crevices; b) at the time of fumigation, to apply a spray treatment to store structures in order to kill all pests not under the gas-proof sheet, and c) at intervals after fumigation to respray store and bag stack surfaces to limit the rate of reinfestation.

The justification for surface spraying in stores is based almost completely on a great many laboratory studies on the effects of pesticide on storage insects. Unfortunately, there has been almost no effort to demonstrate that the actual application of pesticides in stores limits pest increase and that the use of pesticide is more cost effective than reliance on fumigation alone. McFarlane (1980) considered that the surface spraying of bag stacks of milled rice may be of no benefit under tropical conditions. Recent studies on milled rice stocks in Indonesia have been unable to demonstrate any delay to refumigation as a result of respraying store and stack surfaces. It was concluded that reliance on fumigation alone, with a concurrent non-residual spray treatment, would be more cost-effective (Hodges et al., in press).

At the time bag stacks are constructed, each layer of the stack may be dusted or sprayed with insecticide. Although this technique has often been recommended, it would seem to be rarely used because it is both a very time-consuming operation and hazardous to store labourers.

Insecticide admixture has been advocated as a good technique for the protection of bagged commodities (Webley, 1985b) and it certainly has the advantage that insects are likely to have prolonged contact with the treatment. In consideration of a stock protection strategy in South East Asia, Annis and van Graver (1987) recommended admixture of grain protectants for storage of grain for 3-9 months, this duration being the maximum period of biological efficacy for the dose of protectant used. Longer periods would unduly increase the possibilities for the development of insect resistance. Many countries would permit the admixture of insecticides; however, this option is rarely used due to logistical difficulties, double handling costs and in some cases a reluctance to apply pesticide directly to food.
A recent variant of admixture is to treat the insides of bags with a controlled release formulation or to implant in bags strips of plastic tape from which the pesticide is released slowly. To date trials of this method using slow release formulations of malathion or chlorpyrifos have not shown much potential as a stock protection system in large scale storage (Grant et al., 1990).

Fogging of stores to kill flying insects has been advocated but is also rarely used. A variation of this is the

"Pestigas" system, developed by Wellcome, in which insecticide concentrate is delivered into stores, in a carbon dioxide stream, from nozzles located at eaves height. However, for the protection of durable food crops, this method appears to have been used only experimentally. Suharno *et al*. (1987) suggested that the system retards insect population growth to about the same extent as conventional spraying on a three-weekly routine. In view of the fact that conventional respraying is unlikely to be cost-effective (Hodges *et al.*, in press) and that "Pestigas" is in any case a more expensive option, its adoption is unlikely to be justified. However, if tested in relatively airtight stores its performance might be somewhat better.

PROTECTION OF FARM STORED GRAIN

In much of the developing world, particularly in Africa and South Asia, up to three quarters of the durable crop production may be stored in small quantities on smallholder farms, mostly for home consumption. Farm storage losses have, in general been quite low (Tyler & Boxall, 1983) because of the inherent resistance of local varieties to indigenous pests, short storage periods or climatic factors which are adverse to pest proliferation. Consequently, there has been very little use of insecticides on the farm.

The recent trend of governments in developing countries to introduce radical trade liberalisation policies has led to the relaxation of controls on agricultural marketing. Private traders are replacing governmental organisations as the primary buying agents for grain, thus reducing the quantities handled by central storage agencies. These changes are providing incentives for farmers to increase production and to retain the produce on the farm for long periods, in order to gain the benefits of higher selling prices as the post-harvest season progresses. Increased production is very much dependent on the cultivation of high yielding varieties (HYV), which are generally very susceptible to storage insect pests. Farmers are now turning to insecticides to enable them to maintain their stored produce in good condition.

For many years, chemical companies have produced dilute insecticide dusts for use on small farm and this formulation continues to be the one most commonly used. However, dilute dusts which have an acceptable shelf life are extremely difficult to formulate, so that few of these products are available commercially. The active ingredients most commonly employed are pirimiphos-methyl and fenitrothion. For control of the Larger Grain Borer *(Prostephanus truncatus)* in Africa it is recommended that these organophosphorus compounds are combined with a pyrethroid, either permethrin or deltamethrin, to which this pest is particularly susceptible (Golob, 1988).

Few farmers can afford the luxury of purchasing chemicals, even relatively cheap dilute dusts. In the past twenty years there has been an explosion in research undertaken to identify cheap, locally available alternatives, particularly compounds of vegetable origin. When tested in the laboratory and small—scale field trials, several plants have been shown to be efficacious, including *Azadirachta indica* (neem) and *Acorus calamus* (sweetflag) (Golob & Webley, 1980). However, there have been no attempts to scale up these investigations, to determine the cost—effectiveness or practicability of using such materials. More importantly there has been a dearth of information concerning the toxicological hazards of most of the plant extracts. Unless this information becomes available, it will remain difficult to recommend the use of these extracts for crop protection in the developing world.

In the past, fumigation has not been widely promoted for use on farm because of the potential hazards to both untrained users, neighbours and livestock. A further factor has been the inability of farmers to provide or understand the need for gas—tight enclosures. High boiling point liquid fumigants such as ethylene dibromide, carbon tetrachloride and carbon disulphide were marketed in developing countries in quantities appropriate for small—holder farmers. Carbon disulphide was widely used at farm level in Swaziland to fumigate grain stored in gas—tight metal tanks, but during the 1970s was progressively replaced by phosphine. Now, with the more widespread use of metal storage bins, the use of phosphine fumigation has increased. The smallest packs of phosphine fumigants supplied by manufacturers have usually been sufficient for the treatment of approximately 10 tonnes of grain, significantly more than most farmers would wish to treat. Recently, a new formulation known as the 'Tiny Bag' has become available, which produces three grams of phosphine. The product is intended for small scale users and could provide farmers with a much safer option than using individual tablets taken from larger packs. Nevertheless, unless small—holder fumigations are done under sufficiently gas—tight conditions there will be increased risks of poisoning and further development of phosphine resistance.

Many countries do not possess pesticide legislation nor do they have facilities for testing and registering chemicals that the industry attempts to introduce. There is often unrestricted access to chemicals, for example, in West Africa tablets of aluminium phosphide as well as a variety of emulsifiable concentrates can be purchased over the counter from general stores and petrol service stations. The United Nations Food and Agriculture Organisation (FAO) assists governments to design appropriate pesticide legislation and this initiative is helping to combat the problems of misuse. When a compound is approved as a grain protectant its use is governed by specifications issued by the Codex Alimentarius Commission.

PEST CONTROL IN THE FUTURE

In parts of the developing world there will be some shift

from large scale to farm storage. Pesticide use in the future will be determined by the cost consciousness of the user as well as by environmental considerations. Changes that are likely to occur are as follows:

– methyl bromide is likely to be severely restricted because of its effect on ozone depletion;

– phosphine will remain the major gas for fumigation but the development of resistance in insect populations will increase unless improved pest management practices are widely implemented;

– the spraying of store surfaces with residual insecticide will decline because it is generally not cost-effective; the procedure also promotes insecticide resistance;

– smallholder storage practices on farms will improve and this will entail the use of better storage structures, increased use of dilute dusts and a gradual proliferation in the use of fumigation. However, there will be a need for an improvement in extension effort in order that farmers fully understand that poor application techniques lead to a waste of resources and the development of insecticide resistance.

REFERENCES

Andersen, S. O.; Lee–Bapty, S. (1992) Methyl bromide interim technology and economic assessment. Montreal Protocol Assessment Supplement, United Nations Environment Programme.

Annis, P.C.; Banks, H.J.; Sukardi (1984) Insect control in stacks of bagged rice using carbon dioxide treatment and an experimental PVC membrane enclosure. CSIRO Australia Division of Entomology, Technical Paper No 22, pp 38.

Annis, P.C.; van Graver, J. (1987) Sealed stacks as a component of an integrated commodity management system: A potential strategy for continued bag–stack storage in the ASEAN region. *CSIRO Australian Division of Entomology Report* No. 42, 37–43.

Annis, P.C.; van Graver, J. (in press) Suggested recommendations for the fumigation of grain in the ASEAN region. Part 3, Phosphine fumigation of bag stacks sealed in plastic enclosures : an operations manual. CSIRO Division of Entomology, Stored Grain Research Lab. GPO Box 1700, Canberra ACT 2601, Australia.

Chadwick, P.R. (1984) Surfaces and other factors modifying the effectiveness of pyrethroids against insects in public health. *Pesticide Science*, **16**, 383–391.

Champ, B.R.; Dyte, C.E.. (1976) Report of the FAO global survey of pesticide susceptibility of stored grain pests. FAO Plant Protection Series No. 5, FAO Rome, pp 297.

Golob, P. (1988) Current status of the Larger Grain Borer, *Prostephanus truncatus* (Horn) in Africa. *Insect Science and its Application* **9**, 737–745.

Golob, P ; Webley, D.J. (1980) The use of plants and minerals as traditional protectants of stored products. *Report of the Tropical Products Institute* **G138**, vi + 32pp.

Grant, J.A.; Parker, B.L.; Damardjati, D.S. (1990) Controlled-release insecticides for stored-grain pest control in Indonesia II. Warehouse trial. *ASEAN Food Journal*, **5**, 71-78.

Halliday, D.; Harris, A.H.; Taylor, R. W .D. (1983) Recent developments in the use of phosphine as a fumigant for grains and other durable agricultural produce. *Chemistry and Industry*, **12**, 468-471.

Hodges, R.J.; Sidik, M.; Halid, H.; Conway, J.A. (in press) Cost efficiency of respraying store surfaces with insecticide to protect bagged milled rice from insect attack. *Tropical Pest Management* .

Hodges, R.J.; Dales, M. (1991) Report on a investigation of insecticide persistence on grain store surfaces in Ghana 3 April - 10 May 1991. *NRI report R1660 (S)*. Typewritten pp 26.

Holborn, J.M. (1963) The control of grain pests by contact insecticides. *Proceedings of the 1st British pest Control Conference*. pp 16-19.

McFarlane, J.A. (1980) Technical and economical possibilities for simple improvements of maintenance of quality of milled rice in storage. In: *Proceedings of the 3rd Annual Workshop on Grains Post Harvest Technology*, Kuala Lumpur, Malaysia. South East Asian Cooperative Post Harvest Research and Development Programme, 392-398.

Mahmood, T.; Ahmad, M. S.; Javed, M. A.; Iqbal, M. (1992) A simple technique to determine phosphine dosage for resistant stored grain insect pests. Paper presented at a seminar on Grain Storage, Management and Training, Faisalabad, Pakistan, 2- 3 March 1992.

Nataradja, Y.C.; Hodges, R.J. (1990) Commercial experience of sealed storage of bag stack in Indonesia. pp 197-202 In: *Fumigation and controlled atmosphere storage of grain*. (Eds. Champ B.R., Highley E. and Banks H.J.). ACIAR Proceedings No. 25, Canberra.

Suharno, P.; Azis E.; Thojib, A.; Soeroyo (1987) Pestigas application for insect control of stored products in Dolog Jaya. In: *Proceeding of the 10th ASEAN Seminar on Grain Postharvest Technology*, pp 207 220.

Taylor, R.W D.(1989) Phosphine-A major grain fumigant at risk. *International Pest Control*. 31 (1), 10 14.

Tyler, P.S. ; Boxall, R.A.B. (1983) Post-harvest loss reduction programme: a decade of activities, what consequences? *Tropical Stored Products Information* **50**, 4-13.

Tyler, P.S.; Taylor, R. W. D.; Rees, D. P. (1983) Insect resistance to phosphine fumigation in food warehouses in Bangladesh. *International Pest Control* **25**, 45-46.

Webley, D.J. (1985a) Fabric spraying for pest control in grain stores pp 299-302. In: *Pesticides and Humid Tropical Grain Storage Systems* pp (Eds. Champ, B.R. and Highley, E.), ACIAR Proceedings No.14, Canberra.

Webley, D.J. (1985b) Use of pesticides in bag storage of grain, pp 303-311. In: *Pesticides and Humid Tropical Grain Storage Systems* (Eds. Champ, B.R. and Highley, E.). ACIAR Proceedings No 14, Canberra,

Webley, D.J.; Kilminster, K.M. (1980) The persistence of insecticide spray deposits on woven polypropylene and jute sacking. *Pesticide Science*, 11, 667-673.

Winks, R.G. (1987) Strategies for effective use of phosphine as a grain fumigant and the implications of resistance. In: *Proceedings Fourth International Working Conference on Stored Product Protection*, Israel. pp 335-344.

THE INFLUENCE OF STORED FOOD ON THE EFFECTIVENESS OF FARM RAT CONTROL

R.J. Quy, D.P. Cowan, P.Haynes, I.R. Inglis and T. Swinney

Central Science Laboratory,
Ministry of Agriculture, Fisheries and Food,
London Road, Slough Berks SL3 7HJ

ABSTRACT

Rodenticide treatments against farm rats were carried out using difenacoum and bromadiolone inside and outside the area of known difenacoum resistance in central-southern England. Estimates were made of the numbers of rats present during the course of treatments and bait markers were used to estimate the amounts of bait consumed by survivors. Only approximately 10% of survivors consumed sufficient bait to kill fully susceptible animals. The presence of difenacoum resistance thus did not significantly effect treatment outcome. The presence of stored cereal significantly reduced treatment effectiveness. This effect was not apparent when changes occurred in food availability. This study has shown that strategies can be developed that are specifically targeted at the extensive and intractable problem of stored cereal infestation by rats.

INTRODUCTION

The poor performance of second-generation anticoagulant rodenticides, such as difenacoum and bromadiolone, against farm rats (*Rattus norvegicus*) in Hampshire has previously been ascribed to the presence of difenacoum-resistant individuals (Greaves *et al.*, 1982a). Recently, however, the original data used to compare the length of anticoagulant treatments in Hampshire, England with those against warfarin-resistant populations in Powys, Wales were reanalysed by Quy *et al.* (1992). They found that some differences between the two areas were only explicable in terms of variation in behavioural responses towards bait and suggested one potential cause of such behavioural differences was the availability of alternative food. In general, the greater the availability of such food the less likely are rats to consume bait. This study has been undertaken to measure the influence of both difenacoum resistance and alternative food availability on treatment effectiveness. It compares treatments in the area of Hampshire where difenacoum resistance is known to be widespread with treatments in the adjacent county of West Sussex. Here difenacoum resistance is unknown but the ecology of farms is more like those in Hampshire than the farms in Powys considered previously.

Stored cereal is a major potential source of food on many farms. Prickett (1988) found 53% of farm grain stores to be infested with rats. Extensive problems also exist in commercial

grain stores with 41% of sites and 33% of stores infested
(Prickett & Muggleton, 1991). These problems persist despite use
of rodenticides on 78% and 98% of farm and commercial grain
storage sites respectively. There is thus considerable potential
for improving the management of rat infestations in and around
grain stores. There have, however, been no studies of possible
strategies specifically targeted at such infestations. The study
reported here provides some of the data required to develop such
strategies.

METHODS

A total of 42 rodenticide treatments were carried out on
farms in a replicated experimental design. Each replicate
consisted of 6 treatments; three inside the area of known
difenacoum resistance in the county of Hampshire (Greaves *et al.*,
1982b) and three in the adjacent county of West Sussex which is
outside the known area of difenacoum resistance. One of each of
three kinds of treatment was performed in each area for each
replicate. These treatments were: a) seven weeks of laying baits
containing 50ppm difenacoum, b) seven weeks laying baits
containing 50ppm bromadiolone c) three weeks of laying unpoisoned
baits followed by four weeks of baiting with bromadiolone (to
measure bait consumption in the absence of mortality).

For the first three weeks of the treatments all baits
contained 100ppm of the bait marker decachlorobiphenyl (DCBP) and
during the final four weeks all baits contained 100ppm of the bait
marker 2,2',4,4',5,5'-hexachlorobiphenyl (HCBP). Baits consisted
of 90% pinhead oatmeal, 5% sucrose, 2.5% pure corn oil, 2.475%
polyethylene glycol 200, and 0.025% triethanolamine. They were
formulated to contain either 50ppm difenacoum or 50ppm
bromadiolone and 100ppm of either DCBP or HCBP. Baits were tested
for palatability, bioavailability and homogeneity.

Sites were found through contacts in the local farming
communities and the presence of rats confirmed during a
preliminary visit. Selected farms were allocated to one of the
three treatment types. Each farm was surveyed to determine the
size of the infested area and a map was drawn of the farm
buildings and adjacent land. The distribution of potential food
sources for rats was indicated on this map in terms of presence
or absence within a grid of 10m² squares. These food sources fell
into three categories: stored produce, animal feeds or standing
crops in fields adjacent to the farm buildings. Stored produce was
further sub-divided into stored cereal (wheat, oats or barley),
stored seeds (e.g. linseed or grass seed), and other stored
produce (e.g. peas or beans). An additional food type, related to
stored cereal, was waste cleanings or whittlings. Animal feeds
were either silage (maize or apple but not grass as this was
considered to have little attraction to rats), commercial feeds
(pellets or cattle cake) or on-farm feeds (crushed cereals).
Standing crops were either cereal (barley or wheat) or associated
with game cover (maize, kale or artichokes). There was thus a
total of nine different categories of food supply. Any potential
food that appeared to be unavailable to rats, for instance in

rodent proofed grain silos, was not included in the assessment of food availability. All major changes that took place in the availability of food during a treatment were also recorded. A major change was defined as the complete arrival or removal of food to or from a 10m² grid square and movement of food between grid squares.

During week 1 of each trial live-capture cage traps were set for four consecutive days throughout the infested area. Up to 20 animals were removed and housed individually in the laboratory. All these animals were subjected to the blood clotting response test for warfarin resistance (Martin *et al.*, 1979). Any warfarin-resistant individuals were then given a blood clotting response test for difenacoum resistance (Gill *et al.*, in press). During week 2 a pre-treatment census was performed using the tracking plate method developed by Quy et *al.*, (in press).

Bait was laid throughout the infested area, including along any infested hedgerows leading away from the farm buildings, for seven consecutive weeks from the Monday of week 3. Baits were placed in wooden bait boxes. Some baits laid indoors were placed in trays rather than boxes. All bait points initially had 100g of bait. The number of bait points varied between 20 and 94 while bait point density varied between 103 and 236 per infested hectare. This variation reflects the sizes of infested areas and the decisions of the experienced operators involved. The amounts of bait eaten from each bait point were recorded every Wednesday, Friday, and Monday. If all bait was consumed from a bait point the amount laid there was doubled. Conversely, if no bait was removed from a point for two consecutive days the amount of bait laid was reduced by 50% to a minimum of 25g. At the beginning of the fourth week of baiting all bait was removed and replaced with either difenacoum or bromadiolone formulations containing 100ppm HCBP. After the seven weeks of baiting had been completed all baits and bait containers were removed.

Mid-treatment censuses were carried out using the tracking plate method during the third and sixth weeks of baiting. A post-treatment census was carried out during the week following the seventh week of baiting. Daily estimates of the size of the population present on each farm were obtained by linear interpolation between each of the successive census estimates. The experimental design did not allow for estimates of recruitment to the population during the course of treatments through either reproduction or immigration. Hence, the effectiveness of each treatment was estimated in terms of the maximum number of animals that survived. This estimate was derived by expressing the size of the population at the post-treatment census as a percentage of the pre-treatment census. Any treatments for which population size had increased between the pre-treatment census and the post-treatment census were considered to have left 100% of the original population alive at the end of the treatment.

During the week following the post-treatment census live traps were set to catch up to 20 survivors which were tested for resistance to warfarin and difenacoum as described above. During the following three weeks Fenn Mk IV spring traps were used to provide a further sample of surviving animals for analyses of bait markers.

Laboratory studies have shown that a close relationship exists between the amounts of DCBP and HCBP consumed and residues recovered from whole bodies using gas chromatography (CSL, unpublished). The recovery rate is approximately 46% for DCBP over a wide range of exposures (R^2 = 0.99) and 55% for HCBP (R^2 = 0.98) with a detection limit of approximately 0.5g of bait containing 100ppm of marker eaten by a 200g rat. The residues recovered from the bodies of survivors were thus used to estimate the amounts of bait that these animals had eaten during the seven week baiting period. Only data from 432 survivors of the first five replicates (30 treatments) have been processed to date.

All percentages were arcsine square-root transformed before statistical analyses to stabilise variances. In the text, table and figures, mean and standard errors are presented for untransformed data to ease interpretation. All two by two χ^2 tests include Yate's continuity correction. All quoted significance levels are for two-tailed tests.

RESULTS

Infestation characteristics

The mean size of infested areas on 21 Sussex farms of 0.25±0.02ha was not different to that of 0.28±0.02ha for 21 Hampshire farms (t = 0.91, NS). Similarly there was no difference in the mean estimated initial rat population sizes of 104.3±17.0 and 94.2±15.4 rats per farm in Sussex and Hampshire respectively (t = 0.44, NS). Difenacoum resistance was detected on 19 of the Hampshire farms but none of the Sussex farms. The only clear difference regarding food availability was the presence of stored cereal on 14 (66.7%) Hampshire farms compared with only 6 (28.6%) Sussex farms (χ^2 = 4.68, P = 0.031).

Treatment outcome

The mean estimated maximum percentage of the initial population present at the end of the treatments was 59.2±7.7% in Hampshire compared with 29.5±8.5% in Sussex (t = 2.41, P = 0.020). An estimated 57.9±8.8% of the initial population survived on farms where difenacoum resistance was present compared with 33.2±7.9% on the other farms (t = 2.04, P = 0.048). Treatment type did not significantly effect treatment effectiveness ($F_{2,39}$ 0.64, NS). If difenacoum was less effective than bromadiolone against difenacoum-resistant animals then a significant interaction would be expected between treatment type and the presence of difenacoum resistance but this was not the case in a two-way analysis of variance ($F_{1,24}$ 0.13, NS). The only significant effect of food availability was 61.1±9.0% maximum survival in the presence of stored cereal compared with only 29.2±7.1% in its absence (t = 2.83, P = 0.007). Effectiveness was not influenced by the occurrence (n = 11) or absence (n = 31) of major change in food availability during the course of treatments (t = 0.32, NS).

A four-way analysis of variance was performed to examine the effect of four factors on variation in estimates of maximum survival: the type of treatment, the presence or absence of stored cereal on the farm; the presence or absence of major change in food availability during the course of the treatment; the presence or absence of difenacoum resistance amongst rats on the farm. Only the presence of cereal significantly influenced maximum survival as a main effect ($F_{1,27}$ 6.85, $P = 0.014$). Treatment type ($F_{1,27}$ 1.45, NS) and presence of difenacoum resistance ($F_{1,27}$ 2.7, NS) were insignificant as main effects and neither contributed to any significant second order interactions. While change in food availability made an insignificant contribution as a main effect ($F_{1,27}$ 2.34, NS) it exhibited an interesting two-way interaction with the availability of stored cereal ($F_{1,27}$ 6.25, $P = 0.019$). Table 1 shows that in the absence of stored cereal the occurrence of major change in food availability made no difference to effectiveness. However, for treatments in the presence of stored cereal the eight where change occurred were more effective than the other 12 ($t = 2.36$, $P = 0.030$). Stored cereal was available throughout the treatments on seven of the eight farms where both major change occurred and stored cereal was present. On the other it was introduced during the course of the treatment. On none of the farms where stored cereal was present and major change occurred did complete removal of cereal occur, although in all but one instance there were changes in cereal availability.

Table 1. Differences in maximum estimated percentage survival in the presence and absence of stored cereal and whether or not major change occurred in food availability during the course of treatments.

| | Maximum percentage survival | | | |
| | No change in food availability | | Major change in food availability | |
	n	Mean±SE	n	Mean±SE
Stored cereal absent	19	25.4±7.5	3	52.8±18.8
Stored cereal present	12	76.2±10.1	8	38.4±13.7

Patterns of bait consumption

The average consumption of bait per rat for each day of each treatment was calculated by dividing the total bait consumption recorded between visits by the number of days between visits and by the estimated size of the rat population present on that day. Figure 1 shows that for the 28 treatments where either bromadiolone or difenacoum baits were laid for seven weeks there was a difference in the pattern of bait consumption between the 13 in the presence and the 15 in the absence of stored cereal.

Bait consumption was significantly higher over the first 2 days on farms without stored cereal ($t = 3.05$, $P = 0.007$). After four to seven days bait consumption began to decline in the absence of stored cereal, presumably as some animals succumbed to the treatment. Bait take on farms in the presence of stored cereal declined after 9 to 11 days of baiting. Bait consumption per rat appeared to increase again after 16 days of baiting in the absence of stored cereal. This increase was not apparent in the presence of stored cereal.

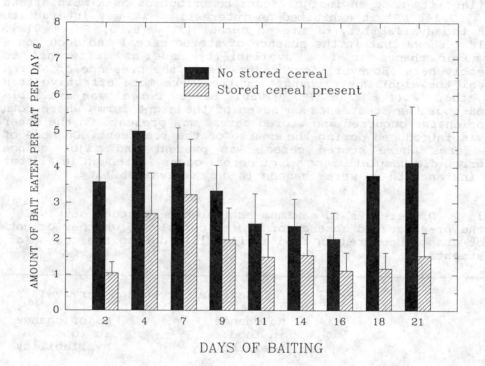

FIGURE 1. Differences in patterns of treated bait consumption over first 21 days of baiting for 15 treatments in the absence of stored cereal and 13 in its presence.

Bait consumption by survivors

Figure 2 shows the estimated amounts of treated bait consumed by 432 survivors of the first five replicates of the study. Forty-eight (11.1%) of survivors had eaten 20g or more of bait. Only three of these were survivors of treatments in Sussex and no survivors of Sussex treatments had eaten more than 50g of bait. Forty-five (18.1%) of survivors of treatments in Hampshire had eaten more than 20g of treated bait (approximately a lethal dose for a fully susceptible animal, see below).

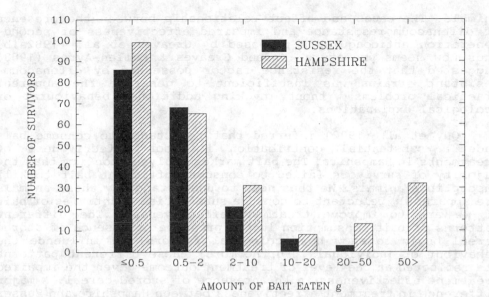

FIGURE 2. The estimated amounts of treated bait eaten by 432
survivors of treatments in Sussex and Hampshire

DISCUSSION

This study is unique in the detail of monitoring undertaken
and the number of comparable treatments performed. As a
consequence quantitative data are, for the first time, emerging
on the relationship between individual differences in bait
consumption and the outcome of treatments at the level of
populations. This is particularly apparent in the analyses of bait
marker residues in the bodies of survivors. Both DCBP and HCBP
have been used previously as qualitative markers (Buckle *et al.*,
1987). Used quantitatively they represent much more powerful
analytical tools. The LD50 of both difenacoum and bromadiolone for
fully susceptible rats are equivalent to a 200g individual eating
20-30g of bait containing 50ppm of active ingredient over a four
day period, allowing for sex specific toxicities (Greaves &
Cullen-Ayres 1988). The 18.1% of survivors on Hampshire farms that
consumed more than 20g of treated bait thus represents the
approximate contribution of second generation anticoagulant
resistance to reduced treatment effectiveness. It is therefore not
surprising that resistance does not contribute significantly to
differences in treatment outcome at the level of populations once
other factors are controlled for. Similarly, in these
circumstances, it might be expected that there would be no
apparent difference in the effectiveness of difenacoum and
bromadiolone against populations containing difenacoum-resistant

animals. The cause and effect relationship between the presence of difenacoum resistance and impaired effectiveness of second-generation anticoagulants proposed by Greaves et al. (1982a,b) thus now seems premature. Indeed Greaves & Cullen-Ayres (1988) suggested that the resistance factor possessed by difenacoum-resistant strains was insufficient to generate the apparent practical problems without invoking additional behavioural or ecological explanations.

Quy et al. (1992) inferred that reluctance to consume bait made a substantial contribution to poor effectiveness of treatments in Hampshire. The bait marker analyses confirm that the majority of survivors failed to consume sufficient bait to kill susceptible animals. We thus need to understand why these animals are apparently reluctant to consume substantial quantities of bait if we are to improve treatment effectiveness. The different patterns of bait consumption in the presence or absence of stored cereal begin to show how ecological factors can influence the behaviour of individuals. Furthermore, these different patterns are reflected at the level of treatment outcome given the impaired treatment effectiveness in the presence of stored cereal. A major difference in treatment effectiveness between Hampshire and Sussex farms is thus explicable in terms of the higher prevalence of stored cereal in Hampshire. Such a difference might also be expected in relation to the predominantly livestock rather than arable farms in Powys, Wales.

What is it about the presence of stored cereal that results in many rats failing to consume substantial quantities of bait? Whole cereals are known to be highly attractive foods for rats (e.g. Palmateer, 1974). It may simply be that the treated baits used in this study failed to compete with a highly attractive alternative food. Another feature of stored cereals, however, is that they tend to be consistently available in the same place for many months from harvest until they are moved off the farm, often not until the following spring. Animals thus have the opportunity to become adapted to a food source that is not only attractive but also consistently available. Against this predictability perhaps the novelty represented by baits elicits not only disinterest but active avoidance. If there is a major change in food availability against this previous background of environmental consistency then interest in any potential food may be enhanced. Such an interpretation is consistent with a risk-sensitive model of foraging behaviour (e.g. Caraco, 1980). This could explain the increased effectiveness of treatments when major change in food availability occurs in the presence of stored cereal. In no case did the observed major change in stored cereal availability involve complete removal. It thus seems likely that consistency rather than just attractiveness contributes to the influence of stored cereal on bait consumption and thus treatment effectiveness.

There is some evidence that the use of poison baits imposes selection pressure favouring individuals that exhibit heightened neophobic responses towards novel foods such as bait (Mitchell et al., 1977). In a diverse and changing environment these animals are likely to be at a disadvantage relative to less cautious individuals. In contrast, the persistent availability of stored cereal on many Hampshire farms may allow animals to fully express neophobic responses. The major changes in food availability recorded in this study are a rather crude measure of environmental stability. In general, much greater change can be expected on farms where livestock are kept compared with predominantly arable concerns. Livestock are fed on a daily basis, food will inevitably be spilt and the general level of activity during the autumn and winter is much greater than around farm buildings that are used only for storing food and machinery. It seems likely that these differences would have existed between farms in Powys and those in Hampshire for the trials reanalysed by Quy *et al.* (1992). The observed differences in effectiveness between these areas are thus explicable in terms of the attractiveness of stored cereal and the stability of its availability.

Strategies for dealing with rat infestations associated with stored cereal begin to emerge from this study. The association of major change in food availability with enhanced success suggests that rodenticide treatments should be timed to coincide with these changes. Rodenticide treatments thus need to be integrated with grain husbandry practices. Perhaps most importantly, all attempts should be made to restrict access of rats to stored cereal, particularly that which is going to be present for many months. Commercially such practices are likely to become more important in the future as tests for grain contamination become more sensitive.

The failure of rodenticide treatments against farm rats has, in the past, often been attributed to anticoagulant resistance without adequate evidence. This study suggests that much closer attention should be paid to ecological factors in terms of the attractiveness and stability of the alternative food supply. The major impact of stored cereals in particular has not previously been recognised. This may explain why problems persist in grain stores despite extensive use of rodenticides. Potential strategies are emerging, however, that can be specifically directed towards the problems posed by rats in the presence of stored cereal. Continuing to improve our understanding of the way patterns of bait consumption by individual animals determine the outcome of treatments will be important for the implementation of such strategies.

ACKNOWLEDGEMENTS

The study would not have been possible without the extensive field experience of Chris Plant. Resistance tests were performed by Erica Gill, Ged Kerins and Robin Redfern. Bait marker analyses were carried out by Gary Dunsford, Ainsley Jones, and Jane Page. Mike Townsend analyzed rodenticide concentrations in formulated baits. The manuscript benefitted from constructive criticism by Pete Smith. Rodenticides were kindly supplied by Rentokil Limited and Sorex Limited. The study was funded by the Pesticide Safety Division of the Ministry of Agriculture, Fisheries and Food.

REFERENCES

Buckle, A.P.; Odam, E.M.; Richards, C.G.J. (1987) Chemical bait markers for the study of bait uptake by Norway rats. In: *Control of Mammal Pests*, C.G.J. Richards and T.Y. Ku (Eds.), Taylor and Francis, London, pp. 199-213.

Caraco, T. (1980) On foraging time allocation in a stochastic environment. *Ecology*, **61**, 119-128.

Gill, J.E.; Kerins, G.M.; Langton, S.D.; MacNicoll, A.D. (in press) The development of a blood clotting response test for discriminating between difenacoum-resistant and susceptible Norway rats (*Rattus norvegicus*, Berk.). *Comparative Biochemistry and Physiology*.

Greaves, J.H; Cullen-Ayres, P.B. (1988) Genetics of difenacoum resistance in the rat. In: *Current Advances in Vitamin K Research*, J.W. Suttie (Ed.), Elsevier, Amsterdam, pp. 389-397.

Greaves, J.H., Shepherd, D.S.; Quy, R. (1982a) Field trials of second-generation anticoagulants against difenacoum-resistant Norway rat populations. *Journal of Hygiene, Cambridge*, **89**, 295-301.

Greaves, J.H., Shepherd, D.S.; Gill, J.E. (1982b) An investigation of difenacoum resistance in Norway rat populations in Hampshire. *Annals of Applied Biology*, **100**, 581-587.

Martin, A.D; Steed, L.C.; Redfern, R.; Gill, J.E.; Huson, L.W. (1979) Warfarin resistant genotype determination in the Norway rat (*Rattus norvegicus*). *Laboratory Animals*, **13**, 209-214.

Mitchell, D.E.; Beatty, E.T.; Cox, P.K. (1977) Behavioural differences between two populations of wild rats: implications for domestication research. *Behavioural Biology*, **19**, 206-216.

Palmateer, S.D (1974) Laboratory testing of albino rats with anticoagulant rodenticides. In: *Proceedings Sixth Vertebrate Pest Conference*, R.W. Marsh (Ed.) pp. 63-72.

Prickett, A.J. (1988) English farm grain stores 1987 Part 1 storage practice and pest incidence. *ADAS Central Science Laboratory Research Report Number 23*, 122pp.

Prickett, A.J.; Muggleton, J. (1991) Commercial grain stores 1988/89 England and Wales Part 2 Pest incidence and storage practice. *HGCA research report number 29*, 99pp+119pp.

Quy, R.J.; Cowan, D.P.; Swinney, T. (in press) Tracking index of rat population size. *Wildlife Society Bulletin*.

Quy, R.J.; Shepherd, D.S.; Inglis, I.R. (1992) Bait avoidance and effectiveness of anticoagulant rodenticides against warfarin- and difenacoum-resistant populations of Norway rats (*Rattus norvegicus*). *Crop Protection*, **11**, 14-20.

ALTERNATIVE STRATEGIES FOR THE CONTROL OF POST HARVEST ROTS IN APPLES AND PEARS

A M BERRIE

ADAS Boxworth R&D Centre, Olantigh Road, Wye, Ashford, Kent, TN25 5EL.

ABSTRACT

The introduction of post-harvest fungicide treatments in the early 1970s in the United Kingdom considerably reduced losses due to rotting in stored apples and pears and resulted in their routine use, regardless of need, in subsequent seasons. Despite the success of such treatments in maintaining average annual losses in stored apples and pears due to rotting to below two per cent, and their obvious advantages environmentally, they are not acceptable to markets or consumers and result in higher levels of residues in the fruit, though usually below the permitted maximum residue levels. Alternative control strategies therefore have to be identified. Surveys carried out on rotting in treated stored Cox apples and Conference pears over the past ten years have identified the fungi responsible, but not the level of losses in the absence of treatment. Alternative control measures are reviewed and discussed in relation to apples and pears, including biological, cultural methods and pre-harvest orchard treatments.

The strategy of integrated control of fruit storage rots is proposed which includes a scheme for assessing the risk of rotting in Cox apples based on fruit mineral analysis, orchard factors and orchard rot history.

INTRODUCTION

The harvesting period for most British apples and pears is restricted to the period mid-September to mid-October. Efficient storage is therefore essential in order to allow the fruit industry to regulate its supply of fruit onto the UK market for most of the year and enable it to compete successfully with the ever-increasing supplies of high quality fruit from other EC countries and outside Europe. Losses due to post-harvest rots can seriously affect the economics of such storage and their effective control is an integral part of efficient storage. In the 1950s and 60s rotting due to Gloeosporium species (Preece, 1967) was the main limitation to extending the storage life of Cox apples. However, the introduction of benzimidazole fungicides (eg. benomyl, carbendazim, thio-phanate-methyl) in the early 1970s as post-harvest fungicide treatments was so effective that the problem was virtually eliminated. Similarly the emergence of Phytophthora rot in the 1970s (Edney, 1978; Upstone, 1978) coincident with the introduction of bare soil management systems in orchards, was controlled by the post-harvest use of metalaxyl in combi-nation with carbendazim. Post-harvest fungicide treatment proved so successful in controlling storage rots that, until recently, almost all apples and pears were routinely dipped or drenched pre-storage. As a result of this success all research into storage rots and alternative means of control virtually ceased. The increased public concern about the use of pesticides in food production has meant that post-harvest treat-ments are unacceptable to consumers and consequently to markets. There is now an urgent need to re-examine control of storage rots in the UK and to develop alternative strategies. This paper aims to review the fungi responsible for losses in store, identify available alternative methods of control and develop a strategy for control that is not dependent on post-harvest fungicides.

CLASSIFICATION OF ROT FUNGI

The main post-harvest rots can be classified into two broad categories - orchard diseases and store diseases. (Table 1)

TABLE 1. Categories of rot fungi

Orchard diseases	Store diseases
Brown rot (*Monilinia fructigena*)	Botrytis rot (*Botrytis cinerea*)
Gloeosporium rot (*Gloeosporium* spp)	Blue mould (*Penicillium expansum*)
Nectria rot (*Nectria galligena*)	Mucor rot (*Mucor pyriformis*)
Phytophthora rot (*Phytophthora syringae*)	Fusarium rot (*Fusarium* spp)
Botrytis rot (*Botrytis cinerea*)	
Black rot (*Botryosphaeria obtusa*)	
Diaporthe rot (*Diaporthe perniciosa*)	

Orchard disease rots usually result from infections that occur in the orchard, but which are latent or escape notice at harvest. Some such as brown rot require wounds for entry, but most are also capable of direct attack. These fungi are present in the orchard either as cankers or mummified fruit or in the soil. Brown rot or Phytophthora rot cause immediate rotting after infection, but Gloeosporium rot or Nectria rot require a latent phase and therefore do not appear as rots in store until several months later. In contrast, store disease rots usually only arise from infections established after the fruit has been picked and put into store. Botrytis rot is categorised in both classes; in the orchard it is visible as an eye rot, originating from infection of senescing petals on the fruit calyx, which usually dries causing a dry eye rot. Store diseases generally need wounds for entry, although Penicillium rot can also enter via lenticels on mature bruised fruit. Store fungi originate in soil, weeds, plant debris and any other form of debris such as leaves and twigs which may be introduced into the bulk bin at harvest. Dirty bulk bins contaminated with the previous season's rot debris are also a source of store disease rots. Orchard diseases are generally well controlled by post-harvest fungicides, but these are usually ineffective against store diseases either because of resistance to fungicides as in the case of Botrytis and Penicillium (Berrie, 1989), or because available fungicides are ineffective (eg. Mucor).

IMPORTANCE OF ROTTING

The main apple (Cox and Bramley) and pear (Conference) cultivars grown are susceptible to most of the storage rot fungi. A survey of losses due to rots in untreated Cox conducted in 1961-65 identified Gloeosporium rot as the main cause of the losses with levels of 30 per cent in worst affected stores (Preece, 1967). *Monilinia fructigena* (brown rot) was also important, but other rots notably *Phytophthora syringae* were insignificant or not present. The considerable advances in Cox storage technology, such as the introduction of controlled atmosphere (CA) low

oxygen storage, improved fruit mineral composition and post-harvest
fungicide treatments, suggest that losses due to rots are unlikely to be
as great now. However, more recent information on losses in non-fungicide
treated Cox is limited. Over the past ten years surveys conducted by ADAS
Wye of rotting in fungicide-treated Cox fruit (Table 2) have shown that
the use of fungicide drenches has maintained losses below two per cent.
Brown rot still causes losses in most seasons, *Gloeosporium* is usually
only present at trace levels, with *Nectria galligena* causing significant
losses in wet seasons (1987/88), despite the use of a drench. In
Conference pears (Table 3) *Botrytis cinerea* is consistently the main cause
of rotting which was adequately controlled by the use of vinclozolin as a
post-harvest drench. The temporary suspension of the approval for
vinclozolin in 1990 has left the industry with no effective products to
control Botrytis rot, with around 60 per cent of isolates resistant to
benzimidazole fungicides (Berrie, 1989).

The susceptibility of the main fruit cultivars Cox apples and
Conference pears to fungal rots and the relatively high rainfall of UK
fruit production areas suggests that significant rotting is likely to
occur in most seasons in long term stored fruit, such that control
measures will be necessary to reduce losses and maintain the economics of
storage.

A new survey in 1991/92 funded by MAFF and the Apple and Pear
Research Council (APRC) of rotting in treated and untreated stored Cox
apples and Conference pears will generate information on the importance of
rotting over the next two seasons.

CONTROL OF ROTS BY POST-HARVEST FUNGICIDE DIPS OR DRENCHES

The development of fungicide dips/drenches to control storage rots
demonstrates how research has contributed to a successful practical system
for growers. Before discussing alternative control strategies it is
important to explore the obvious advantage of fungicide dips/drenches and
identify the problem areas that have resulted in such a successful system
becoming undesirable, mainly due to the increasing public concern over the
environment and the level of pesticide usage.

TABLE 2. Results of Survey in Southern England of mean percentage losses
of fruit numbers due to fungal rots in apple cv. Cox's Orange Pippin
treated with fungicide drenches, 1982-91

Fungal Rots	1982/3	1983/4	1984/5	1987/8	1988/9	1989/90	1990/1
Botrytis	0.1	0.5	1.1	0.6	0.4	0.3	0.3
Monilinia	0.2	0.4	0.1	0.6	0.3	0.5	1.1
Gloeosporium	0.1	0	0	0.6	0	0.1	0
Nectria	0.2	0.2	0.2	4.2	1.1	0.2	0.2
Phytophthora	0.6	0.5	0.4	0.1	0.3	0.8	0.1
Mucor	0.1	0.1	0.4	0	0	0	0
Other rots*	0.2	0.1	0.2	0.2	0.4	0.2	0.6
Total losses due to rots %	1.5	1.8	2.4	6.3	2.5	2.1	2.2
Farms sampled	14	15	18	21	22	30	40

* *Penicillium, Fusarium, Diaporthe*

TABLE 3. Results of survey in South England of mean percentage losses of fruit numbers due to fungal rots in pear cv. Conference in the presence of fungicide drenches, 1980-91

Fungal Rots	'80/81	'82/3	'83/4	'84/5	'87/8	'88/9	'89/90	'90/91
Botrytis	1.0	2.5	1.1	1.8	0.8	0.8	0.9	2.3
Monilinia	0.4	0.4	0.3	0.2	0.5	0.1	0.6	0.2
Nectria	-	0	-	0.1	0.3	0.1	0.1	0
Phytophthora	-	0	-	0.1	0.1	0	0	-
Mucor	0.1	0.2	0.3	0.6	0.1	0.1	0.1	0.1
Other rots	0.1	0.1	0.1	0.3	0.0	0.1	0.3	0.6
Unidentified stalk end rot	-	-	-	-	0.2	-	-	-
Total losses due to rots %	1.6	3.2	1.8	3.1	2.0	1.2	1.9	3.2
Farms sampled	60	12	29	31	12	12	7	42

Post-harvest fungicide dips/drenches have provided a cheap, reliable means of rot control for the past twenty years. Such a system allows the decision on need for treatment and choice of product to be delayed until harvest. Only one treatment is necessary which is targeted on the fruit and not the orchard environment. Benzimidazole fungicides, the main chemical group used for rot control, are reported to be harmful to the predatory mite *Typhlodromus pyri* and to earthworms, both of which are vital parts of integrated orchard protection. The use of post-harvest drenches avoids the use of such products in the orchard. In Germany and the Netherlands, where the use of pre-harvest sprays for rot control is more usual resistance of Gloeosporium rot to benzimidazole fungicides has been reported. (Palm, 1986; van der Scheer & Remijnse, 1988). In the UK it would appear that restricting use of benzimidazole fungicides to post-harvest dips/drenches also reduces the risk to the operator. The use of post-harvest fungicides, however, is not without difficulties. Disposal of the large volumes (around 2,000 litres) of drenching solution, which should be changed regularly (every 200 bins) to avoid debris and fungal spore build-up presents considerable, though not insurmountable, problems. Post-harvest treatments are effective in rot control because they achieve better fungicide cover on fruit and consequently levels of residue on the fruit are higher. MAFF funded studies by ADAS Wye comparing levels of 3 pre-harvest sprays of thiophanate methyl with a single post-harvest dip (Table 4) shows that the residue resulting from the latter is approximately ten times that from pre-harvest sprays although still below the maximum residue level (MRL) permitted of 5 mg/kg. In addition the results of MAFF surveys in 1988-89 (MAFF/HSE, 1990) of pesticide residues in culinary apples (Table 5) show that fungicide residues (usually below the MRL) were detected in over half the samples. Most of these fungicide residues originated from a post-harvest treatment. The presence of a pesticide residue in food, even if well below the MRL, is sufficient to create concern in consumers, despite reassurances on safety. The possible advent of produce labelling may also contribute to the demise of post-harvest treatments. A requirement to label fresh produce with any pesticide treatment applied post-harvest might result in a demand by markets for the abandoning of such practices. Within Europe the use of post-harvest fungicide drenches on fruit are only used in the UK and France and discussion within the EC suggest that Member states may agree to a ban on such treatments in the future (Anon, 1990). Perhaps the greatest problem for the use of post-harvest treatments is the actual concept of drenching fruit with fungicide. It is simply not acceptable to consumers. Therefore, despite the obvious environmental, biological, commercial and scientific advantages of such treatments, their use is likely to decline in the future, as a result of consumer and hence market pressure. The UK fruit industry therefore has to explore alternative strategies for rot control so that it is well prepared for the future.

ALTERNATIVE METHODS OF ROT CONTROL TO POST HARVEST DIPS/DRENCHES

Methods of controlling rots can be categorised as DIRECT METHODS that are aimed at inhibiting the fungus itself and INDIRECT METHODS that enhance the resistance of the fruit to fungal attack.

Direct methods

Other post-harvest treatments

Post-harvest heating to kill or weaken rot fungi offers a pesticide-free method to control post-harvest rots. The technique aims to eliminate fungi on the fruit surface or within the sub-epidermal tissue, without causing damage to the fruit. In the UK limited studies demonstrated that

TABLE 4. Comparison of residues resulting from pre-harvest post-harvest treatment with thiophanate methyl expressed as total carbendazim in apple peel or flesh at various sampling times, (ADAS, Wye, 1990)

	Total carbendazim mg/kg					
	Pre-harvest spray			Post-harvest dip		
Sampling time	Peel	Flesh	Whole apple	Peel	Flesh	Whole apple
Harvest	1.3	n.d*	0.2			
After dipping				14.4	0.3	2.1
After 5 mths store	1.6	n.d	0.2	16.9	n.d	2.3
After 5 mths store + washing	1.1	n.d	0.2	13.7	n.d	2.0

*n.d = not detected (limits of detection = 0.8 mg/kg)
 MRL carbendazim = 5 mg/kg

temperatures of 45°C for ten minutes reduced Gloeosporium rot on Cox apples (Edney & Burchill, 1967) but while the technique offers an alternative to pesticide use, the economics and the likely practical difficulties would make its wide-scale adoption difficult.

The use of thermo-nebulisation techniques for fogging fruit in stores, once they have been loaded have shown promise in investigations in Europe (Bompeix et al, 1986; Nguyen-Thé et al, 1988). Such a method, provided adequate cover could be achieved, would overcome the difficulties of fungicide drench disposal, but would still be confronted with consumer opposition to the concept of post-harvest fungicide use. Likewise, the use of chlorine drenches, though effective in eliminating surface spores of many storage rots, particularly Penicillium and Mucor (Sholberg & Owen, 1991) may also present environmental difficulties.

Pre-harvest fungicide sprays
The effectiveness of pre-harvest sprays of captan or benzimidazole
fungicides (Burchill & Edney, 1972) and dichlofluanid (Edney and Burchill,
1968) in controlling storage rots on Cox apples, mainly *Gloeosporium*,
Nectria and brown rot, was demonstrated in the 1960s and 70s in the UK.
In Europe more recent studies have shown tolyfluanid also to be effective
(Creemers, 1989), but other fungicides such as fenarimol or bitertanol
used for the control of apple scab (*Venturia inaequalis*) were found to be
ineffective (Palm, 1986). One of the main disadvantages of the use of
pre-harvest sprays is the risk of key rot fungi, such as Gloeosporium,
developing resistance to the fungicides used. Benzimidazole-resistant
strains of Gloeosporium have already been identified in Europe but not, so
far, in the UK. Late orchard sprays particularly of captan leave visible
deposits on the fruit creating concern among fruit pickers. In addition
the benzimidazole fungicides are reported to have harmful effects on the
orchard predatory mites *Typhlodromus pyri* and on earthworms (Kennel,
1989). However, recent studies by ADAS Wye to examine the effects of
pre-harvest sprays of captan or thiophanate methyl applied at rates
recommended on the product label, have not shown any significant
reductions in numbers of *Typhlodromus pyri* (Cross & Berrie in lit) or
earthworms (Berrie, 1992) after two seasons of treatment.

**TABLE 5. Working party on Pesticide residues: 1988-89. Residues in UK
produced culinary apples (24 samples)**

Chemical	No. samples with residue	Concentration range mg/kg
carbendazim (MRL* = 5)	12	0.6-1.8
diphenylamine (CAC♦ MRL = 5)	7	0.5-2.9
metalaxyl (CAC MRL = 0.05)	4	0.05-0.17
vinclozolin (MRL = 1)	3	0.5-0.6
phosalone (MRL =2)	1	0.2

*MRL = Maximum Residue Level in mg/kg
♦CAC = Codex Alimentarius Commission

Information on the effectiveness of pre-harvest sprays for control of
pear storage rots in the UK is limited. Preliminary studies in 1991 by
ADAS Wye, funded by Apple and Pear Research Council, suggest that sprays
are much less effective for controlling Botrytis rot on Conference pears
and may need to be applied very near harvest to increase efficacy.

Cultural methods
Many storage rot fungi survive in the orchards on cankers, mummified
fruit, leaf debris or in the soil. Removing such inoculum sources,
picking low hanging fruit separately or mulching herbicide strips to
reduce soil splash will decrease the risk of introducing rot fungi into
store. Bulk bins contaminated with the previous season's mummified rots
are also a source of rot inoculum particularly *Penicillium* or *Botrytis*.

Biological control
Biological control can in theory be achieved by the use of resistant
cultivars, natural plant products or microbial antagonists.

The main apple and pear cultivars grown in the UK, Cox, Bramley and Conference pears, are susceptible to most of the main rot fungi. Breeding programmes at HRI East Malling are screening for resistance to storage rots, but it will be some time before new cultivars which combine resistance to rotting with the required commercial attributes contribute significantly to the UK Market.

The use of naturally occurring anti-microbial plant products has undergone limited investigation overseas (Culter *et al*, 1986). In the UK, Swinburn (1973) has implicated benzoic acid in Bramley in controlling Nectria rot, but little other research has been carried out.

The use of microbial antagonists has been more widely investigated particularly abroad. On apple and pears antagonistic yeasts and bacteria have been identified as giving control of *Penicillium expansum* and *Botrytis cinerea* (Janisiewicz, 1988; Janisiewicz & Roitman, 1988). Such control methods show promise and require further investigation, but are not without difficulties. Formerly the cost of developing biocontrol agents was economically prohibitive, but now with the many problems associated with pesticides this approach may be more attractive. Despite being natural, biocontrol agents are still subject to the same registration requirement as pesticides, and may also suffer from the possible need for produce labelling to record treatment.

Indirect methods

Fruit quality

The importance of the correct mineral composition of apples in maintaining fruit quality and resisting rotting in store is now well understood. Calcium levels are of particular importance; this mineral acts in two ways. Firstly, calcium stabilises the cell wall of the apple maintaining fruit firmness by resisting degradation by enzymes that occur naturally in fruit. Secondly, it also renders the cell wall more resistant to the cell wall degrading enzymes produced by rot fungi (Sharples & Johnson, 1977; Sams & Conway, 1985; Conway *et al* 1991). Fruit of the correct mineral composition are more resistant to lenticel-invading fungi such as *Nectria galligena* or *Gloeosporium* sp (Sharples, 1980).

Many rot fungi particularly brown rot, Penicillium and Mucor rots invade fruits through wounds, either naturally occurring such as cracking or russeting, or those resulting from poor handling at harvest. Good supervision of pickers at harvest can minimise fruit damage and ensure that only sound fruit is selected for long term storage. Careful handling of fruit bins can also minimise damage and avoid fruit being contaminated with soil, which might introduce *Phytophthora syringae* or *Mucor* into store. Preliminary studies at HRI East Malling funded by the APRC (Johnson, 1992, personal communication) shows that considerable reduction in rotting can be achieved simply by good supervision of pickers and selective picking of fruit.

Picking date

The fruit must be picked at the correct state of maturity in order to be suitable for long term storage. Late picked fruit may be over-mature and therefore more liable to rotting. In addition, the longer the fruit remains on the tree, the greater the risk of infection by rot fungi particularly those disseminated by rain.

Store conditions

The development of low temperature, controlled atmosphere (CA) storage for Cox has considerably reduced the level of rotting in store. Low temperatures maintain fruit quality by suppressing senescence and fungal growth. Reducing the oxygen concentration also suppresses fruit senescence (Sharples, 1982; Sams & Conway, 1985). Low oxygen, especially at concentrations of one per cent or less can significantly reduce growth, sporulation and germination in most post-harvest fungi. Experiments at ADAS Wye compared rotting in Cox stored in air or CA (Table 6) following treatment with or without a pre- or post-harvest fungicide. All fungicide treatments reduced rotting, but the greatest reduction occurred in CA storage compared to air. A similar reduction in rotting has been found by Edney, (1964) and Bompeix (1978). To maximise the effect of storage conditions, the store must be loaded quickly and the store conditions rapidly established.

TABLE 6. Control of storage rots in Cox's Orange Pippin with pre-harvest sprays or post-harvest treatments and stored in air at 3-3.5°C or controlled atmosphere storage (1%CO_2. 2% O_2 at 3.5-4.0°C)

Treatments	% rotting (assessed in February)	
	Controlled atmosphere	Air
Untreated	5	16.5
captan orchard spray (3 sprays)	1.2*	6.2*
thiophanate methyl orchard spray (3 sprays)	0.4*	8.8*
thiophanate post-harvest drench	1.3*	9.6*
metalaxyl + carbendazim post-harvest drench	0.9*	8.3*
SED (27 residual dof)		
Fungicide treatment	2.53	
Storage regime	1.60	
Treatment x storage	3.58	

*significantly different from untreated P = 0.05

STRATEGY FOR ROT CONTROL

There are several alternative approaches for tackling the problem of storage rot control. The use of cultural control to reduce orchard inoculum or ensuring correct harvest date, achieving the recommended standards in fruit mineral composition and use of optimum storage conditions individually will not be entirely effective in controlling rots. Similarly, adopting routinely the use of pre-harvest fungicide sprays to reduce rotting, while contributing significantly to control of storage rots, has many disadvantages. However, combining such techniques in an integrated system provides the best strategy for prevention and control of storage rots. MAFF funded research is at present developing a system of rot risk prediction. For apples, this is based on orchard rot history, fruit mineral analysis, and a pre-harvest assessment of orchard disease inoculum levels and fruit quality to determine the likely risk of rotting. In this way problem orchards can be identified and allocated for early marketing while other orchards with a low storage rot risk may only need protective orchard sprays for adequate rot control. For pears, where the main rot is Botrytis rot, developing a rot risk prediction system is more difficult and requires further research.

ACKNOWLEDGEMENTS

The author wishes to thank the Ministry of Agriculture, Fisheries and Food, (MAFF) and the Apple and Pear Research Council for supporting the research cited in this paper.

REFERENCES

Anon, (1990). European Parliament's post-harvest pesticides ban proposals end in compromise. Fresh Produce Journal, September 21.4

Berrie, A.M., (1989). Storage rots of apple and pear in south-east England 1980-1988 incidence and fungicide resistance. Integrated control of Pome fruit diseases, II, IOBC Bulletin XII/6, 229-239.

Berrie, A.M., (1992). Disease control strategies for top fruit production In disease management in relation to changing agricultural practice. Eds A.R. McCracken, P.C. Mercer, SIPP/BSPP, Belfast, April 1992.

Bompeix, G., (1978). The comparative development of Pezicula alba and P. malicorticis on apples and in vitro (air and controlled atmosphere). Phytophologische Zeitschrift, 99, 97-109.

Bompeix, G., Morgat, F and Imbroglini, G., (1986). Traitement des fruits par thermonébulisation. L'Arboriculture Fruitiére, 384, 71-72.

Burchill, R.T. and Edney, K. L., (1972). An assessment of some new treatments for the control of rotting of stored apples. Annals of Applied Biology, 72, 249-255.

Conway, W.S., Sams, C.E., Abbot. J.A., and Bruton, B.D., (1991). Post-harvest calcium treatment of apple fruit to provide broad-spectrum protection against post-harvest pathogens. Plant Disease, 75, 620-622.

Creemers, P., (1989). Chemical control of parasitic storage diseases on apple and pear. Acta Horticulturae, 258. 645-653.

Culter, H.G., Stevenson, R.F., Cole, P.D., Jackson, D.M. and Johnson, A.W., (1986). Secondary metabolites from higher plants. Their possible role as biological control agents. ACS symposium. Ser. pp 178-96. Washington DC. Am.Chem.Soc.

Edney, K.L., (1964). The effect of the composition of the storage atmosphere on the development of rotting of Cox's Orange Pippin apples and the production of pectolytic enzymes by Gloeosporium spp. Annals of Applied Biology, 54, 327-334.

Edney, K.L., (1978). The infection of apples by Phytophthora syringae. Annals of applied Biology, 88, 31-36.

Edney, K.L and Burchill, R.T., (1967). The use of heat to control the rotting of Cox's Orange Pippin apples by Gloeosporium spp. Annals of Applied Biology, 59, 389-400.

Edney, K.L., and Burchill, R.T., (1968). Experiments on the control of Gloeosporium fruit rots by field sprays. Report East Malling Research Station for 1967, 135-137.

Janisiewicz, W.J., (1988). Biocontrol of post-harvest diseases of apples with antagonistic mixtures. Phytopathology, 78, 194-198.

Janisiewicz, W.J., and Roitman, J., (1988). Biological control of blue mould and grey mould on apple and pear with Pseudomonas capacia. Phytopathology, 78, 1697-1700.

Kennel, W, (1989). The integrated use of benzimidazole fungicides to control *Gloeosporium* fruit rot of apple. Integrated control of Pome fruit Diseases II, IOBC Bulletin XII/6, 247-255.

MAFF/HSE, (1990). Report of the working party on pesticide residues 1988-89. Supplement to Issue No. 8, 1990 of The Pesticide Register.

Nguyen-Thé, C., Ripetti, V., Chapon, J.F. and Bompeix, G., (1988). Qualite de la peche. Intérét des traitements post-récolte. Infos Centre Technique Interprofessionel des Fruits et Légumes, 40, 31-34.

Palm, G. (1986). Die aktuelle Bedeutung der Fruchtfäule Erreger an der Niederelbe und Möglichkeiten ihrer Bekämpfung Matt. OVR Alten Landes. 1 14-21.

Preece, T.F., (1967). Losses of Cox's Orange Pippin apples during refrigerated storage in England. 1961-65. Plant Pathology, 16, 176-180.

Sams, C.E., and Conway, W.S., (1985). Effects of controlled atmosphere and calcium infiltration on decay of Delicious apples. Plant Disease, 69, 747-750.

Sharples, R.O., (1980). The influence of orchard nutrition on the storage quality of apples and pears grown in the UK. In: Mineral Nutrition of Fruit Trees, Atkinson, D., Jackson, J.E., Sharples, R.O. and Waller, W.M., (Eds.) Butterworth , 1980. 17-28.

Sharples, R.O., (1982). Effects of ultra-low oxygen conditions on the storage quality of English Cox's Orange Pippin apples. In: Proceedings of the third National controlled Atmosphere Research Conference on controlled atmospheres for storage and transport of perishable agricultural commodities. D.C. Richason and M M Meheriuk, (Eds.) P. 131-138

Sharples, R.O. and Johnson, D.S., (1977). The influence of calcium or senescence changes in apples. Annals of Applied Biology, 85, 450-453.

Sholberg, P.L. and Owen, G.R., (1991). Populations of propagites of *Mucor* spp during immersion dumping of Anjou pears. Canadian Plant Disease Survey, 71, 33-35.

Swinburn, T.K., (1973). The resistance of immature Bramley's seedling apples to rotting by *Nectria galligena* Bres. In: Fungal Pathogenicity and the Plant's Response. R.J.W. Byrde and C.V. Cutting (Eds.) Academic Press, New York. P 365-382

Upstone, M.E., (1978). *Phytophthora syringae* Fruit rot of apples. Plant Pathology, 27, 24-30.

Van der Scheer, H.A. Th. and Remijnse, W., (1988). Aanpassing bestrijding Gloeosporiumschimmels genast. De Fruitteelt, 29, 16-17.

SESSION 4B

ADVANCES IN THE SAFER FORMULATION, PACKAGING AND APPLICATION TECHNOLOGY OF PESTICIDES

CHAIRMAN   DR B. T. GRAYSON

SESSION
ORGANISER   MR P. J. MULQUEEN

INVITED PAPERS   4B-1 to 4B-3

RESEARCH REPORT   4B-4

FUTURE FORMULATION TRENDS - LIKELY IMPACT OF REGULATORY AND LEGISLATIVE PRESSURE

W T C HOLDEN

Schering Agrochemicals Limited, Chesterford Park Research Station, Saffron Walden, Essex CB10 1XL

ABSTRACT

Regulatory and legislative pressures are accelerating the trend to develop safer formulations. Particular emphasis is being placed on the need for products which are safer in handling and use and which minimise environmental impact. These pressures coupled with the need to reduce contaminated packaging waste are leading to the closer integration of formulation, packaging and application technologies to provide safer delivery systems.

At the same time regulatory demands are making it more difficult for new compounds to achieve registration and in consequence opportunities exist to develop safer formulations of existing compounds and to improve their biological efficacy. The evaluation of adjuvants and their incorporation where feasible into crop protection products will become increasingly important.

Lower prices for agricultural commodities will reduce farmer margins and put lower thresholds on the cost acceptability of crop protection products. The formulation chemist must help develop safer products which are cost effective and cost acceptable.

INTRODUCTION

The role of the crop protection industry is to provide cost effective products for farmers and growers as aids to good husbandry. Changes in regulatory and legislative demands are adding to the cost of development of new products and in many cases to the cost of the products themselves. At the same time the Common Agricultural Policy (CAP) in Europe and pressures from GATT are reducing the margins on agricultural commodities.

Formulation is an essential part of the development of any crop protection product and influences factors including, safety, efficacy and cost. This short paper discusses the dilemmas of the formulation chemist and the industry as a whole in providing safer, cost effective/cost acceptable products in the remainder of this decade and beyond. If the cost of any product is perceived to be above the threshold for farmer/grower acceptance then the product will not be used. As a consequence new safer or more effective products may not gain market acceptance.

INCREASED COSTS
(Regulatory/legislative requirements)

Cost acceptability
- -
threshold

REDUCED MARGINS ON AGRICULTURAL
COMMODITIES

REGULATORY AND LEGISLATIVE PRESSURES

My remarks here relate mainly to the situation within Europe, particularly in the UK.

The EC Registration Directive (Uniform Principles) is becoming established. There are increased demands for data to register new products (active materials and formulated products) and maintain registrations on existing products. Particular emphasis is placed on environmental and residues data requirements. Issues relating to inerts will require closer attention.

General environmental concerns have resulted in closer control of water and air quality and in respect of pollution in general. Of relevance to formulation and packaging issues is legislation to control packaging waste, in particular contaminated waste.

In the UK, the Health and Safety at Work Act and the derived COSHH Regulations have brought product handling practices during application into focus. Issues relating to the permeation of protective clothing and the dermal toxicity/irritancy of products are being addressed.

Regulations and codes of practice relating to the transport and storage of products are being tightened. Problems that can arise from fires involving crop protection products were highlighted in a incident in Switzerland back in 1986. EC Regulations demand that a product should have a flash point of more than 55°C to be classed as non-flammable. Certain transport regulations, for example the International Marine Dangerous Goods Regulations (IMDG), define the flammability limit at 61°C. An appropriate target value for the industry is a minimum flash point of 64°-65°C.

On the question of margins on agricultural products, the MacSharry proposals have been reflected in reductions in effective subsidy payments. This is pressure under GATT to further reduce price support. The net effect is a reduction in farmers' margins: current CAP reforms are intended to reduce cereal prices by 29% over the next 3 years.

PROBLEMS TO ADDRESS

Over the past decade the number of new compounds registered for commercial use in Western Europe has been significantly reduced as a result of regulatory pressures. Increasing regulatory demand will increase further the cost and time to clear new compounds. It is, therefore, essential that further formulation effort is devoted to ensuring that best use is made of existing registered compounds as well as new compounds under development.

There are five main areas to be addressed:-

i   Need for safer formulations to minimise problems in transport, storage and general handling.

ii Need for formulations/packs which reduce handling risks during application and minimise disposal problems. Here issues relating to the disposal of containers and used spray/product are under close scrutiny at the present time. Shelf life is also a pertinent question.

iii Environmental concerns - the issues here relate to inerts and application techniques other than hydraulic spraying.

iv Need to optimise the activity selectivity of any new or existing compounds.

v   Need for coformulations either to meet marketing need or to combine active materials of differing modes of action to delay the onset of resistance.

Increasing data requirements for inerts will present difficulties There is the need to ensure that all inerts, surfactants and solvents in particular are supported by an adequate data package in respect of their toxicology, ecotoxicology and environmental fate. Situations may arise where the need for additional data to support the continued use of well established inerts may not be justifiable on cost grounds. More than ever there is the need for formulation chemists to work closely with suppliers particularly of surfactants and solvents to establish that adequate data bases for a particular inert exists and can be maintained at the beginning of any development exercise. It is important that we as formulation chemists do not use inerts which provide for greater hazards or problems than the active material itself. It is encouraging to note that the Uniform Priciples directive has a list of banned Inerts rather than a list of approved inerts.

The need for additional data to support the registration of formulated products themselves must not be overlooked. Although our task here is by no means as onerous as in the case of our toxicological or residue chemistry colleagues, additional work will be required.

BASIC REQUIREMENTS OF A FORMULATED CROP PROTECTION PRODUCT

It is the responsibility of the formulation chemist to design any product to provide the best fit of relevant factors which include:-

*   physical and chemical properties of the compound
*   safety/environment
*   registration requirements
*   biology (activity/crop selectivity)
*   application
*   marketing/user preferences
*   cost
*   suitability for large scale manufacture
*   shelf life.

The issues of particular interest in this paper are those relating to safety/environment, registration and cost/efficacy coupled with the need for coformulations. As far as the safety and environment issues are concerned the formulation chemist cannot work alone. There is and must be a close working relationship between formulation chemist, packaging technologist and applications engineer to provide safe and effective delivery systems for crop protection products.

POTENTIAL SOLUTIONS

Means of resolving the problems raised are set out in tabular form:-

	PROBLEM	REQUIREMENTS	TYPE OF FORMULATION
i	Safety in transport storage and general handling	Non-flammable or non-combustible product. Low dermal toxicity. Low penetration of protective clothing.	Water based liquid formulation (of low or zero solvent content.
			WGs
		Non-dusty	Tablets
		Solids or thickened liquids rather than mobile liquids.	Gels
		EC Dangerous Substances Regulations - unclassified (where possible).	
ii	Handling of products during application, disposal of containers, unused spray liquid and product	Mobile easily metered and rinsed product/ pack combinations (Dutch Covenant).	High quality liquid formulations of low dermal toxicity and good spray tank compatibility.
		Suitable for use in returnable containers.	Single phase systems, SLs, ECs, microemulsions preferred.
		Suitable for use in water soluble packs.	
		Suitable for use in direct injection spray.	
		Products of long shelf life.	

iii <u>Environmental Issues</u>	For conventional spray formulations use of inerts which at rates applied do not accumulate in soil or ground water.	Any type of formulation.
	Control of drift is essentially a sprayer problem (nozzle selection).	Drift control adjuvants.
	Wider use of alternative application techniques.	Seed treatments. Granules. Controlled release.
iv <u>Activity enhancement/ modification</u>	Improved activity/selectivity over basic formulations.	Formulations containing high levels of surfactant/oil.
		Oil dispersions SEs Microemulsions ECs Matrix systems Microcapsular dispersions
		Use of separate adjuvant.
v <u>Coformulations</u>	Particular emphasis on safer types of formulation (water based).	SEs Microcapsular suspensions (SCs and ECs)
	Problems arise where the chemical and physical propertries are dissimilar.	
vi <u>Cost</u>	Simple formulation systems.	SCs, ECs and WPs
	Quick to develop and cheap to manufacture.	

CONCLUSIONS/THOUGHTS ON THE FUTURE

Container disposal is perhaps at this point in time one of the most significant factors in determining which way the industry should move in developing specific types of formulation. If rinsed containers can be regarded as non-hazardous waste and the use of Small Volume Returnable containers (SVR) become accepted for use on larger farms then liquid products have an assured future.

If the disposal issues of standard type containers cannot be satisfactorily resolved then there will be a marked move to solid formulations, WGs in particular. Again the use of water soluble packaging would assume more importance.

In future formulated products must be designed in the context of 3 different types of packing.

i	Conventional	-	Liquid and Solid formulations
ii	SVRs	-	Liquids (possibility granules)
iii	Water Soluble film	-	liquids
		-	solids (WGs WPs)

High quality liquid formulations will be required particularly for SVRs and other large containers.

Where water soluble film is used the potential for product/film compatibility with resultant spray tank problems must not be overlooked. An intriguing point to note here is the possibility of packing water-based products in water soluble film.

The development of low dose active materials will reduce both the quantity of formulation per hectare and the amount of packing material requiring disposal. The use of highly active, high cost compounds will demand that more time is spent in optimising their biological activity. The use of adjuvants in general has been the subject of a recent conference in Cambridge. I will not elaborate on this area other than to state that this area is progressively receiving more attention both in the agrochemical and surfactant/oil industries.

The comments I have made relate to products intended for hydraulic spraying. In environmental terms this application technique is by no means ideal but provides the only practical robust system for treating large crop areas. Hydraulic spraying will continue to be the norm until well into the next century. Opportunity should be taken where the properties of the compound point to make wider use of seed treatment/coating techniques and granular formulations to protect a given crop.

Many references have been made to the use of controlled release systems for crop protection. It is an area worthy of further study but the problems in our industry are much greater than those in human and animal health. Firstly our products have to work under variable conditions of temperature and humidity whereas a specific location inside a mammal or even its exterior surface provides a much more closely controlled environment. Again this is the question of the cost of the delivery system. Seed treatments and granules provide the best options for controlled release formulations in the immediate future.

To conclude it is worthwhile examining some data on formulation types in Western Europe (1989).

Figures based on metric tonnes of formulated product.

WP	29.5%)		
Dust (DP)	10.6%)	Total for dry	
Granules (GR)	12.1%)	formulations - 54.0%	
Other Dry Formulations	1.8%)		
SC	13.7%)	Total for	
SL	6.5%)	water based	
		formulations - 20.3%	
EC	24.7%)	Total for	
Unknown types	1.0%)	solvent	
		based - 25.7%	
	___		___
	100		100

It is revealing to note that in spite of work on alternative systems through the 1980's most of the formulations sold are still of the conventional types. Perhaps this is in part a reflection of the additional time taken to fully develop the more complex types of formulation and particularly to obtain registration.

The agrochemical industry is currently working hard on alternative types of formulation. Work on water-based systems, WGs/tablets, formulations for water soluble packaging and activity enhancement will continue throughout the 1990's. However, it will be interesting to look again at the product breakdown in terms of formulations types at the end of the decade. Although the proportion of more complex water-based, oil based and WG/tablet formulations will increase significantly, I suspect that the conventional types of formulation SC, WP and EC may still predominate. However, a proportion of those conventional formulations will be packed/distributed in water-soluble or returnable packs.

The emphasis must be on safe 'quality' formulations regardless of type. The situation will always apply where the most appropriate formulation is developed for a particular compound(s) for a given use. The emphasis will be cost efficacy/cost acceptance as well as on safety. More than ever before the formulation chemist has to make his silk purse from a sow's ear or even half a sow's ear.

ACKNOWLEDGEMENTS

I would like to thank my colleagues in Schering Agrochemicals Ltd for their help in preparing this manuscript and the Surfactants Division of Hoechst AG for the data on formulation types in Western Europe (1989).

REFERENCES

The EC Registration Directive and Uniform Principles.
EC Directive on Packaging and Packaging Waste (Draft).
Health and Safety at Work etc., Act 1974 (HSW Act).
The Control of Substances Hazardous to Health Regulations 1988 (COSHH).
Council Directive 79/831/EEC amending for the sixth time Directive 67/548/EEC on the
approximation of laws, regulations and administrative provisions relating to the
classification, packaging and labelling of dangerous substances as completed in
Commission Directives 84/449/EEC and 87/302/EEC.
Agrochemical Monitor **No.83** 12.6.92.
Formulation Types in Western Europe (Personal communication -
Hoechst AG/Surfactants Division).

NOVEL FORMULATION AND PACKAGING CONCEPTS-
CUSTOMER NEED OR MARKETING TOOL?

B. Frei

CIBA-GEIGY Ltd., Plant Protection Division, CH-4333 Münchwilen, Switzerland

P. Nixon

CIBA-GEIGY Ltd., Plant Protection Division, CH-4002 Basel, Switzerland

ABSTRACT

In the use of plant protection products, safety for the applicator and the environment must be "Top of mind". Therefore, there is an increasing need for the plant protection industry to continue to develop new products and delivery systems which are optimised with regard to safety, environmental behaviour, biological performance and cost. Novel formulation and packaging concepts will have to make a major contribution for industry to reach these goals. By reduction of organic solvents in liquid formulations, the environmental impact and toxicity of the product may be reduced. A reduction of dermal toxicity may also be obtained by encapsulation of the active ingredient. In most situations liquid products are preferred to powders when preparing spray solutions for several reasons. The use of water soluble film to package powders provides improved worker safety by eliminating dusting during handling. User and environmentally friendly packaging systems include containers which are easy to rinse, packaging of formulations in water soluble films, and small volume refillable containers.

INTRODUCTION

Over the last decade, the plant protection industry has been faced with many changes and, today, it has to meet not only economic, but also social and environmental challenges. With a low growth market situation and increasing regulatory requirements concerning user safety and environmental compatibility of their products, innovative solutions to emerging customer needs become all important if industry players are to reach their economic objectives. From a social point of view it is necessary to inform the public on benefits and risks of products and to aim for continuous improvement of product handling systems with regard to safety for the user. The main targets concerning the protection of the environment include saving resources with better products and manufacturing processes, introducing environmentally compatible products and minimising waste by optimising production processes and packaging designs. To achieve these goals, combined efforts in research, development, production and marketing within our strategic framework will be necessary. As it will be shown by several examples, the development of new formulations and packagings can make an important contribution to the progress in the pursuit of this goal.

The core of each product is the chemical compound which is responsible for the intrinsic biological activity. However, for a safe and optimally targeted application and the development of the biological efficacy of the product, the active ingredient has to be formulated and packed properly. Therefore, the design of formulation and packagings are of fundamental importance. The formulation and packaging concept for a product depends on many factors. The physico-chemical properties of an active ingredient such as the physical state, the chemical stability and the solubility in water and organic solvents determine technically feasible types of formulations, for which the appropriate packagings have to be defined. Further important factors influencing the design of formulations and packagings of a product are the toxicological properties of the active ingredient and, of course, user's needs. As it has been shown in an earlier paper (Urech 1990), the plant protection industry has several "user" groups, namely the society, the farmers, and the regulatory authorities, which have various needs. This paper concentrates on the needs of distributors and farmers as users of plant protection products. They want economic, safe and reliable solutions to problems and no or minimal waste disposal problems. Marketing also has its need to supply the customer with new products which have competitive advantages and generate profit. For positioning a product in the market, in addition to innovations in formulations, new designs of packagings and labels further play an important role.

Today, in the European market most of the plant protection products are still sold as classical formulations such as emulsifiable concentrates (EC), soluble liquids (SL), suspension concentrates (SC), and wettable powders (WP) adding up to over 90% (Diepenhorst *et al.* 1991). Newer product forms such as water dispersible granules (WG) only slowly penetrate the market. In recent years, several active ingredients with low dose rate have been developed using typically only a few g/ha instead of kg/ha. This certainly opens new opportunities for formulation and packaging development. Indeed there has been a rapid increase in the farmer's interest in advanced types of formulations and delivery systems. Furthermore, the high development costs associated with bringing new active ingredients to the market may also push companies to investigate new formulation and packaging technologies in order to extend the life of existing products.

NOVEL FORMULATION AND PACKAGING CONCEPTS
Liquid formulations

It is recognised that liquid formulations are preferred by the farmer for preparing spray solutions for several reasons. They can be measured volumetrically, they are easy to handle, they spontaneously form stable dispersions and, given appropriate container design, most formulations are easy to rinse out of the package.

Emulsifiable concentrates (EC)
Although they are the most applied liquid formulations, EC's also have disadvantages. Some of the organic solvents used in EC's may be harmful because of their toxicity and their flammability. EC's are also coming more and more under regulatory pressure due to the organic solvents.

Suspension concentrates (SC)
These formulations have an advantage over EC's because they are water based and normally contain only small amounts of glycols as antifreeze. However, the preparation of SC's is limited to solid active ingredients having a low water solubility.

Emulsions in water (EW)
For the formulation of hydrolytically stable liquid compounds, EW's are an at-

tractive alternative to EC's. Because they are water based they may be less hazardous for the user and the environment.

Capsule suspensions (CS)

A further step towards more safety for the user may be obtained by encapsulation of the active ingredient. As has been proven for some of our insecticides, capsule suspensions (CS) show a remarkable reduction of the mammalian toxicity compared to the EC's with respect to both oral and dermal exposure. Encapsulation of the active ingredient may also offer an advantage for compounds which are volatile.

Container designs

All liquid formulations have a disadvantage because of the difficulties to dispose of contaminated primary packaging waste. It is important therefore to ensure that single trip containers are rinsed immediately after emptying and the rinsate added to the spray tank. This requires that containers are designed to be rinsed and are easy to rinse. Clean, rinsed containers are easier to be disposed of through municipal waste channels or to be collected for controlled recycling or energy recovery. Industry is in the process of agreeing on container performance standards and specific design criteria aimed at improving handling and rinsability.

Refillable containers

Strategies aimed at reducing the number of single trip containers include the development and eventual introduction to the market of refillable containers. Mini-bulk refillable containers have long been used in the USA and Canada and have contributed to a substantial reduction in the number of single trip containers requiring disposal. Already three years ago, CIBA-GEIGY considered the possibilities of developing small i.e. 20-30 litre refillable containers for fungicides in Europe. Emerging packaging waste legislation i.e. EEC Directive on Packaging Waste, encourages the use of refillable packaging and during 1992, a number of agrochemical companies had development programmes running with small volume refillable (SVR) containers using stainless steel kegs from 10-60 litres sizes. Efforts are being made by industry to standardize fitments attaching SVR containers to sprayer transfer systems.

CIBA-GEIGY is also involved in the development of a 10 litre refillable, closed dispensing container called the 'CIBA-LINK'. The advantages of this systems are due to the fact that no investments in transfer systems or major spray equipment modifications are required. The only modification required is the fitting of a small valve either in the top of the spray tank or in the lid of the induction bowl or hopper. The 'CIBA-LINK' is quick and easy to use, simply inverting the container and engaging the dispensing head into the valve on the sprayer. Applying slight pressure opens the valve and the required amount of product can be dispensed. When the 'CIBA-LINK' is empty it is returned to the bulk site for re-filling.

Clearly the success of SVR containers will also depend on effective logistic systems and getting the economy right. We believe there is an opportunity for refillable containers and that farmers will be quick to see the benefits of such systems when they become available.

Gels (GL)

Gel formulations can be described as thickened EC's packed in water soluble bags (Dez et al., 1990). In some cases, organic solvents may be replaced by natural oils. The viscosity is increased with thickeners up to a range which usually represents a compromise regarding the transport stability in the water soluble bag and the dispersibility in water. This concept offers the plant protection market a new form of product/packaging combination. The first fungicide formulated as a gel is the propiconazole GL 62.5, which was launched under the trade name PRACTIS by CIBA-GEIGY France in 1991. This product provides many benefits, which are highly appreciated by farmers. The premeasured doses in water soluble bags offer advantages in easy handling and increased user safety, and the outer package is not contaminated with product and can be easily disposed of. Because of the higher concentration of the GL 62.5 compared to the EC 500, there are also less organic solvents.

A crucial point for the success of this development was the intense collaboration of formulation and packaging specialists. The challenge for them was to identify a polyvinyl alcohol film as the primary packaging which was compatible with the solvents in the gel formulation and still had a short dissolution time in the spray tank. Furthermore, a multi compartment secondary package had to be developed which provides mechanical protection for the sachet and can be sealed against moisture.

Solid Formulations

Solid formulations have several advantages over liquid ones, in particular, regarding their environmental impact. They are free of organic solvents, easy to recollect in case of spillage, and, in general, there is less packaging waste to dispose of.

Wettable powders (WP)

These are the most common solid formulations. To obtain a stable suspension upon dilution with water, WP's have to be ground to a very fine particle size, which makes them dusty and, therefore, less safe to use, particularly when measuring out. However, worker safety may be improved by packaging the WP's into water soluble bags, which allows the farmer to use premeasured doses and the secondary package is not contaminated by product.

Water dispersible granules (WG)

WG's are slowly becoming established in the plant protection industry. In this formulation type, advantages of liquid and solid formulations are combined. Thus, WG's are easy flowing products with constant bulk density and can therefore be measured volumetrically. They are much less dusty, 2-3 times less voluminous and leave less residues in empty packagings compared to WP's. A drawback for products with high use rates may be the high price of WG's, however, the high processing costs may be balanced by reduced storage costs due to the higher bulk density. Thus, WG's are the formulation of choice for highly active solid products such as sulfonyl ureas.

Effervescent tablets (TB)

As an innovation in solid formulations, effervescent TOPAS tablets have been introduced into the market for disease control in pommefruit and vineyards (Schmutz *et al.*, 1990). As far as handling properties are concerned, tablets are clearly superior to both liquid and powder formulations. Major benefits are a premeasured dose rate, the ease of use and the empty packaging being almost free of product residues. Tablets are also particularly suited for products which are effective at low rates.

Seed treatment formulations

Tailor made formulations for seeds became established at CIBA-GEIGY during the last 10 years and are now increasingly important aspects of plant protection agents application practice. The underlying principle is obvious, placing the chemical as near as possible to where it is required to control seed- or soilborn pests for up-take by the underground parts of the plants. Thanks to the ideal placement of the product direct on the seed, benefits include a more efficient use of product, less environmental contamination and reduced exposure of non-target organisms. Therefore, from an environmental point of view, seed treatment demonstrates clear advantages over granules and soil spray. Particularly with seed treatments, there are advantages associated with indoor application and under controlled conditions by skilled operators, allowing the use of more sophisticated formulations and avoiding the variations caused by weather and different expertise. Two new products, the capsule suspension CS 400 of the insecticide PROMET, which shows reduced toxicity, and various suspension concentrates of the new fungicide BERET have recently been introduced into the market. Furthermore, polymer formulations are being developed as application tools to improve treatment quality.

Seed treatment customers have also a need for improved systems for handling chemical products. Although their needs are quite different from those of the large arable farmer, they share the problem of disposal of empty single trip containers which most often are being stained. In general, customers require high volumes such as 500 - 5000 litres per season, with the need for a closed system for the product to be pumped directly from the container to the seed treatment machine without dilution. Thus, a 500 litre tank for ready to use products was developed and introduced into the market.

CHALLENGES FOR THE FUTURE

Changing customer needs and increasing legislation concerning packaging waste have created the opportunity for companies to re-evaluate formulations and their packaging and encouraged industry to pay more attention to packaging waste management. This situation offers substantial opportunities for companies recognising these changes and which are able to innovate and, at the same time, prepared to accept risks to meet emerging customer needs to gain competitive advantage in the market place.

In the last ten years, much progress has been made in the design and development of new formulations and packagings to meet requirements for user safety and packaging waste reduction. In particular, compacted forms such as WG's are increasing in favour of WP's. Water soluble packaging provides improved user safety by eliminating dusting during handling of powders. It is also essential for gels offering an elegant solution for the handling of the viscous liquid, providing the farmer a pre-measured dose and leaving packaging waste which is not contaminated. Due to concerns for environmental contamination, there will be a trend to use water based instead of solvent based formulations and there will also be a move away from liquid to solid formulations.

There is a great challenge for continuous improvement. The needs of farmers are changing to low dosage, low toxicity and more environmentally friendly products and there are concerns in the public about contamination of ground water and food with plant protection agents. The challenge for R&D is to constantly search for new active ingredients which are biologically more effective and safe. Less environmentally safe products will be phased out. However, until the older products can be replaced, new safer formulations and packagings can certainly offer an intermediary solution to increase the user safety and the introduction of refillable containers will contribute to the goal of packaging waste reduction, as well as reducing user exposure when handling concentrated products. Much is to be gained from industry working together and with governments to establish performance standards in the area of packaging waste management programmes.

In terms of overall packaging strategy, CIBA-GEIGY is committed to waste reduction and improved handling safety. A prime objective is to reduce the number of one-way containers which end up in the solid waste stream. Refillable container programmes aimed at larger growers and custom applicators will contribute to the reduction of one-way packaging and associated secondary packaging. For smaller growers and also for the use of highly active compounds, the introduction of solid formulations and gels, which can be packed in water soluble film, completes the strategy base to achieve a reduction of packaging waste. We have no illusions that developing such innovative solutions and bringing them to market in a short timeframe requires substantial money and effort as well as legislative support to encourage the implementation of emerging packaging waste reduction alternatives.

CONCLUSIONS

New formulation and packaging concepts are definitely a customer need for new and more safe plant protection products. Successfully meeting customer needs is a prime requirement for marketing success and the ability to bring innovation to the market as quickly as possible, a requirement for longer term survival. Solutions have to be offered to the farmer by new products which are optimized with respect to biological efficacy, user safety, environmental aspects and economy. It is our job to maintain our leadership role in these developments and it will be the challenge for marketing to bring these products to the farmer and familiarise him with the benefits of these new technologies.

ACKNOWLEDGEMENT

We would like to thank our colleagues within CIBA-GEIGY for their contributions and for their support in preparing this manuscript.

REFERENCES

Dez, G.; Lerivrey, J.; Schneider, R.; Zurkinden, A. (1991) European Patent Application EP 0449773 A1.

Diepenhorst, P.; Lohuis, H. (1991) Warum die Formulierung der Wirkstoffe immer wichtiger wird. *Pflanzenschutz Praxis 1991*, **3**, 10-12.

Schmutz, P.; Ruess, W.; Heye, C.C.; Arenare, D.; Trespeuch, J. (1990) Effervescent tablets of TOPAS, innovative fungicide formulation technology. *Brighton Crop Protection Conference - Pests and Diseases 1990*, **2**, 537-542.

Urech, P.A. (1990) Industry's achievements in meeting the needs of society and farmers for modern plant protection. *Brighton Crop Protection Conference - Pests and Diseases 1990*, **1**, 283-292.

POLYMERIC FORMULATIONS OF PESTICIDES

P. CHAMBERLAIN

Allied Colloids Ltd., Agricultural Division, PO Box 38,
Bradford, West Yorkshire, BD12 0JZ

ABSTRACT

Novel polymer technology has been developed to
produce aqueous-based pesticide formulations. A
core material is dispersed in an aqueous phase
containing a polymer system designed to coat the
surface of the dispersion, thus stabilising it.
The core material contains the active ingredient,
either alone, with solvent or in a water-insoluble
polymer matrix.

The technique is illustrated by formulations of
chlorpyrifos and cypermethrin. Field trials with
chlorpyrifos and a pot trial with cypermethrin
clearly demonstrate improved efficacy, especially
residual efficacy, over conventional formulations.

INTRODUCTION

Concerns about pesticide safety usually involve two areas,
the environment and the user. To protect the environment there
is a general trend to use reduced levels of active ingredient.
This creates a need for formulations with improved efficacy.
To protect the end-user, safer formulations are required. Thus
for example there is a desire to eliminate solvent-based
formulations.

This paper will describe some novel polymeric formulations
of pesticides, using technology patented by Allied Colloids.
The formulations are aqueous-based, and show improved efficacy
over conventional formulations. The technique is applicable
to a wide range of active ingredients, including liquids and
low melting solids which may be difficult to formulate by other
techniques.

FIGURE 1.

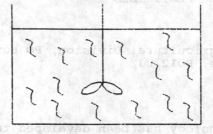

AQUEOUS PHASE CONTAINING POLYMER

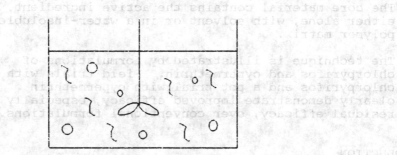

DISPERSION OF CORE MATERIAL.

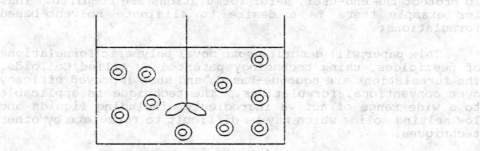

DEPOSITION OF POLYMER ON CORE MATERIAL,

AND DISTILLATION OF VOLATILE SOLVENT

(WHERE APPROPRIATE)

THE FORMULATION PROCESS

The formulation process is straight-forward, consisting of 2 or 3 stages, and is illustrated in Figure 1.

In the first stage, one or more water-soluble polymers is dispersed in an aqueous phase. The polymer system chosen may be of various types, but it must have the ability to stabilize organic droplets dispersed in the aqueous phase. Such systems include Low Critical Solution Temperature (LCST) polymers (Taylor *et al.*, 1975; Priest *et al.*, 1987). Alternatively, a coacervate-forming system may be chosen, (e.g. Nixon *et al.*, 1986).

In the second stage, a water-insoluble 'core' material is added, with high-speed shearing to the aqueous phase. The small core droplets so produced are stabilised by the polymer which deposits on the core material, forming a coating. The core material may consist of an active ingredient

a) alone (for liquids or low melting-point solids).
b) combined with a non-volatile solvent or other crystallisation inhibitor.
c) combined with a volatile solvent and a solvent-soluble, water-insoluble polymer. The polymer is chosen because of its physical compatibility with the active ingredient. In this case, the volatile solvent is distilled out in the third stage without agglomeration of the particles. The active ingredient is thus entrapped within a polymer matrix, forming a glass-like core, with a second polymer wall surrounding it. This forms a unique microcapsule/microbead suspended in water.

Applications of the technique are illustrated below.

CHLORPYRIFOS

Chlorpyrifos has been formulated by the various routes described above, using a range of stabilising polymers. The concentrations of active ingredient in the formulations have been in the range 10%-40% All formulations tested have shown an Acute Dermal LD_{50} (rat) of >2000 mg/kg.

The most interesting formulation to date is a product prepared by the distillation route, with a core of chlorpyrifos in a polymeric glass matrix, coated by a coacervate system.

Electron microscopy shows the presence of discrete spherical particles. A typical particle size distribution shows 90% < 9.0 μm and 50% < 4.5 μm.

Field trial against *Aphis gossypii* on cotton, Egypt 1991

The polymeric formulation (P) was compared with a standard commercial EC formulation. Assessments of activity were made after 24 hours and on day 3, 6, 9, 12 and 15 after spraying. The results are summarised in Table 1.

TABLE 1.   Field trial against *Aphis gossypii*.

Product	Rate (g a.i./ha)	Reduction in aphid population %	
		Initial	Residual
P	240	71	59
	360	82	66
	480	90	75
	600	98	80
EC	240	70	30
	360	80	44
	480	89	57
	600	95	68

INITIAL = 24 hours after spray, RESIDUAL = 3–15 days after spray

The P and EC formulations were equivalent in knockdown activity. Results were similar after 3 days at the highest rate after which the P formulation was better at all rates tested. No phytotoxicity was observed.

Field trial against *Bemisia tabaci* in soybean, Egpyt 1991

The trial was carried out in a manner similar to that described above. Assessments were made after 24 hours and on days 3, 6, 9 and 12 after spraying. The results are summarised in Table 2.

TABLE 2. Field trial against *Bemisia tabaci*

Product	Rate (g a.i./ha)	Reduction in (nymph+adult) population %	
		Initial	Residual
P	600	68	48
	720	76	55
	960	85	64
	1152	91	71
EC	600	62	35
	720	66	38
	960	71	43
	1152	76	48

INITIAL = 24 hours after spray, RESIDUAL = 3-12 days after spray

On this difficult-to-control insect, the P product was immediately superior to the EC, and maintained this superiority to the end of the trial at 12 days.

A second trial against *Bemisia tabaci* on cotton mirrored the results above.

CYPERMETHRIN

A 10% Cypermethrin has been formulated by the distillation route, with a core of cypermethrin in a polymeric matrix, coated by an LCST copolymer.   A typical particle size distribution of the product is 90% < 1.3 μm and 50% < 0.7 μm.

Pot trial against aphids, ADAS, 1992

Winter barley seeds (cv. Bambi) were grown in pots. Immediately prior to treatment, each pot was inoculated with approximately 50 aphids from a mixed colony of *S. avenae*, *R. padi* and *M. dirhodum*.

Pots were sprayed with the polymeric formulation or a commercially available E.C. formulation. Inoculation of the pots was repeated on days 17, 37 and 43. This technique produced very high levels of aphid infestation. Assessments of the aphid population are shown in TABLE 3.

TABLE 3. Pot trial against aphids
Cypermethrin dose = 12.5g a.i./ha

Assessment time	Number of aphids per pot		
(days post insecticide)	Polymer	E.C.	Control
0	4.0	15.0	57.5
17	22.5	95.5	165.5
37	216.0	1185.6	1856.3
43	517.5	1596.3	1325.0

The increase in residual efficacy of the polymeric formulation is clearly demonstrated.

CONCLUSION

Novel aqueous-based polymeric formulations of two insecticides have been developed. Both show improved efficacy, particularly residual efficacy, over the corresponding commercial E.C. formulations. The technique thus offers the potential of improved safety to the user, by eliminating solvents and to the environment, by reducing overall dosage.

ACKNOWLEDGEMENT

The author wishes to thank staff of DowElanco for carrying out the field trials.

REFERENCES

Taylor, L.D.; Cerankowski, L.D (1975) Preparation of Films Exhibiting a Balanced Temperature. Dependence to Permeation by Aqueous Solutions - A Study of Lower Consolute Behaviour. *Journal of Polymer Science* 13, 2551.

Priest, J.H.; Murray, S.L.; Nelson, R.J.; Hoffman, A.S. (1987) Lower Critical Solution Temperatures of Aqueous Copolymers of N-Isopropylacrylamide and other N-Substituted Acrylamides In: *Revisible Polymeric Gels and Related Systems*, American Chemical Society pp 255-264.

Nixon J.R.; Harris M.S. (1986) Coacervation Techniques In: *Development of Drugs and Modern Medicines*, J.W. Gorrod, G.G. Gibson and M. Mitchard (Eds) : Ellis Harwood.

NEW DEVELOPMENTS IN CONTROLLED DROPLET APPLICATION (CDA) TECHNIQUES FOR SMALL FARMERS IN DEVELOPING COUNTRIES - OPPORTUNITIES FOR FORMULATION AND PACKAGING.

J.S. CLAYTON

Micron Sprayers Ltd. Bromyard, Herefordshire, HR7 4HU.

ABSTRACT

The Controlled Droplet Application (CDA) of pesticides using simple hand held spinning disc applicators applying oil-based formulations at Ultra Low Volumes (ULV) of between 1 - 3 l/ha overcame a major constraint in small farmer crop protection by removing the need to fetch and carry large quantities of water to the field as required with conventional application techniques. Although the ULV technique has become widely adopted over the last 25 years in many countries, its use has been largely restricted to cotton and migrant pest control due to a lack of available ULV formulations in other crop situations. To broaden the scope of CDA and avoid formulation constraints, techniques have now been developed to also use water based spray treatments at Very Low Volume (VLV) rates of application (5 - 15 l/ha) using spinning disc sprayers. The use of water based spray treatments has necessitated the development of new spinning disc spray equipment. With recent developments in water dispersible formulations, together with prospects for better packaging, opportunities now exist to combine these developments with the logistical advantages of CDA techniques to improve safety in the use of pesticides by small farmers. The use of CDA techniques with their high work rates, ease of use and increased precision in application offers opportunities for the development of pest control programmes more appropriate to small farmer Integrated Pest Management (IPM).

INTRODUCTION

With increasing demands upon small farmers to maximise crop production it is expected that pesticide use in developing countries will increase markedly over the next few years (Hayes, 1990). Where pesticides need to be applied these products should be used as efficiently as possible and in small holder agriculture appropriate and affordable application methods are required. Traditional techniques for applying pesticides as liquid sprays (as opposed to dusts and granules) rely upon the distribution of the active material in high volumes of water, commonly 300-500 l/ha using hydraulic pressure nozzles as found on manually operated knapsack sprayers. Whilst widely used by small farmers due to their ready availability and versatility such application methods are not necessarily appropriate, particularly in semi-arid areas where water is scarce. The necessity to fetch and carry large volumes of water is labour intensive and time consuming and the sheer drudgery involved means pesticide treatments, if made at all, are often poorly applied and frequently ill-timed (Matthews 1990).

To overcome these constraints techniques have been developed to apply pesticides in minimal spray volumes allowing treatments to be made much more rapidly and with less effort. To apply minimal spray volumes efficiently requires the use of fairly uniform droplet sizes appropriate to the biological target to ensure maximum deposition at the target site and to minimise waste. This is the principle of Controlled Droplet Application (CDA) and applies not only to pest and disease control but also weed control (Matthews 1977, Bals 1978). Simple hand held spinning disc sprayers capable of producing uniform droplets of the appropriate size (which is not possible with hydraulic pressure nozzles) have been developed for this purpose.

This paper reviews the introduction of CDA techniques using spinning disc sprayers with particular reference to small farmer cotton and the requirement to develop new spray equipment in view of recent changes in application techniques. Opportunities exist to accommodate new developments in formulation and packaging to improve safety in pesticide use and these are considered with respect to the needs of small farmers.

DEVELOPMENT OF CDA TECHNIQUES FOR SMALL FARMER USE

Hand held spinning disc sprayers were originally developed over 25 years ago to apply specific oil based formulations (requiring no mixing or dilution by farmers) at Ultra low Volume (ULV) rates of application, commonly 1-3 l/ha (Bals, 1969). Finely atomised droplets are released above the crop canopy and dispersed by the forces of wind and gravity throughout the foliage. The use of such application techniques has been most readily accepted in African small farmer cotton and migrant pest control due to the ease and speed with which spray treatments can be made; typically 1 ha can be treated in 30-45 minutes with improved precision in application. Perhaps the most successful implementation of this technique occurred in francophone sub-saharan Africa where 10 years after its introduction in 1975, 97% of all treated cotton (over 1 million hectares) was protected by ULV treatments with spinning disc hand sprayers (Cauquil, 1987). The rapid development of this technique in cotton and to a lesser extent migrant pest control has been possible due to the existence of an active extension network capable of transferring such methods directly to farmers. The agrochemical industry has also played a significant role in the development of CDA spraying by providing suitable ULV formulations and actively promoting the introduction of such techniques. In other crop situations, however, ULV formulations have not always been readily available. Their generally higher costs in comparison with conventional water dispersible formulations, such as Emulsifiable Concentrate (EC) and Wettable Powders (WP's) has led researchers to examine the possibility of using water based sprays at Very Low Volumes (VLV), typically 5-15 l/ha, with spinning disc sprayers to benefit from the logistical advantages of CDA yet avoid limitations in the availability and cost of ULV formulations.

Introduction of water based spraying

The use of water based sprays with spinning disc sprayers was first used in the early 1970's (Johnstone 1971, King 1976, Mowlam *et.al.* 1975.) to reduce expenditure on pesticides and indeed this technique has been used successfully in Malawi and Zimbabwe for control of cotton pests during the last 20 years. Bateman (1989) indicated cost savings of between 18-43% were made in comparison to ULV formulations available at that time when VLV water based spraying was first introduced into Malawi, Botswana, Zimbabwe and the Gambia. Using this technique gave comparable yields of seed cotton compared with either ULV treatments or indeed high volume knapsack applications (refer to table 1). The water based VLV technique was , however, never fully adopted in other regions of Africa in part due to the success of ULV spraying which whilst initially more expensive was certainly easier to introduce (no mixing of products, measuring or calibration). Recently, however, particularly in francophone Africa the higher costs of ULV formulations in comparison with EC's together with falling cotton prices prompted a re-examination of water based treatments at application volumes of 10 l/ha. Some problems had also been experienced with control of sucking pests (aphids,mites and whitefly) causing sticky residues on the cotton fibres and there was a desire to examine alternative spraying programmes. ULV treatments in West Africa are usually made on a calender basis with 14 day intervals between applications . The onset of spray treatments is selected according to predicted upsurges in major crop pests. With water based spray programmes it is possible to select active ingredients and dosage rates appropriate to the nature and level of pest infestation hence allowing for more flexibility in spray treatments than was possible with preformulated ULV products. Trials began in 1986 in West Africa to assess water based spraying at 10 l/ha in comparison to ULV treatments at 1 and 3 l/ha.

Table 1   Comparison of Knapsack High Volume , VLV and ULV spray treatments at Makoka, Malawi. Yields of seed cotton kg/ha.(after Matthews, 1981)

Year	Knapsack	VLV	ULV
1972	1434	-	1627
1974	1435	1636	1643
1977	1500	1351	
1978	1156	1207	
1979	1286	1247	

With the use of water based treatments larger droplet sizes are normally used to reduce the effects of evaporation. This is usually achieved by increasing the flowrate to the atomiser disc. Spray passes are made every 3 rows as opposed to 4-6 with ULV treatments. Initial trials applied the same active ingredients and dosage rates at 14 day intervals for both ULV and VLV spray treatments. Results from a number of large field trials indicated that biological efficacy in controlling the major crop pests was at least comparable if not slightly better than ULV treatments.

Table 2   Comparison between ULV and VLV spray treatments in West Africa[1987-88]. Biological criteria and Seed cotton yield.- (after Cauquil, 1989.)

Country	No. of Trials	Bollworms	Aphids	Whiteflies	Mites	Yield
Benin	1	-	-	-	-	B
Cameroon	2	A,B	A,A	A,A	-	A,B
C.A.R.	1	-	-	A	-	A
Chad	1	A	-	-	-	B
Cote D'Ivoire	1	-	-	-	A	A
Mali	1	C	A	-	-	B
Togo	2	A,B	A	A	-	A,A

A - VLV superior to ULV   B - VLV equivalent to ULV   C - VLV inferior to ULV

Improved control of certain pests was observed with VLV treatments and it was considered that this may have been due to the use of reduced swath widths as more time is spent treating the crop and less variation in spray deposits will occur. The requirement to train farmers in the mixing of products and the use of higher application volumes was outweighed by the cost savings possible with the water based technique. Cost savings of between 14-33% were achieved in Cameroon with the large scale introduction of VLV spraying despite increased costs in spray equipment and batteries.Two spraying strategies have so far been adopted in West Africa. The first is the use of more frequent spray treatments made on a weekly basis with reduced dosage rates as opposed to fortnightly with

Table 3 Comparative costs of ULV and VLV spray treatments in Cameroon

Costs (CFA) *	1990/1		1991/2	
	1 l / ha	10 l / ha	1 l / ha	10 l / ha
spray equipment / ha	549	1 365	555	1 521
batteries / ha	283	966	297	967
insecticides / ha	14 306	10 899	14 286	7 756
Total costs / ha	15 138	13 230	15 137	10 244
(% saving)		(14%)		(33%)
Surface area (ha)	78 409	11 733	64 907	15 771

* (Central African Francs)   (after Gaudard 1992)

ULV treatments at full dose. The second method is to monitor pest infestation by scouting and applying pesticides only when pest pressure reaches the economic threshold. This latter method involves the much more rational use of pesticides where active ingredients are targeted only at particular insect groups although its implementation demands a high level of farmer training by extension officers. For this reason the adoption of such control strategies is not yet possible in all areas.

Table 4 Comparison of costs/ha of different spray programmes in the region
of Hamakoussou, Cameroon.(1990/91)

	CFA	%
ULV 1 l/ha (14 day interval / full dose)	16 893	100
VLV 10 l/ha (7 day interval / reduced dose)	12 437	74
VLV 10 l/ha (threshold intervention)	9 522	56

Currently a number of countries in West Africa are changing from ULV treatments to the use of VLV spraying largely due to the cost savings possible. Purchasing, for example, 1 litre of EC formulation to be made up to 10 litres with water will invariably be less expensive than using say 3 litres of a ULV formulation (despite applying the same active ingredients and dosage) due to the additional costs of using higher quantities of oil and solvent in ULV formulations. EC formulations being more concentrate can also be less expensive for transportation and being generally available from a greater number of suppliers contributes to their lower costs. This year alone it is expected that around 100,000 ha of cotton will be treated with VLV applications at 10 l/ha in West Africa.

Much of the initial development of the VLV technique used spray equipment which had been developed for ULV applications and whilst having given satisfactory biological results have suffered from a number of deficiencies. The major problems experienced have been due to high battery consumption and poor motor reliability at the higher flowrates being used. Problems have also been experienced with moisture penetration of electric motors in some older sprayer designs. Similar problems were reported during the early development of VLV spraying in Malawi, Zimbabwe and the Gambia where a number of workers concluded that improvements in sprayer design were required for this technique (King, 1976; Bateman, 1989). Moreover, spray equipment generally designed only for ULV treatments does not have the facility to select the appropriate droplet size according to the application technique in use. The choice of droplet size for ULV oil based and VLV water based treatments is quite different.

Droplet size for ULV and VLV treatments

With oil based ULV formulations which are not subject to evaporation to any significant degree, droplet sizes of 50-75µm VMD (Volume Median Diameter) have been employed to ensure adequate coverage on the crop foliage yet avoiding droplet sizes so small that they would drift uncontrollably and fail to impact on the target. Droplets of this size are, however, inappropriate with water as a carrier liquid due to problems of evaporation especially in the hot and dry climates in which they are being used. Larger droplet sizes which sediment more rapidly thus reducing the effects of evaporation are therefore more appropriate with water based sprays. However, as larger droplet sizes contain more liquid volume fewer numbers of droplets can be produced from the same volume of liquid thus higher application volumes are required to maintain droplet coverage. Figure 1 illustrates the theoretical trajectories of falling water droplets undergoing evaporation when released from a height of 1m above the crop canopy.

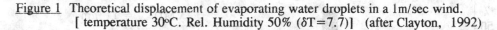

Figure 1   Theoretical displacement of evaporating water droplets in a 1m/sec wind.
[temperature 30°C. Rel. Humidity 50% (δT=7.7)]   (after Clayton, 1992)

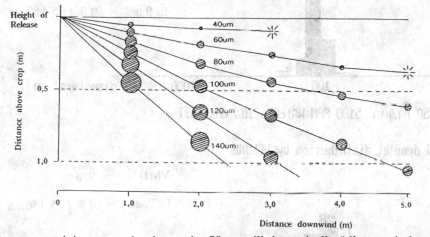

Sprays containing water droplets under 80µm will theoretically fail to reach the target unless the atomiser is lowered to a distance of 0.5m above the canopy. Obviously these sedimentation characteristics are simplified and do not take into account turbulence and convective air currents. The addition of relatively involatile constituents in the pesticide formulation will also limit evaporation to some extent but this will vary from one product to another. Overlarge droplets are wasteful as they are poorly retained upon the plant foliage and will sediment rapidly leading to reduced swath widths and thus lower work rates. For practical purposes previous research has indicated that where water based sprays are used without the addition of an anti-evaporant then droplet sizes should be in the range of 100-150µm VMD to allow for good coverage at volume rates of around 10-15 l/ha. (Picken *et. al.* 1981; Johnstone, 1971; Bateman, 1989). For these reasons new application equipment has been developed to improve motor durability, reduce battery consumption and most importantly allow for the correct choice of droplet size appropriate to the application technique .

DEVELOPMENT OF A NEW HAND HELD CDA SPRAYER

A completely new hand held spinning disc sprayer, the Ulva+ [1], has been developed

---

1   Trademark of Micron Sprayers Ltd.

to meet the demands of water based spraying at higher volume application rates as well as having the facility to alter droplet size according to the application technique, whether ULV or VLV. A new atomiser disc has been developed capable of maintaining good control of the droplet spectrum over a wide rate of flowrates and disc speeds. The essential feature of this new atomiser technology is the arrangement of small internal grooves for liquid distribution and 'teeth' which act as issuing points to control the break-up of spray liquid. Comparison of droplet spectra with the new atomiser and earlier disc designs indicates the improved control of droplet size now possible at higher flowrates.

<u>Figure 2</u>   Comparison of droplet spectra.

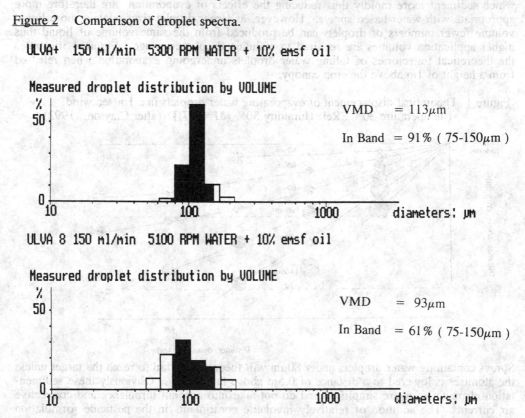

ULVA+ 150 ml/min 5300 RPM WATER + 10% emsf oil

Measured droplet distribution by VOLUME

VMD   = 113μm

In Band = 91% (75-150μm)

ULVA 8 150 ml/min 5100 RPM WATER + 10% emsf oil

Measured droplet distribution by VOLUME

VMD   = 93μm

In Band = 61% (75-150μm)

The graphs illustrate the more uniform distribution of droplet sizes with the new atomiser which should allow for greater recovery upon crop foliage by reducing losses due to evaporation of spray droplets. Droplet size is controlled by adjusting the speed of rotation of the disc by varying the number of battery cells. With the new sprayer 5 batteries are recommended for VLV treatments and 6-8 for ULV treatments. Due to disc design and motor selection power consumption of the Ulva+ sprayer for VLV treatments in comparison to earlier models is greatly improved.(1.5-2.0 watts as opposed to 5-8 watts) and consequently 3-4 fold reductions in battery use have been found; typically 1 local battery is sufficient for almost 2 hectares. This sprayer, introduced early this year, is already in widespread use in West Africa for control of cotton pests using water based sprays.Trials are also being initiated on cowpea and groundnuts. A number of improvements have been incorporated in its design to increase reliability in the field and make maintenance easier.

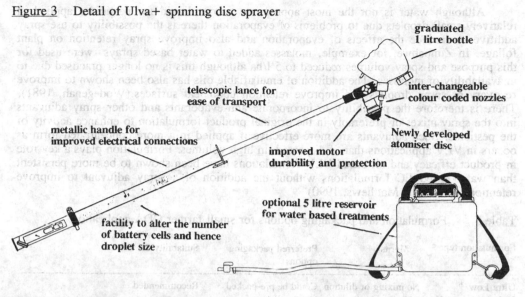

Figure 3   Detail of Ulva+ spinning disc sprayer

graduated 1 litre bottle

inter-changeable colour coded nozzles

telescopic lance for ease of transport

metallic handle for improved electrical connections

Newly developed atomiser disc

improved motor durability and protection

optional 5 litre reservoir for water based treatments

facility to alter the number of battery cells and hence droplet size

PROSPECTS FOR FORMULATION AND PACKAGING

The use of water dispersible formulations with spinning disc applicators overcomes limitations in the availability of specific ULV formulations and may be more appropriate in some circumstances. Whilst Wettable powders and Emulsifiable Concentrates have been successfully used at very low volume rates more recent developments in water dispersible formulations such as suspension concentrates (SC's), micro-encapsulation (CS's) and water dispersible granules (WG's) may also be adapted for CDA use. These offer prospects for improved operator safety by avoiding the use of solvents, reducing toxicity of products to operators and possibilities for improved product handling e.g. micro-encapsulation of organophosphate insecticides can greatly reduce the toxicity of these products to spray operators (Wilkens, 1990). Other formulation techniques such as Concentrated Emulsions (EW's), Micro-Emulsions, Gels and Tablets may also be accommodated with water based CDA treatments. The use of water dispersible formulations can allow for the use of novel products such as certain microbials or organic products which cannot be formulated in oil. Prospects exist to provide pesticides in pre-measured packs for use by small farmers which would alleviate the necessity for farmers to mix products and avoid errors in dosage rate. The need for farmers to mix products is one of the major disadvantages of water based spraying as it is recognised that the necessity to handle products is one of the principle sources of operator contamination. The provision of pesticides in disposable sachets is possible with non liquid formulations. Liquid formulations can be packed in appropriate sized containers sufficient for one application (e.g. 60 - 500ml), such as, tins and bottles although care is required over their disposal. Alternatively products can be supplied in containers with appropriate measuring and dispensing facilities to reduce operator exposure to pesticides. Figure 5 summarises some of the formulation and packaging options for small farmer CDA use. Often such formulation and packaging techniques are not yet available to small scale farmers and frequently their additional cost may preclude their use in the face of cheaper but less desirable alternatives. Product specification at local and national level may be required to encourage their further introduction. One drawback of water based CDA spraying is that it allows some of the more hazardous products sometimes used with knap-sack sprayers to be sprayed at higher concentrations. The use of such products should be discouraged if their availability to small scale farmers cannot be restricted.

Although water is not the most appropriate carrier liquid for pesticides applied in relatively small droplets due to problems of evaporation there is the possibility to use spray additives to reduce the effects of evaporation and also improve spray retention on plant foliage. In Zimbabwe, for example, molasses added to water based sprays were used for this purpose and spray volumes reduced to 5 l/ha although this is no longer practised due to unavailability of molasses. The addition of emulsifiable oils has also been shown to improve recovery of spray droplets and improve retention upon leaf surfaces.(Wodegenah, 1981). There is therefore the possibility to incorporate anti-evaporants and other spray adjuvants into the spray mixes or preferably in the original product formulation to enhance activity of the pesticide. Such adjuvants are more effective if applied in a more concentrated form as occurs in VLV applications than if dispersed in high volumes. Formulation plays a key role in product efficacy and oil based ULV formulations have been shown to be more persistent than water based EC formulations without the addition of a spray adjuvant to improve retention. (Omar and Matthews, 1990)

Table 5   Formulation and packaging options for small farmer CDA application.

Formulation type [a]	Merits	Preferred packaging options	Suitability for CDA
Ultra Low [b] Volume (UL)	No mixing or dilution required by farmers	Could be pre-packed for closed transfer.	Recommended
Wettable Powder (WP)	Low cost Widely available Non liquid	Disposable sachets/ bags	Have been widely used. Problems can occur with agglomerations causing nozzle blockage or deposits accumulating on disc surfaces.
Emulsifiable Concentrate (EC)	Low cost Widely available	Appropriate sized containers.	Have been widely used. Handling concentrate can be hazardous
Water soluble Formulations. (SL) (SP) (SG)	Low cost. Completely soluble in water.	SL-small containers SP,SG -sachets.	Suitable providing products are not hazardous in concentrate mixes.
Suspension Concentrate (SC)	Usually solvent free Small particle size	Appropriate sized containers	Have been used without problems.
Capsule Suspension (CS)	Low toxicity Slow release	Appropriate sized containers	May require adequate dilution to reduce viscosity
Water dispersible Granules (WG)	Low cost packaging Non liquid	Pre-measured packs.	Suitable providing particle size is not large $> 50\mu m$.

Notes: a. Water dispersible formulations may also include: Concentrate Emulsions(EW), Micro-Emulsions Gels, Tablets .

b. Oil based ULV formulations can also include particulate suspensions (FU)e.g. Powders,Microbials.

ULV formulations will continue to be used in many cotton growing areas, due to their simplicity in use, high work rates and familiarity of this technique by farmers, but in some regions will be replaced by water based treatments for reasons of cost. It is unlikely that water based VLV treatments will be generally acceptable in migrant pest control due to difficulties in obtaining and transporting even small volumes of water hence use of ULV formulations will continue to be the standard application method. Improvements in packaging of ULV formulations are also possible by providing products in pre-packed containers ready to fit directly to the sprayer. This would allow for a closed transfer system removing the need for operators to come into contact with products. It was always intended with the introduction of ULV spraying that products would be provided in this manner (Bals, 1969) although largely due to additional costs associated with such packaging this was never fully adopted. To achieve this requires only that suppliers of ULV products and equipment manufacturers standardise on a bottle thread fitting. The exception to this has been the development of the 'Electrodyn [2] ' system where products are supplied in a pre-packed 'Bozzle' which contributes significantly to improved operator safety when handling products (Smith, 1989). As with other application techniques this system has both advantages and disadvantages. By using the forces of electrostatics to deposit droplets on leaf foliage this avoids the need to rely upon the wind for droplet dispersal and impaction as required with spinning disc sprayers. This technique does, however, require even more specialised formulations which have so far only been developed for cotton and cowpea crops and are available from only one supplier. This has restricted the uptake of this technology to some extent (Matthews, 1990).

DISCUSSION AND CONCLUSIONS

The development of application equipment which permits the use of minimal spray volumes is of particular importance to small farmers as they can apply pesticides more quickly and with less effort. To apply minimal spray volumes efficiently requires the use of spray equipment capable of Controlled Droplet Application so that droplet size can be selected appropriate to the pest target. New developments in spinning disc sprayers now offer the choice of using a wider range of formulations and by overcoming problems associated with sprayer reliability and battery consumption, when applying water based sprays, should allow many more farmers to benefit from their use. Novel products such as Bio-pesticides also lend themselves to CDA spraying . Recent research has indicated that such techniques are highly appropriate for application of fungal pathogens in an oil dispersion for control of locust species (Bateman,1992). The prospects of using either ULV oil based formulations or VLV treatments with water based sprays may extend the acceptance of CDA techniques into other small holder crops. Despite encouraging results from field trials with spinning disc sprayers in crops such as groundnuts (Mercer, 1976), vegetables (Quinn et al, 1975), rice (Picken et al , 1981) and cowpea (Raheja, 1976) little large scale introduction of CDA techniques has occurred into these crops due in part to a lack of ULV formulations. Successful spray treatments have also been made in small farmer subsistence crops, e.g. millet, using hand held spinning disc sprayers although the costs of chemicals limited the acceptance of this technique (Jago, 1992). The use of CDA to apply water dispersible formulations may offer an alternative. To successfully develop appropriate crop protection programmes with CDA techniques will require the support of both local extension services and the agrochemical industry in providing farmer training and product recommendations. The use of CDA techniques offer the prospect of improved timing of spray treatments due to their high work rates. This is a crucial element in the successful implementation of Integrated Pest Management (IPM) programmes where often a rapid response to pest and disease infestations can avert the need for later more extensive intervention with pesticides.

REFERENCES

Bals, E.J.(1969) The principles of and new developments in Ultra Low Volume spraying. Proc. 5th Br. Insectic. Fungic. Conf.

Bals, E.J.(1978) The reasons for CDA (Controlled Droplet Application) BCPC Weeds conf

---

2   Electrodyn is a trademark of ICI Plc.

341

Bateman, R.P. (1992) Controlled droplet application of Mycopesticides: an environmentally friendly way to control locusts. Antenna, Jan pp 6-13

Bateman, R. P. (1989) Controlled Droplet Application of particulate suspensions of a Carbamate insecticide. Phd Thesis. Imperial College, London

Cauquil, J. (1987) Cotton Pest Control - a review of the introduction of Ultra Low Volume spraying in Sub Saharan Africa. Crop Prot. No. 6 Feb.

Cauquil, J. (1989) New developments in Cotton crop protection in sub-saharan french speaking Africa. ICAC Conf. Washington,USA,October.

Clayton, J. S. (1992) Une Nouvelle generation de pulverisateur portatif a disque rotatif - le Micron Ulva+ - prevu pour la protection des cultures de petits exploitants. Revue Scientifique du Chad. IRCT/ Reunion phyto. 205-213.

Gaudard, L. (1992) Les traitements insecticides du coton au Nord-Cameroun. Revue Scientifique du Chad. IRCT/Reunion phyto. , 104-107.

Hayes (1990) Global trends in Agrochemicals and seeds. U.S. Co-ops.Soc.Annual conf. Georgia, USA, March 1990.

Jago, N. D. (1992) Integrated Pest Management for Rainfed Millet in North West Mali. In. Integrated Pest Management and African Agriculture. World Bank Tech. paper No. 147

Johnstone, D. R. (1971) Droplet size for Low and Ultra Low Volume spraying. Cott. Cr. 48. 218-33.

King, W. J. (1976) Ultra Low Volume application of insecticides to Cotton in the Gambia. C.O.P.R. Miscellaneous Report N°. 27

Matthews, G. A. (1977) Cda - Controlled droplet Application Pans. 23(4): 387-394.

Matthews, G.A. (1981) Developments in pesticide application for the small-scale farmer in the tropics. Outlook on Agriculture,10,345-349.

Matthews, G. A. (1990) Changes in application techniques used by small scale cotton farmers in Africa. Trop. Prot. Man. 36(2) 166-172.

Mercer, P. C. (1976) Ultra Low Volume spraying of fungicides for the control of Cercospora leafspot of Groundnuts in Malawi. Pans Vol. 22 March

Mowlam, M.D.; Nyirenda,G.K.C.; and Tunstall,J.P. (1975) Ultra low volume application of water based formulations of insecticides to cotton. Cott. Gr. Rev. 52 560-370

Omar, D. and Matthews, G.A.(1990) Influence of formulation and spray droplet size upon the persistence of permethrin deposits on brussels sprouts leaves. Crop protection. Vol. 10. February 1990.

Picken, S. R.; Heinrichs, E. A.; Matthews, G. A. (1981) Assessments of water based controlled droplet application of insecticides on lowland rice. Trop. Pest Man. 27, 257-261.

Quinn, J. G. ; Johnstone, D.R.; Huntingdon, K.A. (1975) Research and Development of High and Ultra-low Volume Sprays to Control Tomato leaf Diseases at Samaru, Nigeria. Pans. Vol. 21 No. 4 Dec.

Raheja (1976) ULV spraying for Cowpea in Northern Nigeria PANS 22(3) 327-332.

Smith, R.K. (1989) The Electrodyn sprayer as a tool for rational pesticide management in smallholder cotton. IN Pest management in cotton. Ed. M.B. Green and D.J. de B. Lyon. SCI Ellis and Horwood Ltd. 227-247

Wilkens, R. M. (1990) Controlled release technology: Safety and environmental benefits. BCPC conf. Pests and Diseases. 1043-1052

Wodagena, A. (1980) The addition of oils to pesticide formulations. Phd. thesis. Imperial college . London.

SESSION 4C

DEVELOPMENT OF PATHOGENS FOR BIOCONTROL

SESSION
ORGANISER   DR N. E. CROOK

POSTERS   4C-1 to 4C-8

DEVELOPMENT OF
PATHOGENS FOR BIOCONTROL

SESSION
ORGANISER   DR N BERROOK

POSTERS   4C-1 to 4C-8

TECHNICAL IMPROVEMENTS TO BIOPESTICIDES

S.G. LISANSKY, J. COOMBS

CPL Scientific Ltd, Science House, Winchcombe Road, Newbury, Berks, RG14 5QX.

ABSTRACT

Although the use of bacteria, fungi and viruses to control insects represents well under 1% of the crop protection market in terms of value, a number of recent developments have improved both the products and the prospects for biopesticides. In particular, the understanding of the mode of action of *Bacillus thuringiensis* (*Bt*), the active ingredient in most of the commercial biopesticides, has increased by the application of biotechnological methods. In addition, the recent steep increase in sales of *Bt* products (up around 80% in the past three years) has been due to improvements in formulation and production which have provided ever more cost-effective products, some of which can compete directly with chemicals. New inventive products are available in 1992 based on conjugation, genetic engineering, endophyte carriers and patented formulations that put well-known and understood pathogens into insect control products for the first time. Our recent survey of the biopesticide field suggests that these developments are likely to make these biological agents into more effective insecticides and disease control agents in the future.

BACTERIA

Bacillus thuringiensis (*Bt*), an aerobic gram-positive spore-forming bacterium, remains the focus of the majority of research on biopesticides. When it was discovered, and until 1978, *Bt* was thought to be active solely against a limited range of *Lepidoptera* and these strains form the basis of a number of well known products from companies such as Abbott, Sandoz and Novo - Dipel™, Thuricide™ and Biobit™ respectively. Cheaper, more active formulations of *Btk* such as Foray™ are increasingly being used to control insects over large areas of forests.

The recent discovery of strains effective against nematodes, animal ectoparasites like mites and endoparasitic protozoans, as well as the earlier discoveries of *Bt* active against *Coleoptera*, particularly the Colorado beetle (*Btt* and *Btsd*), and before that against *Diptera* including disease-carrying mosquitoes (*Bti* or *Bt* H-14), has created a range of major new commercial opportunities - Vectobac™, Teknar™ and Skectal™ based on *Bti* and Diterra™, Trident™ and Novodor™ for use against Colorado beetles. In addition, many new products have been introduced over the past three years; more product launches are planned and it is possible to envisage a steady stream of new products based on the ever more diverse activities of new strains of *Bt*. Bactec, for example, launched the products Bernan I™, II™ and III™ based on novel patented *Bt* strains from the USDA. Field trials over several years suggested the trial product performed well; several of the products have recently received registration in the USA and additional registrations are pending elsewhere.

New products against *Diptera* include Acrobe™ launched by Cyanamid in 1991 and produced with Becker Microbial. It is claimed to have a unique aqueous formulation that can be applied with conventional ground and aerial release equipment.

The use of both genetic engineering and non-recombinant techniques are yielding novel *Bt* strains with increased insecticidal activity as well as novel formulations. Techniques such as mating (conjugation) and partial curing are used to generate strains with a novel combination of plasmids and the agricultural biotechnology company, Ecogen, has launched Condor™, Cutlass™ and Foil™, all based on non-recombinant novel strains. Although historically, non-recombinant methods have raised fewer regulatory issues than the use of recombinant DNA technology, this distinction will become of decreasing importance in the future. Another biotechnology company, Mycogen, has launched recombinant products MVP™ and M-Trak™ based on a Pseudomonad with *Bt* toxin genes incorporated. Killing the bacteria has eased fears about the release of genetically manipulated microorganisms. Recombinant technology has also been used to insert a *Bt* toxin gene into various different hosts, including *Escherichia coli*, *Bacillus subtilis*, a blue-green algae as well as into tobacco, tomato, maize and cotton plants to produce pest-resistant plants.

A novel approach has been taken in the development of InCide™ by Crop Genetics International which is scheduled to be launched in the US in 1993. The product is based on *Clavibacter xyli* var *cynodontis* CGI02, a maize endophyte incorporating a *Bt* endotoxin gene with activity against European corn borer. The endophyte rapidly colonizes the roots, leaves and stems of maize plants where it remains for the duration of the plant's life. It need only be applied in a small dosage (milligrams per hectare) as it multiplies inside the plants. The product functions only within target plants and will not survive outside it and is claimed to be environmentally safe. A range of endophytes are planned which are capable of colonizing maize, cotton, soybeans, wheat, rice and other major crops.

B sphaericus (*Bs*), once a subject for keen interest and then upstaged by *Bt* H-14 is again under active study due to its residual activity against mosquitos and blackfly. Although a number of new products were planned several years ago, none have yet appeared. However, the near future may see the introduction of Sphaerimos™, an as yet unregistered product developed by Duphar, now owned by Novo, for use against *Culex* species of mosquito which are not well controlled by *Bti*. Abbott is reported working on a species of *Bs* for control of mosquitoes in the Rhine.

Another bacterium reaching the market is the streptomycete, *Streptomyces griseoviridis* in Mycostop™, a biofungicide from Kemira. Tests suggest good control of a range of seed-borne and soil-borne pathogens including *Alternaria brassicola*, *Fusarium* on cereals, *Fusarium oxysporum* on carnation and *Botrytis cinerea* on lettuce. The bacteria releases antibiotic substances which inhibit the growth of *Alternaria* spp on cauliflower, *Rhizoctonia solani* on oilseed rape, *Pythium* spp on sugarbeet and cucumber, *Fusarium* spp on carnation, tomato and cereals, *Phomopsis sclerotioides* on cucumber and *Botrytis cinerea* on lettuce and carnation. Other bacteria currently under active study include *Bacillus pumilus* and *B. mycoides* which are being investigated for control of take-all; both worked in greenhouses and, to some extent, in outdoor trials. Strains of *Enterobacter cloacae* and *Erwinia herbicola* have been successful in reducing the incidence of *Pythium* seed rot and pre-emergence damping-off. A strain of the antagonistic bacterium, *Lactobacillus plantarum* has been found to inhibit the plant pathogens, *Xanthomonas campestris*, *Erwinia carotovora* and *Pseudomonas syringae in vitro* by researchers in South Africa. *Pasteuria penetrans* has been reported to give good control of nematodes although the organism is difficult to cultivate.

Genetic engineering may result in the improvement of other species to make them more effective against various targets. Protein engineering is being used for analyzing the molecular basis of toxin specificity to allow new types of toxin to be 'designed'.

FUNGI

Although there are several hundred entomopathogenic fungal species, only about 20 species have been studied as control agents and their commercial development has been slow due to problems of low pathogenicity, reduced viability of inoculum, differences in virulence within a pest species, production problems and constraints imposed by temperature/humidity requirements.

Verticillium lecanii was the first fungus to be commercialized in Europe for use in glasshouses but its temperature and humidity requirements made it unsuccessful for outdoor use and unreliable indoors. However, recent years have seen a new production method, new formulations and new entrants that may restore this fungus' commercial future. At present a number of commercial formulations have been registered. Mycotal™, from Koppert, controls glasshouse and cotton whitefly. The use rate is 3 kg/ha/treatment and 3 treatments per hectare are usually needed. Its companion product, Vertalec™, based on a closely related strain of *Verticillium* is used against aphids. MicroGermin™, from Christian Hansen, is similar to a combination of Mycotal™ and Vertalec™. Engerlingspilz™, from Andermatt-Biocontrol AG, is the first western commercial product based on *Beauveria brongniartii*, presently available only in Switzerland. Grown on barley grains, it controls larvae of the cockchafer, *Melolontha melolontha* at 1-2 applications of 30-50 kg/ha. Asper G™, a powder formulation of *Aspergillus* is being marketed by Shinsyu Creative G Co Ltd. Developed by University of Tokyo's Institute of Applied Microbiology, the fungus produces an insecticidal compound mellezine and is used to control the pine bark beetle *Bursaphelenchus lignicolus*. The product is buried around the base of the tree and is effective for two years.

The recent past has seen a dramatic reversal for *Metarhizium anisopliae* and *Beauveria bassiana*. Although many attempts for many years to make these fungi into viable commercial products had proved fruitless, new production and delivery methods and new formulations will see these fungi finally appearing on Western markets. It is worthwhile noting that neither research on strain selection nor improvement by direct genetic manipulation and protoplast fusion allowed these promising fungi to be commercialized. The clever trick was to find a better way to deliver the fungus to its target.

Bayer, as virtually the only major agrochemical company working on mycoinsecticides, have reported control equivalent to aldicarb with granulated fermenter 'pellets' of a wild-type strain of *Metarhizium anisopliae* against black vine weevil (*Otiorhynchus sulcatus*). The experimental use rate of 0.2 to 1 g/l would require 20- 100 kg/ha to treat the top 1 cm of soil, suggesting that the product's main use for the present will be in high-value horticultural crops. The company began marketing BIO 1020™ on a small scale in Germany in 1991.

EcoScience, a recently funded US biotech company, has developed a novel delivery technology, the Bio-Path™ chamber system. Fungal spores are suspended on upside down petri dishes and the apparatus is designed so that insects, attracted into the device by various means, pick up doses of the lethal fungus. The fungus may also be carried into insect colonies, eliminating the whole population. The idea is to use microorganisms whose activity is well known, but whose formulation and delivery has not yet been effective in practice. EPA approval is being sought for a product for use against cockroaches based on *Metarhizium anisopliae* and the company plans a number of future products based on analogous technology.

Limitations

Experience with all these products, as well as considerable research has established the following key constraints to widespread use of many of the products. Apart from production problems associated with fermentation of active preparations in a consistent way, the main user problem relates to the slow effect. For most of the Deuteromycetes it may be between five and ten days from application before effects are seen. This is often unacceptable to the user who will, on the basis of previous experience using chemical pesticides, expect to find dead insects a short time after application. Even then, effects depend on the conditions, requiring warmth as well as a suitable pH for active growth. Products may be applied as a foliar spray, or as a soil application. With foliar application the effectiveness of the insecticide is influenced by both abiotic and biotic factors. Germination may be affected by the relative humidity or in open situations the spores may be washed off by heavy rain. The spores may also be inactivated by ultraviolet light or by residues of fungicides used previously. In general, our understanding of pathogen/host interaction and the level of customer know-how are not sufficient to obtain optimum performance from fungal insecticides nor are markets likely to grow rapidly.

For those fungi which are applied to the soil major problems may be encountered due to competition between the fungal product and soil flora. This may be a simple competition for available nutrients or actual antagonism by wild type soil microorganisms. The growth of the fungi may be limited by the physical nature of the soil, with such problems augmented again by residues of previously used fungicides and other pesticides.

Marketability and consumer acceptance of these products is also restricted by the present difficulty in defining the efficacy of a preparation or to compare products, or even formulations containing the same active ingredient due to the lack of approved or standardized bioassay procedures. Common techniques include spore counts, viable spore counts, viable percentages, percentage active ingredients vs inerts, etc. None of these show anything at all about efficacy. Other restrictions on the marketability of present products include costs that are high relative to the value obtained; short shelf-lives of almost all fungal products which means the products have to be refrigerated and replaced fairly often; and the highly specific nature of the host range means each product can be sold only for specific problems at specific times. This also makes market forecasting and production planning very difficult. Recently developed products have been aimed at either very specific pests where pesticide resistance is well established or at specific environments such as glasshouse crops or other small-scale trials where their beneficial qualities outweigh their cost and nuisance value. The sales of fungi to control whitefly are likely be between $50,000 and $100,000 for some years due to the reasons cited above plus high production costs, the relatively narrow range of environmental conditions under which it will work, the high level of grower skills required, and the need for substantial product support.

Fungi are widely used for crop protection in developing countries, Eastern Europe and the former Soviet Union. It is very difficult to determine the validity of efficacy data from these countries and until recently, the quality of crop protection and the economics of use may have been different from that required in the West. If production costs are low or unknown, uneconomically high use rates may be applied or, if labour costs are low, frequent re- applications may be feasible. Lenient requirements for registration may also permit the development of 'niche' products that would be uneconomic in the West.

Fungi's future

The main requirements for future research and development include better delivery systems, strain improvement for higher levels of infection, faster kill rates, improved and lower cost methods of production through improved fermentation and improved downstream processing and formulation in order to increase the shelf life and broaden the spectrum of effect. There appears to be no reason at present to think that most of these technical limitations are about to be overcome although progress is evident in the development of specifically formulated niche products like those discussed above.

New products for the near future include an Israeli strain of *Ampelomyces quisqualis* for control of powdery mildew on grapes and apples, presently being tested by E R Butts International. *Entomophaga maimaga* kills 85% of gypsy moth caterpillars attacking oak trees and is being researched by the Boyce Thompson Institute. *Neozygites* strains for the control of spider mites are being investigated by Ecogen. A *Paecilomyces fumosoroseus* which gives 99% control against sweet potato whitefly in all stages of development has been patented by the University of Florida and W R Grace hopes to commercialize the fungus. A strain of *V. lecanii* has been field tested by the USDA to assess its efficacy for the control of soybean cyst nematodes. An Australian sterile red fungus (a Basidiomycete) has been studied in field trials to control take-all. Biotech International are developing a delivery system for the fungus which must be re-inoculated with every new sowing. The same fungus can be used for control of *Fusarium* in carnations, *Pythium* in wild flowers and *Pleiochaeta* in lupins. *Zoophthora radicans* can easily be cultured in liquid medium and attacks *Plutella xylostella* and the leafhopper which it can kill in 3-4 days.

Disease biocontrol

The number of potential biofungicides is increasing, with a number of large companies actively participating in the field. Few products are yet available commercially and the ones that have been on the market have not made much impact thus far. Although some of the claimed benefits of existing and experimental products are doubtful, the products are being sold in niche markets such as fruit trees or soilless glasshouse cropping. Two examples are Binab T™ from Binab which has been on sale in various markets for more than 10 years and F-Stop™ developed by Kodak and Cornell University and registered for sale in the US. However, Kodak is currently seeking to dispose of the product and project to another company. In general, disease biocontrol is more difficult and less well advanced than insect biocontrol.

VIRUSES

Baculoviruses have been the focus for much of the work on viral insect control. No member of the baculovirus family afflicts man or animals so they are believed to be safer than other virus families; extensive testing has revealed no adverse effects on man, animals or plants. The high specificity of baculoviruses also means that they are more environmentally friendly, attacking only one or two species of insect and having no effect on non-target organisms. Effective control of insects relies on a number of factors: the speed with which the virus kills its host and releases new viruses to infect others; the quantity of new virus released; the initial density of the pest insects and their social behaviour; and environmental conditions.

The earliest viral product is Elcar™, now made by Sandoz. New research suggests that using it on weed species early in the season reduces pests by 88-95%. The United States Forest Service has developed, registered and distributed several products for control of forest pests including Gypchek™ against gypsy moth (*Lymantria dispar*) and Neochek™ against pine sawfly (*Neodiprion sertifer*). In the UK, the Natural Environment Research Council also developed an NPV product against pine sawfly which was registered and commercialized as Virox™. The product is effective and can be used at relatively low rates against the gregarious pine sawfly. However, it is used mainly against pests on young trees so the market is small and limited. MicroGenSys (US) introduced Decyde™ for the control of codling moth (*Cydia pomonella*) on apples. Andermatt-BIOCONTROL (CH) produces three virus products for sale only in Switzerland thus far: Capex 2™ based on a granulosis virus used against summer fruit tortrix moth (*Adoxophyes orana*); Madex 2™ (for amateurs) and Madex 3™ (for professionals) based on a granulosis virus of codling moth. Hoechst plans to sell the same GV in Germany as Granupom™. In 1992 Calliope SA of France will be selling in France, Germany, Belgium, Switzerland and the UK a product based on the same virus, Carpovirusine™, and Mamestrin™, based on the cabbage moth (*M. brassicae*) NPV but also claimed effective against cotton boll worm and diamondback moth (*Plutella xylostella*).

The future

The prospects for successful commercialization of viral insecticides have improved significantly within the past few years as technical innovations begin to overcome limitations. At present, large quantities of virus are needed for efficacy. Recent work on combining viruses with conventional insecticides or insect growth regulators and the discovery of 'viral enhancing factor' should reduce the quantities needed. Production of viruses has always been expensive, using live insects either in an insectary or collected from the wild. Recent work suggests that the *in vivo* production costs may now be coming down through the use of alternative host insects with higher productivity. The InStar Division (formerly Espro) of Crop Genetics International, claims to have developed two large-scale commercial processes for the production and purification of consistent quality baculoviruses (*Autographa californica*) which are reported to be successful in field trials against gypsy moth, beet armyworm and codling moth.

Although production *in vitro* using insect cell cultures was even more expensive, these costs may also be coming down through improved fermentation methods that allow cells to be grown continuously and infected with viruses in 'fattening' tanks, and through the use of cheaper nutrients like egg yolk in place of serum. Additional improvements would lower production costs and possibly make viral products cost-competitive with many chemicals.

Use of viruses has been limited by their slow kill, allowing insects to do further damage. Now, viruses have been genetically engineered to produce enzymes or hormones to block moulting, or extra toxins such as *Bt* δ-endotoxin or scorpion toxin to add to their speed and virulence without reducing specificity. The collaboration between NPS Pharmaceuticals (Utah, USA) (formerly Natural Product Sciences) and FMC Corporation (Pennsylvania, USA) has introduced a spider toxin gene. Viruses are also particularly sensitive to UV radiation in sunlight; new formulations that encapsulate them in starch may prolong their effective field life. There is considerable scope for refinement of viral insecticides and improvements in production technology and formulation could generate significant rewards. New, faster acting, higher potency, cheap-to-produce products should be well within the capabilities of a number of companies.

TECHNIQUES FOR QUANTIFYING THE ECOLOGICAL AND PATHOLOGICAL CHARACTERISTICS OF ENTOMOPATHOGENIC FUNGAL STRAINS

D.J. RHODES, J.D. SMITH

ICI Agrochemicals, Jealott's Hill Research Station, Bracknell, Berks. RG12 6EY

J.L. FAULL

Biology Department, Birkbeck College, Malet Street, London WC1E 7HX

ABSTRACT

   In order to classify strains of entomopathogenic Hyphomycete fungi (Beauveria and Metarhizium spp.) according to their ecological characteristics and behaviour during the infection process, a number of techniques have been developed and evaluated. These include the use of in vitro assays to determine the ability of strains to grow at low water potential, fluorescent staining to track the fate of propagules during the infection process, and selective recovery of conidia from soil. When used in conjunction with conventional bioassay approaches, such techniques allow a strain profile to be assembled, based on traits which are required of a successful biopesticide.

INTRODUCTION

   Fungal strains which are to be used as biopesticides must satisfy a number of criteria. The first, and most obvious, of these is virulence towards the target pest. Strains have frequently been selected for field evaluation on the basis of virulence alone, as determined in simple laboratory assays. However, a number of other traits may be equally important in determining the performance of a given strain in the field. Recently, the upsurge in interest in biological control has led to significant progress in expanding the range of characteristics of entomopathogenic fungal strains which can be quantified in laboratory bioassays. The purpose of this paper is to discuss the use of such techniques as part of a strain selection and characterisation programme.

   Although single-dose assays may provide some measure of the intrinsic virulence of a fungal strain, more sophisticated bioassay procedures are likely to yield valuable information on dose/response relationships and speed of kill, both of which may be expected to influence the performance of the strain in the field. A tiered cascade of bioassays was described by Milner (1992) in which strains were assayed firstly for intrinsic pathogenicity, secondly for virulence as assessed by LC50, and finally for efficacy under simulated field conditions.

   Ecological parameters may also be introduced into such a screening cascade. Fungal propagules in the aerial environment may be affected by humidity, light, temperature and the chemical environment. Relative humidity appears to be of particular importance in limiting efficacy of entomopathogenic fungi (Walstad et al., 1970), although there is some evidence that fungal strains may differ in their ability to infect at low humidity, and that this may be affected by the microclimate surrounding the host insect

(Marcandier & Khachatourians, 1987). Soil physics and ecology exert a profound influence on the behaviour of fungi in the soil (Studdert et al., 1990), while the persistence of fungal propagules in the soil may differ between strains (Fargues & Robert, 1995). Attempts have therefore been made to include some measure of infectivity of propagules in soil into screening cascades (Milner, 1992).

CULTURE COLLECTION AND STORAGE

Fungal strains obtained from a variety of sources, including mycosed insects, soils and culture collections, are routinely purified on Sabouraud's Dextrose Agar, which may also be used for isolation from mycosed cadavers. The selective medium of Doberski and Tribe (1980) proved preferable for isolation of Beauveria bassiana from other sources, since it allows colonies of the fungus to be distinguished from other species. Cultures were stored at -20C, using the PROTECT bacterial preservation system. Although designed primarily for storage of bacterial cultures, this non-destructive system appears to be suitable for preservation of conidia of Beauveria and Metarhizium species, at least over the short term.

EFFECT OF WATER POTENTIAL

Despite the available evidence suggesting that moisture is a limiting factor in both infection of insects and the establishment of fungal epizootics, there have been few studies which compare the ability of individual strains to grow across a range of moisture potentials. The objective of this preliminary investigation was to assess whether techniques developed to compare the moisture requirements of spoilage and plant pathogenic fungi could be adapted in order to characterise strains of entomopathogens (Magan & Lacey, 1984).

Relative humidity is related to water potential (expressed in bars) according to the following equation (Papendick and Campbell, 1981):

$$\Psi = RT/V \ (\ln RH)$$

where:
Ψ = water potential (bar)
R = ideal gas constant (8.31×10^{-5} m^3 bar mole^{-1} K^{-1}
T = absolute temperature (K)
V = partial molal volume of water (1.8×10^{-5} m^3/mole at 4°C)

Water potential in vitro may be adjusted by addition of solutes to the medium, taking account of the effect of the major medium components. This in turn may be related to relative humidity according to the above equation. Water potential was adjusted in this study using glycerol, although preliminary experiments suggested that the threshold value for conidial germination of Metarhizium anisopliae was identical whether water potential was adjusted with glycerol, polyethylene glycol or sodium chloride. Replica plating of sporulating colonies on to a series of glycerol-amended plates of Sabouraud's Dextrose Agar, followed by measurement of colony diameter after 9 days, proved to be more effective and reproducible than the use of solute gradients or liquid media in microtitre plates.

By adjusting water potential to values equivalent to relative humidities between 94.5% and 99.5%, growth of Metarhizium anisopliae and Beauveria

<u>bassiana</u> was found to be inhibited by decreasing water potential (Figure 1). Regression analysis indicated that a water potential equivalent to between 90% and 94% r.h. was necessary for growth of the strains tested in this study (Figure 2). Use of this technique allows rapid determination of the ability of entomopathogenic fungal strains to grow across a range of relative humidity values.

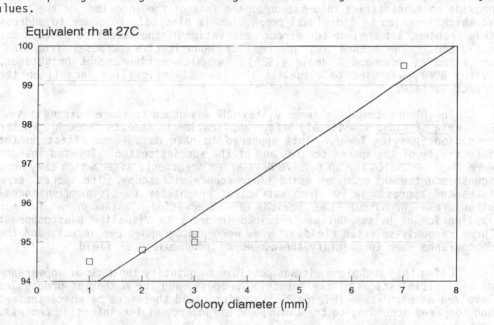

Fig. 1. Effect of water potential on the growth of <u>Beauveria bassiana</u>

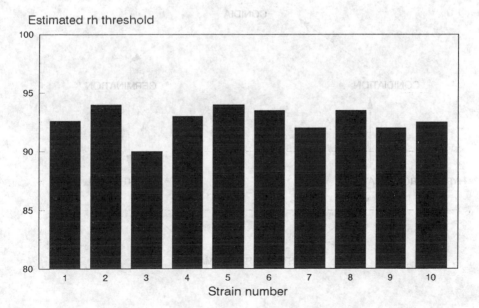

Fig. 2. Threshold water potential for growth of 10 entomopathogenic fungal strains

OBSERVATION DURING PATHOGENESIS

Some measure of the virulence of fungal strains can be obtained by determining LC50 values for a given host in the laboratory, and these undoubtedly vary between strains (Milner, 1992). However, such studies provide no quantitative information on the fate of the inoculum, or the point at which invasion by individual propagules is blocked. In order to address this problem, a technique for direct observation of the infection process was evaluated. The method was adapted for quantititive purposes from that described by Drummond & Heale (1985), in which a fluorescent brightener, Uvitex BOPT, was used to visualise the fungus <u>Verticillium lecanii</u> on the insect surface.

The fluorescent brightener Uvitex BHT was added to spore suspensions of <u>Beauveria bassiana</u> immediately before application to insects through a Potter Precision Spraying Tower. This appeared to have no adverse effect on the infectivity of the spores towards any of the species tested. Treated insects were then incubated for up to five days after treatment, after which they were squash-mounted and examined using fluorescence microscopy. The spores, germ tubes and appressoria retained sufficient brightener to distinguish fungal structures throughout the period of observation, although a further application of Uvitex BHT was required in order to visualise blastospores. Three randomly-selected fields of view were photographed per insect, and the photographs used to quantify the number of propagules per field.

Using this technique, it was possible to quantify the time of appearance of all initial stages of the infection process, and the number of propagules involved at each stage (Figure 3). Strains could therefore be characterised and compared according to the timing and efficiency of the infection process.

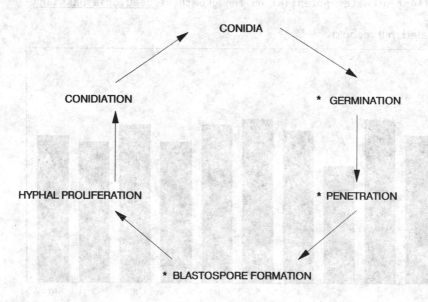

Fig. 3. Infection cycle of <u>Beauveria bassiana</u>. Stages which could be quantified using fluorescence microscopy are marked with an asterisk.

SOIL ECOLOGY

Interactions between fungi and soil are complex. The establishment of entomopathogenic fungal populations in the soil is determined by the chemical and physical properties of individual soils, as well as the properties of the fungal strain (Fargues & Robert, 1985). Characterisation of the behaviour of entomopathogenic fungi in soil is complicated by the fact that total colony counts on selective media fail to distinguish between the infective propagules (conidia) and other forms of fungal biomass. Apparent increases in biomass may therefore be due to saprophytic or parasitic growth, or simply to sporulation of hyphae.

Heat treatment eliminates hyphal biomass while retaining the viability of conidia in the soil (Harrison R.D. et al, unpublished). This allows conidiation, and the persistence of conidia in the soil, to be monitored directly. The proportion of the total propagule count which consists of conidia may vary considerably between soil samples. In field soil artificially infested with hyphal fragments of _Beauveria bassiana_, the proportion of total recoverable propagules which consisted of conidia was found to vary between 16% and 37% (Figure 4).

Use of this technique allows the behaviour of fungi in soil to be characterised and quantified in terms of rate of conidiation, persistence, soil specificity, and susceptibility to variations in the soil environment.

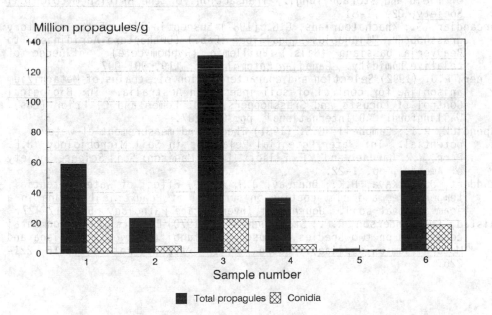

Fig. 4. Total propagule counts and conidial numbers in field soil infested with hyphal fragments of _Beauveria bassiana_.

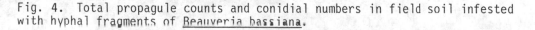

CONCLUSIONS

As the biopesticide industry grows and develops, the screening cascades used to characterise and select candidate microbial strains will undoubtedly become more sophisticated. Significant advances are being made in this field, in terms both of quantifying virulence of entomopathogenic fungi, and of measuring ecological and other properties which contribute to the efficacy of a given strain as a biopesticide. In addition to the techniques discussed here, new approaches such as genetic characterisation and multiple enzyme assays may further contribute to the efficiency of the screening process in the future.

REFERENCES

Doberski, J.W.; Tribe, H.T. (1980) Isolation of entomogenous fung from elm bark and soil with reference to the ecology of Beauveria bassiana and Metarhizium anisopliae. Transactions of the British Mycological Society, 74, 95-100.

Drummond, J.; Heale, J.B. (1985) Vital staining of the entomopathogen Verticillium lecanii on a live insect host. Transactions of the British Mycological Society, 85, 171-173.

Fargues, J.; Robert, P-H. (1985) Persistence des conidiospores des hyphomycetes entomopathogenes Beauveria bassiana (Bals.) Vuill., Metarhizium anisopliae (Metsch.) Sor., Nomuraea rileyi (F.) Samson et Paecilomyces fumoso-roseus Wize dans le sol, en conditions controlees.

Magan, N.; Lacey, J. (1984) Effect of temperature and pH on water relations of field and storage fungi. Transactions of the British Mycological Society, 82, 71-81.

Marcandier, S.; Khachatourians, G.G. (1987) Susceptibility of the migratory grasshopper, Melanoplus sanguinipes (Fab.) (Orthoptera:Acrididae), to Beauveria bassiana (Bals.) Vuillemin (Hyphomycete): influence of relative humidity. Canadian Entomologist, 119, 901-907.

Milner, R.J. (1992) Selection and characterization of strains of Metarhizium anisopliae for control of soil insects in Australia. In: Biological Control of Locusts and Grasshoppers, C.J. Lomer and C. Prior (Eds), Wallingford: CAB International, pp. 200-207.

Papendick, R.I.; Campbell, G.S. (1981) Theory and measurement of water potential. In: Water Potential Relations in Soil Microbiology, J.F. Parr, W.R. Gardner and L.F. Elliott (Eds), Madison: Soil Science Society of America, pp. 1-22.

Studdert, J.P.; Kaya, H.K.; Duniway, J.M. (1990) Effect of water potential, temperature, and clay-coating on survival of Beauveria bassiana in a loam and peat soil. Journal of Invertebrate Pathology, 55, 417-427.

Walstad, J.D.; Anderson, R.F.; Stambaugh, W.J. (1970) Effects of environmental conditions on two species of muscardine fungi (Beauveria bassiana and Metarhizium anisopliae). Journal of Invertebrate Pathology, 16, 221-226.

CONTROL OF THE MIGRATORY LOCUST, *LOCUSTA MIGRATORIA CAPITO,* IN MADAGASCAR: THE POTENTIAL FOR THE USE OF A MYCO-PESTICIDE.

R. SCHERER

Deutsche Gesellschaft für Technische Zusammenarbeit (GTZ), BP 869, Nanisama, Antananarivo, Madagascar.

R.P. BATEMAN, D. MOORE and G.V. McCLATCHIE

International Institute of Biological Control, Silwood Park, Buckhurst Road, Ascot, Berks, SL5 7TA.

ABSTRACT

The potential of a mycopesticide, based on *Metarhizium flavoviride* conidia formulated in oils, to control *L. migratoria capito*, was investigated. Although environmental factors such as ultra-violet radiation reduce conidial viability, there appear to be no major difficulties which could not be overcome. Field trials are recommended for 1993.

INTRODUCTION

The island of Madagascar, lying east of the mainland of Africa, has regular outbreaks of the migratory locust, *Locusta migratoria capito* (L. m. c.) This locust has rearing grounds largely in non agricultural land in the south west of the country but if the hopper bands are not controlled the locusts may aggregate and swarm, fly north and attack the rice producing areas. Major swarms have been reported in 1992; these are being tackled with chemical pesticides.

The Service de la Protection des Végétaux (SPV) of Madagascar, with logistical support from the Deutsche Gesellschaft für Technische Zusammenarbeit (GTZ), have a strategy for treating hopper bands in the transitional phase (as the locusts begin to gregarise) so that major swarms do not develop. The process depends on accurate scouting with a rapid response to enable ground treatment by ULV sprays of fenitrothion or dusting with the methylcarbamate Propoxua (3% D.P.). If ground treatments are inadequate aerial spraying of fenitrothion takes place. In years where only ground treatment takes place the maximum area sprayed is about 20,000 ha; this area may be at least doubled when aerial applications are used.

The International Institute of Biological Control, in conjunction with the International Institute of Tropical Agriculture (IITA) Cotonou, Benin, and the Département de Formation en Protection des Végétaux (DFPV) Niamey, Niger are collaborating on the biological control of locusts and grasshoppers. The strategy envisaged is to formulate spores of entomopathogenic fungi in vegetable or mineral oils, increasing their efficacy (Prior et al, 1988) and decreasing reliance on conditions of high humidity, and apply as a biological pesticide with conventional ultra-low volume (ULV) equipment. Preliminary work resulted in an isolate of *Metarhizium flavoviride* (IMI 330189, isolated from *Ornithacris cavroisi* (Finot) (Orthoptera: Acrididae) in 1988 in Niamey, Niger) being selected as a suitable agent for development. The isolate has a degree of specificity, being more virulent to Acrididae than Pyrgomorphidae and apparently having little virulence to non target organisms at a normal field dose.

In March 1992 a preliminary visit was made to Madagascar to explore the possibility of carrying out a major field trial in 1993. Objectives of the visit included assessing the logistics of application under the prevailing climatic and ecological conditions. This involved spray trials using blank formulation (oil without *M. flavoviride* conidia) and yellow and red tracers on transitional phase locusts.

EXPOSURE TO UV AND TEMPERATURE

Both ultra violet radiation and high temperatures are potentially limiting factors to the use of myco-insecticides (Zimmermann, 1982). In Madagascar temperatures of 55°C in direct sunlight were recorded over the mid-day period and the temperature was over 40°C for at least eight hours each day. The sunlight intensity was assessed by the use of polysulphone films (Davis and Gardiner 1982), the level of UV irradiation being expressed as an equivalent dose of 305nm monochromatic radiation in Wh m^{-2}.

The effects of both environmental factors were studied in the laboratory at IIBC. The effects of UV were assessed using an Oriel sunlight simulator and a comparison made between the level of field irradiation and the loss of conidial viability in formulations exposed to the simulator.. Formulations of oil and *M. flavoviride* were also exposed to temperatures ranging between 50-80°C for various periods of time and conidial viability assessed by germinating conidia on gelatine plates incubated for 24 or 48 hours at 25°C.

RESULTS

Chemical control of L.m.c.

Chemical control has proved successful in achieving good kill of locust bands and this is believed to have prevented the development of swarms during the previous years. The 1992 season had high locust populations and, by the end of March, 50, 000ha were treated with about 25, 000 l of pesticide. However negative environmental and social effects have occurred from past reliance on chemical pesticides. Post application assessments have shown many arthropod predators killed as well as predatory birds. In addition an important social custom amongst people of Southern Madagascar is the wrapping of the dead in silk shrouds for burial ceremonies. The Mahafaly people obtained the silk from the cocoons of two wild species inhabiting the woodlands. Spraying of locusts in previous campaigns is considered to be responsible for the decline in the indigenous silk worm numbers and the virtual elimination of the silk industry in Madagascar (Schomerus-Gernböck, 1981).

Environmental factors.

Work carried out at IIBC showed that conidia of *M. flavoviride* can tolerate short periods of very high temperatures. Five hours of exposure to 60°C failed to cause a significant decline in conidial viability and many conidia survived exposure of 70° and 80°C (Figure 1).

In contrast laboratory studies indicated that direct exposure to sunlight would be very disadvantageous for the conidia. One hour of exposure to simulated solar radiation can dramatically reduce conidial viability (assessed after 24 hours incubation). This reduction is variable according to many features such as age of the fungal culture and whether the fungus is formulated in oils or water (Figure 2). With the configuration used the exposure corresponds to an energy input of 2.358 Wh m^{-2}; this input can be exceeded in a single hour of direct exposure between 10.00-16.00 hours in Madagascar and a single day of direct sunlight would effectively reduce viability to an unacceptably low level (Figure 3).

The results indicated the marked adverse effects of both temperature and U.V. but also indicated the ameliorating effects of a suitable time of application and the nature of the prevailing, largely graminaceous, vegetation. By 15.00 hours the temperature has dropped to only mid 30's and the U.V. dose has decreased from the midday maximum greatly reducing the danger of conidial inactivation by UV.

Application Strategy

An area with locally severe maize crop damage was selected to carry out a preliminary assessment of direct droplet impingement on insects using a hand-held 'Micro Ulva' sprayer. The site was near Analatelo village (22°20' S, 43°45' W), and infested with populations of *L. m. c.* with over 12,000 adults/hectare - mostly in the transiens phase.

The volume application rate was approximately 1 l/ha (flow rate 60 ml/min, swath width 10 m.), and the droplet size 60-70μm VMD (5 batteries producing 10,000 RPM). Spraying took place at 09.40 (windspeed 4-5 km/hr; temperature 32°C, r.h. 38.7%.) A one hectare zone of open grassland (30-50 cm tall) was divided into two 70 x 70m plots and treated with two different ultra-violet tracers (lumogen and flame orange).

This whole area was treated with pesticide approximately 80 minutes later. Fenitrothion was applied with a Piper aircraft fitted with two AU3000 atomisers. Five hours later, moribund and dead locusts were recovered from the central 30 x 30m of each plot for droplet counting. A severe rain storm had occurred during the interval, however being oil-based, the droplets were still discernible with an ultra violet lamp on the following night. Results for locusts recovered in one of the plots are presented in Figure 4.

More than half of the insects examined had four or fewer droplets on them representing at best 0.8 nl of formulation, and nearly 15% of the locusts had no visible traces at all. The wings account for a substantial proportion of the droplet capture, even when the insects are stationary, and infectivity is almost certainly lower for spores deposited on these parts. In order to achieve high (>95%) mortality, secondary uptake would need to be an important means of dose transfer for at least 20% of the insects.

Secondary uptake can be of great importance in the control of locusts with chemical pesticides (Nguyen, 1980). Although the relative importance of direct contact of the spray drops and of secondary uptake from vegetation is not known with our formulation it is likely that the pathogen must contact a mobile host within 24-48 hours to be effective.

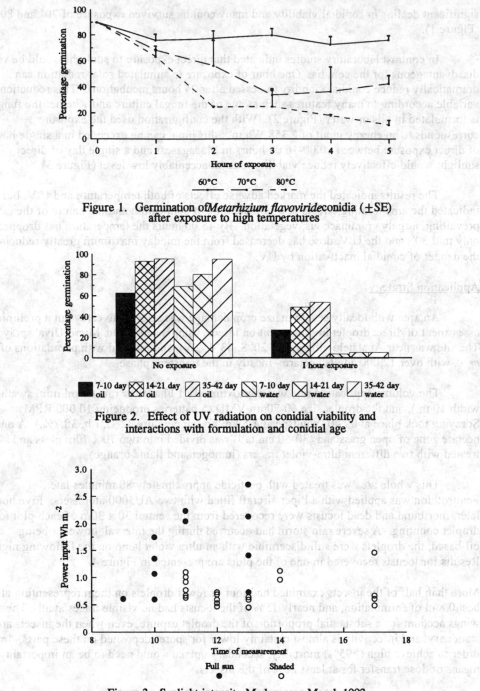

Figure 1.   Germination of *Metarhizium flavoviride* conidia (±SE)
after exposure to high temperatures

Figure 2.   Effect of UV radiation on conidial viability and
interactions with formulation and conidial age

Figure 3.   Sunlight intensity Madagascar March 1992

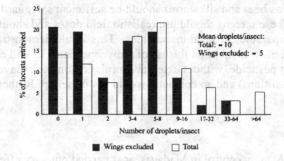

Figure 4. Droplet recovery on *Locusta migratoria capito*

Mid-afternoon spraying ensures that at least 18-20 hours pass before damaging heat and U.V. levels occur on exposed areas and even after that time period dense vegetation will provide further periods of protection. Adverse temperature effects would be unlikely as conidia on vegetation or locusts would not reach the extremes of over 50°C experienced in the open sun.

In reality the period of most danger would be during large scale applications with drums of formulation left in the sun for perhaps a week or two. These could quite rapidly reach temperatures of 50°C or more each day, leading to a reduction in conidial viability (G. V. McClatchie unpublished data). However simple measures would reduce this hazard; shading the drums from direct sunlight, allowing ventilation, using white reflective drums and using evaporative cooling should keep the temperatures down below 40°C. The conidia in the formulation would survive these temperatures for the time covering specific spraying episodes. An alternative strategy would be to store the conidia as a concentrate added to the formulation just prior to application.

Time to kill

One possible disadvantage of a mycopesticide is that kill may take 5-8 days, although certain chemical pesticides may also be slow acting (Bateman 1992). It should be noted that the disease causes a reduction in feeding and flying and hence a kill achieved in 8 days really amounts to the locusts ceasing to be active pests after 5-6 days (Moore et al 1992; E. Seyoum and D. Moore unpublished). In the present situation the problem of slow kill is greatly reduced as the control strategy is to kill locust bands in non-agricultural areas, weeks before the locusts reach the rice producing areas of the north.

Specificity

Although further testing is required it is generally true that *Metarhizium* spp. have varying degrees of specificity. With IMI 330189 the specificity appears to be significant to the family level with the Acrididae being most susceptible, other orthopteran families less so and different orders being infected only rarely and then usually under extreme conditions. *Metarhizium* spp. are notable for the lack of records of severe infections of non-target organisms. The exceptional isolates do occur, but screening of each isolate against a few important species, such as bees and silkworms should be sufficient safeguard to remove those that are non specific. These screens should use realistic field doses and should be carried out in conjunction with comparable chemical insecticides. This would demonstrate the relative safety of the myco-pesticide. In addition the use of a mycopesticide in arid conditions means that it acts like a contact pesticide, without external sporulation on the cadavers (which would occur only in humid conditions) and an epizootic would not be set up, further reducing risk to non target organisms.

CONCLUSION

The strategy of *L. m. c.* control in Madagascar is carried out very effectively but this strategy brings with it environmental problems. Replacement of the chemical pesticide with the mycopesticide would remove these problems. The results of this preliminary visit suggested no reason why the mycopesticide should not be successful and a full scale field trial is planned for 1993.

ACKNOWLEDGEMENTS

The project on biocontrol of locusts and grasshoppers is funded by the Canadian International Development Agency, the Netherlands Directorate General for International Cooperation, the UK Overseas Development Administration and the US Agency for International Development. Thanks are also due to Dr. E. Rabehevitra Rakatobe, Chef du Service de la Protection des Végétaux, Madagascar for cooperation with the initial visit.

REFERENCES

Bateman, R. P. (1992) Controlled droplet application of mycopesticides. In: *Biological Control of Locusts and Grasshoppers*, C.J. Lomer and C. Prior, (Eds.), CAB International Wallingford, pp 249-254.

Davis, A.; Gardiner, D. (1982) An ultra-violet radiation monitor for artificial weathering devices. *Polymer Degradation and Stability*, 4, 145-157.

Moore, D.; Reed, M.; Le Patourel, G.; Abraham, Y. J. and Prior, C. (1992 in press) Reduction of feeding by *Schistocerca gregaria* Försk. after infection by *Metarhizium flavoviride* (Gams & Rozypal). *Journal of Invertebrate Pathology*.

Nguyen, N.T. (1980) Insecticide acquisition by drift sprayed hoppers. *Australian Plague Locust Commission Annual Report Research Supplement, 1970-80*, pp78-85.

Prior, C.; Lomer, C.J.; Herren, H.; Paraïso, A.; Kooyman, C. and Smit, J.J. (1992) The IIBC/IITA/DFPV collaborative research programme on the biological control of locusts and grasshoppers. In: *Biological control of Locusts and Grasshoppers*, C.J. Lomer and C. Prior (Eds.), CAB International Wallingford, pp 8-18

Schomerus-Gernböck, L. (1981) *Die Mahafaly: eine ethnische gruppe im Süd-Western Madagascars*. Reimer, Berlin, 232 pages (See page 115).

BIO 1020: GRANULAR METARHIZIUM - A NEW PRODUCT FOR BIOCONTROL OF SOIL PESTS

K. STENZEL, J. HÖLTERS, W. ANDERSCH,

Bayer AG, Agrochemicals Division/Development, D-5090 Leverkusen, FRG;

SMIT, T.A.M.

Bayer B.V., Agrochemie, NL-3640 AB Mijdrecht, NL.

ABSTRACT

A mycelial granular formulation of a wildtype strain of Metarhizium anisopliae (common name: BIO 1020/Metarhizium anisopliae) has been developed for use in horticulture. The mycelial granules are mixed into the compost at planting, or potting, at an application rate of 1.0 g BIO 1020/litre soil. After application infectious spores form on the granules. BIO 1020 can be used for control of different soil pests but is especially effective against the black vine weevil, Otiorhynchus sulcatus. This pest represents an as yet unsolved problem particularly in horticulture. Trials in greenhouses on ornamentals and in nurseries on nursery stock showed the high efficacy of BIO 1020 against the black vine weevil. Incorporation of the product into the complete compost gave better control than a broadcast application to the soil surface. BIO 1020 showed activity against all stages of O. sulcatus. Plant compatibility was excellent.

INTRODUCTION

Biological control agents are an important means of pest control and can play a part in integrated pest management systems. They require specific environmental conditions and cultural practices to optimise their activity and should, therefore, be targeted first to crops where conditions are favourable. These requirements can be fulfilled, especially in horticulture with its intensive cultivation of plants.

The black vine weevil (Otiorhynchus sulcatus) is of increasing importance in horticulture in many countries, mainly in Central-Europe and North America (Schread 1972, Boehringer 1983, Parella and Keil 1984). Its preferred host plants, for example ornamentals and hardy ornamental nursery stock, are found in professional horticulture as well as house and roof gardens. Yews, 'peat bed' plants such as rhododendrons and azaleas, also grape vine and strawberries are heavily infested.

Feeding by the adult weevils produces the typical indented leaf margins, reducing the commercial value of plants. The main damage to plants is caused by the feeding of larvae on the roots and, particularly, on the stem base which results in impaired plant growth, wilting and finally the death of the plants. Curative treatments applied at the time of symptom development are often unable to prevent damage. Therefore the demand from growers for new strategies is urgent.

BIO 1020, a granular formulation of Metarhizium anisopliae, is under development for use as a biological soil insecticide (Andersch et al. 1990, Reinecke et al. 1990). This paper presents data on the characteristics and biological effectiveness of this product.

MATERIAL AND METHODS

The organism used is a strain (DSM 3884) of the entomopathogenic fungus M. anisopliae. The product (common name: BIO 1020/Metarhizium anisopliae) consists of dust free and insoluble mycelial granules of the fungus which are produced according to a patented procedure (EP 0268177A2). The granules were stored under vacuum at 4°C until testing.

For biological testing the mycelial granules (GR) were mixed in commercial compost as a soil treatment at different application rates. To ensure high sporulation rate of the fungus under unfavourable conditions, e.g. where temperatures were low at potting time, a premixture (PM) was prepared by mixing granules into the compost and incubating it at temperatures between 15°C or 25°C for 7 or 4 days respectively, until sporulation on the granules was completed. The premixture was used for potting directly after this incubation period.

All trials on biological efficacy of BIO 1020 presented in this paper were carried out with the black vine weevil, Otiorhynchus sulcatus. Dependent upon the experiment different stages of O. sulcatus were added at different times before or after treatment. The test plants were planted and either incubated in the greenhouse or placed directly outside. Plants were irrigated and supplied with fertilizer as necessary. No other plant protection agents were applied during the experiments. Efficacy was evaluated according to Abbott's formula.

Sporulation of granules was measured by extracting the spores from soil samples using a 1% (v/v) aqueous solution of Tween 80. Soil extracts were then diluted and inoculated onto a selective medium. Population density of M. anisopliae was expressed as spores (colony forming units) per gram of dried soil. The recovery rate was evaluated for each analysis.

RESULTS

BIO 1020 develops its biological activity in two steps. The first step is the formation of infectious spores on the granules after rehydration and the second is the infection of the pests after contact. Both processes are dependent on environmental conditions, mainly temperature. Soil humidity above the permanent wilting point of ornamentals is in general sufficient for the sporulation and for the infection process. In soil saturated with water sporulation is reduced.

Temperature dependency

When soil temperatures reached 15°C for several hours, more than 10^6 spores/g dried soil were produced within 4-7 days after an application rate of 1 g BIO 1020 granules/litre soil. Lower temperatures, e.g. 10°C, led to an increased time requirement for the production of spore titer sufficient to control black vine weevil. Once sporulation was complete, lower temperatures or even frost during cultivation of the plants, e.g. outside in nurseries in spring, did not influence the viability of the fungal spores. At temperatures higher than 35°C the fungus did not grow.

For the second step, the infection process, temperature was the most important factor. It took one week (at temperatures higher than 14°C) to maximal two weeks (at temperatures of 10°C or 5°C at night/15°C in the day) incubation in a premixture until first reduction of feeding activity of black vine weevil larvae was observed (Table 1). The larvae died some days later. After three to four weeks efficacy was 100% at temperatures of 10°C or higher. At 4°C the effectiveness of BIO 1020 was minimal, since at this temperature the black vine weevil larvae did not feed in treated nor in untreated compost during the incubation period of 32 days.

TABLE 1. Influence of temperature on effectiveness of BIO 1020 measured by feeding activity and mortality of O. sulcatus larvae (L2-3). Larvae were incubated in a BIO 1020-premixture (1.0 g/litre) and feeding activity and mortality were evaluated at different time intervals. Feeding activity of larvae in untreated compost = 100%.

	% feeding activity of larvae during incubation in BIO 1020-premixture at time interval (days)						% mortality of larvae at day	
	0- 5	6- 8	9-12	13-15	16-22	23-32	22	32
4°C	_a	-	-	-	-	-	0	25
10°C	106.6	30.2	20.0	22.9	0	0	17	100
14°C	37.8	21.2	25.5	0	0	0	88	100
18°C	50.3	13.1	1.4	0	0	0	100	100
23°C	18.1	17.2	0	0	0	0	100	100
5°C/15°C[b]	104.3	121.6	25.9	7.6	25.4	0	86	100
8°C/18°C[b]	101.0	12.4	0	0	34.2	0	100	100

[a] no feeding by larvae

[b] Temperature with day/night change (12h/12h)

Mobility in soil

Table 2 demonstrates the limited mobility of spores of BIO 1020 in soil. After several weeks incubation under field conditions, 95.2 to 99.2 % of the spores were recovered from the treated upper soil layer. Biological testing in separated soil layers demonstrated the lack of efficacy in deeper parts of the soil. Efficacy in the upper layers was excellent.

TABLE 2. Mobility of BIO 1020 after surface application and incubation for 4 weeks (in greenhouse pots, containers) or 7 weeks (outdoors in turf) and efficacy in different soil layers against O. sulcatus. Pots and containers were planted with azalea. Treatment and irrigation as follows:

Treatment with BIO 1020		
	Irrigation	
11 cm pot:	0.5 g/pot	30 ml/day
7.5 l container:	7.5 g/container	450 ml/day
turf:	50.0 g/m²	37 mm rainfall in 7 weeks

	layer (cm)	% spores in soil layer	% efficacy in soil layer
11 cm pot	0 - 3	97.9	80
greenhouse	4 - 7	2.1	40
7.5 l container	0 - 6	99.2	82
greenhouse	7 -13	0.4	0
	14 -20	0.4	0
turf	0 - 3	95.2	100
outdoors	4 - 7	4.8	40

Because of the low mobility the efficacy of BIO 1020 was dependent upon the application method (Tab. 3). Protective treatment either by mixing the granules into the compost or using a premixture, gave a mean efficacy of approximately 85 % (Abbott) against black vine weevil larvae. Application of the granules to the soil surface was less effective. The lower efficacy of surface applied granules in comparison to the surface applied premixture in these trials was caused by insufficient sporulation of the granules. These were placed unprotected on the surface of the potting soil and were exposed to high temperature and very low humidity.

TABLE 3. Influence of application method on the efficacy of BIO 1020 against O. sulcatus on different plants. BIO 1020 was applied at 1.0 g/l compost as a soil mix or as a top dressing treatment at an amount appropriate to the soil mix.

Plant	Site	Premix/ Granules	% Efficacy with application method:	
			mix	top dressing
fuchsia	greenhouse	GR	95	57
azalea	greenhouse + outdoors	GR	86	0
grapevine propagation	plastic tunnel	PM	76	51
balcony pots	outdoors	GR	80	26
		PM	83	52

Stage-dependent activity

Often biological measures are effective only against certain developmental stages of an insect. BIO 1020 showed good efficacy against all stages of O. sulcatus (Fig. 1), and even adult beetles were controlled sufficiently. Efficacy against eggs and newly hatched larvae was evaluated by connecting the number of larvae following 8 weeks incubation of a known number of eggs per pot. Infection of eggs by M. anisopliae was proven by microscopic examination in laboratory trials.

Fig. 1: Efficacy of BIO 1020 against developmental stages of O. sulcatus.

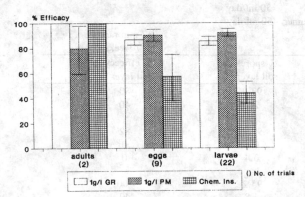

Longterm control

Spores of <u>M.</u> anisopliae survived for a long time in the soil after application. In these trials an activity period of up to 8 months, approximately one vegetation period, was achieved.

Efficacy

For the trials in greenhouses and outdoors all treatments were applied either as the premixture (PM) or as granules (GR) incorporated in the soil. Temperatures during growth of the plants were between 10°C and 30°C in greenhouses and between 5°C and 25°C outdoors. The containers were infested by natural populations or, if necessary, by artificial infestations with eggs, larvae or adults. With natural infestation the efficacy was assessed 6-12 months after treatment. Artificial infestations was carried out immediately or up to 8 months after treatment. Efficacy was evaluated one to three months later. Fig. 2 summarizes 35 trials with BIO 1020 against the black vine weevil. Plant compatibility was excellent on all plants tested so far using the recommended method and rate of application.

In the greenhouse under practical conditions BIO 1020 showed high efficacy. On azalea, fuchsia, chrysanthemum, begonia, impatiens, kalanchoe, parthenocissus veitchii, euonymus and taxus seedlings the number of larvae was reduced by an average of 80% (GR) or 90% (PM) independent of the plant species. The reduction in larvae resulted in reduced plant damage and, therefore, reduced plant loss. The level of control was more variable in cyclamen but an average of 60-70% activity was achieved.

BIO 1020 was also effective in trials under outdoor nursery conditions carried out in the summers of 1989, 1990 and 1991. On rhododendron, taxus, euonymus and in balcony pots on begonia, chrysanthemum and fuchsia 74% (GR) or 81% (PM) control of the black vine weevil was obtained.

Fig. 2: Comparison of the efficacy of BIO 1020 against <u>O.</u> sulcatus on ornamentals in the greenhouse and on nursery stock outdoors.

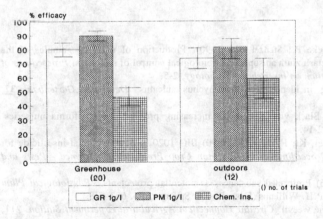

CONCLUSION

BIO 1020 is a new biocontrol product which is easy to handle by the user and, under the conditions of the experiments, showed good and reproducible effectiveness. This product offers a new opportunity to control black vine weevil in horticulture. As expected, the efficacy was better in the greenhouse than outdoors. This is due to the more favourable conditions and confirms previous experience that better results are obtained with biological agents when the environmental conditions are controlled. The premixture was 8-10% more effective than the granule treatment both indoors and outdoors because the conditions for sporulation were more favourable in the premixture.

If the plants are incubated after treatment at soil temperatures below 15°C, the product should be used only as a premix to ensure a protection. Also, for good biological activity in terms of insect infection levels, soil temperatures should not be lower than 15°C. Slow action is a characteristic of all entomopathogenic fungi; an acute, rapid onset cannot be expected. BIO 1020 needs 1-2 weeks at least to develop its full effectiveness and is therefore unsuitable for curative treatment if prompt control of a pest is required.

Efficacy after broadcast application is clearly dependent on feeding behaviour of the pest because of the limited mobility of BIO 1020 in soil. The pest must be present in the treated area e.g. when larvae feed on the stem base, or when adult beetles hide during the day in the upper soil layer. Although some control was obtained when applying the premix to the soil surface of the container, a treatment after planting can only be recommended if the root system of the plants grows near the soil surface (e.g. on roof gardens). The advantage of the immobility of M. anisopliae spores is however the long term control provided.

Like M. anisopliae in general (Zimmermann 1984), BIO 1020 was also less effective on cyclamen. The reasons are, firstly, fungistatic metabolites of cyclamen, the saponins, which are produced in the tubers (Schönbeck and Schlösser 1976) and which impair the development of the fungus (Stenzel, unpubl. data). Secondly, the larvae can migrate into the tuber, thus being prevented from contact with the fungus. Also chemical insecticides often show reduced activity in cyclamen. To ensure a sufficient fungal population at the tuber bases treatment of cyclamen with BIO 1020 should start as early as possible at the seedling stage.

For commercial reasons, particularly in ornamental plants, the absence of phytotoxis of a protection agent is an important criterion. Used correctly with the recommended application rate (1 g/litre), BIO 1020 showed no negative effects on plant growth. The rooting of cuttings was not impaired. Since some trials actually led to the promotion of plant growth, the use of BIO 1020 can be expected to produce positive rather than negative effects.

REFERENCES

Andersch, W.; Hartwig, J.; Reinecke P.; Stenzel, K. (1990). Production of mycelial granules of the entomopathogenic fungus Metarhizium anisopliae for biological control of soil pests. *Proceedings of the Vth International Colloquium on Invertebrate Pathology*, 2-5.

Boehringer, M. (1983) Increasing incidence of Otiorrhnychus sulcatus. *Deutscher Gartenbau*, 37, 698-700.

Parella, M.P.; Keil, C.B. (1984) Black vine weevil: an increasing problem for California nurseries. *California Agriculture*, 38, 12-14.

Reinecke, P.; Andersch, W.; Stenzel, K.; Hartwig, J. (1990) BIO 1020, a new microbial insecticide for use in horticultural crops. *Proceedings of the Brighton Crop Protection Conference - Pests and Diseases 1990*, 1, 49-54.

Schönbeck, F.; Schlösser, E. (1976) Preformed substances as potential protectants. *Physiological Plant Pathology*, R. Heitefuss and P.H. Williams (Eds), Berlin: Springer, pp. 653-678.

Schread, J. C. (1972) The black vine weevil. *Circular Connecticut Agricultural Experiment Station*, 211, 1-8.

Zimmermann, G. (1984) Weitere Versuche mit Metarhizium anisopliae (Fungi imperfecti, Moniliales) zur Bekämpfung des Gefurchten Dickmaulrüßlers, Otiorhynchus sulcatus F., an Topfpflanzen im Gewächshaus. *Nachrichtenblatt des Deutschen Pflanzenschutzdienstes*, 36, 55-59.

SYNERGISM BETWEEN ENTOMOPATHOGENIC FUNGI, *METARHIZIUM* SPP., AND THE BENZOYLPHENYL UREA INSECTICIDE, TEFLUBENZURON, AGAINST THE DESERT LOCUST, *SCHISTOCERCA GREGARIA*

L. JOSHI, A.K. CHARNLEY

School of Biological Sciences, University of Bath, Claverton Down, Bath, Avon, BA2 7AY,

G. ARNOLD, P. BRAIN

AFRC Institute of Arable Crops Research, Long Ashton Research Station, Bristol, Avon, BS18 9AF.

R. BATEMAN

International Institute of Biological Control, Silwood Park, Ascot, SL5 7TH,

ABSTRACT

The entomopathogenic fungus *Metarhizium anisopliae* (applied in an aqueous solution of Tween 80) and the benzoylphenyl urea insecticide teflubenzuron (applied in acetone) can act synergistically to kill 3rd instar desert locusts, *Schistocerca gregaria*. This was apparent from analyses of single dose bioassays but not from experiments involving several doses of fungus and insecticide. However, multidose bioassays with a more specific Acridoid pathogen, *Metarhizium flavoviride* isolate IMI 330184, resulted in significant synergy, when the agents were applied as a combined formulation in mineral oil.

INTRODUCTION

Persistent synthetic chemical pesticides have been used effectively in the past to tackle locust outbreaks. However, the banning of dieldrin has left a significant gap in locust control. Alternative less persistent insecticides have increased costs and reduced efficiency of control (Brader, 1988; Symmons, 1992). In addition scientific and political opinion is against the large-scale spraying of pesticides for locust or grasshopper control. Entomopathogenic fungi, particularly *Metarhizium* spp. show promise as an alternative to chemicals (Lomer and Prior, 1992). However, a mycopesticide would probably be deployed best as part of an integrated programme of measures. The particular strategy addressed here is the combined application of low doses of chemical pesticides with fungi. If the two agents act synergistically, lower doses of both may be used producing more effective and perhaps cheaper control. Benzoylphenyl urea insecticides commend themselves to this approach because; 1. they interfere with chitin synthesis in insects (but not fungi) and thus could facilitate entry of the fungus through weakened host cuticle, 2. insect growth regulators such as chitin synthesis inhibitors are specific and therefore have less environmental impact than many other insecticides, 3. We have shown previously that the benzoylphenyl urea diflubenzuron can act synergistically with *Metarhizium anisopliae* against the tobacco hornworm, *Manduca sexta* (Hassan and Charnley, 1983).

MATERIALS AND METHODS

Locusts were reared on wheat seedlings and bran supplemented with yeast as described previously (Dillon and Charnley, 1986). The fungi *Metarhizium anisopliae* isolate ME1 and *Metarhizium flavoviride* isolate IMI 330189 were cultured on quarter strength Sabouraud's dextrose agar (SDA). For bioassays involving *M. anisopliae*, conidia were harvested in 0.04% Tween 80 in distilled water from 2 week old cultures (Dillon and Charnley, 1986). Newly ecdysed 3rd instar locusts (12h ± 12h old) were immersed for 3s in suspensions of conidia in 0.04% tween. Teflubenzuron (99.5% AI) was dissolved in acetone and applied in a 1µl aliquot topically to metathoracic sternites. Controls were dipped in 0.04% Tween 80 or dosed with 1 µl of acetone. Experimental and control insects were maintained at 30º C and 100% RH for 24h after inoculation then at 30ºC and 30%RH for the duration of the experiment (5d). Fresh wheat seedling was supplied as food.

For bioassays involving *M. flavoviride*, conidia were harvested in the mineral oil ondina EL from 2 week old cultures. Teflubenzuron was dissolved also in mineral oil. A combined formulation was produced by mixing the two preparations. 1µl aliquots of single or combined formulations of the agents in mineral oil were applied to the metathoracic sternites of newly ecdysed 3rd instar locusts (12h ± 12h). Controls were treated with 1µl of mineral oil. Experimental insects were maintained at 30º C and 30%RH throughout the experiment (5d). Fresh wheat seedling was supplied as food.

RESULTS

Initial bioassays were carried out to establish the efficacy of single treatments. The LC50 for *M. anisopliae* was 7.9×10^5 conidia ml^{-1} (95% confidence limits - 1.3×10^5, 41.5×10^5) and the LC50 for teflubenzuron was 0.26 µg/ul (95% confidence limits - 0.11, 0.81).

Combined treatment - agents applied separately

Preliminary experiments showed that teflubenzuron did not significantly affect either germination or growth of *M. anisopliae* at the doses used in the bioassays. The combination experiment was carried out by applying the two agents separately, the insecticide first in acetone, the fungus next in Tween 80. There was no evidence that three replicate experiments behaved differently and thus the data were combined (see table 1).

An independent action model (as defined at the bottom of table 1) was applied to the results. The predicted mortalities are shown in parentheses (table 1). The data differ significantly from the model therefore it may be concluded that fungus and insecticide are acting synergistically.

In a second experiment the insecticide and fungus were again applied separately but at several doses. This enabled a more detailed investigation of the presence of synergy. Once again data were combined from two replicates as there was no evidence of significant residual deviance between the replicates (table 2).

TABLE 1. Effects of combined applications of teflubenzuron and *Metarhizium anisopliae* against 3rd instar locusts

	Metarhizium anisopliae	
	0	3×10^5 conidia ml^{-1}
Teflubenzuron		
0	0 (0)	17 (20.4)
0.003 µg µl^{-1}	1 (1.2)	24 (20.60)

Combined data from 3 replicates. Data are number dead out of 25.
Figures in parentheses indicate mortality predicted by the
independent action model:
proportion killed when insecticide and fungus applied together
$= (1 - (1 - p_M)(1 - p_N))$
where p_M is the proportioned killed by *Metarhizium* alone and p_N is the
proportion killed by teflubenzuron alone

Four models which might reveal synergy were fitted to this data (viz. parallel dose response curves *vs* fungus, parallel dose response curves *vs* insecticide, equivalent doses, independent action). Unfortunately in all cases the data do not deviate significantly from the model so there is no evidence to disprove the hypothesis that the two compounds behave independently.

Bioassays using a combined formulation in mineral oil

Evidence from the two previous experiments was conflicting; in the first experiment synergy was apparent in the second it was not. These bioassays were performed with isolate ME1 of *M. anisopliae*. Although this is a virulent pathogen of locusts it is also pathogenic for other insects including *Calliphora vomitoria* (Diptera) and *M. sexta* (Lepidoptera) (unpubl.; St. Leger *et. al.*, 1988). Therefore we decided to switch our attentions to isolate IMI 330189 of *M. flavoviride*. This isolate appears to have a much more restricted host range than *M. anisopliae* ME1 (unpubl) and it has proven virulence for locusts and a number of other Acridoids.

Bateman *et. al.* (1992) have shown that oil-based ultra low volume sprays containing conidia of *Metarhizium flavoviride* kill locusts at low humidity. This provides the basis for future control programmes of locusts with a mycopesticide. If combined application of fungus and insecticide is to be used practically against locusts, the two agents would be best applied together in a combined formulation (a "tank mix") in mineral oil. Before bioassays were carried out with a combined formulation, the viability of conidia in a mineral oil solution of teflubenzuron was determined. 80% viability was retained for at least 2 months at room temperature and at 6° C (data not shown).

Results of bioassays of the combined formulation of teflubenzuron and *M. flavoviride* in oil against 3rd instar locust hoppers are shown in figure 1. Since an analysis of deviance showed no evidence of differences between the three experiments the data

TABLE 2. Multidose bioassay of teflubenzuron and *Metarhizium anisopliae versus* 3rd instar locusts

	Dose of *M. anisopliae* conidia ml^{-1}			
Dose of Teflubenzuron μg μl^{-1}	0	3x10^3	3x10^4	3x10^5
0	0	-	-	-
0.003	-	2	4	10
0.03	-	0	4	10
0.3	-	6	7	10

Combined data from 2 replicates. Data are number dead out of 10 for each treatment.

have been amalgamated. In dual treatments, increasing dose of insecticide brought about a large increase in mortality over that observed in either single treatment. The approach used to test for synergism in this case was to fit separate dose response lines versus dose with and without teflubenzuron. This analysis showed that the LC50s of insecticide only and fungus-insecticide treatments were significantly different, indicating synergism. If an "independent action" model was the correct model to describe the results of the experiment (ie there was no synergy) the LC50 (the dose which kills 50% of the insects not killed by the fungus, or which die naturally) would be unaffected by the presence of the fungus; it is affected clearly so there is evidence of synergism.

DISCUSSION

The present work establishes that teflubenzuron and *Metarhizium* spp. can act synergistically to kill 3rd instar hoppers of the desert locust. The effect was more marked with the *M. flavoviride* isolate IMI 330189 than with *M. anisopliae* ME1. The effectiveness of a combined formulation in oil suggests that this approach may have practical significance. Locusts are not a perennial problem, though many grasshoppers, particularly in West Africa, are (Fishpool and Popov, 1984). Teflubenzuron proved effective against grasshoppers in field trials in Mali (Krokene, 1991), and *Metarhizium flavoviride* performed well against the grasshopper *Zonocerus variegatus* in Benin (Lomer, pers comm). From which it may be concluded that combined applications of fungus and benzoylphenyl urea insecticide may be useful for grasshopper as well as locust control.

The literature is replete with reports on the interaction between chemical pesticides and microbial pathogens against insects. However, only in comparatively few cases has synergy been shown using established statistical protocols. In most combination experiments the insecticide is purely seen as a general stressor making the insect more prone to disease. Thus it may not be too suprising that the effects of combined treatments are often at best only additive rather than synergistic.

Figure 1. effects of an oil-based formulation of teflubenzuron and *Metarhizium flavoviride* on 3rd instar locusts

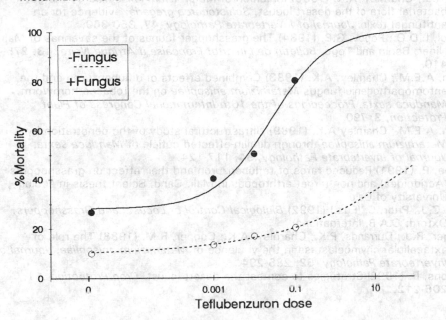

Closed circles = mortality with fungus present (3×10^5 conidia ml^{-1}) as well as insecticide
Open circles = mortality with teflubenzuron alone
Teflubenzuron concentration is in µg ul^{-1}
N = 30 for each treatment

However, in the present case there was good reason to believe that the insecticide may specifically promote invasion of the fungus by weakening the cuticle. Hassan and Charnley (1989) showed in an ultrastructural study that this was the case for *M. sexta* larvae treated with diflubenzuron and infected with *M. anisopliae*. This illustrates the value of a rational rather than an empirical approach to the choice of chemical synergist for a microbial pesticide.

ACKNOWLEDGEMENTS

We would like to thank Chris Vennard for excellent technical asistance and Dr Ray Cannon (Shell Research) for the gift of the teflubenzuron. The work was funded in part by an EEC grant.

REFERENCES

Bateman, R.P.; Godonou, I.; Kpindu, D.; Lomer, C.J.; Paraiso, A. (1992) Development of a novel field bioassay technique for assessing mycoinsecticide ULV formulations. In: *Biological Control of Locusts and Grasshoppers*, C.J. Lomer and C. Prior (eds), Oxford: C.A.B. International, pp. 255-262.

Brader, L. (1988) Control of grasshoppers and migratory locusts. *Brighton Crop Protection Conference - Pests and Diseases 1988*, **2**, 283-288.

Dillon, R.J.; Charnley, A.K. (1986) Inhibition of *Metarhizium anisopliae* by the gut bacterial flora of the desert locust, *Schistocerca gregaria*: evidence for an antifungal toxin. *Journal of Invertebrate Pathology*, **47**, 350-360.

Fishpool, L.D.C.; Popov. G.B. (1984) The grasshopper faunas of the savannas of Mali, Niger, Benin and Togo. *Bulletin de l'Institut Francaise d'Afrique Noire*, **43**, 275-410.

Hassan, A.E.M.; Charnley, A.K. (1983) Combined effects of diflubenzuron and the entomopathogenic fungus *Metarhizium anisopliae* on the tobacco hornworm, *Manduca sexta*. *Proceedings of the 10th International Congress of Plant Protection*, **3**, 790.

Hassan, A.E.M.; Charnley A.K. (1989) Ultrastructural study of the penetration by *Metarhizium anisopliae* through dimilin-affected cuticle of *Manduca sexta*. *Journal of Invertebrate Pathology*, **54**, 117-124.

Krokene, P. (1991) Reduced rates of teflubenzuron and their effect on grasshoppers (Acridoidea) and non-target arthropods in Mali. Cand. Scient thesis in ecology, University of Oslo.

Lomer, C.J.; Prior, C. (Eds.) (1992) *Biological Control of Locusts and Grasshoppers*, Oxford: C.A.B. International.

St. Leger, R.J.; Durrands, P.K.; Charnley, A.K.; Cooper, R.M. (1988) The role of extacellular chymoelastase in the virulence of *Metarhizium anisopliae*. *Journal of Invertebrate Pathology*, **52**, 285-294.

Symmons, P. (1992) Strategies to combat the desert locust. *Crop Protection*, **11**, 206-212.

OPPORTUNITIES FOR A NEW *BACILLUS THURINGIENSIS* BIOINSECTICIDE IN GRAPES

R. SENN, K. BERNHARD, J. BRASSEL, H. BUHOLZER, T. COTTI and C. FLUECKIGER

Plant Protection Division, CIBA-GEIGY Ltd., CH-4002 Basel, Switzerland

ABSTRACT

A new *Bacillus thuringiensis* (BT) bioinsecticide is under development world-wide for control of lepidopterous pests in grapes, tomatoes and cabbage. This product is based upon strain GC-91, serovar. *aizawai*. It was selected for development by CIBA-GEIGY because of its novel spectrum of activity when compared to existing *B. thuringiensis* strains.

In grapes it is used against the second and third generations of the grape moth, *Lobesia botrana* and the vine moth, *Eupoecilia ambiguella*. At the recommended dose of 100 g formulated product/hectolitre, the efficacy is comparable to chemical standards.

INTRODUCTION

In Europe, *Eupoecilia ambiguella* and *Lobesia botrana* are the major pests in grapes. *E. ambiguella* predominates in the cooler wine growing areas of Switzerland, Austria and Germany, whereas *L. botrana* is the major pest in the warmer, Mediterranean climates like Western Switzerland, Italy, France and Spain. Insecticide treatments against larvae of the second and third generation are needed to protect the grapes from losses caused by feeding damage to the berries as well as infection of the damaged berries with the fungus *Botrytis cinerea*. In the past, *Bacillus thuringiensis* insecticides were only infrequently used in grapes because of poor and unreliable efficacy, difficult determination of the proper application time and of the need to add sugar (Charmillot et al.,1991).

MATERIALS AND METHODS

The *B. thuringiensis* strain GC-91

Strain GC-91 was constructed by P. Jarrett and D. Burges (1986) using conjugation between two wild type strains, which produce delta-endotoxins with different insecticidal spectra. It produces delta-endotoxins of both parent strains and is useful for control of a range of lepidopterous pests, broader than the range of either parent. It was patented by Agricultural Genetics Company in Cambridge/U.K. from which CIBA-GEIGY obtained a sole licence. The product based upon GC-91, serovar. aizawai is now developed under the code no. CGA 237'218 and will be commercialized under the trademarks TUREX [TM] and AGREE [TM].

Apart from grapes, it has also been shown to be efficacious in cabbage (*Plutella xylostella, Mamestra brassicae, Pieris rapae, Trichoplusia ni*), tomatoes (*Heliothis armigera, Plusia spp.*), leek (*Acrolepia assectella*) and soya beans (*Anticarsia gemmatalis*) (Flückiger, 1992).

Production of test material

The product based upon GC-91 is produced by cultivating strain GC-91 by deep liquid fermentation. At the end of sporulation, the solids comprising of viable spores, parasporal delta-endotoxin crystals and inert media residues are harvested by centrifugation and spray dried. The powder obtained typically contains 1.2 % w/w delta-endotoxin (Bernhard, 1992) and is referred to as technical product. It is formulated by mixing with an equal amount of inert ingredients. The formulated product is thus referred to as WP 50.

Field trials in grapes

The product was applied as high volume spray at 1000 l/ha. Dosages were 50 - 200 g formulated product/hl. The first application was made at the beginning of egg hatching. In trials with two applications, the second application followed 8 - 12 days after the first. If not stated otherwise, 1 % (w/v) sugar was added to the spray broth as recommended by Charmillot et al. (1992). Evaluation of efficacy occurred by counting larvae on the bunches.

RESULTS

This report summarizes results of 38 tests with strain GC-91 over three years in most of the important European wine growing countries against larvae of all generations of *L. botrana* and *E. ambiguella*. Experimental data of only a selected number of typical trials are shown in this report.

In trials against first generation larvae of *L. botrana* and *E. ambiguella* only 40 - 60% control were achieved. Similar results were obtained with other *B. thuringiensis* preparations and some synthetic insecticides (Data not shown).

Efficacy trials against *E. ambiguella* and *L. botrana*

As shown in figure 1 excellent control of *L. botrana* was achieved against the second generation at 100 g product/hl. Two applications are superior to just one. Good efficacy with two applications was also obtained against second generation larvae of *E. ambiguella* as shown in figure 2. The product was also efficacious against third generation larvae of *L. botrana* in France and Spain (Data not shown).

Figure 1: Efficacy of GC-91 against the second generation of *Lobesia botrana* in Solana de los Barros, Spain 1991

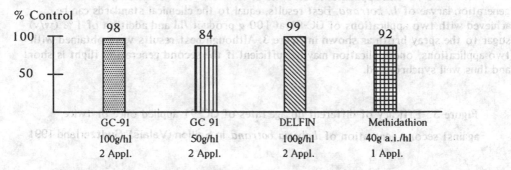

Application dates: 13.6. and 20.6. for GC-91 and DELFIN, 20.6. for methidathion
Untreated check: 53 larvae per 10 bunches

Figure 2. Efficacy of GC-91 against the second generation of *Eupoecilia ambiguella* in Eisental, Germany 1991

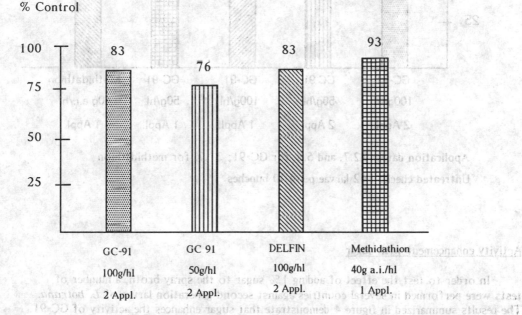

Application dates: 25.7. and 1.8 for GC-91 and DELFIN; 1.8. for methidathion
Untreated check: 20.5% attacked bunches

Dosage rate finding and number of applications

Strain GC-91 was applied once or twice at different dosage rates against second generation larvae of *L. botrana*. Best results, equal to the chemical standards can be achieved with two applications of GC-91 at 100 g product /hl and addition of 1 % (w/v) sugar to the spray broth as shown in figure 3. Although best results were obtained with two applications, one application may be sufficient if the second generation flight is short and thus well synchronized.

Figure 3. Efficacy of different dosage rates of GC-91 applied once or twice against second generation of *Lobesia botrana* in Saillon (Valais), Switzerland 1991

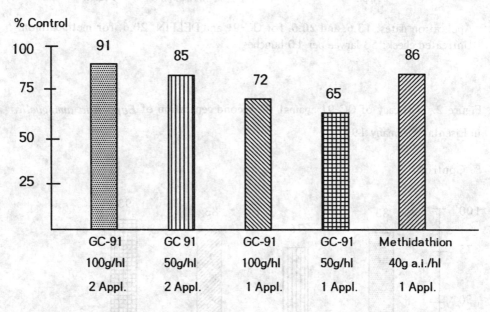

Application dates: 22.7. and 5.8. for GC-91; 31.7. for methidathion

Untreated check: 142 larvae per 100 bunches

Activity enhancement with sugar

In order to test the effect of adding 1 % sugar to the spray broth, a number of tests were performed in several countries against second generation larvae of *L. botrana*. The results summarized in figure 4 demonstrate that sugar enhances the activity of GC-91. It has to be noted however that addition of sugar did not cause a significant effect upon efficacy in all trials.

Figure 4. Efficacy of GC-91 applied at 100 g/hl, alone or with 1% sugar, in 5 trials carried out in France, Italy and Switzerland 1990 against the second generation of *Lobesia botrana*

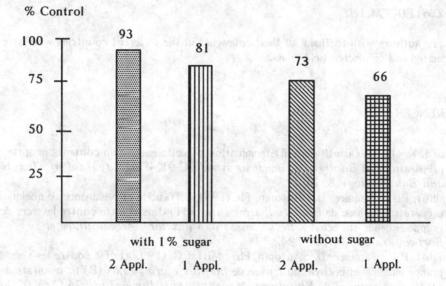

DISCUSSION

Excellent control, equal to the chemical standards against second generation larvae of *L. botrana* and *E. ambiguella* can be achieved with two applications of GC-91 at 100 g product/hl and addition of 1% (w/v) sugar to the spray broth.

In the past *B. thuringiensis* bioinsecticides were not widely used in grapes. The reason was farmer's mistrust based upon poor and unreliable control achieved with older products. Difficulties in determining the proper time of application and the recommendation to add sugar to the spray broth were also deterrents.

With GC-91, control of the first larval generation of *E. ambiguella* and *L. botrana* is 40 - 60 %. Similar results were obtained with other *B. thuringiensis* products and some synthetic insecticides. The relatively weak control is most likely due to long flights of the moths and rapid plant growth at the same time, causing rapid dilution of applied insecticides. Since damage caused by first generation larvae is generally insignificant, no attempts to control them are made in most wine growing areas.

The mode by which sugar enhances activity of *B. thuringiensis* is not well understood. Since enhancement seems to be dependent upon local factors, we recommend to follow advice by the local extension services on whether or not to add sugar to the spray broth.

In some countries farmers are required to cut the green ground cover prior to insecticide application to protect bees. This has a detrimental effect upon predator populations, and is unnecessary if GC-91 is used, which is safe to honey bees. The use of highly efficacious bioinsecticides like GC-91 is therefore also labour saving and helps implementing IPM in grapes.

ACKNOWLEDGEMENTS

The authors wish to thank all their colleagues in the different countries who have coordinated and conducted field trials.

REFERENCES

Bernhard, K. (1992) Quantitative dDetermination of delta-endotoxin contents in spray dried preparations of *Bacillus thuringiensis* strain GC-91. *World Journal of Microbiology and Biotechnology* 8, 24-29.

Charmillot, P.J. ; Pasquier, D. ; Antonin, Ph. (1991) Efficacité et rémanance de quelques préparations à base de *Bacillus thuringiensis* (BT) dans la lutte contre les vers de la grappe eudémis et cochylis. *Revue suisse de Viticulture, Arboriculture et Horticulture* 23 (3), 187-194.

Charmillot, P.J. ; Pasquier, D. ; Antonin, Ph. ; Mittaz C. (1992) Lutte contre les vers de la grappe eudémis et cochylis au moyen de *Bacillus thuringiensis* (BT) : résultats de 1991. *Revue suisse de Viticulture, Arboriculture et Horticulture* 24 (2), 109-116.

Flückiger, C.R. (1992) Resultate der Feldversuche mit TUREX (*Bacillus thuringiensis*) zur Bekämpfung von Schädlingen im Rebbau, auf Tomaten und auf Kohl. *Mitteilungen der Schweizerischen Entomologischen Gesellschaft* 65 (1-2), 197.

Jarrett, P. & Burges, H. D. (1986) *Bacillus thuringiensis* : Tailoring the strain to fit the pest complex on the crop. *BCPC Monograph* No.34 Biotechnology and Crop Improvement and Protection, Cambridge: British Crop Protection Council, pp 259-264.

NovoBtt - A NOVEL <u>BACILLUS THURINGIENSIS</u> SSP <u>TENEBRIONIS</u> FOR
SUPERIOR CONTROL OF COLORADO POTATO BEETLE, AND OTHER LEAF-
FEEDING CHRYSOMELIDAE

N.C.J. SCHMIDT
Novo Nordisk AS, Plant Protection Division, Bagsvaerd, Denmark.

G.W KIRFMAN
Novo Nordisk Entotech Inc., Davis, California, USA.

ABSTRACT

NovoBtt, a novel <u>Btt</u> strain has been developed for the
control of chrysomelid pests. NovoBtt shows a consistent
benefit over competitor strains, both in terms of percent
control, percent defoliation and window of application
when applied against Colorado potato beetle (<u>Leptinotarsa
decemlineata</u>). Examples are given on the use of <u>Btt</u>
against other chrysomelids and in modern pest control
systems.

INTRODUCTION

In 1982, a novel strain of <u>Bacillus thuringiensis</u> was discovered which exhibited activity against larvae of certain
chrysomelid species. It was designated <u>Bacillus thuringiensis</u>
ssp <u>tenebrionis</u> (Btt) (Krieg <u>et al</u>., 1983).

The original patent on <u>Btt</u> was, in November 1991, purchased by Novo Nordisk A/S, and the company now assumes all
rights and license agreements associated with the <u>Btt</u>-products.

NOVODOR is a commercial product based on <u>Btt</u> strain
NovoBtt, produced by Novo Nordisk A/S, Plant Protection
Division.

THE STRAIN

All the commercialised <u>Btt</u> strains produce rhomboidal
crystals containing one major identical protein (delta endotoxin), CryIIIA (Krieg <u>et al</u>., 1987).

TABLE 1. Mean size of protein crystals and delta-
endotoxin production yields (shakeflask trials)
produced by original <u>Btt</u> strain and strain NovoBtt.

	Mean length of crystals μm	Delta endotoxin yield PIA (BTTU/g)
Org. Btt - strain	0,7	1293
NovoBtt strain	2,3	4169

NovoBtt is a mutant obtained by classical techniques. The mutation has resulted in a low sporulating strain, producing crystals which are significantly bigger and have a higher protein content then the crystals produced by the original Btt strain (Table 1).

Activity spectrum

The activity spectrum of Btt is relatively specific within the leaf beetles, chrysomelidae (Krieg et al., 1983; Huger et al., 1986).

The most important species is the Colorado Potato Beetle (CPB), Leptinotarsa decemlineata, but other susceptible species include Alder leaf beetle (Agelastica alni), Cereal leaf beetle (Oulema melanopa), Eucalyptus leaf beetle (Chrysophtharta bimaculata), Elm leaf beetle (Xanthogaleruca luteola) and Large red poplar leaf beetle (Chrysomela populi).

Formulation

NovoBtt is presently available as a FC formulation made from fermenter solids and formulating ingredients. The lead formulation contains 3% active proteins, but in some countries a 2% formulation is available.

Mode of action

Like other Bt strains NovoBtt is a stomach poison. Upon ingestion by the larvae, the crystal proteins are dissolved by the action of the gut juices. They are proteolytically con-verted into the toxic core fragment. The toxins subsequently then bind to specific receptor sites on the midgut epithelial cells, and it is believed that the toxins now induce the for-mation of small pores in the cell membrane. As a result the cells swell and lyse (Höfte & Whiteley, 1989). The larvae nor-mally stop feeding within a few hours after ingestion and die within 2-5 days. The early larval stages (L1-L2) being more susceptible then larger instars (L3-L4).

Safety

Standard toxicological testing has shown NovoBtt to be very safe for workers, mixers and applicators. NovoBtt contains no ß-exotoxin and does not show any pathogenic or infective properties.

Ecotox studies have shown that NovoBtt is not considered to be toxic or pathogenic to mammals, avian wildlife or fresh-water fish, and NovoBtt is not considered to pose any sig-nificant risk to nontarget wildlife like aquatic invertebrates and nontarget insects.

FIELD TRIAL RESULTS

Colorado Potato Beetle (CPB)

A series of trials was carried out in the northeastern states of US during 1991 to compare different dose rates / application timings of NovoBtt (3% FC formulation) to other Bt formulations for the control of CPB. In this region resistant populations of CPB are a severe problem. Control measures include treating the field several times at high dosages at intervals of approx. 7-10 days.

Averaged across all the locations in which treatments were evaluated in at least 3 of the locations, NovoBtt exhibited a clear rate response based on percent control (Figure 1).

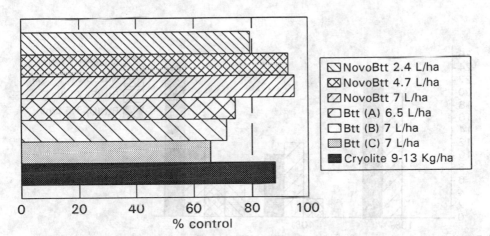

FIGURE 1. Percent control of CPB based on numbers of surviving L3 and L4 larvae. Mean of trials, US 1991.

The average yield improvement based on the trial sites where the information was given shows the best treatments to be cryolite and NovoBtt at 7 l/ha, with an average yield increase of 4,5% and 4,4% respectively.

In one trial the potatoes were planted later than normally, and subsequently experienced a very erratic and uneven distribution of first generation larvae. The larvae population was cleaned up, and a number of CPB adults were collected and released into the plots. This resulted in a very even distribution of second generation eggs throughout the plots. The various treatment were then applied at 10%, 40% and 60% egg hatch, to simulate an early, optimum and a late application scheme.

The optimum timing for Bt's was confirmed to be around 40%, but even at a late application timing, NovoBtt resulted in outstanding control of CPB compared to other Bt products (Figure 2). Defoliation data from the trial shows the same trend (Figure 3).

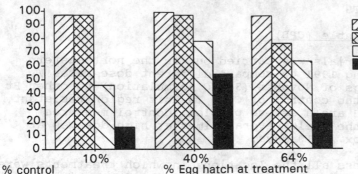

FIGURE 2. Timing Study US 1991. Control of Colorado Potato Beetle based on numbers of surviving L3 and L4 larvae.

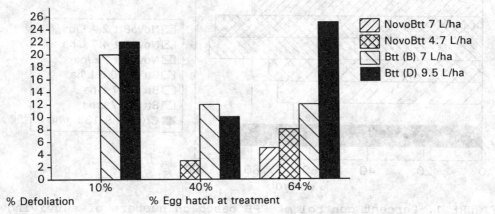

FIGURE 3. Timing study US 1991. Defoliation of potatoes infested by CPB.

All the results presented in figures 1-3 indicate, that applied at comparative dose rates, NovoBtt shows a consistent benefit over competitor formulations, both in terms of percent control, percent defoliation and window of application.

Other chrysomelids

Trials have been undertaken in Hungary during 1990 and 1991 against the Cereal leaf beetle (Oulema melanopa). The outcome of these trials have been, that NovoBtt is now under registration with a proven recommendation for the control of cereal leaf beetles in the dose rates 2 - 4 l/ha.

The eucalyptus leaf beetle (Chrysophtharta bimaculata) is capable of causing extensive damage to the eucalyptus grown

commercially in Tasmania. The standard approved chemical treatment is by using pyrethroids. The knockdown effect of
pyrethoids are much faster, but in spite of the lower effectiveness in % control recorded in the trials for NovoBtt, it
has been shown that NovoBtt is equally effective then cypermethrin in the protection of leaf area. As the aim of the
chrysomelid control is to protect the trees from leaf area loss
(and subsequent improve tree growth), the results of the leaf
area loss assessments are more important then the population
reduction data, in determining the success of each treatment.

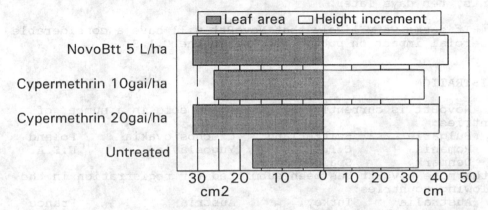

FIGURE 4. Protection of Eucalyptus from leaf beetles. Average
leaf area in cm² and recorded height increment in cm. Tasmania
1989.

USE AREAS
    The different mode of action of Btt's from that of
chemical insecticides, makes them a good tool in resistance
pest management. In the northeastern of USA, Colorado potato
beetle has evolved resistance to important insecticide groups
like organochlorides, carbamates and pyrethoids (Forgash,
1985).

    Bt's containing cryIIIA-proteins are now used as an impor-
tant tool in the resistance management strategy. There have
been no evidence of field resistance to Btt in CPB, and no
indications of cross resistance to any insecticides. On the
contrary, a recent resistance monitoring study in Maryland
concluded, that populations exhibiting a high level of pyrethroid resistance were the most sensitive to Btt. Since there is
no evidence of a related biochemical mechanism involved, it was
presumed that some fitness cost associated with pyrethroid
resistance may be responsible for the increase in Btt sensitivity (Everich et al., 1992)

    Following the Chernobyl Nuclear Accident of 1986, con-
siderable nuclear fallout affected the surrounding agricultural
land of three C.I.S. countries - Ukraine, Byelorussia and Rus-
sia. In view of the resulting impact on the land, it was
decided by the relevant governments not to add further environmental pressure, and so prohibited the use of chemical insecticides.

To protect the vital potato crop from being decimated by the Colorado Potato Beetle, NovoBtt (2% FC) were supplied by Novo Nordisk and equally distributed to the worst affected regions of the three countries. Used at rates of 3-5 litres/ha, NovoBtt gave good control in all the involved areas. For example, from one site in Byelorussia, 61% of plants were infested with 1st & 2nd instars, about 2000 larvae/100 plants (L1L2). Ten days after 5 litres of NovoBtt, there were 142 larvae/100 plants (L3L4). At another site, a 40% infestation with 764 larvae/100 plants had been reduced to 31 larvae/100 plants, ten days later.

It seems very likely that NovoBtt will have a considerable commercial impact on potato growing in the C.I.S.

REGISTRATION

NovoBtt is currently registered and sold in a number of countries:

Bulgaria	Switzerland	Czechoslovakia	Poland
Romania	C.I.S.	Yugoslavia	U.S.A.
Denmark	Spain		

Furthermore NovoBtt has been submitted for registration in the following countries:

| Australia | Turkey | Austria | France |
| Germany | Greece | Hungary | Italy |

REFERENCES

Everich, R.C.; Dively, G.P.; Linduska, L.L. (1992) Baseline monitoring of Colorado Potato Beetle Sensitivity to Bacillus thuringiensis and Associations with Pyrethroid Resistance. Resistant Pest Management, **4**, 1, pp. 14-15.

Forgash, A.J. (1985) Insecticide resistance in the Colorado potato beetle. pp33-53. In: D.N. Ferro and R.H. Voss (Eds) Proceedings of the symposium on the Colorado potato beetle. XVIIth International Congress of Entomology. Res. Bull #704, Mass. Agric. Expt. Sta., Amherst.

Huger, A.M.; Krieg, A.; Langenbruch G.A., Schnetter, W. (1986) Discovery of a new strain of Bacillus thuringiensis var. tenebrionis, effective against Coleoptera. Mitt Biol. Bundesanstalt. Ld. und Forstw., 83-96.

Höfte, H.; Whiteley, H.R. (1989) Insecticidal Crystal Proteins of Bacillus thuringiensis, Microbiological Reviews, **53**,242-255.

Krieg, A.; Huger A.M.; Langenbruch G.A.; Schnetter W. (1983) Bacillus thuringiensis var. tenebrionis: ein neuer, gegenüber Larven von Coleopteren wirksamer Pathotyp., Zschr. angew. Entom., **96**, 500-508.

Krieg, A.; Huger A.M.; Schnetter W. (1987) Bacillus thuringiensis var. san diego Stamm M-7 ist identisch mit dem zuvor in Deutschland isolierten käferwirksamen Bacillus thuringiensis var. tenebrionis Stamm BI 256-82. Zschr. angew. Entom., **104**, 417-424.

IMPROVEMENT OF A BACULOVIRUS PESTICIDE BY DELETION OF THE EGT GENE

D.R. O'REILLY

Imperial College of Science, Technology and Medicine, Department of
Biology, Prince Consort Road, London, SW7 2BB

ABSTRACT

The *egt* gene of the insect baculovirus *Autographa californica*
nuclear polyhedrosis virus (AcMNPV) encodes the enzyme
ecdysteroid UDP-glucosyltransferase. Expression of *egt* enables
the virus to inhibit moulting of its infected host. In this
study, the effect of *egt* on the growth and development of
infected insects has been investigated. These studies revealed
that, since insects normally stop feeding during ecdysis,
expression of *egt* prevents the insect from experiencing this
feeding arrest. Thus, *egt* functions to prolong the length of
time the insect feeds after infection, with a resultant increase
in the weight gain of the insect. Deletion of the *egt* gene
significantly improves the pesticide characteristics of AcMNPV.
Larvae infected with an *egt* deletion mutant display considerably
reduced feeding and earlier mortality than wild-type
AcMNPV-infected larvae.

INTRODUCTION

Insect baculoviruses have been used for the control of several insect
pests (Entwistle & Evans, 1985), and are considered to have great potential
as environmentally benign biological control agents. In general,
baculoviruses infect only arthropods, and individual virus strains infect
only one or a limited number of species (Gröner, 1986). They are not known
to infect mammals, other vertebrates, or any plant species. Despite these
attractive features, the more widespread commercial application of
baculoviruses has been limited for a number of reasons. The length of time
taken to kill the infected insect is particularly problematic; depending on
the strain of virus and the pest species, it may take from several days to
weeks before the infected insect at least ceases feeding. During this
period the insect pest can cause serious damage to the crop. There is
currently intense interest in the possibility of reducing this lag before
feeding arrest by genetic engineering means. A variety of strategies have
been proposed, all based on the concept of engineering the virus to express
new genes which are deleterious to the insect. Genes which have been tested
so far include genes encoding insect-specific toxins, such as *Butheus
eupeus* insect toxin-1 (Carbonell *et al.*, 1988), *Bacillus thuringiensis*
endotoxin (Martens *et al.*, 1990; Merryweather *et al.*, 1990) and the
insect-specific neurotoxin of the straw itch mite (Tomalski & Miller,
1991). In addition, several groups are investigating the potential of
disrupting hormonal regulation by expressing genes such as diuretic hormone
(Maeda, 1989), eclosion hormone (Eldridge *et al.*, 1991), and juvenile
hormone esterase (Eldridge *et al.*, 1992; Hammock *et al.*, 1990).

The *egt* gene of the baculovirus AcMNPV encodes an enzyme known as
ecdysteroid UDP-glucosyltransferase (EGT) (O'Reilly & Miller, 1989). This

enzyme, which is secreted into the haemolymph of infected insects, catalyses the conjugation of ecdysteroids (insect moulting hormones) with glucose or galactose (O'Reilly *et al.*, 1992). The sugar group is attached to the hydroxyl group at position C22 of the ecdysteroid molecule (O'Reilly *et al.*, 1991). The release of ecdysteroids into the haemolymph is the principal trigger for ecdysis. During infection by AcMNPV, EGT circulating in the haemolymph prevents the accumulation of high levels of ecdysteroids, and moulting or metamorphosis of the infected host is prevented (O'Reilly *et al.*, 1992; O'Reilly & Miller, 1989).

In this study, the effects of *egt* expression on the growth and development of infected insects have been characterized. These data reveal that, through the expression of *egt*, AcMNPV ensures that the host insect continues to feed after infection. Thus, the lag time before feeding cessation is actively prolonged by the virus, presumably to facilitate its own propagation. Consequently, the pesticidal properties of AcMNPV can be improved simply by deleting the *egt* gene and impairing the ability of the virus to lengthen feeding of the infected insect. This approach contrasts with other strategies for the improvement of baculovirus pesticides in that it does not involve the insertion of foreign DNA into the virus. These data have been discussed in more detail in O'Reilly & Miller (1991).

INSECT GROWTH AND DEVELOPMENT FOLLOWING INFECTION

To investigate the effects of *egt* expression on the growth and development of infected insects, *Spodoptera frugiperda* larvae were infected by injection with wild-type (wt) AcMNPV or with a recombinant AcMNPV in which the *egt* gene had been destroyed by genetic engineering (O'Reilly & Miller, 1990). Groups of 30 insects were infected approximately 24 hours after ecdysis into the 6th (final) larval instar, and their growth and development were monitored daily. The infected insects were compared to control insects which had been injected with tissue culture fluid containing no virus. The mean weights of the insects are presented in Fig. 1. As expected, the control insects fed and gained weight extensively for the first 2-3 days, but then displayed a dramatic weight loss during the wandering phase preceding pupation. All these insects pupated from 5 to 6 days post-infection (p.i.). The insects infected by the *egt⁻* virus also stopped feeding and displayed significant weight loss after 2 days p.i. These insects developed to a pharate pupal stage but they all died before completing the pupal moult. In contrast, because of the expression of *egt*, none of the wt-infected insects initiated wandering behaviour or stopped feeding. Instead they gained weight until 4 days p.i. and continued to feed until shortly before death. Some of these wt-infected insects attained weights significantly larger than those normally observed in uninfected insects. Similar observations were made with insects infected at the beginning of the penultimate instar. In addition, in both instars, the insects infected with the *egt⁻* virus displayed earlier mortality. Thus, infection by a virus lacking *egt* in either 5th or 6th instar results in reduced feeding and more rapid death of the infected insects.

BIOASSAY IN NEONATE LARVAE

The data presented in Fig. 1 were obtained following injection of 6th instar insects with non-occluded virus prepared in cell culture. We have also compared the virulence and infectivity of wt and *egt⁻* AcMNPV following

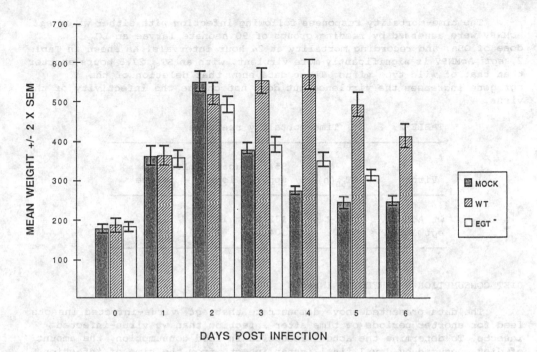

Figure 1. Daily mean weights +/- 2X SEM of control insects (mock) compared to insects infected with wt or egt⁻ AcMNPV.

per os infection of neonate insects with viral occlusion bodies (OBs). For the dose-mortality studies, groups of 60 insects were fed artificial diet containing different concentrations of viral OBs. After 24 hours, the insects were transferred to virus-free diet, and the mortality

TABLE 1.   Dose-mortality response

| Virus | LC_{50}[a] | 95% fiducal limits | | slope |
		upper	lower	
wt AcMNPV	1.42	2.67	0.79	1.59
egt⁻ AcMNPV	2.39	3.75	1.63	0.84

[a] OBs x 10^{-6}/ml of infected diet

at each dose was recorded 9 days later. The data obtained are presented in Table 1. It can be seen from these data that the LC_{50}s of the two viruses do not differ significantly.

The time-mortality responses following infection with either wt or *egt*⁻ AcMNPV were assessed by feeding groups of 90 neonate larvae an LC_{95} dose of OBs, and recording mortality at 24 hour intervals. As shown in Table 2, *egt*⁻ AcMNPV is significantly more virulent, with an ST_{50} 27.5 hours shorter than that of wild-type virus. These data show that deletion of the *egt* gene increases the virulence but does not change the infectivity of the virus.

TABLE 2.   Time-mortality response

Virus	ST_{50}(h)	95% fiducal limits upper	lower	slope
wt AcMNPV	127.2	132.0	122.6	11.5
egt⁻ AcMNPV	99.7	104.1	95.6	9.6

DIET CONSUMPTION BY INFECTED INSECTS

The data presented above demonstrate that *egt*⁻ virus-infected insects feed for shorter periods of time after infection than wt virus-infected insects. To determine the actual reduction in food consumption, the amount of diet consumed by day 1 final instar insects from the time of infection until death was measured. The mean dry weight of diet consumed by insects infected by wt AcMNPV was 402 ± 133 mg. In comparison, *egt*⁻ AcMNPV-infected insects consumed 287 ± 88 mg. This difference was highly significant (p = 0.01) by the Mann-Whitney Wilcoxon test. As expected from the weight gain studies (Fig. 1) there was no significant difference between the amount of food consumed by *egt*⁻ AcMNPV-infected and mock-infected insects (286 ± 79 mg) during this time. These data demonstrate that wt-infected insects consume approximately 40% more diet than insects infected with an *egt*⁻ virus.

CONCLUSIONS

This study demonstrates that *egt* expression by the baculovirus AcMNPV, through the inhibition of ecdysis, maintains the insect in an actively feeding state during infection. From a virological point of view, a critical question is why AcMNPV expresses an *egt* gene. We have found that the prolonged feeding due to *egt* results in an increase of approximately 30% in the yield of progeny OBs per infected insect (O'Reilly & Miller, 1991). Such an increase could certainly confer a selective advantage on the virus. However, these data were obtained in controlled laboratory settings with developmentally synchronous insects which were infected with large virus doses. It remains to be seen whether *egt* expression increases virus yield to the same extent in a field situation, where all these parameters will be highly variable. Other effects of *egt* expression may also be important to the virus. For example, insects which normally leave the host plant to pupate will not do so following infection with an *egt*⁺ baculovirus. Such a behavioural change could be of considerable importance in facilitating the spread of the virus in the field.

Our data show that *egt* deletion accelerates the virus-induced mortality and reduces the insect feeding period (up to 3 to 5 days shorter in 6th instar; Fig. 1). Measurements of the amount of food consumed by the infected insects indicates that, in 6th instar, the prolongation of feeding by wt AcMNPV causes a 40% increase in the amount of diet consumed. This is in good agreement with previous data on food consumption by baculovirus-infected insects (Subrahmanyam & Ramakrishnan, 1981) which also noted that feeding continued until death, and that infected insects consumed more than uninfected controls.

The results presented in this study demonstrate that the pesticidal properties of a baculovirus can be improved simply by deletion of a gene. This represents a novel approach to the engineering of improved baculovirus pesticides, and contrasts with other strategies, all of which have involved the expression of some foreign gene. One of the safety concerns with the generation of recombinant viral pesticides is that introduction of a foreign gene will alter their properties in some undesirable way. We expect therefore, that *egt⁻* baculoviruses will be more easily registered by pesticide regulatory agencies as genetically improved viral pesticides.

ACKNOWLEDGEMENTS

S. frugiperda eggs were kindly provided by D. Perkins (USDA; Tifton, Georgia). This work was supported in part by Public Health Service grant AI 23719 from the National Institute of Allergy and Infectious Disease to Lois K. Miller (University of Georgia, Athens, Georgia).

REFERENCES

Carbonell, L.F.; Hodge, M.R.; Tomalski, M.D.; Miller, L.K. (1988) Synthesis of a gene coding for an insect-specific scorpion neurotoxin and attempts to express it using baculovirus vectors. *Gene*, 73, 409-418.

Eldridge, R.; Horodyski, F.M.; Morton, D.B.; O'Reilly, D.R.; Truman, J.W.; Riddiford, L.M.; Miller, L.K. (1991) Expression of an eclosion hormone gene in insect cells using baculovirus vectors. *Insect Biochemistry*, 21, 341-351.

Eldridge, R.; O'Reilly, D.R.; Hammock, B.D.; Miller, L.K. (1992) Insecticidal properties of genetically engineered baculoviruses expressing an insect juvenile hormone esterase gene. *Applied and Environmental Microbiology*, 58, 1583-1591.

Entwistle, P.F.; Evans, H.F. (1985) Viral Control. In: *Comprehensive Insect Physiology, Biochemistry and Pharmacology, Vol. 12*, G.A. Kerkut and L.I. Gilbert (Eds), Oxford: Pergamon Press, pp. 347-412.

Gröner, A. (1986) Specificity and safety of baculoviruses. In: *The Biology of Baculoviruses. Vol. I*, R.R. Granados and B.A. Federici (Eds), Boca Raton: CRC Press, pp. 177-202.

Hammock, B.D.; Bonning, B.C.; Possee, R.D.; Hanzlik, T.N.; Maeda, S. (1990) Expression and effects of the juvenile hormone esterase in a baculovirus vector. 344, 458-461.

Maeda, S. (1989) Increased insecticidal effect by a recombinant baculovirus carrying a synthetic diuretic hormone gene. *Biochemisty and Biophysics Research Communications*, 165, 1177-1183.

Martens, J.W.M.; Honee, G.; Zuidema, D.; Van Lent, J.W.M.; Visser, B.; Vlak, J.M. (1990) Insecticidal activity of a bacterial crystal protein expressed by a recombinant baculovirus in insect cells. *Applied and Environmental Microbiology*, **56**, 2764-2770.

Merryweather, A.T.; Weyer, U.; Harris, M.P.G.; Hirst, M.; Booth, T.; Possee, R.D. (1990) Construction of genetically engineered baculovirus insecticides containing the *Bacillus thuringiensis* subsp. *kurstaki* HD-73 delta endotoxin. *Journal of General Virology*, **71**, 1535-1544.

O'Reilly, D.R.; Brown, M.R.; Miller, L.K. (1992) Alteration of ecdysteroid metabolism due to baculovirus infection of the fall armyworm *Spodoptera frugiperda*: host ecdysteroids are conjugated with galactose. *Insect Biochemistry and Molecular Biology*, **22**, 313-320.

O'Reilly, D.R.; Howarth, O.W.; Rees, H.H.; Miller, L.K. (1991) Structure of the ecdysone glucoside formed by a baculovirus ecdysteroid UDP-glucosyltransferase. *Insect Biochemistry*, **21**, 795-801.

O'Reilly, D.R.; Miller, L.K. (1989) A baculovirus blocks insect molting by producing ecdysteroid UDP-glucosyl transferase. *Science*, **245**, 1110-1112.

O'Reilly, D.R.; Miller, L.K. (1991) Improvement of a baculovirus pesticide by deletion of the *egt* gene. *Bio/Technology*, **9**, 1086-1089.

O'Reilly, D.R.; Miller, L.K. (1990) Regulation of expression of a baculovirus ecdysteroid UDP-glucosyltransferase gene. *Journal of Virology*, **64**, 1321-1328.

Subrahmanyam, B.; Ramakrishnan, N. (1981) Influence of a baculovirus infection on molting and food consumption by *Spodoptera litura*. *Journal of Invertebrate Pathology*, **38**, 161-168.

Tomalski, M.D.; Miller, L.K. (1991) Insect paralysis by baculovirus-mediated expression of a mite neurotoxin gene. *Nature*, **352**, 82-85.

SESSION 5

NEW COMPOUNDS, FORMULATIONS AND USES – FUNGICIDES

CHAIRMAN   DR K. J. BRENT

SESSION
ORGANISER   DR P. GLADDERS

RESEARCH REPORTS   5-1 to 5-8

PYRIMETHANIL: A NEW FUNGICIDE

G. L. NEUMANN, E. H. WINTER

Schering AG, Pflanzenschutz, Product Development and Marketing,
D-1000 Berlin 65, Germany

J. E. PITTIS

Schering Agrochemicals Limited, Chesterford Park Research Station,
Essex, CB10 1XL

ABSTRACT

Pyrimethanil is a new anilino-pyrimidine fungicide. It is being
developed by Schering AG as a foliar fungicide to control grey
mould (*Botrytis cinerea*) on vine, fruits and vegetables. Pyrimethanil
is highly effective against all strains of *Botrytis* and has not shown
cross-resistance to commercially available botryticides.

INTRODUCTION

Pyrimethanil is the draft ISO common name for N-(4,6-dimethylpyrimidin-
2-yl)aniline, a new anilino-pyrimidine fungicide, property of Schering AG, Berlin,
Germany. It is being developed by Schering AG for the control of grey mould.
This paper describes the properties of pyrimethanil and its performance on
several economically important crops.

CHEMICAL AND PHYSICAL PROPERTIES

Chemical class: Anilino-pyrimidine
Chemical name: N-(4,6-dimethylpyrimidin-2-yl)aniline
Common name: Pyrimethanil (draft ISO)
Structural formula:

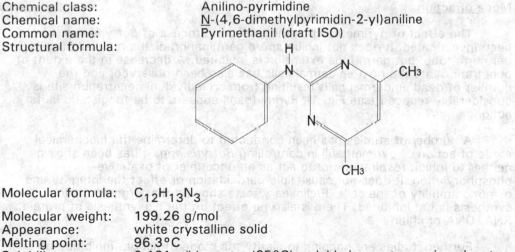

Molecular formula: $C_{12}H_{13}N_3$

Molecular weight: 199.26 g/mol
Appearance: white crystalline solid
Melting point: 96.3°C
Solubility: 0.121 g/l in water (25°C), soluble in most organic solvents
Partition coefficient: log P = 2.48 (n-octanol/water)
Stability: essentially stable within the relevant pH range
Vapour pressure: 2.2 x 10-3 Pa at 25°C

TOXICOLOGY

Pyrimethanil is of very low acute toxicity to a variety of species as follows:

Acute toxicity:	mouse oral LD50	4061-5358 mg/kg
	rat oral LD50	4150-5971 mg/kg
	rat dermal LD50	>5000 mg/kg

Irritation and	rabbit skin irritation	negative
sensitisation:	rabbit eye irritation	negative
	guinea pig skin sensitisation	negative

Mutagenicity: negative in Ames test, *in vitro* cytogenetics assay, *in vivo* micronucleus test and *in vivo* UDS assay.

Teratogenicity: not teratogenic in rats or rabbits.

Wildlife toxicity:	mallard duck and bobwhite quail	LD50 >2000 mg/kg
	mallard duck and bobwhite quail (5 day)	LC50 >5200 ppm
	mirror carp 96 hr LC50	35.36 mg/l
	rainbow trout 96 hr LC50	10.56 mg/l
	earthworm 14 day LC50	625 mg/kg
	honey bee (oral and dermal) LD50	>100 µg/bee

FORMULATIONS

Pyrimethanil is currently available as a flowable formulation (SC 200 and 400 g/l), as well as a water dispersible granule formulation (WG 80 %) and will be marketed under various trademarks including 'Scala'.

BIOLOGICAL ACTIVITY

Mode of action

The effect of pyrimethanil on the infection process of *Botrytis* spp. has been investigated. It does not inhibit spore germination or the number of cells per germ tube, but germ tube extension is inhibited. A decrease in the extent of penetration into the host epidermal cells has also been observed, and the number of dead epidermal cells resulting from an individual penetration site is considerably reduced (see Fig. 1). Pyrimethanil appears to be fungistatic in its action.

A number of studies has been conducted to determine the biochemical mode of action of pyrimethanil in controlling *Botrytis* spp. It has been shown neither to inhibit respiration nor to act as an uncoupler of oxidative phosphorylation. It does not cause lipid peroxidation or affect the integrity and osmotic stability of the cells. Preliminary tests showed that ergosterol bio-synthesis is not inhibited. There is also no effect on the biosynthesis of protein, RNA, DNA or chitin.

Further studies are ongoing to clarify the mode of action. Inhibition of protein secretion by the pathogen has been demonstrated, including reduced levels of some hydrolytic enzymes which are thought to play a role in penetration into and necrosis of the host tissue. These findings are consistent with the observed effects of pyrimethanil on the infection process *in vivo*.

FIGURE 1. Effect of a 48 h pre-inoculation treatment with 200 mg/l of pyrimethanil on the number of epidermal cells killed per penetration site, in four different isolates of *Botrytis fabae*.

(Dr A Daniels, University of Nottingham, 1991)

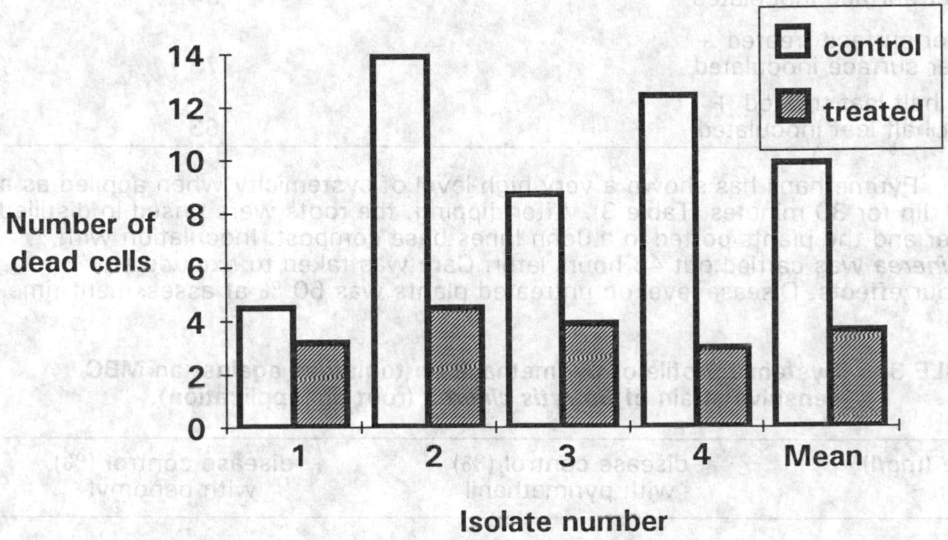

BIOLOGICAL PROPERTIES

Systemicity Data

Pyrimethanil has been shown to exhibit protectant control but no significant systemic activity by leaf to leaf transfer (Table 1).

TABLE 1. Control of *Botrytis cinerea* on tomatoes following a 24 hour protectant spray of pyrimethanil.

Compound	Rate mg/l	% disease control* systemic	protectant
pyrimethanil	250	20	91
	100	13	93
iprodione	250	1	95
	100	0	90

*   Systemic control was assessed on the 3 leaves above the treated leaf. Protectant control was assessed on the treated leaf.

Although the systemic activity from leaf to leaf is negligible, the translaminar activity is significant (Table 2).

TABLE 2.   Translaminar activity of pyrimethanil.

Treatment (pyrimethanil 200 mg/l)	% protection of untreated areas
Lower surface treated + upper surface inoculated	34
Upper surface treated + lower surface inoculated	73
Left half leaf treated + right half leaf inoculated	63

Pyrimethanil has shown a very high level of systemicity when applied as a root dip for 30 minutes (Table 3). After dipping, the roots were rinsed in distilled water and the plants potted in a John Innes base compost. Inoculation with *B. cinerea* was carried out 48 hours later. Care was taken to exclude any vapour effects. Disease level on untreated plants was 60 % at assessment time.

TABLE 3.   Systemic profile of pyrimethanil on tomatoes against an MBC sensitive strain of *Botrytis cinerea* (root dip application).

Rate (mg/l)	disease control (%) with pyrimethanil	disease control (%) with benomyl
50	92	70
25	82	50
5	75	47
1	0	38

Vapour Activity

Vapour activity of the compound has also been observed. Unsprayed tomato plants were placed next to sprayed plants and then enclosed under a plastic cover (Table 4).

TABLE 4.   Control of *Botrytis cinerea* on tomato plants by pyrimethanil applied as a foliar spray.

Rate (mg/l)	% control in treated plants	% control in adjacent untreated plants
100	86	61
50	82	30

Control of Resistant strains

Pyrimethanil is able to control strains of *Botrytis cinerea* resistant to dicarboximides, MBC (benzimidazoles), dicarboximides and MBC, diethofencarb, and diethofencarb and MBC.

In Figure 2, 130 isolates collected from French vineyards have been classified into 6 phenotypes according to their sensitivity to MBC, dicarboximides and diethofencarb + carbendazim. Pyrimethanil was equally active against all strains.

FIGURE 2.   Cumulative IG 50 (50 % control of mycelium growth) distribution values of different phenotypes of *Botrytis cinerea* from vines.

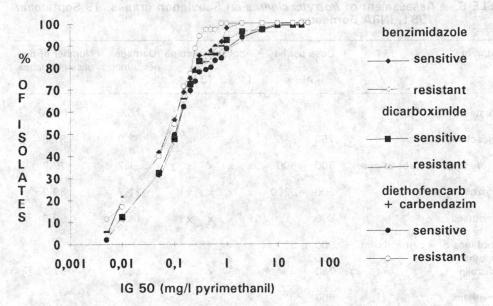

FIFLD TRIALS DATA

Grapes

Pyrimethanil gave outstanding control of *B. cinerea* which was significantly better than the commercial standards (Table 5).

TABLE 5.   Average % control of *Botrytis cinerea* in 64 European trials conducted over 7 years.

Year	85	86	87	88	89	90	91
No. of trials [1]	2	2	4	6	17	13	20
pyrimethanil [2][3]	85	91	90	81	70	74	81
best standard [3]	29	52	30	64	44	51	66
untreated (% infestation)	50	25	33	37	45	40	26

[1]:   trials conducted in France, Germany, Italy, Greece and Spain
[2]:   2 to 4 applications at 50 g AI/hl or 800 g AI/ha
[3]:   same number of applications of vinclozolin 37.5 g AI/hl or diethofencarb + carbendazim 50 + 50 g AI/hl.

Comparison of trials where pyrimethanil alone was used 4 times per season or with sequential spray programmes including other fungicides indicated that the efficacy of sequential spray programmes can be as effective as the use of pyrimethanil alone. Therefore, pyrimethanil can be recommended for use in an alternating spray strategy for resistance management (Table 6).

TABLE 6. Assessment of *Botrytis cinerea* on Sauvignon grapes, 19 September 1991, INRA Bordeaux.

Treatment	Dose per ha g Al	Application stage				Damage per bunch %	Number of diseased bunches %
		T1	T2	T3	T4		
Untreated						76.0	100.0
Vinclozolin	750	x	x	x	x	62.0	97.8
Diethofencarb + carbendazim	500 + 500	x	x	x	x	21.7	72.7
Vinclozolin + thiram	500 + 3200	x	x	x	x	21.7	69.9
Pyrimethanil	800	x	x	x	x	14.7	59.8
Diethofencarb + carbendazim	500 + 500	x					
Pyrimethanil	800		x				
Vinclozolin	750			x	x	16.0	57.7
Pyrimethanil	800	x					
Diethofencarb + carbendazim	500 + 500		x				
Vinclozolin	750			x	x	22.9	74.8
Diethofencarb + carbendazim	500 + 500	x					
Vinclozolin	750		x		x	29.7	82.3
Pyrimethanil	800			x			
Newman & Keuls (5 %)						F = 54.99 C.V. = 10.2%	F = 34.56 C.V. = 7.5 %

Pyrimethanil had no adverse effects on wine fermentation and did not affect the organoleptic quality of the wine in official tests in France, Italy and Germany.

Strawberries

Many trials over 3 years in normal and everbearing varieties have demonstrated an outstanding performance of pyrimethanil for the control of *B. cinerea*. Two examples from official trials conducted in Belgium (Research Station of Gorsem), are shown in Tables 7 and 8.

TABLE 7.   Control of *Botrytis cinerea* on everbearing strawberries (cv. Selva)
on 21 October 1991 after 12 treatments.

Treatment	g AI/ha	% control
Pyrimethanil	800	92
Diethofencarb + carbendazim	250 + 250	94
Procymidone	500	16
Vinclozolin	500	42
Tolylfluanid	1250	75
Thiram	1600	45

In spray programmes, best results, equivalent to pyrimethanil alone, were
achieved in alternation with the best compounds of the above table (Table 8).
The sequence with procymidone was the least effective due to presence of
dicarboximide-resistant strains.

TABLE 8.   Control of *Botrytis cinerea* on everbearing strawberries
(cv. Selva) after different triple sets of treatments
in the spray programme (evaluation on 21 October 1991).

Treatment (rates as Table 7)	% control
3 x P/3 x DC/3 x P/3 x DC	95
3 x P/3 x T/3 x P/3 x T	91
3 x P/3 x Pc/3 x P/3 x Pc	69
P/Pc/DC (continous sequence)	87
12 x P	91

Key: P = pyrimethanil, DC = diethofencarb + carbendazim, T = tolylfluanid, Pc = procymidone

Tomatoes

Pyrimethanil shows excellent activity at 50 g AI/hl or 750-800 g ai/ha in
tomatoes. In Table 9, the results of a typical trial are given. The trial was
conducted under glass in Spain and, due to the vapour activity of pyrimethanil,
2 untreated plots were included: one within the experimental area (4
randomised blocks), and one separate but close to the area of the trial.

TABLE 9.   Control of *Botrytis cinerea* on glasshouse tomatoes after 6 sprays
at 14 d intervals.

Treatment	g AI/ha	% control on dates: $(T_6+8$ d$)$	$(T_6+29$ d$)$	$(T_6+39$ d$)$
Pyrimethanil	750	100	100	100
Vinclozolin	750	62	83	50
Diethofencarb + carbendazim	468	81	96	89
% of infestation in				
Untreated within area of treated		11	12	14
Untreated outside area of treated		22	33	45

The disease levels in untreated plots within the experimental area were
lower than outside the area. This suggests vapour activity.

Onions

Excellent activity has been demonstrated against *Botrytis squamosa* in onions. Table 10 shows the average results of 5 trials conducted in 1991 in the Netherlands using 8 applications.

TABLE 10. Control of *Botrytis squamosa* in onions

Treatment	g AI/ha	% control	% yield
Pyrimethanil	800	69	105
Diethofencarb + carbendazim	250 + 250	50	103
Untreated (% infestation)		31	100

Flower bulbs

An outstanding effect on *B. cinerea* in the Netherlands in artificially infected, forced tulips can be seen in Table 11 (mean of 3 trials). Pyrimethanil treated plants gave the largest yield per pot and the highest number of first class tulips at harvest (max. score 10).

TABLE 11. Control of *Botrytis cinerea* in forced tulips at harvest.

Treatment	g AI/hl	crop yield (g/pot)	1st class tulips (out of 10 per pot)
Pyrimethanil	400	294	9.4
Pyrimethanil	200	303	9.1
Fluazinam	125	275	7.5
Captan	136.5	245	6.7
Procymidone	75	162	4.0
Infected/untreated		180	3.7
Uninfected/untreated		293	9.2

Other crops

Pyrimethanil is highly effective and crop safe at appropriate rates in a number of additional field crops including fodder peas, peas, beans, cucumbers, aubergines and in ornamentals (*Erica, Rhododendron, Begonia, Cyclamen*).

CONCLUSION

Pyrimethanil is a new protective, translaminar and root systemic botryticide for various uses in many crops. It fits very well into seasonal spray programmes. Pyrimethanil has not shown cross-resistance to currently available botryticides and represents a true alternative or partner in a modern *Botrytis* management programme.

ACKNOWLEDGEMENT

The authors wish to thank all their colleagues from many countries, and all the cooperators who have contributed to the data presented in this paper.

BAS 490 F - A BROAD-SPECTRUM FUNGICIDE WITH A NEW MODE OF ACTION

E. AMMERMANN, G. LORENZ, K. SCHELBERGER

BASF AG Landwirtschaftliche Versuchsstation, D-6703 Limburgerhof, Federal Republic of Germany

B. WENDEROTH, H. SAUTER, C. RENTZEA

BASF AG Hauptlaboratorium, D-6700 Ludwigshafen, Federal Republic of Germany

ABSTRACT

BAS 490 F (methyl-(E)-methoximino[α-(o-tolyloxy)-o-tolyl]acetate) is a new synthetic fungicide derived from the fungal secondary metabolite strobilurine. Its broad fungicidal spectrum has demonstrated the following profile in several years of field trials: excellent control of scab in apples and pears, of powdery mildew in apples, grape vine, cucurbits and sugar beet and good control of mildew, scald, net and glume blotch in cereals, of blast and sheath blight in rice, and of downy mildew on grape vine and vegetables. Control of many diseases in several other crops has also been observed. Generally, BAS 490 F has been used safely on mono- and dicotyledoneous crops. In grapes, selectivity of BAS 490 F was good; crop tolerance was slightly reduced only at higher rates.

The fungicidal activity is due to the inhibition of the fungal respiration. The product is safe both to users and to the environment. To date, no adverse toxic effects have been observed.

INTRODUCTION

In 1983, BASF began a programme to evaluate natural products as potential leads for new synthetic pesticides. In the course of this programme, we obtained strobilurine A - a secondary metabolite from the fungus *Strobilurus tenacellus* - from Prof. Anke of the University of Kaiserslautern, FRG in July 1983. Its remarkable in vitro activity (Anke *et al.*, 1977), its new mode of action (Becker *et al.*, 1981), its weak but still measurable fungicidal activity in glasshouse tests and the simplicity of its structure convinced us to focus on this compound as a new fungicidal lead.

At the same time, Prof. Steglich and his group at the University of Bonn, FRG had already succeeded with the synthesis of the first analogues of the β-methoxy-α-phenyl-acrylate type (Schramm 1980, Anke *et al.*, 1989), which also showed some fungicidal activity. Cooperation with the Steglich group led to further structural variations which resulted in several new types of strobilurine analogues (see Appendix) with remarkably enhanced fungicidal properties (Schirmer *et al.*, 1985). Independently, a similar approach to this field of chemistry has been made by others (Beautemont *et al.*, 1991).

Our research in this field has resulted in the fungicide BAS 490 F, which is currently under development (Wenderoth *et al.*, 1986). Its broad-spectrum fungicidal properties, which have been determined in laboratory, glasshouse and field trials, are described below.

CHEMICAL AND PHYSICAL PROPERTIES

Code number	:	BAS 490 F
Chemical name (IUPAC)	:	methyl-(E)-methoximino[α-(o-tolyloxy)--o-tolyl]acetate

Structural formula :

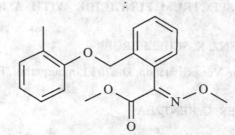

Molecular formula	:	$C_{18}H_{19}NO_4$
Molecular weight	:	313.36
Appearance at 20 °C	:	colourless, odourless crystals
Melting point	:	97.2 - 101.7 °C
Vapour pressure at 20 °C	:	2.3×10^{-8} mbar
Solubility	:	2 mg/l water at 20 °C
Partition coefficient at 25 °C	:	log P = 3.4 (n-octanol/water at pH7)
Stability	:	no hydrolysis at pH7 at 20 °C within 24 h

TOXICOLOGY

Acute toxicity of the technical active ingredient:

Acute oral LD50 rat	:	>5 000 mg/kg body weight
Acute dermal LD50 rat	:	>2 000 mg/kg body weight
Skin irritation rabbit	:	non-irritating
Eye irritation rabbit	:	non-irritating
Ames test	:	negative
Teratogenicity	:	not teratogenic according to the data currently available

FORMULATION

Three formulations have been used: 50 DF, 50 WP with 500 g AI/kg and 500 SC with 500 g AI/l.

BIOLOGICAL ACTIVITY

Material and methods

LC50-values were determined using BAS 490 F-amended agar plates, at a range of concentrations, which had been inoculated with discs of fungal mycelium and assessed by comparison with untreated plates.

In glasshouse experiments, pot grown plants were used which had been cultivated under standard conditions. Inoculations were made by either using aqueous spore suspensions or dusting the plant with spores (*Erysiphe, Puccinia*) with subsequent cultivation under conditions favourable for disease development. Visual assessment of the disease development was made in percent leaf area affected.

The field trials were laid out in randomized blocks with 4 replications. The size of the blocks varied from 10 to 20 m². All trials were sprayed at the beginning of attack either using special small plot tractor-spray equipment or a hand-held precision plot sprayer. Treatments were applied in 200 - 800 l water/ha. A visual assessment of the infected leaves or ears was made in percent for the plot as a whole. Growth stages (GS) are described for cereals according to Zadoks and for other crops according to Weber *et al.*, (1990).

Results

Mode of action
From the literature, the natural lead strobilurine was known to be an inhibitor of mitochondrial respiration by blocking the electron transfer at the cytochrome bc_1 complex (Becker *et al.*, 1981). Detailed studies with the first synthetic analogues by Brandt *et al.* (1988 and 1991) revealed the ubihydroquinone:cytochrome-c oxidoreductase to be the binding site. According to our experiments (Röhl, F., BASF, personal communication), BAS 490 F binds to the same site and thus inhibits respiration. Using a yeast electron transport particle preparation, the rate of cytochrome c reductase was inhibited to 50 % by $2.9 \pm 0.6 \times 10^{-8}$ mol/l BAS 490 F in comparison with an untreated control.

In vitro activity
In in vitro tests, BAS 490 F showed the following activities against a representative group of fungi.

TABLE 1. LC50-values in mg AI/l of a variety of fungi towards BAS 490 F in amended agar plates.

Alternaria solani	< 1	Mucor circinelloides	> 500
Aspergillus niger	> 500	Mycosphaerella fijiensis	< 1
Botryotinia fuckeliana	> 500	Nectria galligena	> 500
Cercospora kikuchii	< 1	Penicillium digitatum	< 1
Chaetomium globosum	< 50	Penicillium expansum	< 1
Choanephora cucurbitarum	< 500	Phaeosphaeria nodorum	< 1
Cladosporium herbarum	< 10	Phomopsis longicola	> 500
Cochliobolus sativus	< 50	Phytophthora cactorum	> 500
Colletotrichum coffeanum	< 50	Phytophthora infestans	< 1
Coniophora puteana	< 1	Pyrenophora avenae	< 10
Corticium rolfsii	< 1	Pyrenophora teres	< 10
Corticium salmonicolor	< 50	Pythium ultimum	> 500
Cylindrocladium scoparium	> 500	Rhizopus stolonifer	< 10
Fusarium culmorum	< 50	Sclerotinia fructigena	> 500
Fusarium oxysporum	< 50	Sclerotinia sclerotiorum	< 1
Glomerella cingulata	< 10	Sclerotium cepivorum	< 1
Guignardia citricarpa	< 1	Serpula himantoides	< 1
Leptosphaeria maculans	< 10	Tapesia yallundae	> 500
Leptosphaeria salvinii	< 1	Thanatephorus cucumeris	< 10
Macrophomina phaseolina	> 500	Trichoderma viride	< 10
Magnaporthe grisea	< 100	Venturia inaequalis	< 1
Monographella nivalis	< 1	Verticillium dahliae	< 10

Glasshouse results
The good and broad activity of BAS 490 F was established in glasshouse tests against plant pathogenic fungi belonging to the Ascomycetes, Basidiomycetes, Deuteromycetes and Oomycetes. Special tests revealed a strong curative activity of BAS 490 F in the control of *Venturia inaequalis* on apple. A single foliar spray-treatment with an aqueous suspension containing 31 mg/l BAS 490 F completely controlled this disease, even 72 h after inoculation. The trial was assessed 14 days after inoculation. Drenching hydroponic rice with BAS 490 F gave no indications for systemic activity against *Pyricularia oryzae* (teleomorph *Magnaporthe grisea*).

Field results in pome fruits

A very good control of scab (*Venturia inequalis*) and powdery mildew (*Podosphaera leucotricha*) in apples (Table 2) has been established. The strong curative properties of BAS 490 F are advantageous under field conditions. No problems of phytotoxicity have been observed in a number of cultivars tested. Equally good results were obtained in Spain in the control of scab on pears (*V. pirina*) using 50 or 100 g AI/ha.

TABLE 2. Control of *Venturia inaequalis* and *Podosphaera leucotricha* in the Federal Republic of Germany, 1991 (cvs. Golden Delicious, Idared, Gravensteiner.).

Treatment[1]	Dose (g AI/ha)	Mean % leaf area affected	
		V. inaequalis	*P. leucotricha*
BAS 490 F	50	4	7
BAS 490 F	100	1	5
Flusilazole +	30 +	9	9
metiram	1200		
Untreated		79	36
Number of trials		3	2

[1] 9 - 10 Treatments (2-4 days after favourable conditions for scab infection).

Grape vine

BAS 490 F has the potential to effectively control powdery (*Uncinula necator*) and downy (*Plasmopara viticola*) mildew on grape vine. Under strong disease pressure, both diseases on the leaves and berries can be significantly reduced.

TABLE 3. Control of *Uncinula necator* in grape vine in Spain 1991.

Treatment[1]	Dose (g AI/ha)	Mean % leaf area or berries affected	
		leaves	berries
BAS 490 F	50	8	9
BAS 490 F	100	3	3
BAS 490 F	150	2	1
Myclobutanil	30	4	4
Untreated		50	70

[1] 4-6 Treatments in 10 - 14 days' interval (Mean of 2 sites).

TABLE 4. Control of *Plasmopara viticola* in grape vine in France and Brazil 1990-1991.

Treatment[1]	Dose (g AI/ha)	Mean % leaf area or berries affected			
		France leaves	berries	Brazil leaves	berries
BAS 490 F	375	12	11	6	5
Metiram	2800	8	15	11	1
Metalaxyl +	200-320 +	5	14	1	1
folpet/mancozeb	800-1280				
Untreated		49	84	51	83

[1] 9 Treatments in France and 5 in Brazil (Mean of 2 sites).

Slight phytotoxicity was sometimes observed on young expanding leaves of grape vine at rates > 200 g AI/ha. This was dependent upon the variety grown and on the prevailing climatic conditions. No phytotoxicity symptoms have been observed on fully developed leaves.

Cereals
BAS 490 F offers good opportunities to control the major diseases in cereals due to its broad spectrum of activity.

TABLE 5. Control of *Erysiphe graminis* (eradicative), *Phaeosphaeria nodorum* (anamorph *Septoria nodorum*) and *Puccinia recondita* (prophylactic) on winter wheat in the Federal Republic of Germany 1990.

Treatment[1]	Dose (g AI/ha)	Mean % leaf area affected			Relative yield
		E.graminis	*P.nodorum*	*P.recondita*	
BAS 490 F	250	3	1	6	150
BAS 480 F +	125 +	6	1	0	154
fenpropimorph	375				
Untreated		28	12	45	100

[1] Applied at GS 32 and GS 51 (Mean of 3 trials).

Field tests revealed the good potential of BAS 490 F to control *Phaeosphaeria nodorum* and *Mycosphaerella graminicola* (anamorph *Septoria tritici*) on leaves and ears in winter wheat. In prophylactic situations, BAS 490 F has a good fungicidal activity against rust diseases in cereals, such as *Puccinia recondita* on winter wheat or rye and *P. striiformis* on winter wheat.
In barley, net blotch (*Pyrenophora teres*) and scald (*Rynchosporium secalis*) are well controlled by BAS 490 F.

TABLE 6. Control of *Pyrenophora teres* and *Rynchosporium secalis* on winter barley in the Federal Republic of Germany 1992.

Treatment	Dose (g AI/ha)	Mean % leaf area affected	
		P. teres [1] 30 DAT	*R. secalis*[2] 30 DAT
BAS 490 F	100	3	10
BAS 490 F	200	2	9
Flusilazole +	160 +	1	4
tridemorph	350		
Untreated		25	19
Number of trials		2	4

[1] One treatment applied at GS 49, [2] one treatment applied at GS 32 - 51.

Rice
In rice, BAS 490 F has a good potential to control blast (*Magnaporthe grisea*, anamorph *Pyricularia oryzae*) and sheath blight (*Corticium sasakii*) by foliar application.

TABLE 7. Control of *Magnaporthe grisea* and *Corticium sasakii* on rice in Taiwan 1991.

Treatment[1]	Dose (g AI/ha)	Mean % leaf area affected			
		M. grisea		*C. sasakii*	
Days after last treatment		8	14	8	14
BAS 490 F	200	6	7	8	20
BAS 490 F	300	3	5	7	12
Kasugamycin + fthalide	10 + 200	9	14	31	53
Pencycuron	125	13	18	6	19
Untreated		19	25	53	74
Number of trials		3		4	

[1] 2-4 Treatments.

Sugar beet
A good control of powdery mildew (*Erysiphe betae*) and leaf spot (*Cercospora beticola*) has been observed with BAS 490 F in sugar beet.

TABLE 8. Control of *Erysiphe betae* on sugarbeet in Spain in 1992.

Treatment[1]	Dose (g AI/ha)	Mean % leaf area affected	
Days after last treatment		0	10
BAS 490 F	100	5	4
BAS 490 F	200	4	1
Difenoconazole	300	4	1
Untreated		52	72

[1] 2 - 3 Treatments in 2-weeks' interval (Mean of 2 sites).

TABLE 9. Control of *Cercospora beticola* on sugarbeet in the Federal Republic of Germany 1991.

Treatment[1]	Dose (g AI/ha)	Mean % leaf area affected		
Days after second treatment		20	30	Relative yield
BAS 490 F	300	13	26	108
BAS 490 F	400	11	23	110
Fentin-acetate + maneb	324 + 96	7	28	108
Untreated		28	30	100

[1] Treatment at the beginning of infection by *C. beticola* at GS 48 and at re-attack at GS 49 (Mean of 3 sites).

Potato

Early and late blight (*Alternaria solani* and *Phytophthora infestans*) in potatoes can be significantly reduced by BAS 490 F.

TABLE 10. Control of *Phytophthora infestans* on potatoes in the Federal Republic of Germany 1991.

Treatment[1]	Dose (g AI/ha)	Mean % leaf area affected		Relative yield
		GS 81	GS 85	
BAS 490 F	400	8	45	111
Metiram	1400	7	40	108
Untreated		31	84	100

[1] 3-5 Treatments (Mean of 3 sites).

TABLE 11. Control of *Alternaria solani* on potatoes in Brazil 1991,1992.

Treatment[1]	Dose (g AI/ha)	Mean % leaf area affected	
		7 DAT	14 DAT
BAS 490 F	200	22	37
	400	15	37
Metiram	1600	49	71
Untreated		59	84

[1] 2 - 4 Treatments (Mean of 3 sites).

Similarly good control of *P. infestans* and *A. solani* in tomatoes has been observed. Good control of other *Alternaria* spp., such as black spot on oil seed rape (*A. brassicae*) and leaf blight on carrots (*A. dauci*), has also been observed; 375 g AI/ha performed clearly better than 500 g AI/ha iprodione.

Cucurbits

Powdery mildews (*Sphaerotheca fuliginea*) on cucurbits are another feature of the fungicidal profile of BAS 490 F.

TABLE 12. Control of *Sphaerotheca fuliginea* on cucurbits in Spain in 1990.

Treatment[1]	Dose (g AI/ha)	Mean % leaf area affected		
		melon 10 DAT	zucchini 10 DAT	cucumbers under glass 7 DAT
BAS 490 F	50	8	30	3
BAS 490 F	100	5	18	1
BAS 490 F	200	3	13	0
Ethirimol	420	3	26	0
Hexaconazole	50	9	41	14
Untreated		43	69	65

[1] 2 - 3 Treatments.

CONCLUSION

BAS 490 F is a new, very active, broad-spectrum fungicide with strong protective, curative, eradicative and long residual disease control. BAS 490 F has excellent potential to control diseases caused by Ascomycetes, Basidiomycetes, Deuteromycetes and Oomycetes in many crops. A pronounced feature is its strong efficacy against *Venturia*, *Uncinula*, *Erysiphe* and *Alternaria* species by foliar treatments. Minor gaps in its fungicidal spectrum can be filled by combinations with other fungicides.

Disease control achieved by the use of BAS 490 F resulted in significant yield increases.

ACKNOWLEDGEMENTS

We would like to express our thanks to those many colleagues who have contributed to the international development of BAS 490 F.

REFERENCES

Anke, T.; Oberwinkler,F.; Steglich, W.; Schramm, G.(1977) The strobilurins - new antifungal antibiotics from the basidiomycete *Strobilurus tenacellus*. The Journal of Antibiotics. **30**, 806 - 810.

Anke, T.; Steglich, W. (1989) "β -*Methoxyacrylate Antibiotics: From Biological Activity to Synthetic Analogues*" in Schlunegger, U.P. (Ed.) "Biologically Active Molecules", Springer Berlin.

Beautement, K.; Clough, J.M.; de Fraine, P.J.; Godfrey C.R.A. (1991) Fungicidal β-methoxyacrylates: from natural products to novel synthetic agricultural fungicides. Pesticide Science **31**, 499-541.

Becker, W.F.; von Jagow, G.; Anke, T.; Steglich, W. (1981) Oudemansin, strobilurin A, strobilurin B and myxothiazole: new inhibitors of the bc_1 segment of the respiratory chain with an E-β-methoxyacrylate system as common structural element. FEBS Letters **132**, 329 - 333.

Brandt, U.; Schägger, H.; von Jagow, G. (1988) Characterisation of binding of the methoxyacrylate inhibitors to mitochondrial cytochrome c reductase. European Journal of Biochemistry **173**, 499 - 506.

Brandt, U.; von Jagow, G. (1991) Analysis of inhibitor binding to the mitochondrial cytochrome c reductase by fluorescence quench titration. European Journal of Biochemistry **195**, 163 - 170.

Schirmer, U.; Karbach, S.; Pommer, E.H.; Ammermann, E.; Steglich, W.; Schwalge, B.; Anke, T. European Patent 203 606 (30.05.1985); European Patent 203 608 (30.05.1985); European Patent 226 917 (20.12.1985) and European Patent 229 974 (20.12.1985).

Schramm, G. (1980) Neue Antibiotika aus höheren Pilzen (Basidiomyceten). PhD Thesis, University of Bonn, FRG.

Weber, E.; Bleiholder, H. (1990) Explanations of the BBCH decimal codes for the growth stages of maize, rape, field beans and peas. Gesunde Pflanzen **42**, 308 - 321.

Wenderoth, B.; Rentzea, C.; Ammermann, E.; Pommer, E.H.; Steglich, W.; Anke, T. European Patent 253 213 (16.07.1986).

APPENDIX

We prefer the term "strobilurine analogues" instead of "β-methoxyacrylates" for two reasons: 1. strobilurine A is structurally the simplest natural lead molecule of this class and 2. the β-methoxyacrylate moiety, in its narrow chemical definition, is not essential for fungicidal activity. Several variations beyond it, e.g. BAS 490 F, have the same mode of action with similar fungicidal activity.

FLUQUINCONAZOLE, A NOVEL BROAD-SPECTRUM FUNGICIDE FOR FOLIAR APPLICATION

P.E.RUSSELL, A.PERCIVAL, P.M.COLTMAN, D.E.GREEN

Schering Agrochemicals Limited, Chesterford Park Research Station, Saffron Walden, Essex CB10 1XL

ABSTRACT

Fluquinconazole, code number SN 597265, is a new quinazolinone based triazole fungicide discovered as a result of a chemical design and synthesis programme aimed at producing novel inhibitors of ergosterol biosynthesis. It possesses a broad spectrum of activity when used as a foliar spray against Ascomycetes, Deuteromycetes and Basidiomycetes, which cause economically important diseases of broad-leaf and cereal crops.
SN 597265 is particularly active against diseases of apple, giving excellent control of *Venturia inaequalis* and *Podosphaera leucotricha*. Other pathogens controlled include powdery mildews, *Monilinia* spp., *Cercospora* spp., *Phoma* spp., *Septoria spp.*, *Pyrenopeziza brassicae*, *Puccinia* spp., *Hemileia* spp., and *Sclerotinia* spp. SN 597265 possesses protectant, eradicant and systemic properties combined with excellent crop safety. It is being developed alone and with various mixture partners in a range of formulations. Expected rates of use are 2.5-15 g Al/hl, and 100-500 g Al/ha, depending on the crop.

INTRODUCTION

SN 597265 is a novel quinazolinone based compound discovered and patented by Schering Agrochemicals Ltd. It arose as a result of a chemical design and synthesis programme aimed at producing novel inhibitors of ergosterol biosynthesis. Early stage research showed SN 597265 to possess excellent fungicidal properties frequently superior to currently available ergosterol biosynthesis inhibitors. This paper presents preliminary data on the chemical and biological properties of SN 597265, with particular emphasis on fungal pathogens of top fruit.

CHEMICAL AND PHYSICAL PROPERTIES

Chemical name (IUPAC)   :   3-(2,4-dichlorophenyl)-6-fluoro-2-(1*H*-1,2,4-triazol-1-yl) quinazolin-4(3<u>H</u>)-one

Draft ISO common name   :   Fluquinconazole

Molecular formula and weight : $C_{16} H_8 Cl_2 F N_5 O$; 376

Appearance and melting point :   Off-white particulate, 191.5-193°C

Vapour pressure   : 6.4×10^{-9} Pa at 20°C

Solubility (g/l at 20°C) : water 0.001, acetone 44, xylene 10, ethanol 3, DMSO 150

Partition coefficient : 3.2 (n-octanol/water)

Structural formula :

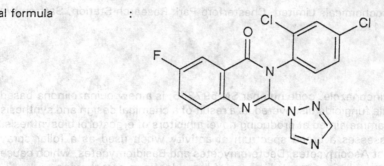

TOXICOLOGY

The acute toxicological profile for SN 597265 is presented in Table 1.

TABLE 1. Acute toxicity summary data: SN 597265

Route		Species	Sex	LD50 mg/kg
Oral		Rat	M	112
			F	112
		Mouse	M	325
			F	180
Dermal		Rat	M	2679
			F	625
Skin irritancy		Rabbit		-ve
Eye irritancy		Rabbit		-ve
Skin sensitisation		Guinea Pig		-ve
Mutagenicity:	Ames test			-ve
	In vitro chromosome aberration test			-ve
	Mouse micronucleus test			-ve
	Unscheduled DNA synthesis test			-ve

SN 597265 shows a wide margin of safety when used as recommended.

BIOLOGICAL ACTIVITY

The biological activity of SN 597265 was first recognised in a series of tests conducted in controlled environment rooms and the glasshouse. Excellent results were achieved in the control of a wide range of Ascomycete, Deuteromycete and Basidiomycete fungi. Control of Phycomycetes was negligible. Of particular note were excellent results obtained in control of diseases of apple. All results presented in this paper relate to the use of a 25% WP formulation.

Activity on apples

The control of diseases of apples poses many problems for the grower. Of these, the requirement to apply fungicide sprays at the correct time is a major factor. In order to help the grower achieve this, various prediction and warning schemes have been devised and will no doubt be refined in the future. In themselves these schemes are excellent but as conditions suitable for disease development and spread are not always perfect for spray application and it is not always possible to respond immediately to a disease warning, the success of the schemes will depend on fungicides with particular biological properties. One of these is the ability to protect uninfected foliage and to eradicate early infections in the period following a disease warning, thus providing the grower with the flexibility in application timing he requires in order to profit from the warning scheme. SN 597265 provides this flexibility, as shown in Table 2.

TABLE 2. Protectant and eradicant activity of SN 597265 against *Venturia inaequalis* (glasshouse trial).

Treatment	Rate mg/l	% disease control 28 days after inoculation
24h protectant	12.5	100
24h eradicant	200	100
48h eradicant	200	100
96h eradicant	200	100

As can be seen, SN 597265 gave total disease control of *V.inaequalis* when applied up to 4 days after inoculation.

Although *Venturia* is the principal disease of apple, powdery mildew caused by *Podosphaera leucotricha* is a major secondary disease which frequently occurs in a complex with *Venturia*. SN 597265 combines excellent *Venturia* control with similarly excellent protectant and eradicant control of *Podosphaera*, as shown in Table 3.

TABLE 3. Protectant and eradicant activity of SN 597265 against *Podosphaera leucotricha* (glasshouse trial).

Treatment	Rate mg/l	% disease control 15 days after treatment
24h protectant	5	100
24h eradicant	100	98 (42)*
5 day eradicant	100	96 (65)
10 day eradicant	100	77 (81)

* Disease levels on untreated at assessment time.

In order to achieve high activity against these diseases, systemicity is a valuable asset. SN 597265 possesses excellent systemic properties on apple as shown by data in Table 4.

TABLE 4. Systemic control of *P.leucotricha* by SN 597265.

Treatment systemic effect evaluated	Rate mg/l	% Disease Control SN 597265	
		Protectant	Systemic
Soil drench, root uptake	2000	-	58
	500	-	57
Leaf to leaf, phloem mobility	200	100	0
	50	100	0
Leaf base to leaf tip xylem transfer	200	100	100
	50	100	100
Leaf tip to leaf base phloem mobility and some xylem diffusion	200	100	22
	50	100	0
Lateral ie leaf side to leaf side	200	100	78
	50	100	63
Translaminar, leaf under surface to leaf upper surface	200	-	97
	50	-	95

These data show that xylem transfer of SN 597265 is extremely good, resulting in highly efficient disease control in areas remote from the site of application. Lateral movement can be explained by leakage from leaf blade vessels to the midrib, followed by xylem vessel transfer to the opposite leaf side. There is no evidence for phloem transfer. The translaminar effect illustrates well that SN 597265 penetrates leaf tissue, is not automatically translocated to remote areas by the xylem vessels but is transported across the leaf tissues to control disease on the opposite surface. This is an important property, ensuring efficient disease control.

Data for field activity are shown in Tables 5 and 6. All sprays were made at 10-14 day intervals with 5-9 applications depending on location. Spray volume was adjusted according to tree size. Initial studies examined dose rates up to 15 g AI/hl. This was soon realised to be too high, with disease control being consistently 100% irrespective of pathogen so lower rates were evaluated.

TABLE 5. Field activity of SN 597265 against *V. inaequalis*.

Treatment	Rate g AI/hl	% Disease control	
		Foliar	Fruit
SN 597265	3.25	82	-
	5.0	90	90
	7.5	94	94
	10.0	95	94
DMI standards (mean)		89	76
Untreated disease level (range)		42 (28-94)	44 (11-90)

(Data from Italy, France, Germany, UK, Spain, Belgium, 1990).

SN 597265 offered excellent control of *Venturia* at dose rates of 5g AI/hl and above. This was particularly noticeable in control of fruit scab, where SN 597265 was consistently the superior product.

TABLE 6. Field activity of SN 597265 against *P. leucotricha*.

Treatment	Rate g AI/hl	% Disease control
SN 597265	5.0	82.6
	7.5	86.1
	10.0	87.3
DMI standards (mean)		83.0
Untreated disease level (range)		43 (12-95)

(Data from France, Germany, UK, Spain, Belgium, 1990).

The activity of SN 597265 applied at 5.0 g AI/hl was at least comparable to that given by the majority of DMI fruit sprays.

The performance of SN 597265 in a *Venturia* spray programme based on scab warnings was evaluated in Belgium in 1991. SN 597265 was used as a mixture with mancozeb. Data are presented in Table 7.

TABLE 7. The activity of SN 597265 plus mancozeb when used in a *Venturia* scab warning spray programme.

Treatment	Rate g Al/hl	% Disease control Time from scab warning		
		4 day	5 days	7 days
SN 597265 + mancozeb	5 + 80	95	93	68
Pyrifenox + mancozeb	4 + 80	92	75	64

SN 597265 gave excellent disease control at the normally accepted spray interval of 4 days, and retained the ability to extend this to 5 days with negligible decrease in efficacy.

During the course of the investigations into control of apple diseases, considerable attention has been paid to crop safety. In all investigations and at dose rates far in excess of those reported here, SN 597265 has shown no problems of crop safety to foliage, pollination processes or final fruit.

Activity on cereals

Data for control of diseases of wheat are shown in Table 8.

TABLE 8. Field control of diseases of wheat by SN 597265.

Treatment	Rate g Al/ha	% Disease control		
		Erysiphe graminis	*Puccinia spp.*	*Septoria spp.*
SN 597265	125	58	84	49
	250	59	84	60
	375	74	94	70
Propiconazole	125	46	78	40
Fenpropimorph	750	68	74	-
Prochloraz	450	-	-	55

(Data from UK, France, Germany, applications made to, and disease control assessed on, the flag leaf).

Control of *E. graminis* on barley was not as good as that on wheat. Control of *Rhyncosporium secalis* and *Pyrenophora teres* was moderate, but inferior to that obtained with prochloraz. SN 597265 gave poor field control of *Pseudocercosporella herpotrichoides* (teleomorph *Tapesia yallundae*) where a mixed W and R type population was present. In common with some other triazoles, SN 597265 showed good laboratory activity against W types but negligible activity against R types.

Activity on vines

SN 597265 has been extensively evaluated for control of vine diseases. Typical trials data are shown in Table 9.

TABLE 9. Control of *Uncinula necator* by SN 597265.

Treatment	Rate g Al/hl	% Disease control
SN 597265	2.5	95
	3.75	97
	5.0	98
Penconazole	1.5	98
Triadimenol	3.75	95

(Data from USA, Germany, France. 14 d spray intervals).

Control of *Uncinula* by SN 597265 was very comparable to that given by the best DMI standards. Although not yet fully evaluated, control of *Uncinula* was frequently associated with control of "rot brenner" (*Pseudopeziza tracheiphila*) and with suppression of *Botrytis cinerea*.

Activity on other crops

The activity of SN 597265 extends to many other crops. On oilseed rape, extensive trials in Germany, France and UK have shown that 250 g Al/ha gives exceptionally good control of *Sclerotinia*, *Pyrenopeziza*, *Phoma* and *Erysiphe* with good control of *Botrytis*. Control of *Alternaria* was only moderate. On sugar beet, control of *Cercospora*, *Ramularia* and *Erysiphe* is excellent at rates of 125-187.5 g Al/ha, while control of *Cercospora* on peanuts in the USA at 125-250 g Al/ha was far superior to that achieved by chlorothalonil.

Other crops where excellent disease control has been achieved include:

			g AI/ha
Coffee	:	*Hemileia vastatrix*	200-500
Turf	:	*Thanatephorus cucumeris*	320
Legumes	:	powdery mildew	125
Rice	:	*Thanatephorus cucumeris*	125-500
		Cercospora spp.	125-500
		Helminthosporium spp.	125-500

			g AI/hl
Stone fruit	:	*Monilinia* spp.	5-10
		powdery mildews	5-10
		Cladosporium carygenum	5-10

FUTURE DEVELOPMENT

SN 597265 is being developed in the markets indicated and evaluated in many more. Where appropriate for reasons of spectrum or activity enhancement, or for fungicide resistance management strategy, it is being developed in a range of mixtures and formulation types with other compounds. The mixture partner and formulation type is being decided according to the crop and pathogen involved.

METCONAZOLE, AN ADVANCE IN DISEASE CONTROL IN CEREALS AND OTHER CROPS

A.J. SAMPSON

Shell Research Ltd, Sittingbourne Research Centre, Sittingbourne, Kent,
ME9 8AG

A. CAZENAVE

Shell Forschung Gmbh, D-6507 Schwabenheim, Federal Republic of Germany

J-P. LAFFRANQUE

Agrishell, 14, rue Professeur Deperet - 69160 Tassin, France

R. GLYN JONES

Shell Chemicals U.K. Ltd. Agricultural Division, Heronshaw House, Ermine
Business Park, Huntingdon, Cambs. PE18 6YA

S. KUMAZAWA, T. CHIDA

Kureha Chemical Industry Co.Ltd. Nishiki Research Laboratories
Iwaki, Japan

ABSTRACT

Metconazole, (1RS,5RS;1RS,5SR)-5-(4-chlorobenzyl)-2,2-dimethyl-1-
(1H-1,2,4-triazol-1-ylmethyl)cyclopentanol, is a new broad
spectrum triazole. With its systemic properties, it gives
excellent control of foliar infections of Septoria spp., Puccinia
spp., Rhynchosporium secalis and Pyrenophora teres, and seed-borne
infections of Tilletia caries, Ustilago spp. and Pyrenophora spp.
Useful control of other diseases on cereals is also obtained.
A major characteristic of the compound is its outstanding
performance against Septoria and rust diseases on cereals. The
high prophylactic and strong therapeutic activity have proved to
be particularly useful against Septoria spp. Uses on a wide range
of other crops are under evaluation.

INTRODUCTION

Fungicidally active substituted azole derivatives have been studied for
more than twenty years. The large number of possible substitutions on the
molecules have encouraged many chemical companies to synthesise related
molecules, looking for variations in the levels of biological activity or
in the spectrum of activity. Metconazole, the subject of this paper, is
one such material, first synthesised and patented by the Kureha Chemical
Industry Co.Ltd. and under development with the Shell Group of companies.

CHEMICAL AND PHYSICAL PROPERTIES

Structural formula:

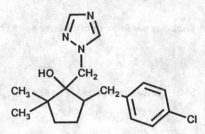

Chemical name (IUPAC):   (1RS,5RS;1RS,5SR)-5-(4-chlorobenzyl)-2,2-dimethyl-1-
(1H-1,2,4-triazol-1-ylmethyl)cyclopentanol

Common name (BSI/ISO):   metconazole

Shell code: WL136184 is the cis (1RS,5SR) isomer of metconazole,
with the hydroxy and benzyl groups on the same side
of the cyclopentyl ring, and for which all data
applies unless otherwise stated

Empirical formula: $C_{17}H_{22}ClN_3O$

Molecular weight: 319.8

Physical state: crystalline solid

Melting point: 110-113∃C

Colour: white

Odour: odourless

Solubility in water: 15 mg/kg

Stability: good thermal and hydrolytic stability

TOXICOLOGY

<u>Acute toxicity for technical material</u>

Acute oral LD50 to rat: 1459 mg/kg

Acute dermal LD50 to rat: >2000 mg/kg

Skin irritancy to rabbit: not irritant

Eye irritancy to rabbit: slight irritant

Skin sensitisation: negative

Ames test: negative

BIOLOGICAL ACTIVITY

Mode of action

Metconazole is, in common with most other azole fungicides, an ergosterol biosynthesis inhibitor. However, the spectrum of disease control and inherent fungicidal activity varies considerably between the different azole molecules.

Laboratory testing

Initial in-vitro tests with metconazole identified it as an extremely active molecule against a very large range of species. At the same time, cis and trans isomers were identified and produced separately. Both were found to be fungicidally active. Against some diseases the isomers had similar activity, but, overall, the cis isomer was shown to be substantially more active. Data were produced using cultures on freshly prepared potato, sucrose and agar (PSA) media, all at pH 6.0. Temperatures and incubation periods varied from fungus to fungus but were mainly 28°C and three days. Examples of the activities determined in these tests are given for the separate isomers in Table 1. Data are expressed as the mycelial growth inhibition concentration (MIC) in concentrations of mg/l.

TABLE 1. In-vitro activities of metconazole isomers.

Pathogen	MIC in mg/l	
	cis	trans
Alternaria alternata	25	100
Botryotinia fuckeliana	1.6	12.5
Cercospora beticola	25	>100
Cochliobolus miyabeanus	25	25
Fusarium oxysporum f.sp. cucumerinum	1.6	12.5
Fusarium oxysporum f.sp. niveum	3.1	25
Fusarium oxysporum f.sp. raphani	1.6	6.3
Glomerella cingulata	1.6	12.5
Nakataea sigmoidea	25	100
Leptosphaeria nodorum	<0.8	<0.8
Pyricularia oryzae	6.3	12.5
Thanatephorus cucumeris	100	>100
Monilinia laxa	<0.8	1.6
Sclerotinia sclerotiorum	1.6	25
Valsa ceratosperma	<0.8	1.6

In-vivo activity

Some similar differences were observed in pot tests in the glasshouse. For example, disease control obtained with the isomers in same-day applications against grey mould on kidney beans and brown rust on wheat, (see Table 2 below), also shows the cis isomer to be substantially more active than the trans isomer against these diseases.

TABLE 2. Preventive activity of metconazole isomers.

Treatment	mg AI/l	% disease control Botrytis cinerea	Puccinia recondita
cis isomer	7.8	50	100
	31.3	79	100
	125	100	100
trans isomer	7.8	5	90
	31.3	44	98
	125	60	100

Field testing

Because of the differences demonstrated above, the cis isomer, code number WL136184, was selected for further evaluation in field programmes. It is still referred to as metconazole in the remainder of this report. Table 3 gives a broad view of the activity spectrum determined in field tests to date. Trials reported were conducted in the U.K., France and Germany.

TABLE 3. Metconazole fungal activity spectrum.

Crop	Pathogen	Disease control rating
Cereals (seed treatment)	Fusarium spp.	**
	Puccinia striiformis	***
	Pyrenophora gramineum	***
	Leptosphaeria nodorum	***
	Tilletia spp.	***
	Ustilago spp.	***
Cereals (foliar spray)	Erysiphe spp.	**
	Fusarium spp.	**
	Pseudocercosporella spp.	*
	Puccinia spp.	***
	Pyrenophora teres	***
	Rhynchosporium secalis	***
	Septoria spp.	***
Sugar beet	Cercospora beticola	***
	Erysiphe betae	***
	Ramularia betae	***
Apple	Podosphaera leucotricha	**
	Venturia inaequalis	***

* low activity ** moderate activity *** high activity

Cereal seed treatments

As a seed treatment on wheat and barley, metconazole provided good control of the major diseases. It was highly active against <u>Tilletia caries</u> and <u>Ustilago</u> spp., normally giving complete control with doses of 2.5 g AI/100 kg of seed, and often with much less. Good levels of control of <u>Pyrenophora graminea</u> and <u>Puccinia striiformis</u> have also been obtained in the field, and in pot tests in France good activity was shown against <u>Leptosphaeria nodorum</u> and <u>Fusarium roseum</u>, and moderate activity against <u>Fusarium nivale</u>. Examples of the interesting activity against leaf stripe and yellow rust are given in Tables 4 and 5. Most of the data were produced from 'wet' treatments using a 100 g/litre EC.

TABLE 4. The effect of metconazole seed treatment on leaf stripe (<u>Pyrenophora graminea</u>) on barley.

Treatment	g AI/100 kg seed	% effect 1991	pre 1991
Metconazole	2.5	71	71
Metconazole	5.0	91	86
Metconazole	7.5	92	91
Triadimenol	30	7	5
Triadimenol + triazoxide + anthraquinone	30+2+50	98	-
Oxine-copper	20	60	46
Untreated (% infected plants)		16	15
Number of trials (all in France)		3	4

TABLE 5. The effect of metconazole seed treatment on yellow rust (<u>Puccinia striiformis</u>) on wheat, cv. Slejpner.

Treatment	g AI/100 kg seed	% effect
Metconazole	0.5	73
Metconazole	1.0	79
Metconazole	2.5	79
Metconazole	5.0	83
Triadimenol	30	71
Untreated (% infection)		33

Mean of 2 U.K. trials assessed at the early booting stage.

Barley foliar treatments

Data collected from winter barley trials showed good control of the four main diseases which infect this crop. Brown rust, <u>Puccinia recondita</u> <u>f.sp. hordei</u>, was sometimes present as a late infection. This was controlled well, virtually 100% effect being achieved by all doses for five weeks after spraying. Control of the other diseases, <u>Rhynchosporium</u> <u>secalis</u>, <u>Pyrenphora teres</u> and <u>Erysiphe graminis</u> f.sp. <u>hordei</u>, are shown in Table 6. These results are all based on assessments made four to six weeks after spraying, mostly from a single spray using a 60 g/l SL. All of the trials summarised in Table 6 were located in England.

TABLE 6. Disease control with metconazole treatments on winter barley.

Treatment	g AI/ha	% control on -		
		R.secalis	P.teres	E.graminis
Metconazole	30	72	-	-
Metconazole	48	84	72	89
Metconazole	60	-	75	93
Metconazole	72	88	76	94
Metconazole	90	89	-	-
Tebuconazole	250	74	81	95
Cyproconazole	100	-	60	93
Untreated (% infection)		76	25	8
Number of trials		2	6	5

Wheat foliar treatments

With the exception of powdery mildew, foliar diseases of wheat are also well controlled. Infections of <u>Erysiphe graminis</u> f.sp.<u>tritici</u> may be moderately well controlled by prophylactic treatments, but on varieties sensitive to mildew, therapeutic treatments, in common with most other azoles, need a specific mildewicide partner.

Brown rust, (<u>Puccinia recondita</u> f.sp.<u>tritici</u>), is an excellent indicator species for the persistance of azole treatments in wheat. In most trials all metconazole treatments resulted in complete rust control for a long period. Yellow rust (<u>Puccinia striiformis</u>) was also very well controlled.

In addition to rusts, the strength of metconazole is it's activity against the septorias. Data presented in Table 7 are from high natural infections of <u>Septoria tritici</u> and <u>Leptosphaeria nodorum</u>. Data from two U.K. trials which were inoculated with <u>L.nodorum</u> are given in Table 8.

TABLE 7. Activity of metconazole against the _Septoria_ spp.

Treatment	Dose g AI/ha	% control on leaves 1 and 2		
		S. tritici	_L. nodorum_	
Metconazole	48	81	-	-
Metconazole	60	83	-	-
Metconazole	72	87	84	53
Metconazole	90	-	87	62
Tebuconazole	250	82	86	65
Cyproconazole	100	82	-	-
Flusilazole+ carbendazim	200+100	-	84	-
Untreated (% infection)		60	39	28
Trials/country/years		8 U.K. 91/92	9 FR 92	5 GE 91/92

TABLE 8. Activity of metconazole against inoculated _Leptosphaeria nodorum_.

Treatment	Dose g AI/ha	L. nodorum % control			
		prophylactic		therapeutic	
		Ear	Leaf	Ear	Leaf
Metconazole	48	53	86	46	87
Metconazole	60	63	90	54	88
Metconazole	72	65	89	58	92
Tebuconazole	250	60	85	13	8
Cyproconazole	100	46	62	36	57
Untreated (% infection)		15	60	32	93
Treatment timing		10 days pre-inoculation		4 days post-inoculation	

Cereal yield responses

Cereal yield responses were usually very good, reflecting the differences in infection levels between control plots and the treatments. In seed-treatment trials with high infection levels, yields from treated plots were often several times that of untreated.

In the U.K. trials from which the above foliar disease data were taken, average yield increases of 25% were achieved in winter barley (mean control yield 6.5 t/ha) and 13% in winter wheat (mean control yield 8.9 t/ha) giving 1.6 t/ha and 1.2 t/ha extra grain respectively. Similar yield responses to disease control were seen in France and Germany.

DISCUSSION & CONCLUSIONS

The above data demonstrate that metconazole has a high level of activity and a wide spectrum of activity for this class of compound. Doses as low as 10 g per tonne of seed can completely control some seed-borne diseases. It is active against all diseases in cereals, although, in common with most other azoles, control of established mildew in sensitive wheat cultivars is not adequate. Mixtures of metconazole with mildew-specific products overcome this weakness, although data have not been presented in this paper. In barley, all diseases are well controlled, and activity against <u>Rhynchosporium secalis</u> is particularly high. In wheat, strong prophylactic and therapeutic activity combine to give high and persistent activity, particularly against the rusts and septorias. Persistence of disease control for more than six weeks may allow the use of a single treatment for effective crop protection in many wheat growing areas.

Metconazole is not just another azole, but a useful addition to the armoury against cereal diseases.

Trials to define the activity of metconazole against diseases in broad-leaved crops are continuing.

MON 24000: A NOVEL FUNGICIDE WITH BROAD-SPECTRUM DISEASE CONTROL

P.O'REILLY

Monsanto Technical Centre Europe, rue Laid Burniat, 1348 Louvain-la-Neuve, Belgium

S.KOBAYASHI, S.YAMANE

Monsanto Japan Ltd., Agriculture Research Station, P.O.B.28, Ryugasaki, Japan

W.G.PHILLIPS, P.RAYMOND, B.CASTANHO

The Agricultural Group of Monsanto Company, Chesterfield Village, 700 Chesterfield Village Parkway, St.Louis MO 63198, USA.

ABSTRACT

MON 24000 is a new thiazolecarboxanilide fungicide. It is being developed by the Agricultural Group of Monsanto Company as a foliar fungicide for rice, cereals, field crops and turf, and as a seed treatment for both cereal and non-cereal crops.

An extensive field testing programme carried out during 1989-1992 has revealed the excellent activity of MON 24000 against a wide range of diseases, especially the Basidiomycete fungi. Efficacy as a foliar application has been observed particularly against plant pathogenic fungi in the genera *Rhizoctonia*, *Puccinia* and *Corticium* and as a seed treatment at low rates against species of *Ustilago*, *Tilletia* and *Pyrenophora*. The mode of action of this compound is by inhibition of the enzyme succinate dehydrogenase in the tricarboxylic acid cycle of fungi.

INTRODUCTION

MON 24000 is a new thiazolecarboxanilide fungicide which was discovered and patented by the Agricultural Group of Monsanto Company. It is being developed as a fungicide for foliar, seed and soil treatment. The biological properties of MON 24000 have been evaluated since 1989 on a wide range of crops including rice, cereals, potatoes, peanuts and turf. This paper is a review of its performance against diseases of major importance in these crops.

CHEMICAL AND PHYSICAL PROPERTIES

Chemical Class: Thiazolecarboxanilide
Chemical Name: 2',6'-dibromo-2-methyl-4'-trifluoromethoxy-4'-trifluoromethyl-1,3-thiazole-5-carboxanilide

Structural Formula:

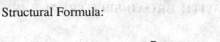
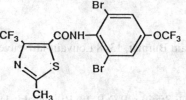

Molecular Formula:	$C_{13}H_6Br_2F_6N_2O_2S$
Molecular Weight:	528.1
Appearance at 20°C:	White to light brown powder
Melting Point:	177.9 - 178.6 °C (pure material)
Solubility in water at 20°C:	1.6 mg/l
Partition Coefficient:	log P = 4.1 (n-octanol/water)
Hydrolysis:	Stable at pH 5.0 - 9.0

TOXICOLOGY AND ENVIRONMENTAL STUDIES

Mammalian toxicity

Acute oral LD_{50} rat:	> 5000 mg/kg
Acute dermal LD_{50} rabbit:	> 5000 mg/kg
Eye irritation rabbit:	moderately irritating
Skin irritation rabbit:	slightly irritating

Mutagenicity

Ames test:	negative
Micronucleus (mouse):	negative

Toxicity to wildlife

Avian	Bobwhite quail LC_{50} > 5620 ppm, practically non-toxic
	Mallard duck LC_{50} > 5620 ppm, practically non-toxic
Aquatic	Blue sunfish LC_{50} (96 h), 1.2 mg/l, moderately toxic
	Rainbow trout LC_{50} (96 h), 1.3 mg/l, moderately toxic
	Daphnia magna LC_{50} (48 h), 1.6 mg/l, moderately toxic
	Carp LC_{50} (96 h), 2.9 mg/l, moderately toxic

MODE OF ACTION

MON 24000 inhibits the enzyme succinate dehydrogenase in the tricarboxylic acid cycle of fungi. Efficacy within the Basidomycete sub-division of fungi is not restricted to particular strains of any genus as evidenced by its activity against all anastomosis groups of *Rhizoctonia*.

FORMULATIONS

Several formulations of MON 24000 will be available including a wettable powder formulation (WP 25) as well as water based flowable formulations (SC 20, SC 50), granules (G02, WG50) a dust (DL 0.85) and a flowable concentrate for seed treatment use (FS15).

BIOLOGICAL ACTIVITY

Materials and methods

Rice

The trials were conducted using a randomized block design with 4 replicates, on plots 5-10 m². One or two applications were made from panicle differentiation to late heading using spray volumes of 200-400 l/ha. Disease assessments were made at grain maturation (20-30 days after heading)

Cereals

All foliar trials reported had plot sizes of 10-20 m² with 4-5 replications using randomized complete block design. Treatments were applied at GS 30-32 (stem base) or GS 37-59 (foliar). Spray volume was 200-300 l/ha. Disease severity was assessed on stems, leaves or ears as appropriate. Seed treatment applications were made using a fluidised bed or mini rotostat machine.

Potatoes

Trials were conducted using a randomized block design with 4 replicates. Plot sizes were 10-40 m² and treatments were applied prior to planting as an ultra low volume mist at a rate of 2 l/tonne. The severity of both stem canker and black scurf was assessed.

Peanuts/Turf

Trials had plot sizes of 2-20 m² with 4 replications using randomized complete block design. Treatments were applied as foliar sprays in volumes of 600-1500 l/ha. Peanut white mould trials were evaluated at lifting. Disease severity was measured as the number of disease loci per plot. Turf brown patch trials were assessed as percent disease severity at intervals appropriate to application timing .

Coffee

Trials were conducted using randomized complete block design with 4 replicates. Plot sizes were 5-10 m². Applications were made using a spray volume of 1000 l/ha. Disease assessments were performed six to seven weeks after the last application.

Results and discussion of field trials

Rice

MON 24000 gave outstanding control of rice sheath blight (*Thanatephorus cucumeris*) as a foliar application in both Asia and USA. (Table I). The compound was also effective as a granule applied to paddy water at 50 to 20 days before heading. In the 75 official trials performed by the Japan Plant Protection Association since 1989, MON 24000 obtained a class "A" or "B" category in 73 of these tests, confirming its strong potential for practical use.

TABLE I.   Control of sheath blight on rice in USA and Asia 1990-1991.

| | | % sheath blight | | |
Treatment	Dose g AI/ha	USA 1990	USA 1991	ASIA 1990-1991
Untreated		83	56	36
MON 24000	100	-	-	3
MON 24000	140/130*	17	29	3
MON 24000	280	15	16	-
Benomyl	1120	56	43	6
Pencycuron	560/330*	32	22	4
Number of trials		12	7	4

*   Dose in USA and Asia respectively

Cereals

MON 24000 has consistently shown good activity against the common stem base disease sharp eyespot (*Rhizoctonia cerealis*). In high disease situations, foliar applications at GS 30-31 gave optimum control and yield benefits of 5% (Table 2).

TABLE 2.   Control of sharp eyespot on winter wheat 1990-1991.

| | | 1990 | | 1991 |
Treatment	Dose g AI/ha	%stem infection	Yield (t/ha)	%stem infection
Untreated		34	6.3	25
MON 24000	125	12	6.6	-
MON 24000	150	-	-	8
MON 24000	200	-	-	6
MON 24000	250	8	6.6	-
Prochloraz	450	28	6.7	20
Flusilazole	200	27	6.7	20
Number of trials		8*	8*	28

Average of trials in France, UK, Denmark, Belgium and Ireland
* Yields and efficacy originated in same trials

Stem disease surveys conducted by Monsanto of 100 commercial winter wheat crops randomly sampled at GS 75 in France and UK in 1990 and 1991 revealed a high incidence of sharp eyespot (Table 3). A low incidence of this disease was observed in Germany and Denmark in 1991. In France and UK, 20-30% of crops sampled recorded significant levels of the disease. Wheat, oilseed rape and legumes as previous crops were found to be equally conducive to sharp eyespot development.

TABLE 3.   Incidence of sharp eyespot in 100 winter wheat crops in France, UK, Germany and Denmark 1990-1991.

Country	% crops with sharp eyespot	
	1990	1991
France	92	60
UK	92	70
Germany	-	43
Denmark	-	26

MON 24000 also provides control of cereal rusts especially *Puccinia recondita* (Table 4). Good control of *Ustilago* spp and *Tilletia caries* has been observed when used as a seed treatment at 7.5-30 g AI/100 kg seed (Table 5). Suppression of barley leaf stripe (*Pyrenophora graminea*) also was noted.

TABLE 4.   Control of *Puccinia recondita* and *P.striiformis* on winter wheat 1990-1992.

Treatment	Dose g AI/ha	% leaf infection*	
		P.recondita	*P.striiformis*
Untreated		24.7	16.3
MON 24000	125	2.0	-
MON 24000	150	-	4.6
MON 24000	200	0.5	3.9
MON 24000	250	0.8	-
Cyproconazole	60	-	1.4
Fenpropimorph	562	3.3	1.7
Number of trials		6	4

Average of trials in France, UK and USA
* Assessed 20-40 days after last treatment

TABLE 5.   Control of *Ustilago nuda* and *Pyrenophora graminea* on winter barley and *Tilletia caries* on winter wheat 1990-1991.

Treatment	Dose g AI/100 kg seed	% infection		
		U.nuda	*P.graminea*	*T.caries*
Untreated		13.10	18.0	15.9
MON 24000	7.5	-	-	0
MON 24000	15	-	6.8	0
MON 24000	30	0.03	7.4	0
MON 24000	60	0	9.5	0
Carboxin	60	0.11	-	0
Imazalil	5	-	2.2	-
Triadimenol + fuberidazole	37.5 + 4.5	0	0	0
Number of trials		5	2	4

Average of trials in France, UK, Belgium and Ireland

Potatoes

MON 24000 at 50 g AI/tonne seed gave control of stem canker (*Thanatephorus cucumeris*) superior to reference compounds pencycuron and tolclofos-methyl (Table 6). Good activity also was observed on the black scurf phase of the disease.

TABLE 6.   Control of stem canker and black scurf on potatoes 1989-1990.

Treatment	Dose g AI/tonne	% infection	
		Stem canker	Black scurf
Untreated		16.0	34.1
MON 24000	50	0.9	1.4
MON 24000	100	0.6	1.4
MON 24000	150	0.3	2.0
Tolclofos-methyl	125	6.4	0.7
Pencycuron	150	4.2	0.3
Number of trials		3	4

Average of trials performed in UK, Belgium and Ireland

Peanuts

Activity against white mould (*Corticium rolfsii*) has been observed. Foliar broadcast applications at pegging at rates of 280-560 g AI/ha demonstrated control of this devastating disease superior to the reference compound quintozene (Table 7). Control of limb rot (*T.cucumeris*) and rust (*Puccinia arachidis*) also has been observed.

TABLE 7.   Control of white mould and limb rot on peanuts USA 1989-1991.

Treatment	Dose g AI/ha	% Disease	
		C.rolfsii*	T.cucumeris
Untreated		30	27
MON 24000	280	20	15
MON 24000	560	17	12
Quintozene	5600	26	-
Tebuconazole	500	-	17
Number of trials		5	3

*Mean disease loci per 10-30 linear m of row

Turfgrass

MON 24000 has been shown to provide long duration control of brown patch (*T.cucumeris*) on turf. Rates of 1500-3000 g AI/ha gave 21 to 28 day control of the disease at least equal to commercial standards (Table 8). MON 24000 is also effective in controlling red thread (*Laetisaria fuciformis*).

TABLE 8.   Control of brown patch on turfgrass at various times after treatment USA 1989-1990.

Treatment	Dose g AI/ha	14 DAT	% Disease 21 DAT	28 DAT
Untreated		-	19.7	17.9
MON 24000	1500	-	2.8	3.9
MON 24000	3000	-	2.9	2.3
Iprodione	3000	-	2.8	11.1
Chlorothalonil	9500	3.9	-	5.4
Number of trials		3	3	6

Coffee

MON 24000 at 250 g AI/ha gave control of leaf rust (*Hemileia vastatrix*) equal to the reference compound triadimefon and superior to copper (Table 9). Activity was observed at least 40 days after the last treatment application.

TABLE 9.   Control of leaf rust on coffee in Brazil 1991-1992.

Treatment	g AI/ha	% leaf infection* 1991	% leaf infection* 1992
Untreated		48	46
MON 24000	250	24	25
Triadimefon	250	26	22
Copper	3528	-	38
Number of trials		2	1

*   Assessed 44-47 days after last treatment

Other Diseases

MON 24000 applied as a foliar, seed or soil treatment has shown activity against the following other disease targets : wheat take-all, Rhizoctonia damping-off of cotton and canola, and aerial blight of soyabeans. Excellent efficacy against Rhizoctonia rot of poinsettias also has been observed, representing strong potential for use of MON 24000 against Basidiomycetes in a wide range of high value vegetable and ornamental crops.

CONCLUSIONS

MON 24000 has shown excellent activity in the last three years in a number of crops especially against the Basidiomycete fungi. Its mode of action makes it particularly attractive for use alone or in mixtures with existing products.

ACKNOWLEDGMENTS

The authors are indebted to many Monsanto colleagues who contributed to the international development of MON 24000, especially A.Amano, G.Barnes, M.Halsey, J.N.Mutz, M.O'Keeffe, H.Rasmussen, J.Rejda-Heath, R.Schumacher, B.Shortt, and C.Stride. We also thank cooperators who have contributed data presented in this paper.

ICIA5504: A NOVEL, BROAD SPECTRUM, SYSTEMIC β-METHOXYACRYLATE FUNGICIDE

J.R. GODWIN, V.M. ANTHONY, J.M. CLOUGH, C.R.A. GODFREY

ICI Agrochemicals, Jealott's Hill Research Station, Bracknell, Berkshire.

ABSTRACT

ICIA5504 (methyl (E)-2-{2-[6-(2-cyanophenoxy)pyrimidin-4-yloxy] phenyl}-3-methoxyacrylate) is a highly active fungicide providing a broad spectrum of disease control. LC_{95} values below 1 mg AI/l have been demonstrated against major ascomycete, basidiomycete, deuteromycete and oomycete plant pathogens in glasshouse in vivo studies. ICIA5504 has a novel mode of action and controls fungal pathogen strains resistant to the 14-demethylase inhibitors, phenylamides, dicarboximides or benzimidazoles.

ICIA5504 has eradicant, protectant, translaminar and systemic properties, offering the potential for use as a foliar, seed, soil or paddy water treatment. The breadth of spectrum of ICIA5504 has been demonstrated in field trials against a wide range of economically important crop pathogens.

INTRODUCTION

Becker *et al.* (1981) first reported that the fungicidal activity of the natural products strobilurin A, strobilurin B, oudemansin A and myxothiazol, all derivatives of β-methoxyacrylic acid, stemmed from their ability to inhibit mitochondrial respiration by blocking electron transfer between cytochrome b and cytochrome c_1. Indeed, subsequent work has established that these natural products bind at a specific site on cytochrome b (Mansfield & Wiggins, 1990). No compounds currently sold as agricultural fungicides have the same specific mode of action, a feature which should preclude cross-resistance between the β-methoxyacrylates and other classes of fungicide. Therefore, ICI was particularly interested in the β-methoxyacrylates as an area for fungicide synthesis.

Samples of oudemansin A and myxothiazol (kindly provided by Prof. T.Anke and Dr.H.Reichenbach respectively) were tested by ICI in 1982 and shown to have fungicidal activity *in vivo*. Although no sample of strobilurin A was available, we felt it important to determine whether this was similarly fungicidally active since it is structurally the simplest of the natural β-methoxyacrylates and, consequently, the most attractive starting point for the synthesis of analogues. In preparing a sample of strobilurin A for testing *in vivo*, we established that the wrong configuration had previously been assigned to the strobilurins. Subsequently, we were able to assign the correct configuration (Beautement & Clough, 1987). Disappointingly, strobilurin A showed no in vivo fungicidal activity in glasshouse tests. Nevertheless, it was active against fungi growing on agar in the dark and strongly inhibited mitochondrial respiration *in vitro*. Tests showed that the lack of in vivo fungicidal activity of strobilurin A stemmed from its photochemical instability and relatively high volatility.

We have designed and synthesised analogues of the strobilurins in which the structural features responsible for fungicidal activity have been retained, while those responsible for photochemical instability and volatility have been modified (Beautement *et al.*, 1991). During the course of an extensive chemical synthesis programme, we have established the relationships between structure and fungicidal activity for the β-methoxyacrylates and this has led to the preparation of ICIA5504, the subject of this paper.

CHEMICAL AND PHYSICAL PROPERTIES

Chemical name (IUPAC) : Methyl (E)-2-{2-[6-(2-cyanophenoxy)pyrimidin-4-yloxy]phenyl}-3-methoxyacrylate.

Code number : ICIA5504

Structural formula :

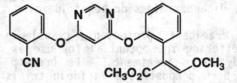

Molecular formula and weight:	$C_{22}H_{17}N_3O_5$; 403.4
Physical state:	White crystalline solid
Melting point:	118-9°C
Density:	1.33 g/cm^3
Water solubility:	10 mg/l at 25°C
n-Octanol-water partition coefficient:	440 (logP = 2.64)
Vapour pressure:	<< 10^{-5} Pa at 20°C

TOXICOLOGY

Rat acute oral LD50:	>5000 mg/kg (males and females)
Rat acute dermal LD50:	>2000 mg/kg (males and females)
Rabbit skin irritation:	slight
Rabbit eye irritation:	slight
Guinea pig skin sensitisation:	negative
Mutagenicity:	Ames negative

BIOLOGICAL PROPERTIES

Test methods

Laboratory, glasshouse and field study methods closely follow those described in previous publications by ICI Agrochemicals (Heaney *et al.*, 1988; Waller *et al.*, 1990).

Spectrum and features of activity

In vivo glasshouse tests highlight the breadth of spectrum and level of activity of ICIA5504, with excellent fungicidal activity displayed against ascomycetes, basidiomycetes, deuteromycetes and oomycetes (Table 1). ICIA5504 shows protectant, eradicant, translaminar and systemic properties.

TABLE 1. Glasshouse efficacy *in vivo*.

Pathogen	Plant host	Type of application	LC95 value (mg AI/l) ICIA5504	Commercial standard	
Ascomycetes					
Erysiphe graminis f.sp. *tritici*	Wheat	Erad,01	4	7	Tebuconazole
Mycosphaerella graminicola	Wheat	Prot,01	0.3	2	Tebuconazole
		Erad,05	0.3	2	Tebuconazole
Pyrenophora teres	Barley	Prot,01	0.3	6	Flusilazole
		Erad,01	20	10	Flusilazole
Venturia inaequalis	Apple	Prot,01	2	5	Hexaconazole
		Erad,03	5	0.6	Hexaconazole
		Xlam,01	11	2	Hexaconazole
Basidiomycetes					
Puccinia recondita	Wheat	Prot,01	0.2	0.7	Tebuconazole
		Erad,05	3	7	Tebuconazole
		Syst,02	4	34	Tebuconazole
Thanatephorus cucumeris	Rice	Prot,01	1	3	Pencycuron
		Syst,02	35	33	Flutolanil
Deuteromycetes					
Pyricularia oryzae	Rice	Prot,01	0.03	0.9	Tricyclazole
		Erad,02	1	0.6	Kasugamycin
		Syst,02	0.9	4	Pyroquilon
Alternaria solani	Tomato	Prot,01	0.1	3	Hexaconazole
Oomycetes					
Plasmopara viticola	Vine	Prot,07	1	8	Mancozeb
		Erad,01	13	1	Cymoxanil
		Syst,02	8	2	Cymoxanil
Phytophthora infestans	Potato	Prot,01	0.4	109	Mancozeb

Erad = Foliar eradicant   Syst = Root drench (systemic) protectant
Prot = Foliar protectant   Xlam = Translaminar protectant
01 = 1 day between inoculation and chemical application (02=2 days etc.)

ICIA5504 is a particularly potent inhibitor of spore germination and, in addition to its ability to inhibit mycelial growth, also shows marked anti-sporulant activity.

Uptake into leaves

Foliar uptake of ICIA5504 into wheat, barley and vines is low with typically ≤ 10% AI penetrating the leaf by 24 hours after application.

Photostability

In a simulated sunlight test, ICIA5504 did not suffer the photoinstability of strobilurin A (time for 50% loss of ICIA5504 = 24 hours cf. strobilurin A = 12 seconds).

Translocation in wheat

FIGURE 1. Distribution along wheat leaf (*Puccinia recondita* bioassay)

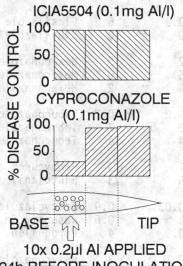

Bioassays to examine movement of AI along the leaf in wheat highlight the systemic properties of ICIA5504; disease control at the leaf tip can be achieved within 24 hours of application of ICIA5504 to a zone at the leaf base (Figure 1). In addition, and in contrast to highly systemic fungicides such as cyproconazole, disease control is retained at the zone of application with ICIA5504 in this test. The uniformity of distribution of ICIA5504 within the cereal leaf ensures an excellent persistence of biological effect without rapid AI accumulation at the leaf tip.

FIGURE 2. Distribution along wheat
leaf (radiolabel)

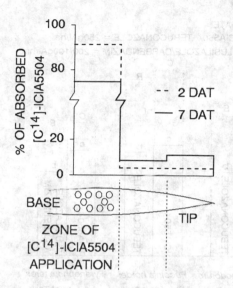

Studies with $[C^{14}]$-ICIA5504 have confirmed that translocation of the AI takes place acropetally only and occurs slowly, resulting in uniform distribution of ICIA5504 throughout the leaf (Figure 2).

Translocation in vines

Plasmopara viticola bioassays and radiolabelled studies showed ICIA5504 to have penetrant and local redistribution properties in vine leaves.

Field performance

Cereal foliar spray

Representative data from European cereal field trials confirm the very good efficacy of ICIA5504 against *Puccinia* spp., *Mycosphaerella graminicola* (*Septoria tritici*), *Leptosphaeria nodorum* (*Septoria nodorum*) and *Pyrenophora teres* (Figure 3). The persistence of fungicidal effect with ICIA5504 was impressive, maintaining the green leaf area of the upper foliage until late in the season. A similarly high level of protection was afforded to the ear by sprays applied at GS 55-59. Consequently, particularly large yield benefits have been achieved (Figure 3).

Despite only moderate control of wheat and barley powdery mildews (*Erysiphe graminis*) on the foliage, ICIA5504 applied at GS 55-59 has regularly given good control of wheat powdery mildew on the ears. ICIA5504 showed negligible activity against true eyespot (*Tapesia yallundae)* but was highly effective against sharp eyespot, caused by *Rhizoctonia cerealis.*

ICIA5504, applied over a wide range of application timings and environmental conditions, has consistently been very crop safe on wheat and barley.

FIGURE 3. Disease control and associated yield increases on wheat and barley
in five representative trials

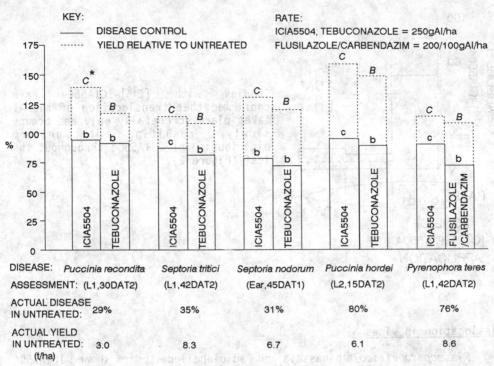

KEY:
—— DISEASE CONTROL
······ YIELD RELATIVE TO UNTREATED

RATE:
ICIA5504, TEBUCONAZOLE = 250gAI/ha
FLUSILAZOLE/CARBENDAZIM = 200/100gAI/ha

DISEASE:	*Puccinia recondita*	*Septoria tritici*	*Septoria nodorum*	*Puccinia hordei*	*Pyrenophora teres*
ASSESSMENT:	(L1,30DAT2)	(L1,42DAT2)	(Ear,45DAT1)	(L2,15DAT2)	(L1,42DAT2)
ACTUAL DISEASE IN UNTREATED:	29%	35%	31%	80%	76%
ACTUAL YIELD IN UNTREATED: (t/ha)	3.0	8.3	6.7	6.1	8.6

*DIFFERENT LETTERS INDICATE SIGNIFICANT DIFFERENCES AT 5% LEVEL BETWEEN TREATMENTS
WITHIN INDIVIDUAL TRIALS (UNTREATED EQUIVALENT TO A OR a)
L = LEAF NUMBER (NUMBERING DOWN FROM FLAG LEAF =L1)
30 DAT2 = 30 DAYS AFTER SECOND TREATMENT etc

Rice
ICIA5504 is unique in showing control of both rice blast (*Pyricularia
oryzae* on the leaves and panicles) and sheath blight (*Thanatephorus
cucumeris*). ICIA5504 has been effective in Japanese field trials when applied
either as granules directly to the paddy water (Table 2) or as a spray to the
foliage.

Vines
Under high disease pressure in France, ICIA5504 at 25 g AI/hl applied
on a prophylactic schedule has typically given control of vine downy mildew
(*Plasmopara viticola*) on the leaves and bunches superior to the commercial
standards (Table 3). In a representative Italian trial, ICIA5504 applied at
a rate of 12.5 g AI/hl has given good control of a heavy attack of vine
powdery mildew (*Uncinula necator*) on the leaves and bunches (Table 3). Its
performance was superior to sulphur, but slightly inferior to hexaconazole.

ICIA5504 may cause transient chlorotic symptoms on younger foliage.
Fruit quality and/or quantity has not been adversely affected and no
phytotoxic symptoms have been seen on the fruit at any stage of development.

TABLE 2 Control of rice diseases by granule application to paddy water.

		% disease control		
Treatment	Rate (g AI/ha)	Leaf blast (37 DAT)	Panicle blast (36 DAT2)	Sheath blight (23 DAT)
Untreated (% disease)		0 A (23)	0 A (45)	0 A (38)*
ICIA5504	1600	-	-	66 B
	1800	91 B	79 B	-
Probenazole	2400	96 B	78 B	-
Flutolanil	2000	-	-	50 B

* Mean lesion height (cm)
Treatment means within data columns followed by different letters indicate
significant differences at the 5% level.
36 DAT2 = 36 days after second treatment etc.
-     = treatment not in specified trial.

TABLE 3 Control of vine diseases.

		% disease control			
Treatment	Rate (g AI/hl)	*Plasmopara viticola* Leaves (15 DAT9)	Bunches (15 DAT9)	*Uncinula necator* Leaves (13 DAT7)	Bunches (13 DAT7)
Untreated (% disease)		0 A (46)	0 A (69)	0 A (30)	0 A (96)
ICIA5504	12.5	-	-	90 C	92 C
	25	98 B	99 B	-	-
Mancozeb	280	87 B	91 B	-	-
Cymoxanil + mancozeb	12+ 140	80 B	87 B	-	-
Sulphur	280	-	-	77 B	61 B
Hexaconazole	2	-	-	100 D	100 C

Treatment means within data columns followed by different letters indicate
significant differences at the 5% level.
15 DAT9 = 15 days after ninth treatment etc.
-     = treatment not in specified trial.

Potatoes
     A prophylactic schedule of ICIA5504 at 200 g AI/ha has typically given
control of potato late blight (*Phytophthora infestans*) equivalent to the

commercial standard, mancozeb. ICIA5504 applied at rates up to 500 g AI/ha on a range of potato varieties has shown no phytotoxic symptoms.

Apples
ICIA5504 applied at 120 mg AI/l on a prophylactic schedule has provided equivalent foliar and superior fruit scab (*Venturia inaequalis*) control to captan or flusilazole. At the higher rate of 200 mg AI/l, ICIA5504 has given control of *Alternaria mali* equivalent to a bitertanol/thiram/ziram mixture.

ICIA5504 has caused no phytotoxic effects on apples, with the exception of a limited number of varieties on which necrosis of young leaves and buds has been observed.

Cereal Seed Treatment
ICIA5504 applied as a seed treatment to winter barley at 100 mg AI/kg seed has shown good crop safety and given powdery mildew control equivalent to the commercial standard, ethirimol + flutriafol + thiabendazole ('Ferrax'), in UK field trials. Clarification of the potential for ICIA5504 as a cereal seed treatment continues.

CONCLUSIONS

ICIA5504 is a broad spectrum fungicide which has displayed good efficacy in field trials against a wide range of economically important crop diseases, often matching or outperforming the best current commercial standards. Crop safety, except on a limited number of apple varieties, has been good to excellent. Other exciting features of ICIA5504 are its systemic properties, novel mode of action and persistence of fungicidal effect.

ACKNOWLEDGEMENTS

The authors would like to thank their many colleagues in ICI Agrochemicals who have participated in the ICIA5504 project.

REFERENCES

Beautement, K.; Clough, J.M. (1987) Stereocontrolled syntheses of strobilurin A and its (9E)-isomer. *Tetrahedron Letters*, **28**, 475-478.
Beautement, K.; Clough, J.M.; de Fraine, P.J.; Godfrey, C.R.A. (1991) Fungicidal ß-methoxyacrylates : from natural products to novel synthetic agricultural fungicides. *Pesticide Science*, **31**, 499-519.
Becker, W.F.; von Jagow, G.; Anke, T.; Steglich, W. (1981) Oudemansin, strobilurin A, strobilurin B and myxothiazol: new inhibitors of the bc_1 segment of the respiratory chain with an E-ß-methoxyacrylate system as common structural element. *FEBS Letters*, **132**, 329-333.
Heaney, S.P.; Shephard, M.C.; Crowley, P.J.; Shearing, S.J. (1988) ICIA0001: a novel benzamide fungicide. *Proceedings 1988 Brighton Crop Protection Conference - Pest and Diseases*, **2**, 551-558.
Mansfield, R.W.; Wiggins, T.E. (1990) Photoaffinity labelling of the ß-methoxyacrylate binding site in bovine heart mitochondrial cytochrome bc_1 complex. *Biochimica et Biophysica Acta*, **1015**, 109-115.
Waller, C.D.; Eschenbrenner. P.; Godwin, J.R. (1990) Hexaconazole - a new flexible cereal fungicide. *Proceedings 1990 Brighton Crop Protection Conference - Pests and Diseases*, **2**, 447-454.

XRD-563 - A NOVEL FOLIAR APPLIED FUNGICIDE FOR THE CONTROL
OF POWDERY MILDEW IN CEREALS

W.R. ARNOLD, D. JOHNSON

DowElanco, P.O. Box 708, Greenfield, Indiana, USA

P. DANIAU

DowElanco S.A., 6 Avenue Charles de Gaulle,
Hall B/1er etage, 78150, Le Chesnay, France

C. LONGHURST

DowElanco Europe, Research and Development Laboratory,
Letcombe Regis, Wantage, OX12 9JT

ABSTRACT

XRD-563 is a novel benzamide fungicide
discovered by DowElanco. It is effective
against wheat and barley powdery mildew
(Erysiphe graminis f.spp. tritici and hordei
respectively).

The fungicide can be applied as a foliar
spray and penetrates into plant tissue very
rapidly where it is translocated acropetally.
XRD-563 shows curative, eradicant and
protectant activity against mildew.

XRD-563 shows similar activity to morpholine
fungicides under field conditions when
applied at equivalent rates. No
phytotoxicity has been observed on any of the
cereal cultivars tested. In laboratory and
field trials XRD-563 was effective against
powdery mildew showing reduced sensitivity to
EBI (DMI) fungicides.

The compound has been mixed with azole
fungicides to give products for broad-spectrum
disease control in cereals. The tank-
mixtures also afford valuable resistance
management tools to reduce the resistance
risk to both components of the mixture. The
product, alone or in mixture, will provide a
valuable new chemistry to combat cereal
powdery mildews.

INTRODUCTION

XRD-563 is a new systemic fungicide discovered by
DowElanco. This paper describes the properties and

performance of XRD-563, under both glasshouse and field
conditions, against powdery mildew of wheat and barley.

CHEMICAL AND PHYSICAL PROPERTIES

Chemical name(IUPAC):   2,6-dichloro-N-(4-trifluoromethyl-
                        benzyl)benzamide

Structural formula:

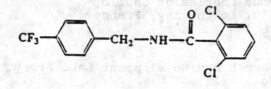

Molecular formula: $C_{15} H_{10} Cl_2 F_3 NO$

Molecular weight: 348.154

Solubility   :   water 3.5 mg/l
               :   readily soluble in organic solvents
                     eg methanol, acetone

TOXICOLOGY PROPERTIES

Technical material

    Mammals
    Acute oral - rat :   LD50 > 5000 mg/kg
    Acute oral - mice: LD50 > 500 mg/kg
    Acute dermal - rabbit: LD50 > 2000 mg/kg
                          (no mortality at this level)

    Reproduction studies
    Rat teratology study: 1000 mg/kg daily - no evidence of
                            teratogenicity

    Irritation
    Rabbits
       Primary eye: slight conjunctives cleared in 72 hr
       Primary skin: slight erythema cleared in 72 hr.

    Mutagenicity
    Gradient Plate Assay (Modified Ames) test with/without
    metabolic activation:negative
    DNA repair assay in primary rat hepatocytes:negative

    Avian
    Bobwhite (adult): Acute Oral - LD50 > 2000 mg/kg (no
                      mortality at this level).
                      Dietary - 8 day exposure LC 50 > ca.
                      4990 ppm in the diet

Aquatic
Bluegill: LD50 (96 h) > 100 mg/l)
Rainbow trout: LD50 (96 h) between 50 and 100 mg/l
Daphnia: 24 h static test - LD50 > 100 mg/l

BIOLOGICAL PROPERTIES

Glasshouse studies

Wheat or barley plants, grown in a glasshouse at 18-20°C under a 16 h light: 8 h dark regime were inoculated with Erysiphe graminis f.sp. tritici or f.sp. hordei five days before treatment (eradicative), two days before treatment (curative) or two days after treatment (protective). Treatments of XRD-563 or reference fungicides were applied with a deVilbiss spray gun. XRD-563 was tested as either technical material or as a 120 g/l EC. Standard fungicides were fenpropimorph 750 g AI/l EC, fenpropidin 750 g AI/l EC, tridemorph 750 g AI/l EC, propiconazole 250 g AI/l EC, triadimenol 250 g AI/l EC and nuarimol (technical material). Unless otherwise stated in the Tables, formulated material was used in laboratory and field studies.

XRD-563 showed eradicative, curative and protectant activity against Erysiphe graminis f.sp. tritici on wheat rates comparable to reference fungicides (Table 1). A similar range of activity could be demonstrated against Erysiphe graminis f.sp. hordei on barley (Table 2).

TABLE 1. The eradicative, curative and protectant activity of XRD-563 and reference fungicides against Erysiphe graminis f.sp. tritici of wheat (cv. Rapier) under glasshouse conditions.

Treatment	Dose mg AI/l	% Disease control 14 d after inoculation		
		eradicative	curative	protectant
XRD-563	6.25	94	99	42
	25.0	94	99	77
Fenpropidin	6.25	94	99	54
	25.0	98	99	88
Propiconazole	6.25	98	95	86
	25.0	94	99	94
Tridemorph	6.25	31	50	31
	25.0	66	96	42
Disease in controls		36%	63%	54%

TABLE 2. The eradicative, curative and protectant activity of XRD-563 and reference fungicides against _Erysiphe graminis_ f.sp. _hordei_ of barley (cv. Golden Promise) under glasshouse conditions.

Treatment	Dose mg AI/l	% Disease control 14 d after inoculation		
		eradicative	curative	protectant
XRD-563	6.25	82	79	59
	25.0	89	100	79
Fenpropidin	6.25	85	97	83
	2.50	91	99	95
Propiconazole	6.25	91	95	79
	25.0	93	99	95
Tridemorph	6.25	56	48	18
	25.0	68	99	73
Disease in controls		59%	60%	46%

The efficacy of the compound is not affected by rainfall when applied as either formulated or technical material (Table 3). Plants were treated with doses ranging from 25 to 100 mg/l and allowed to dry before subjecting to 12.5 mm of artificial rainfall. The efficacy of the compound to control wheat powdery mildew was excellent under the rainfall conditions.

TABLE 3. The efficacy of XRD-563 on the control of wheat powdery mildew (_Erysiphe graminis_ f.sp. _tritici_) after plants had received rainfall.

Treatment	Rate mg AI/l	Disease Control Rating*	
		No rain	12.5 mm rain
XRD-563 EC	25	8	7
	50	8	8
	100	9	8
XRD-563 Tech	25	8	7
	50	8	8
	100	8	8
Control	0	1	1

*Rating scale=1-9; where 1=no control, 9=100% control

It has been demonstrated that the compound is readily translocated in leaves. In laboratory experiments, the application of technical XRD-563 in a known concentration on a small portion of the upper leaf surface resulted in the control of mildew on untreated acropetal portions of the upper and lower surface of the leaf blade.

XRD-563 demonstrated excellent control of wheat powdery mildew conidia as shown in Table 4. These data suggest the material is fungicidal rather than fungistatic.

TABLE 4. The efficacy of XRD-563 on wheat powdery mildew (Erysiphe graminis f.sp. tritici) conidia after exposure for 15 min*.

Treatment	Rate mg/l	Disease Control Rating♦
XRD-563 Tech.	10	1
	100	9
Nuarimol Tech.	10	2
	100	9
Control blank	0	1

*Wash conidia from wheat; add compound; let stand 15 minutes; spin down; wash conidia with distilled water; inoculate wheat plants.
♦Rating scale=1-9; where 1=no control, 9=100% control

FIELD ACTIVITY

XRD-563 was evaluated in field trials in France, United Kingdom and U.S.A. using 15-25 m^2 plots and 3-4 replicates. Applications were made with Azo sprayers fitted with medium flat fan nozzles. In the trials reported in this paper, two applications of XRD-563 and reference materials were made on a 21-28 day schedule.

XRD-563 at rates in excess of 225 g AI/ha gave control of Erysiphe graminis f.sp. tritici comparable to the reference powdery mildewicides, propiconazole, triadimenol and tridemorph (Table 5). Data for each trial reported under each experiment show a similar rate range of control in both the U.K. and France.

TABLE 5. The efficacy of XRD-563 and reference fungicides against *Erysiphe graminis* f.sp. *tritici* of wheat in field trials in France and U.K.

Treatment	Dose g AI/ha	% Disease Control 35 Days after Treatment 1					
		206*	212*	123*	822♦	823♦	411♦
XRD-563	112	43	75	73	73	54	75
	224	84	91	80	93	70	91
	338	91	88	83	97	73	96
	450	93	94	84	97	81	96
Tridemorph	750	84	86	80	62	58	73
Triadimenol	125	91	90	84	94	80	–
Propiconazole	125	81	79	75	84	48	91
Disease in Controls		34%	51%	52%	87%	65%	60%

* Trial code number, UK. ♦ Trial code number, France.

Good control of *Erysiphe graminis* f.sp. *hordei* was provided by XRD-563. In trials where triazoles (propiconazole, triadimenol) were not providing good mildew control (207R-208R, Table 6), indicating the presence of DMI insensitive mildew, XRD-563 continued to provide good control.

TABLE 6. The efficacy of XRD-563 and reference fungicides in controlling *Erysiphe graminis* f.sp. *hordei* of barley in field trials in France and U.K.

Treatment	Dose g AI/ha	% Disease Control 35 Days after Treatment 1					
		204*	018*	824♦	824♦	207R*	208R*
XRD-563	112	43	85	71	57	20	18
	224	84	87	78	87	51	59
	338	85	91	82	87	71	79
	450	93	92	85	97	95	93
Tridemorph	750	96	99	85	97	95	93
Triadimenol	125	83	88	85	70	20	10
Propiconazole	125	73	97	87	73	51	38
Disease in Controls		55%	14%	20%	7%	91%	90%

* Trial code number, UK. ♦ Trial code number, France.

MIXTURES WITH AZOLE FUNGICIDES

Cereals are attacked by a complex of diseases in addition to powdery mildew. These include rusts (eg _Puccinia recondita_, _P.striiformis_) and _Septoria_ spp. in wheat and _Rhynchosporium secalis_ and rusts in barley. Broad-spectrum disease control can be achieved with XRD-563 by either tank-mixing or co-formulating it with broad-spectrum azole fungicides.

XDE-563 has been successfully tank-mixed (Table 7) at low rates with the recommended rate of propiconazole to provide broad-spectrum disease control. As well as providing broad-spectrum disease control these combinations will also provide a 'Resistance Management Strategy' analogous with that provided by mixtures of azoles with morpholines (Heany _et al._, 1988).

TABLE 7. Field activity of XRD-563, alone or in combination with propiconazole, against a range of cereal diseases.

Treatment	Dose g AI/ha	Mean % disease control			
		Puccinia recondita wheat(5)*	_Erysiphe graminis_ wheat(3)	Rhyncho-sporium secalis barley(7)	_Erysiphe graminis_ barley(4)
XRD-563	225	8	84	0	64
XRD-563+ propiconazole♦	225+ 125	82	82	80	70
Fenpropimorph+ propiconazole♦	375+ 125	83	81	88	77
Propiconazole	79	79	70	79	65

()* Number of trials   ♦ Tank-mix

CROP SAFETY

XDE-563 has been evaluated at rates up to and including 1000 g AI/ha in over 100 trials in wheat and barley in Europe and the U.S.A. No injury has been reported on any cultivar tested.

CONCLUSIONS

XRD-563 will provide a safe new chemistry, which is highly selective to the crop, to combat powdery mildew of cereals. This is particularly important in view of the widespread reduced sensitivity to DMI compounds (eg Locke, 1986) and reports (Brown et al., 1990; de Waard et al., 1992) of population shifts to reduced sensitivity of Erysiphe graminis to morpholine fungicides.

REFERENCES

Brown, J.K.M.; Slater, S.E.; Howe, P.M.; See, K.A. (1990). Mildew of Barley. **U.K. Cereal Pathogen Virulence Survey, 1989 Annual Report, Cambridge: U.K. Cereal Pathogen Virulence Survey Committee**, 24-31.

De Waard, M.A.; Banga, M.; Ellis, S.W. (1992). Charaterisation of the sensitivity of Erysiphe graminis f.sp. tritici to Morpholines. **Pesticide Science**, 34, 374-376.

Heany, S.P.; Martin, T.J.; Smith, J.M. (1988). Practical approaches to managing anti-resistance strategies with DMI fungicides. **Proceedings of the 1988 Brighton Crop Protection Conference - Pests and Diseases** 3, 1097-1106.

Locke, T. (1986). Current incidence in the United Kingdom of fungicide resistance to pathogens of cereals. **Proceedings of the 1986 British Crop Protection Conference - Pests and Disease** 1, 781-786.

A NEW CONCEPT IN CROP PROTECTION : AN ACTIVE ADJUVANT FOR
FUNGICIDES - THE CASE OF COPPER TALLATE

J-L. SOYEZ

Proval S.A.R.L., 75012 Paris, France

ABSTRACT

   Copper tallate is a combination of copper hydroxide
   with the acid distillate (fatty and resin acids)
   from pine wood. Low in toxicity, it has been
   extensively tested in France since 1985, in the
   first instance as a fungicide. However, its main
   interest lies in its excellent properties as a
   surfactant and its synergy with a number of foliar
   fungicides including benzimidazoles, chlorothalonil,
   cymoxanil, folpet, fosetyl-aluminium and prochloraz.
   Copper tallate's mode of action has not been fully
   explained, but as little as 50g Cu metal/ha gives
   statistically significant improvements in efficacy.
   Registered in France as an *active* adjuvant to
   fungicides used against Botrytis and downy mildew of
   grapes, it is expected to be of interest in
   fungicide programmes in top-fruit, horticulture,
   cereals and many tropical crops.

INTRODUCTION

   This research programme on copper tallate started in 1985
and has demonstrated that its fungicidal activity is less
interesting than its secondary characteristics such as
surfactant activity. The improvement in efficacy of several
fungicide molecules by the addition of copper tallate is such
that a true synergy is demonstrable in many cases. This led
to the new concept of active surfactant or *active* adjuvant, a
category of surfactant with biological efficacy and
synergistic effect with potential for the reduction of rates
of some fungicide partners. This potential is of interest for
various reasons, particularly where fungicide resistance
problems occur. Up until now, available wetting agents,
surfactants and other additives have been intrinsically
inactive in applications in which they are used.

CHEMICAL AND PHYSICAL PROPERTIES

Derivation and Formulation

   The acid distillation of pine or other resinous trees
results in an acid liquid, tall oil, which reacts with copper
derivatives. Tall oil contains two types of products, fatty
acids, mainly oleic, linoleic and linolenic, and resin acids,
mainly abietic. Varying the conditions of the distillation
affects the exact ratios obtained of the different fatty and

resin acids. Fatty acids help the penetration of many molecules into animal or vegetal cells. Resin acids aid the sticking of the spray mixture on the plant. The copper tallate described in this paper is a proprietary formulation that has been developed by Proval S.A.R.L, derived by acid distillation of *Pinus maritimus* from the Les Landes region of France. It contains 50g copper metal/l, typically 650g copper tallate /l. Copper tallate has a strong terpene odour and is an eye irritant. It can leave green stains on plastic but these can be removed by aromatic solvents. The formulation has a long shelf life and is not sensitive to low temperatures.

Surfactant Properties

As shown in Figure 1, when diluted at registered rates, droplets of copper tallate are much smaller than those formed by other copper fungicides. Copper tallate droplets are typically in the range 0.3-0.9μm, droplets of inorganic copper derivatives in the range 2.5-4.3μm, giving clear benefits in terms of biological efficacy.

FIGURE 1.   Comparison of droplet sizes of copper fungicides.

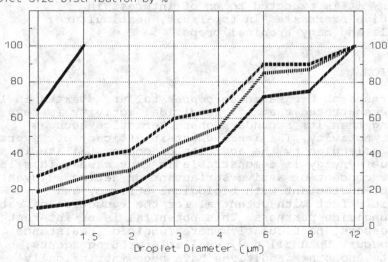

Droplet Size Distribution by %

Copper tallate   Copper sulphate   Copper oxychloride   Copper hydroxide

Preliminary, unpublished results of a study currently being conducted by Dr. Doux, ENSA, Toulouse, show that
(1) the diameter of water droplets is doubled by addition of copper tallate, thereby giving better surface coverage.
(2) copper tallate greatly increases the time for spray droplets to dry, i.e. it is a desiccation retardant.
(3) copper tallate prevents copper sulphate crystals from forming, thus avoiding loss of efficacy of copper sprays.
(4) a drop of copper tallate spray at usual dose rates shows a contact angle of 20-25° versus ±90° for copper sulphate.

Environmental Characteristics and Compatibility

Applications of copper tallate in crop protection use much smaller quantities of copper metal per hectare, 50-100g/ha for use as an active adjuvant, 175-200g/ha as a fungicide, when compared with traditional, inorganic copper derivatives. One application of Bordeaux mixture will use up to 10 times more copper metal per hectare than copper tallate for an equivalent level of efficacy. It is generally accepted that thiram and copper fungicides should not be sprayed together. This also applies to copper tallate. High-nitrogen liquid fertilizers are not compatible with copper tallate.

APPLICATIONS IN VINES

Botrytis

Copper tallate was first registered as an active adjuvant for foliar fungicide treatments on vines to help solve the Botrytis resistance problems experienced with dicarboximide fungicides. INRA Bordeaux established the synergy between copper tallate and vinclozolin (Soyez, 1992). An application rate of copper tallate equivalent to 100g Cu metal/ha is the optimum required, although 175g Cu/ha is necessary in areas where there is appreciable resistance to dicarboximides such as the vineyards of North East France and in some areas of Bordeaux. In 1991, the Service de la Protection des Végétaux conducted trials to establish the benefits brought by copper tallate when applied with dicarboximide fungicides. This is summarised in Figure 2.

FIGURE 2. Comparison of vinclozolin alone and with copper tallate for Botrytis control at various sites in France.

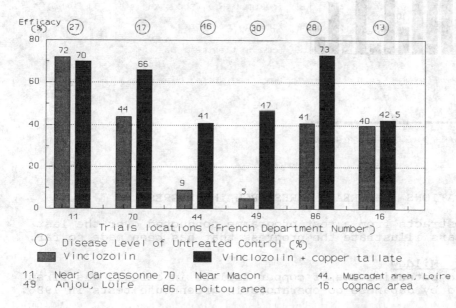

11. Near Carcassonne 70. Near Macon   44. Muscadet area, Loire
49. Anjou, Loire   86. Poitou area   16. Cognac area

In 4 out of 6 vineyards, a marked improvement in efficacy was reported. Another part of the trials programme showed that copper tallate (100-175g Cu metal/ha) could replace thiram at 3.2kg a.i./ha without reduction in efficacy against Botrytis.

Downy Mildew

The potential uses of copper tallate in programmes for the control of downy mildew are considerable. A rate of 1l/ha copper tallate (50g copper metal/ha) is sufficient to increase the efficacy of ethylenebisdithiocarbamates, phthalimides, cymoxanil and fosetyl-aluminium, with or without inorganic copper compounds. It is especially noteworthy that the improvement in efficacy is evident on grape berry downy mildew as well as on leaf downy mildew. This is shown in Figure 3, the summarised results of field trials conducted by INRA Bordeaux in 1990 and 1991 with spray intervals of 14 days.

FIGURE 3. Downy mildew trials with copper tallate as adjuvant.

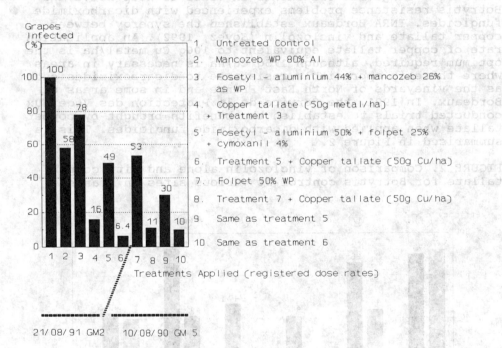

1. Untreated Control
2. Mancozeb WP 80% AI
3. Fosetyl - aluminium 44% + mancozeb 26% as WP
4. Copper tallate (50g metal/ha) + Treatment 3
5. Fosetyl - aluminium 50% + folpet 25% + cymoxanil 4%
6. Treatment 5 + Copper tallate (50g Cu/ha)
7. Folpet 50% WP
8. Treatment 7 + Copper tallate (50g Cu/ha)
9. Same as treatment 5
10. Same as treatment 6

21/08/91 GM2   10/08/90 GM 5

APPLICATIONS IN CEREALS - RESEARCH IN PROGRESS

Abstracts from a test programme conducted over the last six years illustrate the progress that has been made so far:

Powdery Mildew

The potential use of copper tallate in cereals was first studied by Japanese co-operators in greenhouse tests in 1986.

Complete efficacy was shown against *Erysiphe graminis* on barley with copper tallate at a concentration of 125mg/l (9.6mg copper metal/l) and triadimefon at 50mg/l.

Glasshouse tests carried out in the UK in 1989 showed enhanced performance of registered mildewicides when 2.5l copper tallate (50g copper/l) was added. Copper tallate itself showed some activity against mildew for a period of at least 14 days. Similar tests were repeated in the UK in 1992 using a reduced rate of copper tallate, 1l/ha (50g copper metal/ha), together with fungicides used at half the commercially recommended rates. The conclusions were:
1. Copper tallate, alone at both 50 and 250g copper metal/ha, was comparable with a reduced rate of tridemorph at 14 and 21 days after treatment on barley under low disease pressure.
2. The addition of 1l/ha copper tallate to reduced rates of carbendazim or prochloraz showed a trend towards increasing efficacy against powdery mildew on two barley cultivars over a two-week period. The carbendazim improvement was maintained on one cultivar for three weeks. These effects now need to be confirmed under field conditions.

Septoria tritici

Prochloraz and copper tallate
Two tests carried out by ITCF in 1988 showed that a programme of two treatments with prochloraz, 750g AI/ha followed by 450g AI/ha, could be replaced by two treatments with an experimental formulation with prochloraz at 225g AI/ha, copper tallate at 125g copper/ha, and carbendazim at 200g AI/ha. The efficacy was 56% in both trials and the wheat yields obtained with the experimental formulation exceeded those from the prochloraz treatments alone.

Chlorothalonil and copper tallate
Four tests carried out in 1990 were designed to study the activity of chlorothalonil, at reduced rates, in combination with copper tallate. For the first treatment, chlorothalonil was sprayed alone at 1100g AI/ha and at 750g AI/ha with copper tallate at 125g copper metal/ha. For the second treatment, chlorothalonil was applied at 1100g AI/ha together with fenpropimorph at 750 g AI/ha. The competitive programme was chlorothalonil at 750g AI/ha with copper tallate at 125g copper metal/ha. On ten ratings taken on various leaves, the efficacy, 60%, was the same for both programmes. From these four tests, it was concluded that:
(1) chlorothalonil at 750g AI/ha in presence of copper tallate at 125g copper metal/ha was equivalent to chlorothalonil at 1100g AI/ha.
(2) in presence of copper tallate the second fenpropimorph treatment was not needed.

Tapesia yallundae

INRA, Rennes, tested copper tallate in 1989 and 1990 against eyespot and concluded that it was not active against this disease. However, five other separate trials were conducted in 1989 to investigate the activity of reduced rates of carbendazim with copper tallate in areas where there was disease resistance to carbendazim. Carbendazim at 125g AI/ha with copper tallate at 125g copper/ha was compared against the registered rate of carbendazim, 200g AI/ha, and, overall, proved to be more effective. Moreover, the proprietary formulation used for *Septoria tritici* control, using only 225g AI prochloraz/ha, in two application, gave 72% control of eyespot, equivalent to prochloraz alone at 750g AI/ha followed by 450g AI/ha.

POTENTIAL FOR USE AS AN ACTIVE ADJUVANT

The experimental results suggest that copper tallate has wide potential. As general guide, copper tallate should be considered for use in the following cases:
1. As with other copper fungicides.
2. Where a disease can be controlled by fungicides that are synergised by copper tallate, e.g. benzimidazoles, dicarboximides, ethylenebisdithiocarbamates, chlorothalonil, cymoxanil, fosetyl-aluminium. The use of copper tallate in these cases allow application rates to be reduced.
3. In areas of disease control where there are problems of fungicide resistance, toxicology or economics. Many fungal and bacterial diseases of crops such as potato, tomato, hops, apple, stone fruit, beet and banana could be treated by adding an active adjuvant, such as copper tallate, to the basic fungicide treatment.

Rates of 1l/ha copper tallate (50g copper metal/ha) should be studied in cases (2) and (3), for use as an active adjuvant. Rates of 1l/ha and 2.5l/ha should be studied in case (1), where copper tallate is used as a fungicide and where increasing the rate may increase the control.

CONCLUSIONS

The concept of *active adjuvant* is opening up new areas of research and could:
- complement the registered rates of many fungicides while increasing their biological efficacy
- help reduce the number of fungicide applications in the same season or, in certain cases, the application rates of fungicides necessary to give good control
- assist in resolving situations where fungicide residues in crops must be lowered
- contribute to overcoming disease resistance problems

REFERENCES

Soyez, J-L. (1988) European patent number 0364529, based on French patent number 8803163.

Soyez, J-L. (1992) Le tallate de cuivre - un adjuvant utile en viticulture. *Phytoma*, _439_, 36-38.